SPOT GLOBE 2000

Edited by
STEEN B. BÖCHER and HENRIK B. HOFFMEYER

Geographical section: Steen B. Böcher, Ph.D., Professor
Historical section: Henrik B. Hoffmeyer, M.A.
Calculator of latitude   Leif Tang Lassen, Teacher
and longitude:
Illustrator: Arne Gaarn Bak, Illustrator and Cartographer
Cover: Erling Nederland, Illustrator

© Scan-Globe A/S, Denmark, 1974
16th Edition, 1982
Printed by P. J. Schmidts Printing House, Vojens
ISBN 87-87343-26-6
Printed in Denmark

SPOT GLOBE 2000 – a New Concept

Is it really possible? Can we find fresh ideas about globes? Is not one globe like any other? Not always, new ideas keep cropping up and Spot Globe 2000 has completely new possibilities and offers scope for innumerable ways of use.

One of the problems with globes has been that it was limited how many place names could be printed in such a small area. Spot Globe 2000 has solved that problem and now it is possible to locate a great many more geographical names. Any place on earth can be pinpointed if the latitude and longitude is known. Given these two facts it is possible to adjust the two scales to the given figures of latitude and longitude. This causes a pinpoint of light to indicate where the place lies.

Having made this big step forward, we come to the next problem to be solved. What if the latitude and longitude is not known? How do we overcome this difficulty? The obvious solution seems to be to provide a book where these figures can be found. In this way anybody can locate all the places in the index.

The day has passed when a globe was an exceptional possession, owned only by noblemen and a few scientists. By now, many of us have realized that a globe gives the most correct picture of the world and one where distances and directions are accurate. This point has been enlarged upon in the section on Air Traffic (p. 60). The exact length of plane routes can be measured and, given the speed of the plane, calculations can be made with the help of the time dial to find the flying time.

A globe is essential in the world of modern man where air flight has made travel to all parts of the world possible and where daily news is received from all over through television, radio and newspapers. A globe has become part of the inventory of the modern home just like an atlas. It is nor surprising that the sale of globes has increased tenfold in Europe in the last ten years.

It happens almost daily that we hear of an event in a place which is unfamiliar to us and we do not even know its position. First we can look for it in the index of this book. If it is not there it is likely that another place has been mentioned in the locality and that this can be found in the index. Should the distance between two places be given in miles, we only need to remember that 1° of latitude is 68.3 miles (=110 km).

There are many other things we want to locate besides international events. The book offers other subjects which may be of interest. The table of contents shows the many topics introduced in this book and it must be emphasized that this is only a limited selection to whet the appetite for further studies with the globe. For that reason the book contains some blank pages where additional information on localities can be noted. Perhaps a step of progress will be that, in the future, encyclopedias and dictionaries give latitude and longitude of place names.

We have feeling that when one first

begins to work with Spot Globe 2000 and the accompanying book it will become a new game. All the family can sit together around the globe and find out where the various places lie. There is no need to be limited to the subjects in the book. Hobbies like travel, ham radios and stamp collections will lead to other investigations of the globe.

It must be mentioned that the size of the pinpoint of light (3mm/0,039″ in diameter) gives some inaccuracy in localization. However, together with an atlas with large scale maps, one can first locate the place on the globe and then use the atlas to get a more accurate position. A globe is not used for its great exactitude but to help locate places in relation to other places. The right impression of this can only be given by a globe.

Now try to find the location of Europe's longest bridge, 56.0° N. and 16° E. It is 8.07 miles long.

The idea for Spot Globe 2000 was developed at 55.5° N. 12.5° E. It lies in the country of – – – –

We hope that you have many pleasant hours with your globe.

Steen B. Böcher

Contents

INFORMATION

Locating places with the globe 7
Time dial 9
Adjustment of the scales.......................... 10
Replacing the bulb 11

QUIZ 12

THE EARTH

Physical Features of the Earth
The seas 14
Sea floor and sea trenches 16
Capes and peninsulas 18
Islands 20
Deserts 22
Lakes and glaciers 24
Rivers 26
Mountains and passes 28
Earthquakes 30
Meteors and meteorites 32

Climate, Plant and Animal World
Climate and climate records 34
Plant and animal world, Cultivated
    plants and domestic animals 36

Continents, Countries and Towns
Continents and countries 38
The biggest cities of the world 40

World Resources
Sources of energy.................................... 42
Iron ore 44
Precious metals 46
Other metals 48
Other minerals 50

Industry and Traffic
Industrial zones 52
Oil refineries and atomic energy plants 54
Shipping 56
Tunnels, bridges and dams 58
Air traffic 60

ARCHAEOLOGY AND HISTORY

Prehistoric man 62

Ancient History
Mesopotamia, Egypt, Greece and
    the Roman Empire 64

The Middle Ages
Famous towns and fortresses, etc. 68
Famous buildings outside Europe 70

Modern History
Voyages of discovery and historic
    battlefields 72
National parks and game reserves 74
Events that shook the world 76

INDEX 79

BIOGRAPHY OF DISCOVERERS 163

Locating Places with the Globe

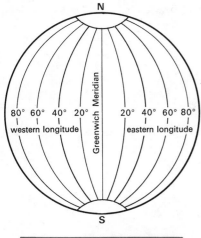

To find the position of a place on earth one uses two groups of imaginary lines. First, lines of longitude or meridians which are half-circles connecting the North and South Poles and secondly, lines of latitude which are parallel circles to the equator. The equator itself is a parallel. Lines of latitude and lines of longitude intersect each other at practically right angles.

A complete circle is divided into 360° (1° = 1 degree). Longitude is divided in the following way: the meridian which runs through the observatory at Greenwich, London, has been chosen as prime meridian (0°) and from here one calculates 180° to the east and 180° to the west, (altogether 360°). The location of a place is described by giving its longitude calculated from the Greenwich meridian, together with information whether it lies to the east or west of the Greenwich meridian. This is abbreviated to E. or W.

Spot Globe 2000 has two horizontal scales, the upper one for time and the lower one for longitude. The Greenwich meridian is marked as 0° on the lower scale. From 0°, this scale is sub-divided into 15°, 30°, 45° etc. to 180° both to east and west.

In this book is a register of names giving latitude and longitude. To find a place's longitude, turn the lower scale to the figure of the place's longitude, remembering whether it lies to the east or west of the Greenwich meridian.

Locating Places with the Globe

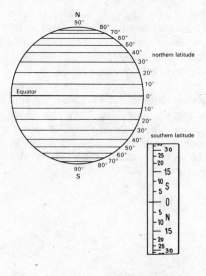

Lines of latitude are calculated from the equator which is called 0°. From here 90° are calculated to the north and 90° to the south, altogether 180°.

North of the equator is described as the northern latitudes and those to the south as the southern latitudes, (abbreviated as N. and S.).

A place's latitude indicates its location in relation to the equator. N. or S. will show whether it lies to the north or south of the equator.

Spot Globe 2000 has a vertical scale for degrees of latitude starting with 0° which represent the equator and a graduated scale above and below for north and south.

The second figure given at the side of a place in the index indicates the longitude which is located by moving the lower horizontal scale. (See page before). The first figure in the index gives latitude. The vertical scale is adjusted to this figure. When both scales are adjusted to the latitude and longitude of a place a pinpoint of light will indicate its position on the globe.

Normally, a globe can only give a limited number of names. Spot Globe 2000 can locate more than 20,000 names with the help of the index and the two scales.

In addition, one can adjust the pinpoint of light to a place such as New York and read on the scales what the corresponding latitude and longitude will be.

The Time Dial

The sun rises in the East and sets in the West because the earth rotates on its axis from west to east. It is this rotation that gives us *day and night*.

Meridian means the noon line, and the earth is divided into 360° of longitude. It takes 24 hours for the earth to make a complete rotation so one hour represents 15°. (360° ÷ 24 = 15° per hour), or 1° of longitude is equal to 4 minutes (60 minutes ÷ 15° = 4 minutes per degree).

When the sun is highest in the sky it is noon and all points that lie on the same meridian have noon at the same time. For practical purposes the world is divided into time zones which have the same hour. Each zone is 15° wide and covers 7½° on either side of 0°, 15°, 30° etc..

Spot Globe 2000 is provided with a *time dial showing hours*. The time dial is placed above the lower horizontal scale for longitude as a time shift of 1 hour is the same as 15° of longitude. If, for example, the longitudinal scale is placed on 25° E. (Helsinki) and the time dial at 14.00, it

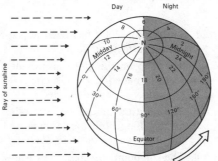

will be possible to read the time for all the other longitudes in relation to Helsinki at 14.00.

If one fixes the pinpoint of light on London (51° N, 0,5° W) by means of the two scales of latitude and longitude and adjusts the time dial to 10.00, one can find the corresponding time in New York (42°N. 75°W.) by moving the pinpoint of light there. The time dial will show the corresponding New York time. The difference in time is calculated by simple subtraction.

Spot Globe 2000 is also provided with a *day* and *night scale* placed at the North Pole.

That scale has hours on it and one

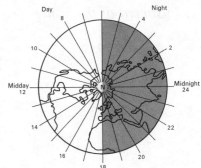

half gives day and the other half, night. By adjusting the day and night scale to 10.00 on London's longitude (0,5°W.) the day and night scale will show whether it is day or night elsewhere in relation to 10.00 London.

Adjustment of the Scales

1. Spot Globe 2000 has been adjusted at the factory.
2. The map on the globe is provided with a network of latitude and longitude.
3. The adjustment can be controlled by installing both the latitude and longitude scales on 0°.
4. The pinpoint of light will show on the equator (0° lat.) and the Greenwich meridian (0° long.).
5. Apart from damage, there can only be one reason for re-adjusting the longitudinal scale and that will be after a change of light bulb if the globe has been re-set 180° wrong.
6. Adjustment will be easiest if
    a. The pinpoint of light is put on the equator (0° lat.).
    b. The globe is turned so that the ligth shows 0° longitude (Greenwich meridian).
    c. The globe is held firmly in this position.
    d. The scale for longitude, which is tight, is twisted to its 0° position so that 0° on the scale is next to the indicator.
    e. The scale for longitude is now adjusted to the globe's network.

Replacing the Bulb

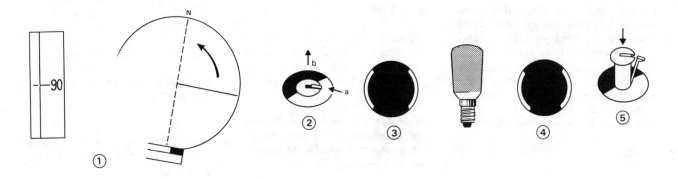

1. Adjust the vertical scale wheel for latitude to 90°N. so that the pinpoint light would indicate the North Pole, if lit. This will bring the swivel arm of the lens system, which is connected to the pinpoint of ligth, into an upright position so that it can pass through the hole at the South Pole.
2. Push the pawl at the North Pole towards the centre of the globe; withdraw the plastic tube and remove the day and night scale.
3. The loosened shell of the globe should now be twisted until it is free from the main chassis so that it can be lifted past the cord, bulb socket, dimmer and lens arm.
4. After changing the bulb, the shell of the globe is replaced over the internal mechanism. The two indentations at the South Pole on the shell are now placed over the two projections on the revolving piece of the main support. Avoid twisting the globe 180°.
5. Place the plastic tube through the day and night scale and the hole at the North Pole. Push the tube gently into locking position.

With Spot Globe 2000 and this book all the family can make their own course of programmed instruction with every member providing a question and answer. Here are some ideas for a quiz, but many more can be made using Spot Globe 2000 and the accompanying book as a source for questions and answers. Here is *education and entertainment for all.*

1. **Which lies most north – Madrid or New York?**

Adjust the pinpoint light to Madrid and then turn the globe so that the light lies on the longitude that goes through New York. Read off.

2. **What are the degrees of latitude and longitude for the most southerly points of Australia, Africa and South America?**

Adjust the light to these points and read the scales.

3. **When it is 12.00 in Hamburg, what is the time in Tokyo?**

Adjust the light to Hamburg and the time dial to 12.00. Then adjust the light to Tokyo and read off the time dial.

4. **How deep is the Philippine Trench and where does it lie?**

See the section "Sea Floor and Sea Trenches".

5. **Where is Christmas Island?**

See the section in the book on "Islands".

6. **What is the name of the biggest lake in Africa? In which country does it lie?**

See section on "Lakes".

7. **In which country is the world's highest waterfall?**

See the section of "Rivers".

8. **Which place has the most hours of sunshine in the year?**

See "Climate Records".

9. **Which gold mine has the highest production?**
   See "Precious Metals".

10. **What is "Golden Gate"? Position?**
    See "Tunnels, Bridges and Dams".

11. **Which airport is the biggest? London or Paris?**
    See "Air Traffic".

12. **What is Altamira? Where does it lie?**
    See "Prehistoric Man".

13. **Where is the Petrified Forest?**
    See "National Parks and Game Reserves".

14. **Where is the Kruger National Park?**
    See "National Parks and Game Reserves".

15. **Where and when did the airship "Hindenburg" burn?**
    See "Events that Shook the World".

16. **What is Canossa? Where does it lie?**
    See "Middle Ages".

17. **What is the name of the country whose capital lies 64,10°N. and 21,55°W?**

18. **When it is 8.00 in San Francisco, is it morning or evening in London? In Karachi (Pakistan)?**
    Use time dial and day and night scale.

19. **Where is the mountain Mauna Kea?**
    See "Mountains".

20. **The highest pass in the world is Cumbre or Uspallata (3760 m/ 12340 feet). Give its position in latitude and longitude.**
    See "Mountains".

The Seas

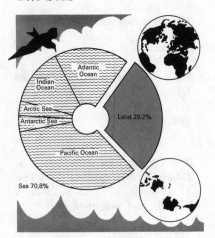

The greatest part of the earth's surface, 70,8% is covered with water.

This area is divided into three oceans: the Pacific Ocean, the Atlantic Ocean and the Indian Ocean. In addition, there are a series of border seas which are separated from the oceans by island chains, and inland seas like the Mediterranean Sea which are almost completely surrounded by land. There is some doubt as to which category the Arctic Sea belongs as it is very big and opens into both the Pacific and Atlantic Oceans. It can be considered as an inland sea of the Atlantic Ocean or made a special case and called the Arctic Ocean. The sea around Antarctica is divided between the three great oceans.

Connections between the various seas are called straits or sounds. Many of these are the busiest shipping areas like the English Channel, the Straits of Gibraltar, the Straits of Malacca, etc. Indentations of water into the land are called gulfs (large) or fjords (small), but some of the gulfs are so large that it would be more correct to call them inland seas, (e.g. Gulf of Mexico) or border seas, (e.g. Hudson Bay or Gulf of California). On the other hand, there are some small seas which should be called straits, (e.g. Kattegat or Marmara Sea).

As we all know, sea water is salty but it is not equally salty in all parts of the world. The salt content of the oceans is generally about 3%. But in seas, like the Red Sea, where evaporation is great and the in-flow of river water low, the salinity can rise to about 4%. In contrast, the salinity of the Baltic in some areas is very low, only 1%.

Some examples of the various types of seas are given on the opposite page. As many of the seas are very big, the latitude and longitude is located about the middle of each sea.

Some Seas, Straits, etc.

Ocean	Latitude	Longitude
PACIFIC OCEAN *(with subsidiary seas):* 179,7 mill. km² (68,36 mill. sq. miles) surface.		
BORDER SEAS		
Sea of Okhotsk	55° N	150° E
Sea of Japan	40° N	135° E
INLAND SEAS		
Gulf of California	27° N	112° W
East China Sea	36° N	123° E
STRAITS		
Sunda Strait	6° S	105° E
Strait of Malacca	3° N	101° E
Bering Strait	66° N	170° E

Ocean	Latitude	Longitude
ATLANTIC OCEAN *(with subsidiary seas):* 106,5 mill. km² (41,11 mill. sq. miles) surface.		
BORDER SEAS		
North Sea	56° N	6° E
Gulf of Mexico	25° N	90° W
INLAND SEAS		
Baltic Sea	57° N	18° E
Mediterranean Sea	37° N	20° E
Hudson Bay	58° N	85° W
STRAITS		
English Channel with Irish Sea	50° N	0°
Kattegat	57° N	11° E
Straits of Gibraltar	36° N	6° W
INDIAN OCEAN *(with subsidiary seas):* 74,9 mill. km² (28,91 mill. sq. miles) surface.		
INLAND SEAS		
Red Sea	20° N	38° E
STRAITS		
Bab-el-Mandeb	13° N	53° E
Strait of Malacca	3° N	101° E

Sea Floor and Sea Trenches

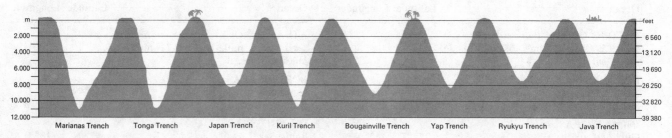

From the coasts, the sea floor drops evenly down to a depth of about 660 feet. From here it descends more steeply down to the ocean floor which in average is about 13126–19690 feet below sea-level. These descending slopes are called continental shelves. As the name suggests they are linked to the continents. The seas that cover the area above the shelf where the depth is under 660 feet are called transgressive seas. Politically, USA and other countries consider this shelf as part of the adjourning land. This distinction is made because of future oil drilling, etc... For the same reason, the North Sea has been divided up between the countries that border on it.

Movements of the earth's crust have caused the ocean floor to sink into trenches in some places. This is most common near land masses. It is here that the oceans' greatest depths have been measured with the aid of echo sounders. Such movements of the earth's crust have also caused the rise of volcanos on the ocean floor and special types of under-water mountain ranges. The Mid-Atlantic Ridge is the best example of an under-water mountain range with volcanos. In fact, Iceland lies on the Mid-Atlantic Ridge where it has emerged above the surface of the ocean. Other islands on the Mid-At-

lantic Ridge have been formed in this way too.

Earlier, it was believed that the ocean floor was fairly even, but systematic research with echo sounders on the ocean floor has proved that this is far from true. Countless under-water ridges, mostly discovered in this century, show that the oceans are divided into a series of basins.

Opposite is a list of the best known deep-sea trenches in the various ocean beds. It must be remembered that the figures are adjusted from time to time when new measurements are presented.

The Deepest Sea Trenches

Ocean	Depth in m/feet	Latitude	Longitude
PACIFIC OCEAN			
Marianas Trench	11 022/36 174	13° N	143° E
Tonga Trench	10 822/35 715	20° S	172° W
Tonga-Kermadec Trench	10 047/32 974	15–35° S	175° W
Kuril-Kamchatka Trench	10 542/34 599	45° N	150° E
Philippine Trench	10 540/34 592	9° N	127° E
Bougainville Trench	9 140/29 997	7° S	155° E
Yap Trench	8 597/28 215	10° N	138° E
Japan Trench	8 142/26 722	34° N	142° E
Aleutian Trench	7 822/25 672	52° N	170° E–148° W
Atacama Trench	7 820/25 665	24° S	72° W
Ryukyu Trench	7 507/24 638	26° N	128° E

Ocean	Depth in m/feet	Latitude	Longitude
ATLANTIC OCEAN			
Puerto Rico Trench	9 219/30 257	19° N	67° W
South Sandwich Trench	8 264/27 122	57° S	26° W
Cayman Trench	7 680/25 206	19° N	80° W
Romanche Trench	7 370/24 188	0°	17° W
INDIAN OCEAN			
Java Trench	7 455/24 467	10° S	100–120° E

Capes and Peninsulas

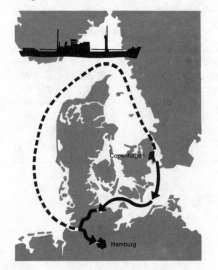

Coastal formations like islands, bays, capes and peninsulas have always been important to seafarers. This can be seen even on the early maps of the Pacific islands made by the Polynesians. The wooden maps from Greenland show capes and indentations. Ancient seafarers like the Phoenicians and Greeks have probably made similar ones and we know that the early sea explorers laid great importance on the capes that they passed. This is shown by the names they were given. Cornwall's west point: Land's End, Eire's west point: Cape Clear, Spain's west point: Cap Finisterre (Land's End), Greenland's south point: Cap Farvel (Cape Goodbye) and the Cape of the Good Hope which was thought to be South Africa's most southern point.

In many parts of the sea the peninsulas extend far out and make it necessary for the boats to circumnavigate a large area. For example, to go by sea from Hamburg to Stockholm it was necessary to sail round Skagen until the Kiel Canal was built. To go by sea from New York to New Orleans one has to sail round the peninsula of Florida and Cape Key West. To reach Rangoon from Bangkok by sea, ships must sail far south of the Malacca Peninsula and Singapore. At suitable places along such routes important harbours have developed.

Capes

Cape	Country	Latitude	Longitude
Nordkapp	Norway	71° N	26° E
Lands End	England	50° N	6° W
Cape Clear	Eire	51° N	9° W
Cabo Finisterre	Spain	43° N	9° W
Cabo da Roca	Portugal	39° N	10° W
Capo de Maroqui	Spain	36° N	6° W
Capo Passero	Italy	37° N	15° E
Mys Tjukotskij (East Cape)	USSR	66° N	171° W
Cape Comorin	India	8° N	77° E
Dondra Head	Sri Lanka	6° N	82° E
Cap Blanc	Tunisia	37° N	10° E

Cape	Country	Latitude	Longitude
Cap Vert	Senegal	15° N	17° W
Cape Aghulas	South Africa	35° S	20° E
Cape York	Australia	11° S	142° E
South East Cape	Australia	42° S	146° E
North Cape	New Zealand	34° S	146° E
South West Cape	New Zealand	47° S	168° E
Kap Morris Jesup	Greenland	83° N	35° W
Kap Farvel	Greenland	59° N	44° W
Cape Prince of Wales	Alaska	66° N	168° W
Cape Hatteras	USA	35° N	76° W
Key West	USA	25° N	82° W
Cape Horn	Chile	57° S	67° W

Islands

We learn in school that an island is a piece of land surrounded by water. It can lie in a lake or in the sea. Some islands are so big that it is only on a map or globe that they can be conceived as islands. Greenland is the biggest island. Australia is still bigger but it has been decided to name it the smallest continent in the world.

Most islands are connected with the continents because they lie on the continental shelf. (See p. 16). But there are more small islands in the middle of oceans and these are generally of volcanic origin. At least, the base is nearly always a volcano and in warm seas coral reefs have grown over this. Coral formations can also be formed in shallow water near the coast.

Generally, coral islands lie together in groups, called an archipelago, whereas volcanic islands tend to lie completely isolated.

Many small rocky islands were eroded by the Ice Age glaciers and if they lie together they are called skerries. We find some of these off the coast of Finland. It is certain that many Danish islands have been caused by glaciers, but they were not eroded and consist nearly wholly of glacial deposits with the tips sticking out of the sea. This is called a morraine archipelago.

On the right-hand page is a list of the world's largest islands and their area, together with some of the smaller well-known islands.

The Earth's Largest Islands

Name of Island	Area in km² / sq. miles		Latitude	Longitude	Name of Island	Area in km² / sq. miles		Latitude	Longitude
Greenland	2 175 000	839 550	59–83° N	11–73° W	Luzon	105 000	40 520	16° N	121° E
New Guinea	785 000	303 010	5° S	143° E	Island	103 000	29 758	64° N	170° W
Borneo	735 000	283 710	1° N	103° E	Mindanao	95 000	36 670	8° N	125° E
Madagascar	590 000	227 740	20° S	47° E	Ireland	84 000	32 424	53° N	8° W
Baffin Island	570 000	220 020	67° N	70° W	Haiti	77 000	29 722	18° N	72° W
Sumatra	450 000	173 700	0°	102° E	Sakhalin	75 000	28 950	51° N	143° E
Great Britain	230 000	88 780	53° N	2° W	Tierra del Fuego	72 000	27 792	54° S	67° W
Honshu (Japan)	225 000	86 850	36° N	138° E	Tasmania	68 000	26 248	43° S	147° E
Celebes	180 000	69 480	2° S	120° E	Sri Lanka	66 000	25 476	8° N	81° E
New Zealand *(South Island)*	150 500	58 093	44° S	172° E	Svalbard (Western Spitzbergen)	40 000	15 440	79° N	18° E
New Zealand *(North Island)*	115 000	44 390	38° S	177° E	Sicily	25 000	9 650	37° N	14° E
Newfoundland	110 000	42 460	49° N	57° W	Sardinia	24 000	9 264	40° N	9° E

Some Well-known Smaller Islands:

		Latitude	Longitude
Galapagos Islands		0°	90° W
Easter Island		27° S	110° W
Christmas Islands		2° N	157° W
St. Helena		16° S	6° W
Gough Island		40° S	10° W

Deserts

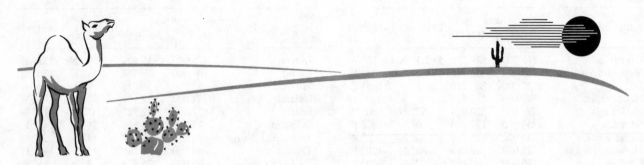

A desert is a territory where for one reason or another there is little or no growth of plant life. The most important causes are drought or cold. Cold deserts are found in polar regions like the whole of Antarctica, but many of the high mountains are cold deserts too.

Most of the great desert areas of the world are caused by lack of rain. This does not mean that it never rains but that there can go many years between the single showers of rain. When making a map of the world's deserts it is apparent that these are generally found in areas where cold air moves towards warmer regions. Consequently it can hold more moisture without condensation. The winds can blow towards the Equator. These are called Trade Winds. Or the winds can blow from the cold seas onto the warm west side of continents. Finally, it may be that the air during passage over mountain ranges or large areas of land has released so much condensation that there is nothing left. When an area gets less rainfall because it lies in the lee of a mountain range, in relation to the prevailing wind, it is said that it lies in the rain shadow.

Opposite is a list of the most important deserts and some oases. Oases are places in the middle of deserts where there is some water and plants can thrive. (Wells, rivers, etc.)

Deserts

Desert	Area in 1000 km² /	1000 sq. miles	Latitude	Longitude
SAHARA				
Libyan Desert	2 000	772	15–30° N	18–35° E
Nubian Desert	400	154	27° N	25° E
OASES in Sahara				
Cufra	–	–	24° N	23° E
Siwah	–	–	29° N	25° E
ARABIAN DESERTS				
Rub-al-Khali	132	51	18° N	50° E
An Nefud	–	–	28° N	42° E

Desert	Area in 1000 km² /	1000 sq. miles	Latitude	Longitude
AUSTRALIAN DESERTS				
Great Sandy Desert	–	–	20° S	125° E
Great Victoria Desert	–	–	28° S	130° E
Simpson Desert	145	56	25° S	137° E
Gibson Desert	–	–	24° S	125° E
Gobi	2 000	760	43° N	105° E
Kalahari	800	304	23,5° S	23° E
Takla Makan	500	190	40° N	77° E
Karakum	280	106	40° N	60° E
Thar	120	46	27° N	72° E
Atakama			23° S	70° W

Lakes and Glaciers

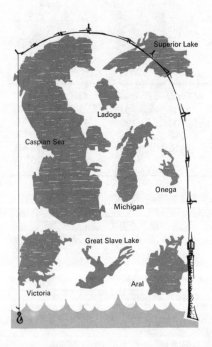

When a river flows through an area that is lower than the river's level, the area will be filled with water before the river can flow on. Many lakes must have been formed in this way, but hollows that lie below the ground water level will also generally be filled with water.

The lake water will become salty if the evaporation from the lake is greater than the flow-in, because incoming water always holds a little salt in solution. Eventually the quantity of salt will become so great that saturation is reached and salt is precipitated. Most of the world's sources of salt have been created in this way either recently or at earlier periods of geology.

If snow falls in areas where it is so cold that the snow cannot melt away, it will eventually accumulate and form an ice cap. As ice under pressure becomes plastic, the ice will under its own weight push outwards and downwards in the form of glaciers. The biggest coherent masses of ice are in Antarctica and Greenland.

The list opposite gives the names of some of the biggest glaciers and some of the world's greatest lakes. The lakes marked with S are salt-lakes.

The Largest Lakes

Lake	Area in 1000 km² /	1000 sq. miles	Latitude	Longitude
EUROPE				
Ladoga Lake	18	7	62° N	32° E
Lake Onega	10	4	63° N	36° E
AFRICA				
Lake Victoria	68	26	2° S	33° E
Lake Tanganyika	34	13	7° S	30° E
Lake Malawi	31	12	13° S	35° E
NORTH AMERICA				
Lake Superior	82	32	48° N	88° W
Lake Huron	60	23	45° N	83° W
Lake Michigan	58	22	43° N	87° W
Great Bear Lake	30	12	66° N	120° W
Great Slave Lake	29	11	62° N	115° W
Lake Erie	26	10	42° N	82° W
Lake Winnipeg	24	9	53° N	98° W
USSR				
Caspian Sea (S)	371	143	42° N	51° E
Aral Sea (S)	67	26	45° N	60° E
Lake Baykal	32	12	54° N	107° E

Some of the Largest Glaciers

Glacier	Country	Area in km²	sq. miles	Latitude	Longitude
Vatnajökul	Iceland	8 800	3 397	64° N	17° W
Malaspina	Alaska	1 990	768	61° N	141° W
Nabesna	Alaska	1 350	521	62° N	147° W
Fedtchenko	Pamir	1 150	444	38° N	74° E
Siachen	Karakorum			35° N	77° E
Aletsch	Alps	115	44	46° N	8° E

Rivers

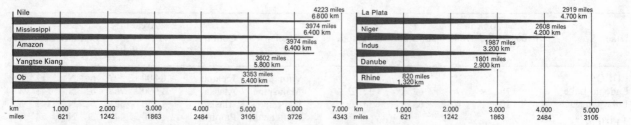

Geographically, the word "River" means any water course during its flow from its source to its estuary. The latter may be in a salt lake or in the sea. Some even end in sand, but these are generally dry river beds or wadis that do not contain water all the time.

The river's source can be a spring or rain fissure that has eroded down to the sub-surface water table or it can be formed by melted water that comes from a glacier.

Some rivers erode their surrounding area (basin) and carry away the material mostly as silt. This material is deposited either in the lakes or out in the sea. Such sediment deposited at the river mouth forms a delta and this stretches further out into the sea if not removed by tidal or other currents or if the coast-line is sinking. If the coast-line sinks a funnel-shaped estuary is formed.

Some river beds are so hard in places that they cannot be eroded. Here waterfalls are formed but gradually these become worn down and eventually disappear. Low waterfalls or eddies are often called cataracts.

Main rivers are those which have the biggest volume of water, but some tributaries can be longer than the main river. The Nile is considered to be the world's longest river, unless tributaries are included. In that case the Mississippi-Missouri is the longest.

The Greatest Rivers

River	Length in		Basin Area in		Latitude	Longitude
	km	/ miles	1000 km²	1000 sq. miles		
Nile (with Kagera)	6 800	4 223	2 900	1 119	32° N	31° E
Mississippi (with Missouri)	6 400	3 974	3 250	1 255	29° N	89° W
Amazon	6 400	3 974	7 200	2 779	0°	50° W
Yangtse Kiang	5 800	3 602	1 800	695	32° N	122° E
Ob	5 400	3 353	3 000	1 158	83° N	74° E
Hwang Ho	4 900	3 043	750	290	38° N	118° E
La Plata (with Parana)	4 700	2 919	3 100	1 197	34° S	58° W
Mekong	4 500	2 795	800	309	10° N	107° E
Lena	4 400	2 732	2 500	965	74° N	126° E
Amur	4 400	2 732	1 850	714	54° N	142° E
Congo	4 300	2 670	3 700	1 428	6° S	13° E
Niger	4 200	2 608	2 100	811	4° N	6° E
Yenisey (with Angara)	4 100	2 546	2 600	1 004	83° N	80° E
Yukon	3 700	2 298	850	328	63° N	165° W
Volga	3 700	2 298	1 400	540	46° N	48° E
Mackenzie	3 500	2 174	2 100	811	69° N	135° W
St. Lawrence	3 400	2 111	1 250	489	47° N	72° W
Indus	3 200	1 987	1 000	386	24° N	68° E
Danube	2 900	1 801	820	317	45° N	30° E
Ganges	2 700	1 677	1 100	425	22° N	90° E
Zambesi	2 700	1 677	1 330	513	18° S	36° E
Rhine	1 320	820	250	97	52° N	4° E

The highest waterfall in the World: Angel Falls (Venezuela)					6° N	62° W
The waterfall with the biggest volume of water: Stanley Falls (Zaïre)					0°	25° E

Mountains and Passes

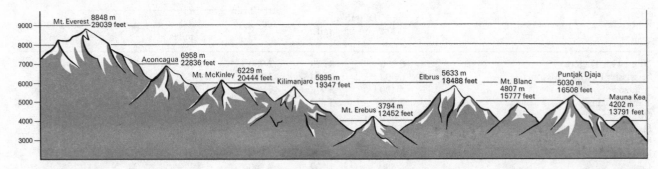

The area of the earth's surface that lies more than 660 feet above sea level is called highland. If this has an uneven surface it is termed a mountainous area whereas high-lying flat areas are called plateaux.

Mountains are of various origins and periods. They can have been caused by volcanism or by movements of the earth's crust which caused fold-mountains and fault block mountains. The youngest fold-mountains, mostly from the Tertiary Period, are the Alpine Folds and include the world's highest mountains and longest mountains ranges. The highest are the Himalayas and the longest range is the Cordilleras in North and South America. As these foldings were often accompanied by volcanism some of the mountains in the chain can have been of volcanic origin. The older fold-mountains have become more or less completely eroded, but with later faults along lines of fracture they can be uplifted into fault block mountains again.

Mountain ranges are obstacles for communication between countries, but even in olden times people, especially the Romans, were able to find places where there were gaps between the peaks. These were called passes and here it was easier to cross the mountains. The best passes are those which can be used all the year round like the Brenner Pass.

The list opposite contains the names of some of the highest mountains in various parts of the world. V after the name indicates active or extinct volcanos. The names of some passes are given too.

The World's Highest Mountains

Mountain	Height in m* / feet*		Latitude	Longitude
EUROPE				
Mount Blanc	4 807	15 777	45° N	6° E
Etna (V)	3 340	10 962	37° N	15° E
USSR				
Elbrus	5 633	18 488	43° N	42° E
Peak of Communism	7 495	24 599	38° N	72° E
AFRICA				
Kilimanjaro (V)	5 895	19 347	2° S	36° E
Mount Kenya (V)	5 200	17 066	0°	37° E
ASIA				
Mount Everest	8 848	29 039	28° N	86° E
Fuji (V)	3 776	12 393	35° N	138° E
NORTH AMERICA				
Mount McKinley	6 229	20 444	63° N	151° W
Citlaltepetl (V)	5 700	18 707	19° N	97° W
SOUTH AMERICA				
Aconcagua (V)	6 958	22 836	32° S	70° W
Huascaran (V)	6 768	22 213	9° S	77° W
AUTRALIA				
Mount Cook	3 764	12 353	43° S	170° E
Mount Kosciusko	2 230	7 319	36° S	148° E
ANTARCTICA				
Mount Erebus (V)	3 794	12 452	77° S	167° E

Mountain	Height in m* / feet*		Latitude	Longitude
OCEANIA				
Puntjak Djaja	5 030	16 508	3° S	137° E
Mauna Kea (V)	4 202	13 791	19° S	155° W

Passes

Mountain Range	Pass	Height in m* / feet*		Latitude	Longitude
Alps	Mount Cenis	2 083	6 836	45° N	7° E
Alps	Gt. St. Bernhard	2 469	8 103	46° N	7° E
Alps	St. Gotthard	2 091	6 863	46,5° N	8,5° E
Alps	Brenner	1 372	4 503	47° N	11,5° E
Pyrenees	Roncevalles	1 053	3 456	43° N	1° W
Trans-Sylvanian Alps	Turno Rozu	352	1 155	46° N	24° E
Balkans	Shipka	1 370	4 496	43° N	26° E
Sulajman Range	Khyber	1 070	3 512	34° N	71° E
Andes	Cumbre Uspallata	3 760	12 340	32° S	69° W

* All indications of height must be taken with reservations as these can vary a great deal.

Earthquakes

The displacements, horizontal and vertical, that occur in the earth's crust (see p. 28) do not only take place slowly and imperceptably. Along the faults and under the folds of mountain ranges tensions may occur that can be released very suddenly causing a tectonic earthquake. From the centre of the earthquake, the hypocentrum, waves are spread that are transmitted through the earth's core and through the earth's crust. This is registered as a shock and is strongest just above the centre of the earthquake, in the so-called epicentrum, and fades with distance from it. The strongest earthquakes can be registered all over the world at seismatic stations with seismographs. From the resulting graphs of the earthquake it can be established how far away from the station the earthquake occurred. The centre of the earthquake can be fixed with graphs from several stations. Most earthquakes occur in the area around the Alpine Folds. This shows

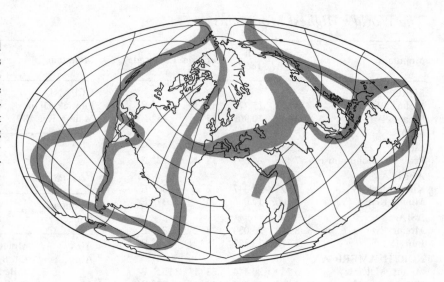

that the earth's surface is by no means quiescent and folding and faulting occur all the time.

Fortunately few earthquakes cause catastrophes but in some earthquakes thousands of people have lost their lives. Hardly any areas are totally free from earthquakes but in many cases these are very weak and may be caused by the sinking of the sub-soil's bed.

The beds of the seas can be affected by earthquakes. These make great movements of water, seismatic sea waves – Tsunami – that can cause great damage when they reach the shore.

Earthquakes Disasters

Locality	Year	Number of Deaths	Latitude	Longitude
Japan	1730	137 000	36° N	140° E
Lisbon	1755	32 000	39° N	10° W
Calabria	1783	50 000	39° N	16° E
San Francisco	1906	1 000	35° N	122° W
Messina (Italy)	1908	75 000	35° N	16° E
Avezzano (Italy)	1915	30 000	42° N	13° E
Kansu (China)*	1920	180 000	36° N	104° E
Kwanto-Ebene (Japan)**	1923	145 000	36° N	140° E
Kansu (China)	1932	70 000	36° N	104° E
Quetta (Pakistan)	1935	50 000	30° N	66° E
Erzingan (Turkey)	1939	45 000	39° N	39° E
Agadir (Morocco)	1960	12 000	31° N	10° W
East Turkey***	1966	3 000	39° N	43° E
East Iran***	1968	10 000	28° N	60° E
Peru***	1970	50 000	12° S	77° W

* The earthquake released great landslides and these caused the many casualties.

** Material damage done in the area, which included Tokyo, was estimated at £ 1.000.000.000.

*** Localization not certain.

Meteors and Meteorites

Meteors are pieces of stone or metal which enter the earth's atmosphere at enormous speed. Friction with the earth's atmosphere causes fire and we can see their light. People call meteors "shooting" or "falling" stars.

The majority of meteors burn out before they reach the earth's surface. Others reach it and explode on impact. A meteor that reaches the earth is called a meteorite.

It is calculated that about 200 million visible meteors come into the atmosphere of the earth every day and that these increase the earth's weight by about 1000 tons, daily. Meteors belong to the solar system and occur in swarms. They are common at certain periods of the year at intervals which coincide with comet periods. It is thought that they are the remains of comets.

The majority of the known meteorites seem to be composed of iron and nickel. Their surfaces show signs that they have been glowing on their descent towards earth. Stone meteorites are of very varied substances but these seem volcanic in character.

On the opposite page is a list of the most well-known meteorites together with a list of craters on the earth's surface that are believed to have been caused by meteorites.

Here it might be mentioned that many of the craters to be found on the moon are definitely meteorite craters. As the moon has no atmosphere the meteorites cannot burn away and all reach the surface of the moon.

Meteorites

Meteorite	Approx. Tonnage	Latitude	Longitude
The greates recorded meteorite was found near Hoba in the neighbourhood of Grootfontein, (South West Africa).	60 t	19° S	18° E
"The Tent" ⎤	30,4 t		
"The Woman" Cape York	3,0 t		
"The Dog" (Greenland)	0,4 t	76° N	67° W
"Savic" ⎦	3,4 t		
"Agpallilik" (near Thule)	20 t	77° N	69° W
Found near Mexico	27 t	26° N	108° W
Tanzania (East Africa)	26 t	5° S	35° E
Oregon (USA)	14 t	43° N	120° W
Mexico	14 t	29° N	106° W
Chihuahua (Mexico)	11 t	29° N	106° W
Cranbourne (Australia)	3,5 t	25° S	130° E
Magura (Czechoslovakia)	1,5 t	49° N	17° E

Meteorite Scars and Craters

	Latitude	Longitude
Vanavara near Podkamenuaya or Stony Tunguska (Siberia), 1908	62° N	90° E
Sikhota, Alin, 1947	46° N	136° E
Deep Bay, Saskatchewan, (Canada)	55° N	105° W
Nastapoga Island, Hudson Bay (Canada)	57° N	77° W
Coon Butte or Barringer Crater, Winslow, Arizona (USA)	35° N	111° W

Climate and Climate Records

The climate of a place is generally described by its temperature, wind forces and rainfall. Temperatures are the most important factors, but in reality the average temperature of a place does not give a true picture.

For example, the average temperature for Cambridge, England for June is given as 58.5° F. Yet, the average monthly extremes for June over a period of years range from 38–82° F. ref. Meteorological Office Data.

The temperature of a place is influenced by the sun's rays; that is hours of sunshine and height of the sun. Strangely enough the warmest places on earth do not lie on the Equator where there is generally a lot of cloud. The hottest places are to be found in the desert areas on both sides of the Equator where there is little cloud ceiling.

The winds are caused by difference in air pressure as air masses move from places with high air pressure to places with lower air pressure. Because of the rotation of the earth the wind is deflected to the right in the Northern Hemisphere and to the left in the Southern Hemisphere. The greater the difference in air pressure, the stronger the wind. The greatest wind forces are reached in typhoons and hurricanes.

Rain occurs when an air mass holding a certain amount of vapour is chilled so that the vapour condenses to form drops of water which fall as rain.

Climate Records

Temperature

Highest in the shade	58°C	Al Aziziyah (Libya) 32° N lat. 13° E long.
Highest yearly average	31,1°C	Lugh Ganana (East Africa) 4° N lat. 43° E long.
Lowest temperature	−88,3°C	Wostok (Antarctica) 82° S lat. 105° E long.
Lowest yearly average temperarature	−17,5°C	Wostok (Antarctica) 82° S lat. 105° E long.

Air Pressure:

Highest	1079 mb	Barnaul (Mid-Siberia) 53° N lat. 84° E long.
Lowest	877 mb	near Guam (Oceania) 13° N lat. 145° E long.

Windforce on Earth's Surface:

Highest 372 km/231 miles per hour	Mt. Washington (USA) 44° N lat. 71° W long.
Most windy place with wind force over 300 km/186 miles per hour	George V Coast (Antarctica) 70° S lat. 150° E long.

Rainfall:

Greatest per minute	2,12 cm/0,1″	Unionville (North America) 40° N lat. 115° W long.
Greatest per day	173 cm/65″	Reunion (Indian Ocean) 22° S lat. 56° E long.
Greatest per year	3246 cm/1278″	Cherrapunji (Assam) 28° N lat. 92° E long.
Greatest yearly average	1200 cm/472″	Cherrapunji 28° N lat. 92° E long.
Greatest number of rainy days per year	348	Bahia Felix (Chile) 45° S lat. 74° W long.
Lowest rainfall	0 cm	Atacama Desert (Chile) 24° S lat. 69° W long.

Greatest snowfall in one day:	193 cm/76″	Silver Lake (USA) 43° N lat. 121° W long.
Greatest snowfall per year:	2541 cm/1001″	Mt. Rainier (USA) 47° N lat. 121° W long.

Sunshine:

Maximum: 4300 hours per year	Libyan Desert 27° N lat. 25° E long.
Minimum: 6 minutes in one month	London December 1890 51,5° N lat. 0°

Plant and Animal World, Cultivated Plants and Domestic Animals

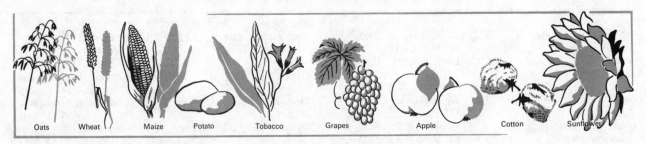

Oats   Wheat   Maize   Potato   Tobacco   Grapes   Apple   Cotton   Sunflower

To locate the origin of plants and animals on a globe is nearly impossible, because few species of plants and animals are associated with one single place. They do have special areas where they grow but these are not constant. Natural spreading and growth of plants and animals is becoming limited, because human beings are encroaching. In fact, some species are already lost and others are nearly wiped out and soon it will only be possible to say where they were seen last.

On the other hand, some plants and animals, especially cultivated plants and domestic animals have been widely spread by people and this happened even in prehistoric times. For many years we believed that maize was indigenous to the Americas, but it has been proved that it originated in East Asia.

Zoologists, botanists, geneticists and geographers have been trying for years to find out where the various plants and animals of the world first grew. This is difficult because the cultivated forms often look very different to the original species. It is of great importance to find the sources of these because wild forms are of use in cross fertilization.

Probable Place of Origin Cultivated and Domestic Animals

	Place of origin	Latitude	Longitude		Place of origin	Latitude	Longitude
Cultivated Plants				Olive	Turkey	37° N	37° E
Wheat	Iraq	35° N	45° E	Sesame	Ethiopia	10° N	40° E
Barley	Near East	35° N	40° E	Sunflower	USA	35° N	95° W
Rye	Near East	40° N	40° E	Oil Palm	West Africa	5° N	15° E
Oats	Armenia	40° N	45° E	Coconut Palm	Columbia	10° N	75° W
Millet	China	35° N	115° E	Groundnut	Brazil	15° S	45° W
Maize	Assam	28° N	95° E	Flax	Near East	40° N	45° E
Rice	Thailand	15° N	105° E	Cotton	Sudan	10° N	30° E
Potatoes	Peru	10° S	78° W	Sisal	Mexico	20° N	90° W
Sugarcane	Bangladesh	24° N	90° E	Jute	Bangladesh	24° N	90° E
Sugar beet	Baltic Coast	54° N	12° E				
Coffee	Ethiopia	5° N	40° E	*Domestic Animals*			
Cocoa	Brazil	0°	70° W	Horse	Caucasia	45° N	45° E
Tea	Assam	26° N	93° E	Sheep	Afghanistan	33° N	65° E
Tobacco	Bolivia	12° S	65° W	Goat	Near East	40° N	40° E
Grapes	Armenia	42° N	42° E	Cattle	Near East	40° N	40° E
Dates	Arabia	30° N	40° E	Donkey	North Africa	20° N	35° E
Figs	Arabia	15° N	45° E	Lama	South America	12° S	72° W
Apple	Central Europe	52° N	12° E	Chicken	Malaysia	4° N	103° E
Citrus fruits	Burma	23° N	97° E				
(e.g. Lemon)	South China	23° N	115° E				

Continents and Countries

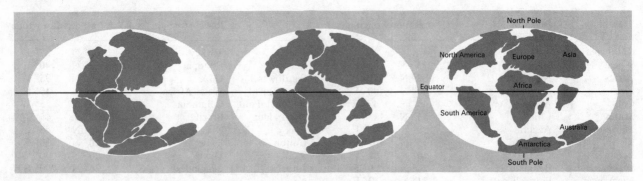

Many million years ago it is quite possible that all the land masses were concentrated in the same area. They became split by strong internal movements of the earth. Looking at a map it seems likely that North and South America have been connected with Europe at some time.

The great land masses are called continents, but there is not complete agreement where the divisions should be made. It would be more natural to say Eurasia instead of Europe and Asia. This would overcome the difficulty of the fact that USSR lies in both continents. But Europe is like-ly to continue its status as a continent, even though it should be called a sub-continent like India.

There are seven continents: Asia, Africa and Europe which are the Old World, North and South America which make the New World and Australia and Antarctica which might be called the Newest World. Statistically, it has been most expedient to talk of Europe without USSR and Asia without USSR and give figures for USSR alone. Discussion about Australia seems to indicate that it should be included in the area of the Pacific Ocean and called Oceania.

The continents are split up into countries, politically. Most of these are independent or constituent states, examples of the latter being USA, Brazil, Jugoslavia and West Germany. There are some colonies in existence which have not yet gained their independence.

The biggest countries are USSR, Canada, China, USA, Brazil, Australia and India. Other countries are so small that it is difficult to find them on the map. The following list shows some of these.

Small States

Continent	Area in 1000 km²	/ 1000 sq. miles	Latitude	Longitude
EUROPE				
Albania	29	11.2	42° N	20° E
Andorra	0.4	0.19	43° N	2° E
Liechtenstein	0.16	0.06	47° N	9° E
Luxembourg	2.6	1.00	49° N	7° E
Malta	0.3	0.116	36° N	14° E
Monaco	0.0015	0.00058	43° N	7° E
San Marino	0.06	0.0232	43° N	13° E
Vatican City	0.0004	0.0002	42° N	12° E
ASIA				
Bahrain	0.6	0.232	26° N	51° E
Israel	21	8.1	32° N	35° E
Quatar	24	8.5	25° N	52° E
Kuwait	16	6.2	29° N	57° E
Lebanon	10	3.86	33° N	36° E
Maldive Islands	0.3	0.116	6° N	73° E
Singapore	0.6	0.232	2° N	104° E
Cyprus	9.3	3.59	35° N	33° E

Continent	Area in 1000 km²	/ 1000 sq. miles	Latitude	Longitude
AFRICA				
Equatorial Guinea	28	10.8	2° N	10° E
Burundi	28	10.8	4° S	30° E
Gambia	11	4.2	13° N	15° W
Lesotho	30	11.58	29° S	28° E
Mauritius	2	0.77	20° S	57° E
Ruandi	26	10.04	3° S	30° E
Swaziland	17	6.56	27° S	32° E
AMERICA				
Barbados	0.4	0.154	13° N	60° W
El Salvador	21	8.11	14° N	88° W
Haiti	27	10.4	14° N	73° W
Jamaica	11	4.25	18° N	77° W
Trinidad and Tobago	5.1	1.97	11° N	62° W
AUSTRALIA and OCEANIA				
Fiji	18	6.95	17° S	179° E
Nauru	0.02	0.0077	0°	166° E
Tonga	0.7	0.27	21° S	175° E
West Samoa	2.8	1.98	14° S	172° E

The Biggest Cities of the World

Tokyo   New York   Shanghai   Paris   Buenos Aires   Mexico City   London   Moscow   Calcutta   Chicago   Bombay   Berlin

Due to the rapid expansion of industry since the nineteenth century, most towns in the industralized countries of the world have increased quickly too. For example, in Germany the urbanized population of the country is more than 80 % (1816:25 %, 1900: 55 %). In USSR about 60 % of the people live in towns whereas in 1900 only 12 % lived there. This urban explosion has spread to the lesser developed countries and they have many big cities too, that is towns with more than 100,000 inhabitants. The reason for all this urbanization is that land dwellers have moved to the big cities where there are greater employment possibilities and social opportunities.

This urbanization has lead not only to the founding of single towns but also to groups of towns (conurbation). Well-known examples of this development are the Ruhr area of Germany, the Midlands of England and Randstad Holland, which is the area around Amsterdam, The Hague and Rotterdam. Many towns are surrounded by planned suburbs where the population often grows more rapidly than the actual town area. Consequently it is not always easy to calculate the actual population of a big town and often the population of the suburbs is included. On the opposite page it will be noticed that the initials "I.S" have been printed after certain population figures. This indicates "Including Suburbs".

Of the 2000 big cities of the world there are 180 cities with over a million people. Most of the cities are in USSR, USA, China, India, Japan, Germany and Great Britain. Until 1957, New York was the biggest city in the world. Now it is Tokyo.

The Biggest Cities of the World

City	Country	Inhabitants in Millions i.s. = including suburbs	Latitude	Longitude
Tokyo	Japan	12,0 i.s.	35° N	139° E
New York	USA	11,5 i.s.	40° N	74° W
Shanghai	China	10,7	31° N	121° E
Paris	France	10,6 i.s.	48° N	2° E
Buenos Aires	Argentina	8,8 i.s.	34° N	58° W
Mexico City	Mexico	8,9 i.s.	19° N	99° W
London	Great Britain	7,4 i.s.	51° N	0°
Moscow	USSR	7,7 i.s.	55° N	37° E
Calcutta	India	7,0 i.s.	22° N	88° E
Chicago	USA	7,0 i.s.	41° N	87° W
Los Angeles	USA	8,4 i.s.	34° N	118° W
Peking	China	7,6	40° N	116° E

City	Country	Inhabitants in Millions i.s. = including suburbs	Latitude	Longitude
Bombay	India	6,9 i.s.	19° N	72° E
Cairo	Egypt	5,0 i.s.	30° N	31° E
Philadelphia	USA	4,8 i.s.	44° N	75° W
Rio de Janeiro	Brazil	4,4	23° S	43° W
Detroit	USA	4,2 i.s.	42° N	83° W
Leningrad	USSR	4,3 i.s.	60° N	30° E
Tientsin	China	4,3	39° N	117° E
Delhi	India	3,6 i.s.	28° N	77° E
Berlin (West and East)	Germany	3,0	52,5° N	13,5° E

* Underlined cities are capitals.

Sources of Energy

By sources of energy we mean the raw materials which can be developed for heat, industry, transport, etc., but we do not refer to the sources of nourishment which gives energy to man and animal.

In earlier times hauling was done by man and beast, and heat made by wood and peat. Quite early, people learnt to utilize water power and, later, wind forces. These became inadequate when the Industrial Revolution started about 1800. Soon the problem of sufficient energy was solved at that time by the invention of steam engines heated by coal. About 1900, petrol and oil-driven machines were introduced. Earlier, water wheels were used to provide power, but by the end of the Nineteenth Century water was used to make hydraulic power. The introduction of alternating current at the beginning of 1900 meant that power from hydro-electric plants could be carried great distances to industrialized areas. It was not long before steam turbines and internal combustion engines contributed power to the increasing net of hydro-electric power lines. Power plants could now be built at places where raw materials for energy were found and at points where they could be easily transported, e.g. harbours. Later came the development of utilizing atomic energy for the production of electric power.

The lands which possess such raw materials have great advantages today because they can use them for their own industries or export the raw materials to other lands which have insufficient. The demands for these materials grow greater all the time.

Location of Sources of Energy

Coal	Country	Latitude	Longitude
Yorkshire	Great Britain	55° N	1° W
Durham	Great Britain	54° N	1° W
Ruhr	West Germany	51° N	7° E
Slask	Poland	51° N	19° E
Donezbasin	USSR	48° N	35° E
Kusnezbasin	USSR	55° N	90° E
Karaganda	USSR	60° N	75° E
West Virginia	USA	38° N	82° W
Pennsylvania	USA	41° N	77° W
Illinois	USA	40° N	88° W
Ranchi	India	22° N	86° E
Fuschun	China	41° N	123° E
Newcastle	Australia	38° S	152° E

Uranium	Country	Latitude	Longitude
Johannesburg	South Africa	27° S	28° E
Katanga	Zaïre	8° S	25° E
Irkutsk	USSR	53° N	104° E
Fergana	USSR	41° N	71° E
Uranium City	Canada	59° N	109° W
Beaver Lodge	Canada	63° N	115° W
Port Radium	Canada	66° N	118° W
Shiprock	USA	37° N	109° W
Rum Jungle	Australia	13° S	131° W
Jachymov	Czechoslovakia	50° N	13° E

Oil	Country	Latitude	Longitude
Baku	USSR	41° N	50° E
New Baku	USSR	64° N	78° E
Kirkuk	Iraq	36° N	45° E
Kuwait		29° N	48° E
West Iran		31° N	50° E
Ghawar	Saudi Arabia	25° N	50° E
Palembang	Indonesia	3° S	105° E
Maracaibo	Venezuela	10° N	72° W
Oficina	Venezuela	8° N	66° W
Trinidad		10° N	62° W
Gulf Field	USA	24–31° N	87–97° W
Mid Continent Field	Texas	33–35° N	97° W
Pembina	Canada	34° N	118° W
Hassi-Messaud	Algeria	31° N	6° E
Zelten	Libya	28° N	19° E

Iron Ore

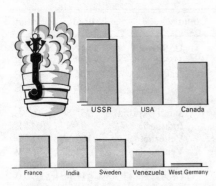

Iron is one of the most abundant elements of the earth's crust and the most important ore in industrial use. In ancient times iron was smelted over charcoal and mass production first began with the introduction of blast furnaces where coke was used for the conversion of iron. The invention of blast furnaces is as important as that of steam engine.

Places where both coal and iron were found in the earth became obvious areas for the establishment of heavy industry.

Iron ore is of varying quality, the best containing over 60% and the poorest having less than 20%. The latter, usually brown iron ore, could not be used economically in earlier times, but recently cheap methods have been found which help to enrich the iron content and this has made it an economical proposition now.

Most iron is converted into steel and steel works are placed near iron works to save transport. For the production of the many varieties of steel many other metals are used with iron. These enhance the quality of the steel (e.g. makes it rustless). Metals which are used in alloys are manganese, chromium, nickel etc.

The chart opposite gives the figures for the production of iron ore in the various countries for 1975 and to simplify comparison all figures quoted give the amount of iron extracted.

Country	Iron Ore (in 1000 tons)	Area or Location	Latitude	Longitude
USSR	233 000	Krivoi Rog	45° N	34° E
		Magnitogorsk	53° N	59° E
USA	76 906	Mesabi Range	47° N	94° W
		Wisconsin	44° N	90° W
Australia	37 115	Hamersley Range	16° S	127° E
		Middleback Range	34° S	137° E
Canada	49 415	Schefferville	55° N	67° W
		Labrador City	62° N	68° W
Brazil	58 460	Minas Gerais	19° S	46° W
China	22 000	Anschan	41° N	123° E
Sweden	30 900	Kiruna	68° N	20° E
		Gällivare	60° N	14° E
India	36 000	Bihar/Orissa	25° N	85° E
France	54 260	Lorraine	49° N	6° E
Liberia	17 480	Bomi Hills	5° N	10° W
Venezuela	26 200	Cerro Bolivar	6° N	63° W
West Germany	1 804	Salzgitter	52° N	10° E

Precious Metals

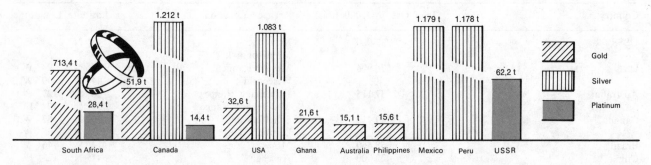

Gold		
Silver		
Platinum		

Under this heading we refer to platinum, gold and silver. They are called "precious" because they do not combine with the oxygen of the air and are almost chemically inactive. From earliest times these qualities led to the use of gold and silver for personal ornaments, jewelry etc. and later for coins and measures of value. Until recent years, most countries had gold standards of currency, some few had silver standards, and during currency crises there is still a great buying up of gold.

Gold and silver have been used in the production of jewelry because both are quite ductile and therefore malleable. In many cases the ductile quality of these two metals has been hardened by alloying them with other harder metals, like copper. In contrast, platinum is very hard and is used for the setting of very valuable jewelry. It has many technical uses in alloy form as it is resistant to corrosion.

Most platinum and gold and some silver are found in pure form and less frequently as ore with other metals. Extraction of platinum and gold can be made partly by extraction and partly by washing out. Grains of gold can be separated from grains of sand because gold is heavier.

Opposite is a list of the most important countries for the production of gold, silver and platinum.

	Country	Annual production in tons	Location of mine	Latitude	Longitude
Gold	South Africa	713,4	Witwatersrand	27° S	27° E
			Oldendalsrus	29° S	28° E
	Canada	51,9	Porcupine	48° N	80° W
			Val d'Or	48° N	78° W
			Yellowknife	62° N	114° W
	USA	32,6	Fairbanks	65° N	147° W
			Yuba	39° N	121° W
	Ghana	21,6	Obuasi	6° N	1° W
			Prestea	5° N	2° W
	Australia	15,1	Victoria	37° S	144° E
			Kalgoorlie	32° S	122° E
	Philippines	15,6	North Luzon	17° N	122° E
	Japan	4,3	Mombetsu	44° N	143° E
	Columbia	6,3	Frontino	2° N	77° W
	Mexico	4,5	San Dimas	24° N	106° W
Silver	Canada	1212	Sudbury	47° N	81° W
			Kootenay	49° N	117° W
	USA	1083	Butte	46° N	112° W
	Mexico	1179	Chihuahua	29° N	106° W
	Peru	1178	Cerro de Pasco	10° S	77° W
	USSR	1150	Sadon	43° N	44° E
Platinum	USSR	62,2	Norilsk	69° N	88° E
	South Africa	28,4	Rustenburg	26° S	27° E
	Canada	14,4	Sudbury	46° N	81° W

Other Metals

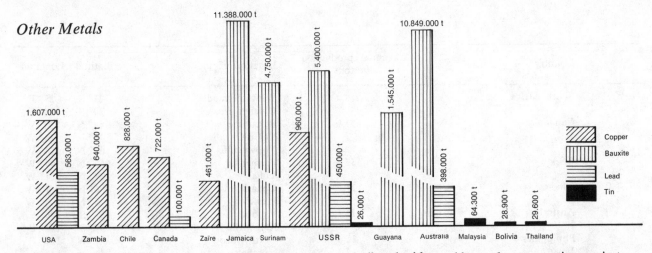

The importance of other metals depends on their industrial uses. Their properties vary a great deal and this determines whether they can be used economically or not.

Copper is good conducting agent of heat and electricity and much copper is used for wires, cables and tubes. Copper is also used in alloyed forms as bronze and brass and both these products are used extensively in our daily life.

Aluminium is another important metal which is used because of its lightness. It is also used alloyed with iron to make aluminium steel which is both hard and light and used in the making of aircraft. The main sources of aluminium is in bauxite, which is a clay-like mineral often red in colour. A great deal of electricity is needed for the extraction of aluminium and most works are situated near hydraulic power plants.

Lead is heavy and soft. Earlier, it was used for water pipes because of its resistance to corrosion. Today, it is used as covering for all types of cables and as protection against radio-active rays and X-rays. Thick layers of lead cover reactors of atomic energy plants and X-ray machines are protected with lead plate.

As zinc does not rust it is used in the galvanizing of iron.

Other metals especially manganese, chrome and nickel and even the more rare vanadium, titanium, wolfram, molybdenum etc., are used primarily as alloys. Chrome, nickel and tin are used as coating metals in the car and canning industry.

	Country	Annual production in 1000 tons	Location	Latitude	Longitude
Copper	USA	1 607	Bingham	40° N	112° W
			Morenci	33° N	110° W
			Butte	46° N	112° W
	USSR	960	Dzhezkazgan	48° N	68° E
	Chile	828	Chuquieamata	22° S	64° W
			El Teniente	36° S	72° W
			Potrerillos	27° S	71° W
	Canada	722	Sudbury	46° N	81° W
			Flin Flon	55° N	102° W
	Zambia	640	Copper Belt	13° N	27° W
	Zaïre	461	Katanga	10° S	27° E
Bauxite	Jamaica	11 388		18° N	77° W
	Australia	10 849	Weipa	35° S	148° E
	Surinam	4 750		4° N	56° W
	USSR	5 400	Krasnoturinsk	60° N	68° E
			Pawlodar	56° N	63° E
	Guayana	1 545	Mackenzie	7° N	58° W
Lead	USA	563	South East Missouri	37° N	90° W
	USSR	450	Leninogorsk	51° N	84° E
	Australia	398	Mt. Isa	21° S	139° E
			Broken Hill	32° S	141° E
	Canada	100	Kootenay	49° N	117° W
Tin	Malaysia	64,3	Kintatal	4° N	103° E
	Bolivia	28,9	Potosi	20° S	66° W
	USSR	26,0	Borsja	50° N	127° E
	China	23,0	Nanning	23° N	108° E
	Thailand	29,6	Pilok	17° N	103° E
	Indonesia	22,6	Bangka	3° S	107° E

Other Minerals

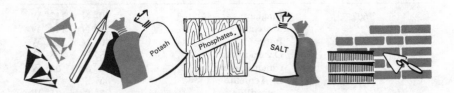

Some minerals are common all over the world and cannot be placed in any special locality, others are more rare. Amongst the latter are two forms of crystallized pure carbon: diamonds and graphite. These have widely different qualities. Diamonds are the hardest material known whereas graphite is soft and greasy. Diamonds are used as abrasives in industry. In addition they are much valued as precious stones because of their quality of reflecting light when they are cut properly. Graphite is used in lubrication, as a moderator in atomic piles, and in making lead pencils.

One of the more common minerals is mica which is used as insulating material in electrical equipment. Another is asbestos which cannot burn and is used for protection against high temperatures. Workers in blast furnaces use asbestos clothing.

A large group of minerals are used in the fertilizer industry. These are potassic salt (potash), chilean nitrate, phosphates and chalk. The latter is used a great deal in the building industry, in the form of cement.

In addition, sulphur and ordinary kitchen salt must be included as they are used in the chemical industries. Kitchen salt is of importance in the human diet, too.

	Country	Area or location	Latitude	Longitude
Diamonds	South Africa	Kimberley	29° S	25° E
		Premier	27° S	29° E
	Namibia (South West Africa)	Lüderitz	27° S	15° E
		Rosh Pinah	28° S	17° E
	Zaïre	Tsikapa	9° S	21° E
		Mbuji-Mayi	7° S	23° E
	USSR	Mir	55° N	31° E
		Udachnaja	64° N	102° E
		Yakutia	63° N	134° E
Potash	Germany	Lengede near Hannover	52° N	10° E
		Bernburg/Saale	52° N	12° E
	France	Bollwiller in Alsace	45° N	6° E
	USSR	Solikamsk	56° N	56° E
	Canada	Esterhazy	51° N	102° W
	USA	Carlsbad	32° N	104° W
Phosphates	Morocco	Khouribga	33° N	7° W
		Youssoufia	32° N	9° W
	USSR	Kirovsk	68° N	34° E
		Chulok-Tau	45° N	67° E
	USA	Mulberry	27° N	82° W
Common salt	Poland	Wieliczka	50° N	20° E
	Austria	Salzkammergut	47° N	13° E
	Israel	Dead Sea	32° N	36° E

Industrial Zones

There is every reason for calling our present times the Industrial Age. Since the middle of the 19th Century industry has become more dominant and in many countries more people are employed in industry than any other form of labour. This may no longer be the case now as we are entering a new phase where services of different kinds begin to take over the employment lead. But it must be emphasized that this is only possible because mass production has made consumer goods of every sort available to all.

At the beginning of the industrial period there was a tendency to group industries together. This was influenced by the location of raw materials, especially coal and iron, and by the availability of labour. Many industries remain where they started but new ones have developed especially in areas where there is a good market for industrial products.

Many industries are dependent on each other and it can be an advantage if they lie near to each other so that transport costs are less. This collaboration between the different industries has been studied scientifically and the results have influenced the placement of new factories, grouping them together in larger units. In big industrial areas many combinations have been developed. Certain industries such as knitwear employ female labour and these are placed in the same area as heavy industries where it is more general to employ men. In this way there is employment for both men and women in the same area.

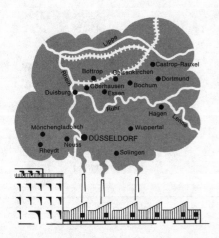

Industrial Locations	Town	Latitude	Longitude
Midlands	Birmingham	52° N	2° W
(U. K.)	Coventry	52° N	1° W
Lancashire	Manchester	53° N	3° W
(U. K.)	Preston	53° N	2° W
Yorkshire	Sheffield	55° N	1° W
(U. K.)	Leeds	54° N	1° W
Ruhr	Dortmund	52° N	7° E
(West Germany)	Bochum	51° N	7° E
	Gelsenkirchen	51° N	7° E
	Essen	51° N	7° E
	Oberhausen	51° N	7° E
	Duisburg	51° N	7° E
Randstad	Rotterdam	52° N	5° E
(The Netherlands)	Amsterdam	52° N	5° E
	The Hague	52° N	4° E
	Utrecht	52° N	5° E

Industrial Locations	Town	Latitude	Longitude
Upper Silesia	Katowice	50° N	19° E
(Slask)	Zabrze	50° N	19° E
(Poland)	Gliwice	50° N	19° E
Donetsk Basin	Donetsk	48° N	38° E
(USSR)	Makeyevka	48° N	35° E
	Gorlovka	48° N	33° E
	Voroshilovgrad	50° N	36° E
Industrial belt	Detroit	43° N	83° W
round Lake Erie	Toledo	42° N	84° W
(USA)	Cleveland	42° N	82° W
	Pittsburgh	41° N	80° W

Oil Refineries and Atomic Energy Plants

Oil has become an important world product in the past few years. At first oil refineries were built in areas where oil was found. But these areas had little practical use for it whereas in other areas the chemical industry was developing many new products from raw oil. Transportation of oil became more efficient with the building of pipe lines and super tankers. It is more practical to transport the raw oil instead of the many finished oil products so refineries were built outside the oil producing areas. Such refineries are economic assets and even small countries have refineries now.

Another modern industrial phenomenon is the atomic energy plant. Developments in this field have made it of economic value to build such plants in countries which use a great deal of electricity. Atomic plants are very expensive to build, but use of atomic energy leads to a saving of other raw materials originally used in the production of energy. Due to the risk of radio-active fallout etc., most plants are built in under-populated areas.

Oil Refineries

Location	Country	Latitude	Longitude
Grangemouth	Great Britain	56° N	3° W
Liverpool	Great Britain	53° N	3° W
Fawley	Great Britain	51° N	10° W
Thames estuary	Great Britain	51° N	10° E
Europort	The Netherlands	52° N	40° E
Antwerpen	Belgium	51° N	4° E
Ruhr	West Germany	52° N	5° E
Hamburg	West Germany	54° N	10° E
Karlsruhe	West Germany	49° N	8° E
Ingolstadt	West Germany	49° N	11° E
Le Havre	France	49° N	0°
Marseilles	France	43° N	5° E
Genoa	Italy	44° N	9° E
Augusta	Sicily	37° N	15° E
Abadan	Iran	31° N	48° E

Location	Country	Latitude	Longitude
Kuweit		29° N	48° E
Tokio	Japan	36° N	140° E
Philadelphia	USA	40° N	75° W
Chicago	USA	42° N	88° W
Houston	USA	30° N	95° W
Los Angeles	USA	33° N	110° W
San Francisco	USA	38° N	123° W
Tampico	Mexico	22° N	95° W
Trinidad		11° N	61° W
Curaçao	Dutch West Indies	12° N	69° W
Amuay	Venezuela	12° N	70° W
El Cardon	Venezuela	12° N	71° W
Baku	USSR	41° N	50° E
Ufa	USSR	55° N	56° E
Kuybyschew	USSR	54° N	50° E

Atomic Energy Plants

Location	Country	Latitude	Longitude
Berkeley	Great Britain	52° N	2° W
Calder Hall	Great Britain	54° N	3° W
Hinkley Point	Great Britain	51° N	4° W
Chinon	France	47° N	0°
Marcoule	France	44° N	5° E
Kahl/Main	West Germany	50° N	8° E
Stadersand/Elbe	West Germany	54° N	9° E

Location	Country	Latitude	Longitude
Rheinsberg	DDR	53° N	13° E
Rheinfelden	Switzerland	48° N	8° E
Voronezh	USSR	55° N	40° E
Tokai Mura	Japan	58° N	33° E
Sioux Falls	USA	43° N	96° W
Browns Ferry	USA	40° N	76° W
Sequoyah Site	USA	35° N	121° W

Shipping

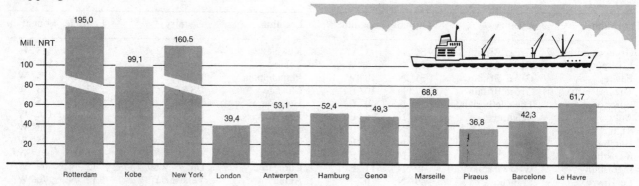

The cheapest form of transport is by boat. It is not as quick as other forms of transport, but this is not important for heavy and non-perishable goods.

At the beginning of the Industrial Age, it was important to transport coal, iron and industrial goods as cheaply as possible. Horses and wagons were not very suitable, especially as the roads were badly made at that time. Consequently water transport was used and wherever possible canals were built across countries. Some of these have importance today but many remain only as tourist attractions. Inland canals which have remained important must be able to take big boats. The network in USSR which links Moscow to the Baltic, White, Black and Caspian Seas is one example.

Deep-draught ship canals which can take ocean-going boats are of greatest value. Many of these have been cut through isthmuses so that long sailing distances have been saved. (Panama, Suez and Kiel Canals.) Others have been cut into the land. (Manchester Ship Canal, St. Lawrence Seaway, etc.)

For shipping, it has always been important that harbours were sheltered so that ships do not have to ride at anchor at the open roadsteads. Generally harbours have been developed where they could supply a large industrial hinterland. It is easy to understand why Rotterdam with Europort has become the biggest harbour in the world having a yearly turnover of goods of about 225 millions.

Canals

	Latitude	Longitude
Suez Canal	31° N	33° E
Volga-Don Canal	48° N	44° E
Kiel Canal	54° N	9° E
Houston Canal	29° N	95° W
Alphonse XIII. Canal (to Seville)	37° N	6° E
Panama Canal	9° N	80° W
Manchester Canal	53° N	2° W
Welland Canal (by Niagara Falls)	43° N	79° W

The Most Important Ports

Turnover in mill. t. net. per year (1976)	Latitude	Longitude
Rotterdam	195,0	52° N	4° E
Kobe	99,1	69° N	135° E
New York	160,5	41° N	74° W
Yokohama	181,2	35° N	139° E
Singapore	111,4	1° N	104° E
Nagoya	57,8	35° N	137° E
Osaka	84,2	35° N	135° E
London	39,4	51° N	0°
Antwerpen	53,1	51° N	4° E
New Orleans	36,9	30° N	90° W
Marseilles	68,8	43° N	5° E
Hamburg	52,4	53° N	6° E
Los Angeles	59,4	33° N	118° W
Aden	9,9	13° N	45° E
San Francisco	29,4	38° N	123° W
Le Havre	61,7	49° N	0°
Genoa	43,9	44° N	9° E
Boston	14,5	42° N	71° W
Bremen	39,4	53° N	9° E
Santos	18,8	24° S	46° W
Piraeus	36,8	38° N	24° E
Southhampton	33,0	51° N	1° W
Curaçao	24,0	12° N	69° W
Barcelone	42,3	41° N	2° E
Houston	41,9	30° N	95° W
Aruba	23,1	12° N	70° W
Montreal	33,6	46° N	73° W
Copenhagen	14,4	55° N	12° E

Tunnels, Bridges and Dams

Golden Gate

The great artificial fall of water at the barrage itself is used to make electricity. Artificial irrigation is one of the most important uses of the lake and it can be used for fishing. If a sluice canal is built to circumnavigate the fall, the lake can be used for water transport. These lakes give the landscape a new scenic beauty and such areas are used for recreation. A great many of such lakes have been made in USA.

Mountains and water have always been obstacles to any form of road transport. The first way of crossing mountains was made by using the passes on the lowest parts of mountains. (See p. 28 Mountains). Later tunnels were built.

Large stretches of water have always offered difficulties as these could only be crossed by boat or ferry. Bridges can be built over fjords, straits and big rivers where the amount of traffic justifies this expense. Tunnels can be built under water and these are of greatest value where there is much shipping in the area.

New features in the landscape of today are artificially-built lakes. First, a barrage is constructed at a suitable point on the river. The water rises behind this barrage to form a big lake.

		Location		Latitude	Longitude
Tunnels					
through mountains	Simplon	Switzerland Italy		46° N	8° E
	Apennin	Bologna Florence		44° N	11° E
	St. Gotthard	Switzerland		47° N	9° E
Tunnels					
under water	Seikan	Tsugaru Strait (Japan)		41° N	141° E
	Kammon	Shimoseki (Japan)		34° N	131° E
	Mersey	Liverpool Birkenhead (England)		53° N	3° W
Bridges					
	Öland Bridge	Sweden		56° N	16° E
	Verrazano-Narrows	Brooklyn (New York)		41° N	74° W
	Golden Gate	San Francisco		38° N	123° W
	George Washington	Hudson River		42° N	74° W
	Salazar Bridge	Lisbon		39° N	9° W
	Forth Bridge	Firth of Forth (Scotland)		56° N	4° W
	Severn	England		52° N	3° W
Dams					
		Country	*River*		
	Igurskaya	USSR	Iguri	55° N	33° E
	Nurek	USSR	Vakhsh	38° N	69° E
	Vaioul	Italy	Piave	46° N	13° E
	Mauvoisin	Switzerland	Rhônequelle	46° N	8° E
Some big					
artificial lakes	Kariba	Zimbabwe		17° S	28° E
	Bratsk	USSR		58° N	101° E
	Aswan	U.A.R.		24° N	33° E
	Akosombo	Ghana		6° N	0°

Air Traffic

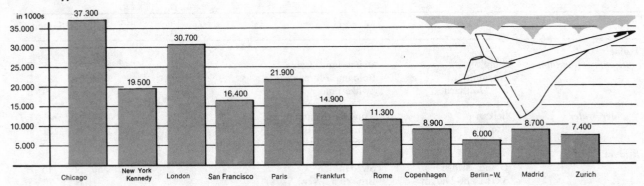

in 1000s

Chicago 37.300
New York Kennedy 19.500
London 30.700
San Francisco 16.400
Paris 21.900
Frankfurt 14.900
Rome 11.300
Copenhagen 8.900
Berlin-W. 6.000
Madrid 8.700
Zurich 7.400

Today, we say that "the world has become smaller," and this is true. First telecommunications have made it possible for us to contact each other over great distances in a matter of seconds. Secondly, almost as soon as news is made in any part of the world it is reported to us through the medias of radio and television.

Lastly, and most important we have reduced the size of the world by the speed with which we can get from one place to another by air. Travel that took days and months now only takes a few hours. It is not surprising that the number of trans-Atlantic ship

passengers has fallen greatly. In 1954, 63% of the travellers came to Europe by boat but by 1967 only 9% made use of this way of travel. This is not only due to the speed of modern planes but also because planes take more direct routes from airport to airport.

It is difficult to find the distance of this circular arc between two airports on a map, but on a globe it is easy. Take a piece of string and hold it tightly on the globe between the two airports. The string will lie in a arc and the length of string between the two airports will give the distance.

This can be calculated in kilometres as each degree of latitude is 110 km (=69,3 miles).

Airports

	Passengers (in 1000s) 1976	Latitude	Longitude
USA			
Chicago	37,3	42° N	88° W
Los Angeles	23,7	33° N	118° W
New York (Kennedy)	19,5	40° N	74° W
Atlanta	25,3	34° N	84° W
San Francisco	16,4	38° N	123° W
New York (La Guardia)	13,2	41° N	74° W
Miami	12,1	26° N	80° W
Dallas	16,1	32° N	96° W
Washington D.C.	11,2	39° N	77° W
Boston	10,5	42° N	71° W

	Passengers (in 1000s) 1976	Latitude	Longitude
Europe			
London	30	51° N	0°
Paris	21	49° N	2° E
Frankfurt	14	50° N	9° E
Rome	11	42° N	12° E
Copenhagen	8	55° N	11° E
Palma	7	39° N	3° E
Berlin-West	6	52° N	13° E
Amsterdam	8	52° N	5° E
Madrid	8	40° N	4° W
Zurich	7	47° N	9° E

Prehistoric Man

We do not know how long man has existed on earth. But there are signs that the first creature we can describe as man – because he used tools – lived about two million years ago. In this connection it is worth remembering that the first written evidence about man is only 5000 years old and was found in Mesopotamia, now Iraq.

Judging from present day standards, these first creatures that inhabited the earth in earliest times were more like apes than people. This type of creature has been named Australo-Pithecus (South Ape), as the most important discovery of this extinct group was made in Africa.

From about 500,000 BC there is evidence of a more human group, Pithecanthropus, first found in Java. Later, came Sinathropus, (the Peking Man), which is a probable variant of "Homo Erectus". The Heidelberg Man, of which only the lower jaw was found, comes from a later period.

From about 60,000 BC the Neanderthal Man seems to have dominated. This is known from many discov-

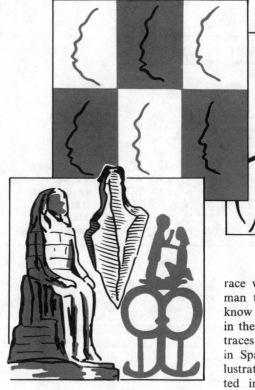

eries of his remains in Europe and North Africa. Finally, from about 25,000 BC came the Cro-Magnon race who resembled the present day man to a much greater degree. We know much more about them because in the last Ice Age some of them left traces in the caves where they lived in Spain and France. They have illustrated the animals that they hunted in cave paintings and statues. Amongst these were mammoth, bison, reindeer, wild horse, rhinoceros, bear and hart.

Excavations of Extinct Human Races

Race	Place of Discovery	Latitude	Longitude
Australopithecus	Olduvai	3° S	35° E
Pitecanthropus erectus	Java	3° S	107° E
Sinanthropus (Peking-man)	near Peking	40° N	115° E
Heidelberg-man	near Heidelberg	49° N	9° E
Neanderthal-man	Neanderthal	51° N	7° E
Cro Magnon	Les Eyzier	45° N	1° E

Caves with Paintings

Place	Country	Latitude	Longitude
Altamira	Spain	43° N	4° W
Lascaux	France	45° N	1° E
Font de Gaume	France	45° N	1° E
Pech Merle	France	44° N	2° E

Famous Sculptures etc.

Venus of Willendorf	Austria	48° N	15° E
La Venus de Laussel	France	45° N	1° E
Stonehenge	England	51° N	2° W

Mesopotamia, Egypt, Greece and the Roman Empire

EGYPT   PAESTUM   UR   POMPEI

Mesopotamia and Egypt

Most historical remains of ancient times are to be found in the areas where civilization reached its greatest heights. This happened where artificial irrigation was used. The big artificial irrigation areas were developed on the banks of rivers. Through ingenious canal networks the water was lead into flat river valleys and used for agriculture. As the river brought fertile sediment along with it, there was no necessity to use additional fertilizer. Thus two needs for plant growth were satisfied and high temperatures were provided by nature itself.

The conditions for establishing and maintaining an artificial irrigation system demanded a highly organized community which could keep the rules about when and how much water should be given to each place. Many of these communities grew up in the Middle East, in the so-called "Fertile Half-Moon" which stretches from the Euphrates and Tigris valleys to Egypt. The rulers of these kingdoms have left impressive monuments in the form of graves, pyramids, fortresses and towns.

Jericho is thought to be the oldest of these urbanized communities.

About 7000 BC there was a village which gradually developed into a town, economically based on the artificial irrigation-farming of the Jordan valley. Almost as old is Ur, Abraham's town, which lay in the land of the Sumers. In 3000 BC it consisted of small clay-lined huts flanking small streets. The town was surrounded by a wall. Dominating the whole town was a great temple – the Ziggurat – This must have been an impressive sight with its base of 60 by 45 meters (197 by 148 feet) and height of 21 meters (69 feet). We can still see some of the wealth that was collected by the kings of the town as relics have been found in the form of 16 royal graves with valuable burial deposits. Lagash was another of the city-states of the Sumers.

About 2000 BC, the dominant rule of the Sumers collapsed in Mesopotamia and the Amonites became the leaders. Their most important town was Babylon, which like Ur, had a temple as focal point. This was the Marduk Temple. About 1600 BC a

new group of people, the Hittites conquered Babylon. The greatest part of their kingdom lay in Asia Minor and from here they conquered both Syria and Lebanon, including Aleppo. The Assyrians lived on the upper reaches of the Tigris river where Assur was the capital. Later Nineveh became the capital. At the end of 2000 BC the Assyrians had conquered Babylon, Syria, Palestine and even Egypt at one point.

In Egypt there are traces of civilization from 5000 BC, but the first real town settlements were developed just before 3000 BC. The first capital of the whole country was Thebes. Later Memphis became the capital. The era from Egypt's foundation about 3000 BC to the time when Alexander the Great conquered the land in 332 BC is divided into about 30 dynasties of which there were three main periods: the Old Kingdom (about 3000-2280 BC), the Middle Kingdom (2050-1778 BC), and the New Kingdom (about 1567-1085 BC). Interspersed between these were periods of decline and disruption. Much of our knowledge of these old Kingdoms comes from the inscriptions on clay tablets written in Egyptian script, hieroglyphics. In 1799 AD, at Rosetta on the Nile delta, a find was made of a stone with three texts: one in Greek, one in hieroglyphics and one in Demotic, a later Egyptian script. A suspicion that all three sets of writing might have the same text lead to the deciphering of hieroglyphics and paved the way to a greater knowledge of ancient history.

The most beautiful monuments from these Kingdoms are the Pyramids, many of which are at Gizah. The biggest of these is the Cheops Pyramid from about 2650 BC: circumference 233 meters (765 feet) and original height 146 meters (400 feet). In the period of the New Kingdom, the capital was moved from Thebes to Tell el Amarna, for 20 years. Many important finds from this period have been discovered including paintings, portraits and cuneiform writing. The Temple at Abu Simbel is from the New Kingdom's period too. It was built about 1250 BC by the great Pharaoh, Ramses II.

Greece

In ancient times, the greatest cultural development in Europe took place in Greece. A civilization developed in the last century BC which was above anything else in the rest of Europe. The development started with the arrival of the Dorians about 1100 BC and culminated in 5-3 BC. Because of the many mountains that divide the country, a series of city-states developed and these at various periods had contact and co-operation with each other. Countless relics from the various periods have been preserved and consequently only a few of the well-known can be listed here.

The towns of Mycenae and Troy are from the period before the Doric migration. There was a group of fortified towns on the Argive Plain and each was ruled by a king. The best known of these are Mycenae and Tiryns, both of which were surrounded by great battlements. Some of these towns still remain. According to Homer, the King of Mycenae was a kind of over-lord King who could call the land to war as Agamemnon did when hostilities against Troy broke out. This is described in the Iliad.

The foundation of the Golden Age

of Greece was laid between 750-500 BC. City-states like Athens and Sparta developed on their own lines. Their power and influence over the other city-states was considerable. A wave of emmigration started from Athens to the coastal regions of the Western Mediterranean.

Closeness in cultural interests was maintained in many ways such as the joint athletics meeting at Olympia. Gatherings of religious importance were held too. One religious centre was Delphi were there was an Apollo cult with an oracle which interpreted the Gods' prophecies about the future.

Political agreement within Greece was strengthened when the war with the Persians took place in 499-450 BC and an attack from the East was successfully repelled by the Greeks. Among the famous battlefields was Marathon, about 42 km (26 miles) from Athens.

The Roman Empire

The Roman Empire became Greece's successor as a cultural influence in Europe. It was greatly influenced by the earlier Greek period. Originally, the Empire only consisted of Rome and the surrounding countryside. Gradually, it developed so that at the beginning of the Christian era it covered the whole of the Mediterranean coastal area, all of present-day Western and Southern Europe, the Black Sea area, Asia Minor and all the Italian peninsula. The Roman Empire expanded again in the first hundred years AD and reached its greatest power during Emperor Trajan's reign (98-117 AD). At that time the empire included England, all areas south of the Rhine and the Danube, plus parts of Dacia, Egypt and Mauretania which were incorporated into the empire.

The Roman harbour, Ostia, was situated on the coast of Italy near Rome and here many important relics have been found in recent years. Pompei has been an invaluable source of knowledge about the Roman way of life at that time. The town was completely buried when Vesuvius erupted in 79 AD. From the Greek colonization period, we have Paestum where a great many temples from the 5th Century BC have been preserved. Taranto, too, was one of the important Greek colonies. In a similar way, Syracuse on Sicily was a source of Greek culture. In the 2nd and 3rd Century BC Glanum in Southern France was developed as a Greek town and later was occupied and expanded by the Romans. The town was destroyed in 300 AD, but is now partially excavated.

Carthage, which lay on the north coast of Africa, was Rome's greatest enemy in the 3rd and 2nd Centuries BC. The town was founded by the Phoenicians, who were great traders and controlled all the shipping routes on the Mediterranean at that period. After many wars, the Punic Wars, Carthage was totally destroyed by the Romans in 146 BC.

Mesopotamia and Egypt

	Latitude	Longitude		Latitude	Longitude
Aleppo	36° N	37° E	Abu Simbel	22° N	32° E
Assur	36° N	43° E	El Faijum	29° N	31° E
Babylon	33° N	45° E	Gizah	30° N	31° E
Jericho	32° N	35° E	Memphis	30° N	31° E
Telloh	31° N	47° E	Rosetta	31° N	30° E
Nineveh	36° N	43° E	Tell el Amarna	28° N	31° E
Ur	31° N	46° E	Thebes	26° N	33° E

Greece

	Latitude	Longitude		Latitude	Longitude
Athens	38° N	24° E	Glanum	44° N	5° E
Delphi	38° N	23° E	Carthage	37° N	10° E
Marathon	38° N	26° E	Ostia	42° N	12° E
Mycenae	38° N	23° E	Pompei	41° N	15° E
Pergamon	37° N	27° E	Paestum	40° N	15° E
Sparta	37° N	22° E	Syracuse	37° N	15° E
Troy	40° N	26° E	Taranto	41° N	17° E

Roman Empire

Famous Towns and Fortresses etc.

Carcassonne

Strasbourg

In the Middle Ages, Europe was a peasant society ruled by two powerful groups: one consisting of emperors, kings and noblemen and the other being the Catholic church. All the wealth and power was concentrated in these two groups and there are only a few relics to help us depict the life of the European peasant at this time. On the other hand, despite centuries of war and destruction, there are buildings of all sizes showing us how the aristocracy and clergy lived. The nobles built fortresses, castles and walled towns like York and Aigues Mortes. The clerics built churches, great and small, and monasteries in all parts of the Western world. The clerics were important, not only as spiritual influences, but also for their many innovations of practical value. Many monasteries were the leading agricultural influence of the area and the monks were experts on matters like drainage and ploughing, types of plants and all the technical developments of agriculture.

The monasteries were organized into religious orders guided by a Mother foundation. At first the majority of the cloisters lay in the country but, later in the Middle Ages, monasteries became part of the towns too. This gave their field of work a greater significance in social and educational areas.

Places of the Middle Ages

		Latitude	Longitude				Latitude	Longitude
Towns	Aachen	51° N	6° E	*Churches*	Le Puy	45° N	4° E
	Avignon	44° N	5° E		Lincoln	53° N	1° W
	Bamberg	50° N	11° E		Lund	56° N	13° E
	Bruges	51° N	3° E		Rouen	49° N	1° E
	Canterbury	51° N	1° E		Santiago	43° N	9° W
	Hastings	52° N	1° E		Wells	51° N	3° W
	Hildesheim	52° N	10° E				
	Pavia	45° N	9° E	*Monasteries*	Canossa	44° N	10° E
	Salzburg	48° N	13° E		Cluny	46° N	5° E
	Strasbourg	49° N	8° E		Citeaux	47° N	5° E
	Toulouse	44° N	1° E		Grande Chartreuse	45° N	6° E
	Trier	50° N	7° E		Hirsau	49° N	9° E
	York	54° N	1° W		Ravenna	44° N	12° E
Fortresses	Aigues Mortes	44° N	4° E				
	Carcassonne	43° N	2° E				
	Tower (London)	51° N	0°				

Famous Buildings Outside Europe

There are many buildings from earlier cultural periods throughout the world. Even today, some of these like Mecca and Medina have a great influence on cultural life.

In the ancient Asian empires many magnificent edifices were built. temples, castles, monuments, etc. Many of these were of an impressive size. The architecture of these buildings still has influence on the buildings of newer times. Our list includes both older and newer buildings so as to give an impression of the importance of building traditions. In some cases only the name of the town is given, e.g. Nanking, as the town has a great many characteristic buildings. In addition, from China we have included the Chinese Wall which is a structure whose dimensions have never been surpassed.

A small group of towns from both Mexico and Peru are listed. As in Asia, many of these old buildings have had a considerable cultural influence and, in spite of the erosion of time, there are many impressive remains.

In some cases there are only traces of town ruins. In others, like Cuzco, people are living in these old buildings although it must be added that these are people of an entirely different culture.

One of the modern cities of South America must be mentioned. This is Brazilia, the new capital of Brazil, which is well-known as an example of modern architecture and town planning.

Famous Buildings in Other Parts of the World

		Latitude	Longitude
Asia	Agra (Taj Mahal)	27° N	78° E
	Ajanta (Grotto)	20° N	76° E
	Angkor Vat	13° N	104° E
	Ayutthaya	14° N	101° E
	Jaipur (Hawa Mahal)	21° N	86° E
	The Chinese Wall	39° N	110° E
	Kyoto (the Nijo Castle)	35° N	136° E
	Nanking	32° N	119° E
	Peking	40° N	116° E
	Rangoon (the Golden Pagoda)	17° N	96° E
	Medina	25° N	40° E
	Mecca	22° N	40° E

		Latitude	Longitude
America	Brasilia	16° S	48° W
	Cuzco	14° S	72° W
	Oaxaca (Monte Albán)	17° N	97° W
	Easter Island	28° S	144° W
	San Juan Teotihuacán (Mexico)	20° N	99° W
	Uxmal	20° N	90° W

Voyages of Discovery and Historic Battlefields

From a European point of view, one of the greatest steps forward was made when voyages of discovery really became profitable about 1500 AD. This gave an extended knowledge of the world and increased the wealth of the countries which sent out the expeditions and merchant ships. Spain (e.g. Columbus) and Portugal pioneered such expeditions followed by the Netherlands, England and France. Some localities which became known through voyages of discovery are listed opposite. Many places have retained their original names but others have been named after the European who first arrived there.

The first voyages from Europe, apart from the Vikings who sailed to Greenland and North America, were down the coast of Africa. Areas like the Gold Coast were known to Europeans long before that terrible chapter of slave trade. This started about 1600 and from West Africa alone, during the 16th-19th Century more than 15,000,000 slaves were shipped to the American continent. The original reason for the voyages was to find the passage to India. Vasco da Gama, a Portuguese, succeeded in doing this in 1497-1498 after sailing round the Cape of Good Hope.

The European advance in America was made via the West Indies. To the North, Virginia became a favourite gateway for emigrants into the hinterland. The French founded a colony at Quebec, Canada.

The Spanish colonization of South America reached its peak after Pizarro, in 1531, conquered the Incas and their capital of Cuzco and thus gained countless riches in gold, found in the Inca empire.

One of the Europeans who gave his name to a Strait was Magellan who made a most daring voyage. In 1519 he sailed with five ships from Spain down the coast of South America round the cape into the Pacific Ocean and reached the Philippines. In 1522, he was killed there in a fight with the natives. A year later, his successor sailed home round Africa with one ship carrying 18 of the original crewmen. This was the first circumnavigation of the world.

(See also page 163)

Discoveries

	Latitude	Longitude
Bahia	12° N	42° W
Bantam	7° S	106° E
Bering Straits	66° N	170° W
Cuzco	14° S	72° W
Gold Coast	4° N	2° W
Magellan Straits	53° S	75° W
Malabar Coast	11° N	75° E
Quebec	47° N	71° W
Tanjore	11° N	49° E
Torres Straits	10° S	143° E
Virginia	51° N	76° W
West Indies	17° N	63° W

Historic Battlefields

	Latitude	Longitude
Austerlitz	49° N	17° E
El Alamein	21° N	29° E
Gettysburg	40° N	77° W
Golan Heights	33° N	36° E
Hiroshima	35° N	133° E
Stalingrad	49° N	44° E
Narva	59° N	28° E
Normandy	49° N	0°
Pearl Harbour	21° N	158° W
Poltava	50° N	35° E
Tilsit	55° N	22° E
Trafalgar	36° N	6° W
Verdun	49° N	5° E
Versailles	49° N	2° E
Waterloo	51° N	4° E

History of Europe

Europe's history of the last three hundred years has been dominated by the avarice of the different nations for colonies, and this with other factors often led to wars. The longest and most cruel ones were the Thirty Years War (1618–1648), the Napoleonic Wars (1792–1815), World War I (1914–1918), and finally World War II (1939–1945). The main actors in these wars were the European Great Powers who with changing luck defended their motherland and their colonies. Even though these wars as such did not bring any progress, many of the battlefields have become famous and are now part of history. Thus, the list contains places where the Europeans have shown their clear superiority as well as places where they have displayed their worst qualities.

National Parks and Game Reserves

Today, industry dominates the landscape and many breeds of animals will soon be wiped out. It has become an important task not only for the industralized countries like USA and those of Europe but also for the under-developed countries to set up reserves where nature is left unspoilt and where plants and animals may not be destroyed. Different titles have been given to these areas round the world but their purpose is the same.

USA has been a pioneer in this type of project and already in 1872 she passed a law about Yellowstone National Park. This law has become a pattern for all later laws on national parks which are grouped under a special commission: the National Parks Service. In this way much important scenery has been saved as well as historical places in USA.

Preservation in Western Europe is done in the same way but few of these areas are on the same scale as the USA.

It is of special importance that the big mammals be preserved. This is not for the sake of the animals alone but also to attract tourists and thus increase the revenue of foreign currency for many under-developed lands.

One of the first National Parks for animals was made in South Africa: the Kruger National Park. This has been copied by many other countries, especially in East Africa. Here, the landscape is being preserved too and we have areas like the Murchison Falls Game Reserve in Uganda. The waterfall on the Nile, the Murchison Falls, is part of this Park.

National Parks and Game Reserves

	Country	Latitude	Longitude
Yellowstone National Park	USA	45° N	110° W
Grand Canyon National Park	USA	36° N	112° W
Glacier National Park	USA	49° N	114° W
Zion National Park	USA	37° N	112° W
Petrified Forest National Park	USA	35° N	110° W
Lassen Volcanic National Park	USA	40° N	121° W
Rocky Mountains National Park	USA	40° N	104° W
Lüneburger Heide	Germany	53° N	10° E
Upper Engadine	Switzerland	47° N	10° E
Peak District	England	53° N	1° W
Sareks National Park	Sweden	67° N	16° E
Krugers National Park	South Africa	24° S	32° E
Serengeti	Tanzania	3° S	35° E
Ngorongoro	Tanzania	3° S	36° E
Murchison Falls	Uganda	2° N	32° E

Events that Shook the World

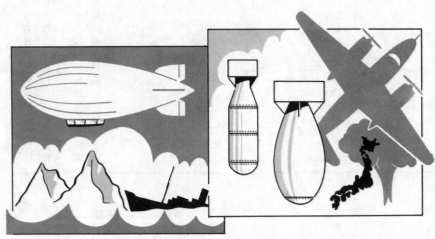

All too frequently shattering, world-shaking events come into our living rooms via newspapers, television and radio. But where did the event take place? Probably the daily paper shows a map of the afflicted area but does not give its position in relation to the rest of the world. However, if we are given the name of an important near-by town, we can locate the area with the help of the globe.

World-shaking events have happened before, but at the time these seemed remote. Now, we help you to localize some of these by giving you the latitude and longitude. All have had an impact on the world.

		Latitude	Longitude
14.4.1865	Murder of President Abraham Lincoln at the Ford Theatre, Washington, DC.	39° N	77° W
14./15.4.1912	Titanic, the biggest ship of that period, sank on her maiden voyage. She hit an iceberg about 2.500 km. (1560 miles) N. E. of New York. About 1500 people lost their lives.	50° N	48° W
28.6.1914	Murder of the Austrian Archduke Franz Ferdinand and his wife. The assasination started World War I. It happened in the Bosnian town of Sarajevo.	44° N	18° E
6.5.1937	After several years of routine flights between Europe and USA, the airship Hindenburg burst into flames over Lakehurst, New Jersey. All aboard were killed.	40° N	74° W
6.8.1945	The town of Hiroshima in Japan was destroyed by the world's first atom bomb.	34° N	132° E
Sept. 1961	United Nations' General Secretary, Dag Hammarskjöld was killed in a flying accident over Zambia.	12° S	22° E
22.11.1963	President J.-F. Kennedy assasignated in Dallas/Texas	33° N	97° W
1972	War in Vietnam and the uprising in East Pakistan that ended with its secession as the new state of Bangladesh. Many localities have been referred to, the most important being the three capitals:		
	North Vietnam: Hanoi	21° N	105° E
	South Vietnam: Saigon – Ho Chi Minh City	11° N	106° E
	Bangladesh: Dacca	24° N	90° E
1973:	In the war between Israel and Syria the decisive battles took place in the peninsula of Sinai	29° N	34° E
	and the Golan heights	33° N	36° E
4.11.1979	Occupation of the US Embassy in Teheran and seizure of hostages	36° N	51° E
August 1980	Strikes in Poland, in particular at the Lenin shipyard in Danzig	54° N	19° E

A.S.S.R. – Autonomous Soviet Socialist Republic
Ala. – Alabama
Alas. – Alaska
Ang. – Angola
Arch. – Archipelago
Arg. – Argentina
Ariz. – Arizona
Ark. – Arkansas
B. – Baie, Bahía, Bay, Boca, Bucht, Bugt
B.C. – British Columbia
Br. – British
C. – Cabo, Cap, Cape
C.A.E. – Central African Empire
C. Prov. – Cape Province
Calif. – California
Chan. – Channel
Col. – Colombia
Colo. – Colorado
Conn. – Connecticut
Cord. – Cordillera
D.C. – District of Columbia
Del. – Delaware
Dep. – Dependency
Des. – Desert
Dist. – District
Dom. Rep. – Dominican Republic
E. – East
Eng. – England

Fd. – Fjord
Fed. – Federal, Federation
Fla. – Florida
Fr. – France, French
G. – Golfe, Golfo, Gulf, Guba
Ga. – Georgia
Gt. – Great
Hants. – Hampshire
Hd. – Head
Hts. – Heights
I.(s) – Ile, Ilha, Insel, Isla, Island (s)
Id. – Idaho
Ill. – Illinois
Ind. – Indiana
J. – Jezero (L.)
K. – Kap, Kapp
Kans. – Kansas
Kep. – Kepulauan (I.)
Kól. – Kólpos (B.)
Ky. – Kentucky
L. – Lac, Lacul, Lago, Lagoa, Lake, Limni, Loch, Lough
La. – Louisana
Ld. – Land
Mad. P. – Madhya Pradesh
Man. – Manitoba
Mass. – Massachusetts
Md. – Maryland
Me. – Maine
Mich. – Michigan
Minn. – Minnesota

Miss. – Mississippi
Mo. – Missouri
Mont. – Montana
Mt.(s) – Mont, Monte, Monti, Muntii, Montaña, Mountain (s)
Mys. – Mysore
N. – North, Northern
N.B. – New Brunswick
N.C. – North Carolina
N.D. – North Dakota
N.H. – New Hampshire
N. Ire. – Northern Ireland
N.J. – New Jersey
N. Mex. – New Mexico
N.S.W. – New South Wales
N.Y. – New York
N.Z. – New Zealand
Nat. Park – National Park
Nebr. – Nebraska
Neth. – Netherlands
Nev. – Nevada
Newf. – Newfoundland
Nic. – Nicaragua
Nig. – Nigeria
O.F.S. – Orange Free State
Okla. – Oklahoma
Ont. – Ontario
Oreg. – Oregon
Os. – Ostrov (I.)
Oz – Ozero (L.)
P. – Pass, Passo, Pasul

P.N.G. – Papua New Guinea
Pa. – Pennsylvania
Pak. – Pakistan
Pass. – Passage
Pen. – Peninsula
Pk. – Peak
Plat. – Plateau
Pol. – Poluostrov
Port. – Portugal, Portuguese
Prov. – Province, Provincial
Pt. – Point
Pta. – Ponta, Punta
Pte. – Pointe
Que. – Quebec
Queens. – Queensland
R. – Rio, River
R.S.F.S.R. – Russian Soviet Federal Socialist Republic
Ra.(s) – Range(s)
Reg. – Region
Rep. – Republic
Res. – Reserve, Reservoir
S. – South
S. Africa – South Africa
S.C. – S. Carolina
S.D. – South Dakota
S. Leone – Sierra Leone
S.S.R. – Soviet Socialist Republic
Sa. – Serra, Sierra
Sask. – Saskatchewan
Scot. – Scotland

Sd. – Sound
Sp. – Spain, Spanish
St. – Saint
Str. – Strait, Stretto
Switz. – Switzerland
Tanz. – Tanzania
Tas. – Tasmania
Tenn. – Tennessee
Terr. – Territory
Tex. – Texas
U.K. – United Kingdom
U.S.A. – United States of America
U.S.S.R. – Union of Soviet Socialist Republics
Ut. P. – Uttar Pradesh
Va. – Virginia
Vdkhr. – Vodokhranilishche (Res.)
Ven. – Venezuela
Vic. – Victoria
Vt. – Vermont
W. – West
W. Va. – West Virginia
Wis. – Wisconsin
Wyo. – Wyoming
Yorks. – Yorkshire
Yug. – Yugoslavia

An open square □ signifies that the name refers to an administrative division of a country while a solid square ■ follows the name of a country.

A

Aachen .... 50 47N 6 4 E
A'Âlâ en Nîl □ ... 8 50N 29 55 E
Aalsmeer .... 52 17N 4 43 E
Aalst .... 50 56N 4 2 E
Aalten .... 51 56N 6 35 E
Aarau .... 47 23N 8 4 E
Aare, R. .... 47 37N 8 13 E
Aarschot .... 50 59N 4 49 E
Aba .... 5 10N 7 19 E
Aba Saud ...... 17 15N 43 55 E
Abadan .... 30 22N 48 20 E
Abai 25 58s 55 54w
Abakaliki ...... 6 22N 8 2 E
Abakan .... 53 40N 91 10 E
Abarqu .... 31 10N 53 20 E
Abasan .... 31 19N 34 21 E
Abashiri .... 44 0N 144 15 E
Abashiri-Wan, G. . 44 0N 144 30 E
Abay .... 49 38N 72 53 E
Abaya, L. ...... 6 30N 37 50 E
Abaza .... 52 39N 90 6 E
Abba Hillèl ..... 31 42N 34 38 E
Abbeville, Fr. .... 50 6N 1 49 E
Abbeville, U.S.A. . 30 0N 92 7w
Abbottabad ..... 34 10N 73 15 E
Abéché .... 13 50N 20 35 E
Åbenrå .... 55 3N 9 25 E
Abeokuta ...... 7 3N 3 19 E
Aberayron 52 15N 4 16w
Aberdare 51 43N 3 27w
Aberdeen,
  Australia .... 32 9s 150 56 E
Aberdeen, S. Africa 32 28s 24 2 E
Aberdeen, U.K. .. 57 9N 2 6w
Aberdeen, Id. ... 42 57N 112 50w
Aberdeen, Miss. . 33 49N 88 13w
Aberdeen, S.D. .. 45 28N 98 29w
Aberdeen, Wash.. 46 59N 123 50w
Aberdovey 52 33N 4 3w
Aberfeldy 56 37N 3 50w
Abergavenny 51 49N 3 1w
Aberystwyth 52 25N 4 6w
Abhâ .... 18 0N 42 34 E
Abidjan 5 26N 3 58w
Abilene, Kans. .. 39 0N 97 16w
Abilene, Tex. 32 22N 99 40w

Abingdon 51 40N 1 17w
Abkhaz A.S.S.R.. . 43 0N 41 0 E
Abkit .... 64 10N 157 10 E
Abocho .... 7 35N 6 56 E
Abohar .... 30 10N 74 10 E
Aboisso 5 30N 3 5w
Abomey .... 7 10N 2 5 E
Abong Mbang ... 4 0N 13 8 E
Abonnema 4 41N 6 49w
Aboso 5 23N 1 57w
Abou Deïa ...... 11 20N 19 20 E
Aboyne 57 4N 2 48w
Abqaiq .... 26 0N 49 45 E
Abrantes 39 24N 8 7w
Abrud .... 46 19N 23 5 E
Abruzzi □ ...... 42 15N 14 0 E
Abū al Khasib ... 30 25N 48 0 E
Abu Arish ...... 16 53N 42 48 E
Abu Dis .... 19 12N 33 8 E
Abū Ghōsh ..... 31 48N 35 6 E
Abu Hamed ..... 19 32N 33 13 E
Abu Tig .... 27 4N 31 15 E
Abû Zabad ..... 12 25N 29 10 E
Abū Zabī ...... 24 28N 54 36 E
Abuja .... 9 16N 7 2 E
Abyad, Gebel, Reg. 17 30N 28 0 E
Abyssinia■=
  Ethiopia ■ ..... 8 0N 40 0 E
Acajutla 13 36N 89 50w
Acámbaro 20 0N 100 40w
Acaponeta 22 30N 105 20w
Acapulco 16 51N 99 56w
Acará 1 57s 48 11w
Acatlan 18 10N 98 3w
Acayucan 17 59N 94 58w
Accra 5 35N 0 6w
Accrington 53 46N 2 22w
Aceh □ .... 4 50N 96 0 E
Achill 53 56N 9 55w
Achill, I. 53 58N 10 5w
Achinsk .... 56 20N 90 20 E
Acklins I. 22 30N 74 0w
Acme 51 33N 113 30w
Aconcagua, Mt. .. 32 39s 70 0w
Acre=Akko ..... 32 55N 35 4 E
Acre □ 9 1s 71 0w
Ad Dam .... 20 33N 44 45 E
Ad Dammam .... 26 20N 50 5 E
Ad Khālis ...... 33 40N 44 55 E

Ada, Ghana ..... 5 44N 0 40 E
Ada, U.S.A. 34 50N 96 45w
Adale .... 2 58N 46 27 E
Adamaoua,
  Massif de l' .... 7 20N 12 20 E
Adamello, Mt. .. 46 10N 10 34 E
Adams, N.Y. 43 50N 76 3w
Adams, Wis. 43 59N 89 50w
Adams, Mt. 46 10N 121 28w
Adam's Bridge .. 9 15N 79 40 E
Adam's Pk. ..... 6 55N 80 45 E
Adana .... 37 0N 35 16 E
Adaut .... 8 8s 131 7 E
Adda, R. .... 45 8N 9 53 E
Addis Ababa=
Addis Abeba .... 9 2N 38 42 E
Addis Abeba .... 9 2N 38 42 E
Adebour .... 13 17N 11 50 E
Adelaide, Australia 34 52s 138 30 E
Adelaide, S. Afr. .. 32 42s 26 20 E
Adelaide Pen. ... 67 40N 98 0w
Adelaide River... 13 15s 131 7 E
Aden= Al 'Adan .. 12 50N 45 0 E
Aden, G. of .... 13 0N 50 0 E
Adige, R. ...... 45 10N 12 20 E
Adirondack Mts. .. 44 0N 74 15w
Adjohon .... 6 41N 2 32 E
Admiralty, G. ... 14 20s 125 55 E
Admiralty Inlet .. 48 0N 122 40w
Admiralty I. 57 50N 134 30w
Admiralty Is. ... 2 0s 147 0 E
Ado .... 6 36N 2 56 E
Ado-Ekiti ...... 7 38N 5 12 E
Adoni .... 15 33N 77 18 E
Adour, R. 43 32N 1 32w
Adra 36 43N 3 3w
Adrano .... 37 40N 14 19 E
Adrar des
  Iforas, Mts. .. 19 40N 1 40 E
Adrian 41 55N 84 0w
Adriatic Sea .... 43 0N 16 0 E
Adzhar A.S.S.R. . 42 0N 42 0 E
Ægean Sea ..... 37 0N 25 0 E
Æolian Is.=
  Eólie o Lípari, I. 38 30N 14 50 E
Aerhtai Shan, Mts. 48 0N 90 0 E
Afghanistan ■ ... 33 0N 65 0 E
Afgoi .... 2 7N 44 59 E
Afikpo .... 5 53N 7 54 E
Africa .... 5 0N 20 0 E

Afuá 0 15s 50 10w
Afula .... 32 37N 35 17 E
Afyon .... 38 20N 30 15 E
Agadez .... 16 58N 7 59 E
Agadir 30 28N 9 25w
Agapa .... 71 27N 89 15 E
Agartala .... 23 50N 91 23 E
Agats .... 5 34s 138 5 E
Agboville 5 55N 4 15w
Agde .... 43 19N 3 28 E
Agege .... 6 37N 3 20 E
Agen .... 44 12N 0 38 E
Agnew .... 28 1s 120 30 E
Agnibilekrou 7 10N 3 11w
Agra .... 27 17N 77 58 E
Ağri Daği, Mt. .. 39 50N 44 15 E
Agrigento ...... 37 19N 13 33 E
Agrinion .... 38 37N 21 27 E
Agua Clara 20 25s 52 45w
Agua Prieta 31 20N 109 32w
Aguadas 5 40N 75 38w
Aguadilla 18 27N 67 10w
Aguanish 50 14N 62 2w
Aguas Blancas .. 24 15s 69 55w
Aguascalientes .. 22 0N 102 20w
Aguascalientes □ . 22 0N 102 20w
Aguilas 37 23N 1 35w
Agulhas, K. ..... 34 52s 20 0 E
Agur .... 31 42N 34 55 E
Ahaggar, Reg. ... 23 0N 6 30 E
Ahaura .... 42 20s 171 32 E
Ahmadabad .... 23 0N 72 40 E
Ahmadnagar .... 19 7N 74 46 E
Ahuachapán 13 54N 89 52w
Ahvāz .... 31 20N 48 40 E
Ahvenanmaa=
  Åland , I. ..... 60 15N 20 0 E
Ahwar .... 13 31N 46 42 E
Aibaq .... 36 15N 68 5 E
Aichi □ .... 35 0N 137 15 E
Aigues-Mortes .. 43 35N 4 2 E
Aihun .... 49 55N 127 30 E
Aijal .... 23 40N 92 44 E
Aiken 33 44N 81 50w
Ailsa Craig, I. .. 55 15N 5 7w
Aim .... 59 0N 133 55 E
Aimorés 19 30s 41 4w
Ain □ .... 46 5N 5 20 E
Aïn Beida ..... 35 50N 7 35 E
Ain Dăr .... 25 55N 49 10 E

Ainabo .... 9 0N 46 25 E
Aïr .... 18 0N 8 0 E
Airdrie 55 53N 3 57w
Aire, R. 53 44N 0 44w
Aisne, R. ...... 49 26N 2 50 E
Aisne □ .... 49 42N 3 40 E
Aitush .... 39 54N 75 40 E
Aiud .... 46 19N 23 44 E
Aix-en-Provence . 43 32N 5 27 E
Aix-les-Bains ... 45 41N 5 53 E
Ajaccio .... 41 55N 8 40 E
Ajana .... 27 56s 114 35 E
Ajanta Ra. ..... 20 28N 75 50 E
Ajdâbiyah ..... 30 54N 20 4 E
'Ajlun .... 32 18N 35 47 E
Ajman .... 25 25N 55 30 E
Ajmer .... 26 28N 74 37 E
Ajo 32 18N 112 54w
Ajua 4 50N 1 55w
Akaba .... 8 10N 1 2 E
Akaroa .... 43 49s 172 59 E
Akashi .... 34 45N 135 0 E
Akershus □ ..... 60 10N 11 15 E
Aketi .... 2 38N 23 47 E
Akhelóös, R. .... 38 36N 21 14 E
Akhisar .... 38 56N 27 48 E
Akhmîm .... 26 31N 31 47 E
Akimiski I. 52 50N 81 30w
Akita .... 39 45N 140 0 E
Akita □ .... 39 40N 140 30 E
Akjoujt 19 45N 14 15w
Akko .... 32 55N 35 4 E
Akkol .... 43 36N 70 45 E
Aklavik 68 25N 135 0w
Akō, Japan ..... 34 45N 134 24 E
Ako, Nigeria .... 10 19N 10 48 E
Akola .... 20 42N 77 2 E
Akordat .... 15 30N 37 40 E
Akosombo Dam .. 6 20N 0 5 E
Akpatok I. 60 30N 68 0w
Akranes 64 19N 22 6w
Akron 41 7N 81 31w
Aksaraka ...... 66 31N 67 50 E
Aksehir .... 38 18N 31 30 E
Aksenovo
  Zilovskoye ... 53 20N 117 40 E
Aksu .... 41 4N 80 5 E
Aksum .... 14 5N 38 40 E
Aktogay .... 44 25N 76 44 E
Aktyubinsk .... 50 10N 57 3 E

Aku .... 6 40N 7 18 E
Akure .... 7 15N 5 5 E
Akureyri 65 40N 18 5w
Akyab .... 20 15N 92 45 E
Al 'Adan .... 12 50N 45 0 E
Al Amārah ...... 31 55N 47 15 E
Al 'Aqabah ..... 29 37N 35 0 E
Al Barah .... 31 55N 35 12 E
Al Basrah ...... 30 30N 47 55 E
Al Baydā .... 32 30N 21 40 E
Al Buraimi ..... 24 15N 55 53 E
Al Hadithan .... 34 0N 41 13 E
Al Hadr .... 35 35N 42 44 E
Al Hasa, Reg. .. 25 40N 50 0 E
Al Hasakah ..... 36 35N 40 45 E
Al Hauta .... 16 5N 48 20 E
Al Hawra .... 13 49N 47 37 E
Al Hillah, Iraq ... 32 30N 44 25 E
Al Hillah,
  Saudi Arabia .. 23 35N 46 50 E
Al Hilwah ...... 23 24N 46 48 E
Al Hindiyah .... 32 30N 44 10 E
Al-Hoceïma 35 15N 3 58w
Al Hufūf .... 25 25N 49 45 E
Al Jahrah ...... 29 25N 47 40 E
Al Jalāmid ..... 31 20N 39 45 E
Al Jazir 18 30N 56 31N
Al Jazirah, Reg. . 26 10N 21 20 E
Al Jubail ...... 27 0N 49 50 E
Al Juwara ...... 19 0N 57 13 E
Al Khābūrah .... 23 57N 57 5 E
Al Khalaf ...... 20 30N 57 56 E
Al Khums .... 32 40N 14 17 E
Al Kūt .... 32 30N 46 0 E
Al Kuwayt ...... 29 20N 48 0 E
Al Lādhiqiyah .. 35 30N 35 45 E
Al Lith .... 20 9N 40 15 E
Al Madīnah ..... 24 35N 39 52 E
Al Mafraq ...... 32 17N 36 14 E
Al Manamah ..... 26 10N 50 30 E
Al Marj .... 32 25N 20 30 E
Al Masīrah ..... 20 25N 58 50 E
Al Matamma ..... 16 43N 33 22 E
Al Mawsil ...... 36 15N 43 5 E
Al Mazra' ...... 31 18N 35 32 E
Al Miqdādiyah .. 34 0N 45 0 E
Al Mubarraz .... 25 30N 49 40 E
Al Muharraq .... 26 15N 50 40 E
Al Mukha .... 13 18N 43 15 E
Al Qamishli .... 37 10N 41 10 E

Al Qatif .... 26 35N 50 0 E
Al-Qatrūn .... 24 56N 15 3 E
Al Qunfidha ..... 19 3N 41 4 E
Al Ubailah ...... 21 59N 50 57 E
Al 'Ugaylah ..... 30 12N 19 10 E
Al Wakrah .... 25 10N 51 40 E
Al Wari 'ah ..... 27 50N 47 30 E
Ala Shan, Reg. .. 40 0N 104 0 E
Alabama, R. 31 8N 87 57w
Alabama □ 31 0N 87 0w
Alagôa Grande ... 7 3s 35 35w
Alagôas □ 9 0s 36 0w
Alagoinhas 12 0s 38 20w
Alajuela 10 2N 84 8w
Alakurtti .... 67 0N 30 30 E
Alameda 35 10N 106 43w
Alamogordo 32 59N 106 0w
Alamosa 37 30N 106 0w
Åland, I. .... 60 15N 20 0 E
Ålands hav ...... 60 0N 19 20 E
Alapayevsk ...... 57 52N 61 42 E
Alashanchih ..... 38 58N 105 14 E
Alaska □ 65 0N 150 0w
Alaska, G. of ... 58 0N 145 0w
Alaska Pen. 56 0N 160 0w
Alaska Ra. 62 50N 151 0w
Alatyr .... 54 45N 46 35 E
Alausi 2 0s 78 50w
Alawoona .... 34 45s 140 30 E
Alba .... 44 41N 8 1 E
Alba-Iulia ...... 46 4N 23 35 E
Albacete 39 0N 1 50w
Albania ■ .... 41 0N 20 0 E
Albany,
  Australia ..... 35 1s 117 58 E
Albany, Ga. 31 40N 84 10w
Albany, N.Y. 42 40N 73 47w
Albany, Oreg. ... 44 41N 123 0w
Albany, R. 52 17N 81 31w
Albardón 31 20s 68 30w
Albarracin 40 25N 1 26w
Albarracin, Sa. de . 40 30N 1 30w
Albemarle 35 27N 80 15w
Alberche, R. 39 58N 4 46w
Alberni 49 20N 124 50w
Albert 45 51N 64 38w
Albert, L.=
  Mobutu Sese
  Seko, L. ...... 1 30N 31 0 E
Albert Lea 43 32N 93 20w

Albert Nile, R. .... 3 36N 32 2 E
Albert Town 18 17N 77 33w
Alberta □ 54 40N 115 0w
Albertinia .... 34 11s 21 34 E
Alberton .... 38 35s 146 40 E
Albertville=
Kalemie .... 5 55s 29 9 E
Alberz, Reshteh-
Ye-Kūkhā-Ye,
Mts. .... 36 0N 52 0 E
Albi .... 43 56N 2 9 E
Albina, ... 5 37N 54 15w
Albion 42 15N 84 45w
Alboran, I. 35 57N 3 0w
Ålborg .... 57 2N 9 54 E
Albuquerque 35 5N 106 47w
Albury .... 36 3s 146 56 E
Alcalá de Henares . 40 28N 3 22w
Alcalá la Real ... 37 27N 3 57w
Alcaníz .... 41 2N 0 8 E
Alcântara, Brazil . 2 20s 44 30w
Alcântara, Sp. ... 39 41N 6 57w
Alcaraz, Sa. de .. 38 40N 2 20w
Alcaudete 37 35N 4 5w
Alcazar de San
  Juan 39 24N 3 12w
Alcira 39 9N 0 30w
Alcobaça 39 32N 9 0w
Alcoy 38 43N 0 30w
Aldabra Is. ...... 9 22s 46 28 E
Aldan, R. .... 63 28N 129 35 E
Aldeburgh .... 52 9N 1 35 E
Alderney, I. 49 42N 2 12w
Aldershot 51 15N 0 43w
Aleg 17 3N 13 55w
Alegrete 29 40s 56 0w
Aleisk .... 52 40N 83 0 E
Aleksandrovsk-
Sakhalinskiy ... 50 50N 142 20 E
Aleksandrovskiy
Zavod .... 50 40N 117 50 E
Aleksandrovskoye . 60 35N 77 50 E
Alençon .... 48 27N 0 4 E
Alenuihaha Chan. . 20 25s 156 0w
Aleppo=Ḥalab ..... 36 10N 37 15 E
Alert Bay 50 30N 127 35w
Alès .... 44 9N 4 5 E
Alessandria ...... 44 54N 8 37 E
Ålesund .... 62 28N 6 12 E

Aleutian Is. 52 0N 175 0w
Alexander Arch. .. 57 0N 135 0w
Alexander Bay .... 28 36s 16 33 E
Alexander City ... 32 56N 85 57w
Alexander I. 69 0s 70 0w
Alexandra .... 45 14s 169 25 E
Alexandria=El
  Iskandarîya .... 31 0N 30 0 E
Alexandria,
  Canada 45 19N 74 38w
Alexandria,
  S. Africa ...... 33 38s 26 28 E
Alexandria, La. .. 31 20N 92 30w
Alexandria, Minn. . 45 50N 95 20w
Alexandria, Va. .. 38 47N 77 1w
Alexandria Bay ... 44 20N 75 52w
Alexandroúpolis ... 40 50N 25 24 E
Alford .... 53 16N 0 10 E
Alfreton 53 6N 1 22w
Alga .... 49 46N 57 20 E
Algarve, Reg. 37 15N 8 10w
Algeciras 36 9N 5 28w
Algemesí 39 11N 0 27w
Alger .... 36 42N 3 8 E
Algeria ■ .... 35 10N 3 0 E
Alghero .... 40 34N 8 20 E
Algiers=Alger .... 36 42N 3 8 E
Algoabaai .... 33 50s 25 45 E
Algonquin Prov.
  Park 45 35N 78 35w
Alhama de
  Murcia 37 51N 1 25w
Alhambra 34 0N 118 10w
Aliákmon, R. ..... 40 30N 22 36 E
Alicante 38 23N 0 30w
Alicante □ 38 30N 0 37w
Alice 27 47N 98 1w
Alice Arm 55 29N 129 23w
Alice Downs ...... 17 45s 127 56 E
Alice Springs .... 23 40s 135 50 E
Alicedale .... 33 15s 26 4 E
Aligarh .... 27 55N 78 10 E
Aligudarz .... 33 25N 49 45 E
Alingsås .... 57 56N 12 31 E
Alipur .... 29 25N 70 55 E
Alipur Duar ...... 26 30N 89 35 E
Aliquippa 40 38N 80 18w
Aliwal Nord ...... 30 45s 26 45 E
Aljustrel 37 55N 8 10w
Alkamari .... 13 27N 11 10 E

Alkmaar .... 52 37N 4 45 E
All American
  Canal 32 45N 115 0w
Allada .... 6 41N 2 9 E
Allahabad .... 25 25N 81 58 E
Allan 51 53N 106 4w
Allanridge ...... 27 45s 26 40 E
Allard Lake 50 40N 63 10w
Allegheny Mts. .. 38 0N 80 0w
Allegheny, R. ... 40 27N 80 0w
Allende 28 20N 100 50w
Allentown 40 36N 75 30w
Alleppey .... 9 30N 76 28 E
Aller, R. .... 52 57N 9 11 E
Alliance, Nebr. . 42 10N 102 50w
Alliance, Ohio .. 40 53N 81 7w
Allier, R. ...... 46 58N 3 4 E
Allier □ .... 46 25N 3 0 E
Alligator Creek . 19 23s 146 58 E
Alliston 44 15N 79 55w
Alloa 56 7N 3 49w
Alma, Canada 48 35N 71 40w
Alma, U.S.A. 43 25N 84 40w
Alma Ata .... 43 15N 76 57 E
Almada 38 40N 9 9w
Almaden .... 17 22s 144 40 E
Almadén 38 49N 4 52w
Almansa 38 51N 1 5w
Almanzor, P. de . 40 15N 5 18w
Almazán 41 30N 2 30w
Almeirim, Brazil . 1 30s 52 0w
Almelo .... 52 22N 6 42 E
Almendralejo 38 41N 6 26w
Almería 36 52N 2 32w
Almirante 9 10N 82 30w
Alnwick 55 25N 1 42w
Alon .... 22 12N 95 5 E
Alonsa 50 50N 99 0w
Alor, I. .... 8 15s 124 30 E
Alor Setar ...... 6 7N 100 22 E
Aloysius, Mt. ... 26 0s 128 38 E
Alpena 45 6N 83 24w
Alpes-Maritimes □ 43 55N 7 10 E
Alpes-de-Haute-
  Provence □ .... 44 8N 6 0 E
Alpha .... 24 8s 146 39 E
Alpi Carniche, Mts. 46 36N 13 0 E
Alpine 30 35N 103 35w
Alps, Mts. ...... 47 0N 8 0 E
Alroy Downs ..... 19 20s 136 5 E

Alsace, Reg. ...... 48 15N 7 25 E
Alsasua 42 54N 2 10w
Alston 54 48N 2 26w
Alta .... 69 55N 23 12 E
Alta Gracia ...... 31 40 s 64 30w
Alta Lake 50 10N 123 0w
Altaelv, R. ...... 69 57N 23 17 E
Altagracia 10 45N 71 30w
Altai, Mts. ...... 48 0N 90 0 E
Altai, Mts.=
    Aerhtai Shan,
    Mts. .... 48 0N 90 0 E
Altamira 3 0s 52 10w
Altanbulag ...... 50 19N 106 30 E
Altea 38 38N 0 2w
Alto-Alentejo,
    Reg. 38 50N 7 40w
Alto Araguaia .... 17 15 s 53 20w
Alton, U.K. 51 8N 0 59w
Alton, U.S.A. 38 55N 90 5w
Altona .... 53 32N 9 56 E
Altoona 40 32N 78 24w
Altus 34 30N 99 25w
Altyn Tagh, Mts. .. 39 0N 89 0 E
Alula .... 11 50N 50 45 E
Alusi .... 7 35 s 131 40 E
Alva 36 50N 98 50w
Alvarado 18 40N 95 50w
Alvear .... 29 5 s 57 40w
Alvesta .... 56 54N 14 35 E
Alvie .... 38 15 s 143 30 E
Älvkarleby .... 60 34N 17 35 E
Älvsborgs □ ...... 58 30N 12 30 E
Älvsbyn .... 65 39N 20 59 E
Alwar .... 27 38N 76 34 E
Alyat Pristan .... 39 59N 49 28 E
Alyth 56 38N 3 15w
Am-Timan .... 11 0N 20 10 E
Amadjuak 64 0N 72 50w
Amadjuak L. 65 0N 71 0w
Amagasaki ...... 34 42N 135 20 E
Amakusa-Shotŏ,
    Is. .... 32 15N 130 10 E
Åmål .... 59 2N 12 40 E
Amalner .... 21 5N 75 5 E
Amangeldy ...... 50 10N 65 10 E
Amapá 2 5N 50 50w
Amapá □ 1 40N 52 0w
Amarante .... 6 14 s 42 50w
Amargosa .... 13 2 s 39 36w

Amarillo 35 14N 101 46w
Amaro, Mt. ...... 42 5N 14 6 E
Amassama .... 5 1N 6 2 E
Amasya .... 40 40N 35 50 E
Amatikulu ...... 29 3 s 31 33 E
Amatitlán 14 29N 90 38w
Amazon=
Amazonas, R.... 2 0s 53 30w
Amazonas, R.... 2 0 s 53 30w
Amazonas □ .... 4 20 s 64 0w
Ambala .... 30 23N 76 56 E
Ambalavao ...... 21 50 s 46 56 E
Ambanja .... 13 40 s 48 27 E
Ambarchik ...... 69 40N 162 20 E
Ambaro, B. d' .... 13 23 s 48 38 E
Ambata-Boéni .... 16 28 s 46 43 E
Ambato .... 1 5 s 78 42w
Ambatofinandrahana20 33 s 46 48 E
Ambatolampy .... 19 20 s 47 35 E
Ambatondrazaka .. 17 55 s 48 28 E
Ámbelos, Ákra ... 39 56N 23 55 E
Amberg .... 49 25N 11 52 E
Ambergris Cay ... 18 0N 88 0w
Amberley .... 43 9 s 172 44 E
Ambikapur ...... 23 15N 83 15 E
Ambleside 54 26N 2 58w
Ambohimanga
    du Sud .... 20 52 s 47 36 E
Amboise .... 47 25N 0 59 E
Ambon .... 3 35 s 128 20 E
Ambositra .... 20 31 s 47 25 E
Ambovombé ...... 25 11 s 46 5 E
Amboy 34 33N 115 51w
Ambre, C. d' .... 12 40 s 49 10 E
Amby .... 26 30 s 148 11 E
Amderma .... 69 45N 61 30 E
Ameca 20 30N 104 0w
Ameland, I. ..... 53 27N 5 45 E
Amen .... 68 45N 180 0 E
American Falls ... 42 46N 112 56 E
American Samoa, I. 14 20 s 170 0w
Americus 32 0N 84 10w
Amersfoort, Neth . 52 9N 5 23 E
Amersfoort, S. Afr. 26 59 s 29 53 E
Amery, Australia .. 31 9 s 117 5 E
Amery, Canada .. 56 45N 94 0w
Ames 42 0N 93 40w
Amga, R. .... 62 38N 134 32 E
Amgu .... 45 45N 137 15 E
Amherst, Burma .. 16 0N 97 40 E

Amherst, Canada .. 45 48N 64 8w
Amherstburg 42 6N 83 6w
Amiens .... 49 54N 2 16 E
Amirantes, Is. .... 6 0′s 53 0 E
Amlwch 53 24N 4 21w
'Ammān .... 32 0N 35 52 E
Ammi'ad .... 32 55N 35 32 E
Amorgós .... 36 50 25 57 E
Amos 48 35N 78 5w
Amoy=Hsiamen . 24 25N 118 4 E
Ampanihy .... 24 40 s 44 45 E
Amper .... 9 25N 9 40 E
Amqui 48 28N 67 27w
Amroati .... 20 55N 77 45 E
Amreli .... 21 35N 71 17 E
Amritsar .... 31 35N 74 57 E
Amroha .... 28 53N 78 30 E
Amsterdam,
    Neth. .... 52 23N 4 54 E
Amsterdam, S. Afr. 26 35 s 30 45 E
Amsterdam, U.S.A. 42 58N 74 10w
Amsterdam, I. .... 37 30 s 77 30 E
Amu Darya, R. ... 43 40N 59 1 E
Amukta Pass. 52 25N 172 0w
Amundsen G. 70 30N 123 0w
Amundsen Sea ... 72 0 s 115 0w
Amur, R. .... 52 56N 141 10 E
An Najaf .... 32 3N 44 15 E
An Nasiriyah .... 31 0N 46 15 E
An Nhon .... 13 53N 109 6 E
An Nu'ayriyah ... 27 30N 48 30 E
An Uaimh 53 39N 6 40w
Anabta .... 32 19N 35 7 E
Anaconda 46 7N 113 0w
Anacortes 48 30N 122 40w
Anadarko 35 4N 98 15w
Anadolu, Reg. ... 38 0N 39 0 E
Anadyr .... 64 35N 177 20 E
Anadyr, R. ...... 64 55N 176 5 E
Anahim Lake 52 28N 125 18w
Anakapalle ...... 17 42N 83 6 E
Anakie .... 23 32 s 147 45 E
Analalava .... 14 35 s 48 0 E
Anambas, Kep. .. 3 20N 106 30 E
Anambra □ ..... 6 30N 7 30 E
Anan .... 33 54N 134 40 E
Anantnag .... 33 45N 75 10 E
Anápolis .... 16 15 s 48 50w
Anar .... 30 55N 55 13 E
Anatolia, Reg.=

Anadolu, Reg. .. 38 0N 39 0 E
Añatuya .... 28 20 s 62 50w
Anchorage 61 10N 149 50w
Ancohuma, Mt. .. 16 0 s 68 50w
Ancona .... 43 37N 13 30 E
Ancud 42 0s 73 50w
Ancud, G. de .... 42 0 s 73 0w
Andalsnes .... 62 35N 7 43 E
Andalusia 31 51N 86 30w
Andaman Is. .... 12 30N 92 30 E
Andenne .... 50 30N 5 5 E
Anderson, Calif. '.. 40 30N 122 19w
Anderson, Ind.... 40 5N 85 40w
Anderson, S.C.... 34 32N 82 40w
Anderson, R. 69 43N 128 58w
Andes, Mts. ..... 20 0 s 68 0w
Andevoronte ..... 18 57 s 49 6 E
Andhra Pradesh □ 15 0N 80 0 E
Andizhan .... 41 10N 72 0 E
Andkhui .... 36 52N 65 8 E
Andorra ■ .... 42 30N 1 30 E
Andorra .... 42 31N 1 32 E
Andover 51 13N 1 29w
Andradina .... 20 54 s 51 23w
Andreanof Is. 51 0N 178 0w
Ándria .... 41 13N 16 17 E
Andriba .... 17 30 s 46 58 E
Andros, I. 24 30N 78 4w
Ándros I. .... 37 50N 24 50 E
Andros Town 24 43N 77 47w
Andújar 38 3N 4 5w
Anécho .... 6 12N 1 34 E
Anegada I. 18 45N 64 20w
Anegada Pass. ... 18 15N 63 45w
Aneto, Pico d .... 42 37N 0 40 E
Angamos, Pta. ... 23 1s 70 32w
AngankI .... 47 .9N 123 48 E
Angara, R. ...... 58 6N 93 0 E
Angarsk .... 52 30N 104 0 E
Angaston .... 34 30 s 139 8 E
Ånge .... 62 31N 15 35 E
Angel de la
    Guarda, I. 29 30N 113 30w
Angeles .... 15 9N 120 33 E
Ängelholm ...... 56 15N 12 58 E
Angels Camp 38 8N 120 30w
Ångermanälven, R. 62 48N 17 56 E
Angers .... 47 30N 0 35 E
Anglesey, I. 53 17N 4 20w
Ango .... 4 10N 26 5 E

Angoche .... 16 8s 40 0 E
Angol .... 37 48 s 72 43w
Angola ■ .... 12 0s 18 0 E
Angoulême ...... 45 39N 0 10 E
Angoumois, Reg. . 45 30N 0 25 E
Angren .... 41 1N 69 45 E
Anguilla, I. 8 14N 63 5w
Angurugu .... 14 0 s 136 25 E
Angus, Braes of . 56 51N 3 0w
Anhsien .... 31 30N 104 35 E
Anhwei □ .... 33 15N 116 50 E
Anie .... 7 42N 1 8 E
Anivorzno ...... 18 44 s 48 58 E
Anjou, Reg. 47 20N 0 15w
Anjozorobé ...... 18 22 s 47 52 E
Anju .... 39 36N 125 40 E
Anka .... 12 13N 5 58 E
Ankang .... 32 38N 109 5 E
Ankara .... 40 0N 32 54 E
Ankaramina ..... 21 57 s 46 39 E
Ankazoaba ...... 22 18 s 44 31 E
Ankazobé .... 18 20 s 47 10 E
Anking .... 30 31N 117 2 E
Ann Arbor 42 17N 83 45w
Anna Plains ..... 19 17 s 121 37 E
Annaba .... 36 50N 7 46 E
Annam, Reg.=
    Trung-Phan, Reg. 16 30N 107 30 E
Annan 54 59N 3 16w
Annan, R. 54 59N 3 16w
Annapolis 38 59N 76 30w
Annapolis Royal .. 44 44N 65 32w
Annecy .... 45 55N 6 8 E
Anning .... 24 58N 102 30 E
Anniston 33 45N 85 50w
Annobón=Pagalu . 1 35s 3 35 E
Anoka 45 10N 93 26w
Anorotsangana .. 13 56 s 47 55 E
Anping .... 23 0N 120 6 E
Ansbach .... 49 17N 10 34 E
Anshan .... 41 3N 122 58 E
Anshun .... 26 2N 105 57 E
Ansi .... 40 21N 96 10 E
Anson, B. ...... 13 20 s 130 6 E
Ansongo .... 15 25N 0 35 E
Ansonville 48 46N 80 43w
Anstruther 56 14N 2 40w
Ansuda .... 2 11 s 139 22 E
Anta .... 46 18N 125 34 E
Antakya .... 36 14N 36 10 E

Antalaha .... 14 57s 50 20 E
Antalya .... 36 52N 30 45 E
Antalya Körfezi ... 36 15N 31 30 E
Antananarivo ..... 18 55s 47 35 E
Antarctica 90 0s   0   0
Antarctic Pen. 67 0s 60 0w
Antequera 37 5N   4 33w
Anthony 32 1N 106 37w
Anthony Lagoon .. 18 0s 135 30 E
Anticosti I. 49 20N 62 40w
Antigo 45 8N 89 5w
Antigonish 45 38N 61 58w
Antigua 14 34N 90 41w
Antigua, I. 17 0N 61 50w
Antilla 20 40N 75 50w
Antimony 38 7N 112 0w
Antioquia 6 40N 75 55w
Antipodes Is. ..... 49 45s 178 40 E
Antofagasta 23 50s 70 30w
Antongil, B. d' ... 15 30s 49 50 E
António Enes=
    Angoche .... 16 8s 40 0 E
Antrim 54 43N   6 13w
Antrim □ 54 55N   6 10w
Antrim, Mts. of ... 54 57N   6 10w
Antsalova .... 18 40s 44 37 E
Antsirabe .... 19 55s 47 2 E
Antsohihy .... 14 50s 47 50 E
Antung .... 40 10N 124 18 E
Antwerp=
    Antwerpen ..... 51 13N   4 25 E
Antwerpen .... 51 13N   4 25 E
Antwerpen □ ..... 51 15N   4 40 E
Anupgarh .... 29 10N 73 10 E
Anuppur .... 22 58N 81 44 E
Anuradhapura .... 8 22N 80 28 E
Anvers=
    Antwerpen ..... 51 13N   4 25 E
Anvik 62 40N 160 12w
Anyang .... 36 7N 114 26 E
Anyer-Lor .... 6 6s 105 56 E
Anyi .... 28 50N 115 31 E
Anzhero
    Sudzhensk .... 56 10N 83 40 E
Ánzio .... 41 28N 12 37 E
Aomori .... 40 45N 140 45 E
Aomori □ .... 40 45N 140 40 E
Aosta .... 45 43N   7 20 E
Aozou .... 21 49N 17 25 E
Apam 5 17N   0 44w

Apapa .... 6 25N   3 25 E
Aparri .... 18 22N 121 38 E
Apatzingán 19 0N 102 20w
Apeldoorn .... 52 13N   5 57 E
Apenam .... 8 35s 116 13 E
Apennines, Mts.=
    Appennini, Mts.. 41 0N 15 0 E
Apia 14 0s 171 55w
Apizaco 19 26N 98 9w
Apollonia=
    Marsa Susa .... 32 52N 21 59 E
Apostle Is. 47 0N 90 30w
Apóstoles 27 55s 55 45w
Apoteri 4 2N 58 32w
Appalachian Mts. . 38 0N 80 0w
Appleby 54 35N   2 29w
Appleton 44 17N 88 25w
Approuagne 4 20N 52 0w
Apucarana 23 55s 51 33w
Aq Chah .... 37 0N 66 5 E
'Aqaba .... 29 31N 35 0 E
'Aqaba, Khalj al .. 28 15N 33 20 E
Aqiq .... 18 14N 38 12 E
Aqraba .... 32 9N 35 20 E
Aquidauana 20 30s 55 50w
Ar Rab' al Khālī .. 21 0N 51 0 E
Ar-Ramthā .... 32 34N 36 0 E
Ar Raqqah .... 35 56N 39 1 E
Ar Riyād .... 24 41N 46 42 E
Ar Ruska .... 23 35N 53 30 E
Ar Rutbah .... 33 0N 40 15 E
Arab, Bahr el, R. .. 9 2N 29 28 E
Arabia, Reg. ..... 25 0N 45 0 E
Arabian Des. ..... 28 0N 32 30 E
Arabian Sea ...... 16 0N 65 0 E
Aracajú 10 55s 37 4w
Aracataca 10 38N 74 9w
Aracati 4 30s 37 44w
Araçatuba 21 10s 50 30w
Aracena 37 53N   6 58w
Araçuai 16 52s 42 4w
'Arad .... 31 17N 35 12 E
Arad .... 46 10N 21 20 E
Arafura Sea ...... 10 0s 135 0 E
Aragón, R. 42 13N   1 44w
Aragon, Reg. 41 0N   1 0w
Araguacema 8 50s 49 20w
Araguaia, R. 5 21s 48 41w
Araguari 18 38s 48 11w
Arak .... 34 0N 49 40 E

Arakan Coast ..... 19 0N 94 0 E
Arakan Yoma,
    Mts. .... 20 0N 94 30 E
Araks, R. .... 40 1N 48 28 E
Aral Sea=
    Aralskoye More . 44 30N 66 0 E
Aralsk .... 46 50N 61 20 E
Aralskoye More .. 44 30N 60 0 E
Aran, I. 55 0N   8 30w
Aran Is. 53 5N   9 42w
Aranjuez 40 1N   3 40w
Aransas P. 28 0N 97 9w
Aranyaprathet .... 13 41N 102 30 E
Arapongas 23 29s 51 28w
Araranguá 29 0s 49 30w
Araraquara 21 50s 48 0w
Ararat .... 37 16s 143 0 E
Ararat, Mt.=
    Ağri Daği, Mt. . 39 50N 44 15 E
Arauca 7 0N 70 40w
Araxá 19 35s 46 55w
Araya, Pen. de ... 10 40N 64 0w
Arbatax .... 39 57N   9 42 E
Arbīl .... 36 15N 44 5 E
Arbroath 56 34N   2 35w
Arcachon 44 40N   1 10w
Arcadia 44 13N 91 29w
Arcata 40 55N 124 4w
Archangel=
    Arkhangelsk .... 64 40N 41 0 E
Archers Post ...... 0 35N 37 35 E
Arcola 49 40N 102 30w
Arcos de los
    Frontera 36 45N   5 49w
Arcot .... 12 53N 79 20 E
Arcoverde 8 25s 37 4w
Arctic Bay 73 2N 85 11w
Arctic Ocean 78 0N 160 0w
Arctic Red River .. 67 15N 134 0w
Arda, R. .... 41 39N 26 29 E
Ardabīl .... 38 15N 48 18 E
Ardèche □ .... 44 42N   4 16 E
Ardee 53 51N   6 32w
Ardennes, Reg. ... 49 30N   5 10 E
Ardennes □ .... 49 35N   4 40 E
Ardestan .... 33 20N 52 25 E
Ardgour, Reg. 56 45N   5 25w
Ardlethan .... 34 22s 146 53 E
Ardmore, Australia 21 39s 139 11 E
Ardmore, U.S.A. .. 34 10N 97 5w

Ardnacrusha 52 43N   8 38w
Ardnamurchan Pt.. 56 44N   6 14w
Ardrossan 55 39N   4 50w
Ards □ 54 35N   5 30w
Ards Pen. 54 30N   5 25w
Arecibo 18 29N 66 42w
Areia Branca 5 0s 37 0w
Arenal .... 39 28N   2 47 E
Arendal .... 58 28N   8 46 E
Arequipa 16 20s 71 30w
Arero .... 4 41N 38 50 E
Arévalo 41 3N   4 43w
Arezzo .... 43 28N 11 50 E
Argentia 47 18N 53 58w
Argentine Basin,
    Reg. .... 44 0s 51 0 E
Argentina ■ 35 0s 66 0w
Argentino, L. 50 10s 73 0w
Arges, R. .... 44 10N 26 45 E
Argo .... 19 28N 30 30 E
Argolikós Kól. .... 37 20N 22 52 E
Argonne, Mts. .... 49 0N   5 0 E
Árgos .... 37 40N 22 43 E
Argostólion ...... 38 12N 20 33 E
Arguello, Pt. 34 34N 120 40w
Argun, R. .... 43 22N 45 55 E
Argungu .... 12 40N   4 31 E
Argyle, L. .... 16 20s 128 40 E
Århus .... 56 8N 10 11 E
Arica, Chile 18 32s 70 20w
Arica, Col. 1 30s 75 30w
Arid, C. .... 34 1s 123 10 E
Arida .... 33 29N 135 44 E
Ariège □ .... 42 56N   1 30 E
Arima 10 38N 61 17w
Arisaig 56 50N   5 40w
Arizona 35 45s 65 25w
Arizona □ 34 20N 111 30w
Arjona 10 14N 75 22w
Arka .... 60 15N 142 0 E
Arka Tagh, Mts. .. 36 30N 90 0 E
Arkadelphia 34 5N 93 0w
Arkaig, L. 56 58N   5 10w
Arkansas, R. 33 48N 91 4w
Arkansas □ 35 0N 92 30w
Arkansas City 37 4N 97 3w
Arkhangelsk ...... 64 40N 41 0 E
Arklow 52 48N   6 10w
Arles .... 43 41N   4 40 E
Arlington, S. Afr. . 28 1s 27 53 E

Arlington, U.S.A. . 44 25N 97 4w
Arlon .... 49 42N   5 49 E
Armadale .... 32 12s 116 0 E
Armagh 54 22N   6 40w
Armagh □ 54 16N   6 35w
Armagnac, Reg. ... 43 44N   0 10 E
Armavir .... 45 2N 41 7 E
Armenia 4 35N 75 45w
Armenian S.S.R. □ 40 0N 41 10 E
Armidale .... 30 30s 151 40 E
Armstrong, B.C. .. 50 25N 119 10w
Armstrong, Ont. .. 50 20N 89 0w
Arnhem .... 51 58N   5 55 E
Arnhem, B. .... 12 20s 136 10 E
Arnhem Land .... 13 0s 135 0 E
Arno, R. .... 43 31N 10 17 E
Arnprior 45 23N 76 25w
Arrabury .... 26 45s 141 0 E
Arrah .... 25 35N 84 32 E
Arran, I. 55 34N   5 12w
Arras .... 50 17N   2 46 E
Arrecife 28 59N 13 40w
Arrée, Mts. d' 48 26N   3 55w
Arrino .... 29 30s 115 40 E
Arrowhead 50 40N 117 55w
Arrowtown .... 44 57s 168 50 E
Arshan .... 46 59N 120 0 E
Árta .... 39 8N 21 2 E
Artemovsk .... 48 35N 37 55 E
Artesia 32 55N 104 25w
Arthur, Pt. .... 22 7s 150 3 E
Artigas 30 20s 56 30w
Artois, Reg. ...... 50 20N   2 30 E
Artvin .... 41 14N 41 44 E
Aru, Kep. .... 6 0s 134 30 E
Arua .... 3 1N 30 58 E
Aruanã 15 0s 51 10w
Aruba, I. 12 30N 70 0w
Arunachal
    Pradesh □ ..... 28 0N 95 0 E
Arusha .... 3 20s 36 40 E
Arvada 44 43N 106 6w
Arvayheer .... 46 15N 102 48 E
Arvida 48 16N 71 14w
Arvidsjaur .... 65 35N 19 10 E
Arvika .... 59 40N 12 36 E
Arys .... 42 26N 68 48 E
Arzamas .... 55 27N 43 55 E
Arzew 35 50N   0 23w
As Salt .... 32 2N 35 43 E

As Samawah ...... 31 15N 45 15 E
As Sulaimānīyah .. 24 8N 47 10 E
As Sulaimānīyah ... 35 35N 45 29 E
As Suwaih .... 22 10N 59 33 E
As Suwayda .... 32 40N 36 30 E
As Suwayrah ...... 32 55N 45 0 E
Asaba .... 6 12N 6 38 E
Asahikawa .... 43 45N 142 30 E
Asamankese 5 50N 0 40W
Asansol .... 23 40N 87 1 E
Asbestos 45 47N 71 58W
Asbury Park 40 15N 74 1W
Ascension, B. de la 19 50N 87 20W
Ascension, I. 8 0S 14 15W
Aschaffenburg ... 49 58N 9 8 E
Ascoli Piceno .... 42 51N 13 34 E
Aseb .... 13 0N 42 40 E
Ash Fork 35 14N 112 32W
Ash Shāmiyah ... 31 55N 44 35 E
Ash Sharma ..... 28 1N 35 18 E
Ash Shuna ...... 32 32N 35 34 E
Asha .... 35 10N 33 38 E
Ashanti □ 7 30N 2 0W
Ashburton .... 43 53S 171 48 E
Ashburton, R. .. 37 52S 145 5 E
Ashburton Downs . 23 25S 117 4 E
Ashby-de-la-Zouch 52 45N 1 29W
Ashdod .... 31 39N 34 35 E
Ashdot Yaaqov ... 32 39N 35 35 E
Asheboro 35 43N 79 46W
Asheville 35 39N 82 30W
Ashford .... 51 8N 0 53 E
Ashikaga .... 36 28N 139 29 E
Ashington 55 12N 1 35W
Ashkhabad ...... 38 0N 57 50 E
Ashland, Ky. 38 25N 82 40W
Ashland, Ohio 40 52N 82 20W
Ashland, Oreg. ... 42 10N 122 38W
Ashland, Wis. 46 40N 90 52W
Ashquelon ...... 31 42N 34 55 E
Ashtabula 41 52N 80 50W
Ashton 44 6N 111 30W
Ashton-under-
Lyne 53 30N 2 8W
Asia .... 45 0N 75 0 E
Asilah 35 29N 6 0W
Asinara, G. dell' . 41 0N 8 30 E
Asinara, I. ..... 41 5N 8 15 E
Asino .... 57 0N 86 0 E
Asir, Ras .... 11 55N 51 0 E

Asir, Reg. .... 18 40N 42 30 E
Asira esh
Shamaliya ..... 32 16N 35 16 E
Askersund .... 58 58N 14 8 E
Asmar .... 35 10N 71 27 E
Asmera .... 15 19N 38 55 E
Aspiring, Mt. 44 23S 168 46W
Assam □ .... 25 45N 92 30 E
Asse .... 50 54N 4 6 E
Assen .... 53 0N 6 35 E
Assiniboia 49 40N 106 0W
Assiniboine, Mt. .. 50 52N 115 39W
Assiniboine, R. ... 49 53N 97 8W
Assis 22 40S 50 20W
Assisi .... 43 4N 12 36 E
Assynt, L. 58 25N 5 10W
Astara .... 38 30N 48 50 E
Asti .... 44 54N 8 11 E
Astipálaia, I. ..... 36 32N 26 22 E
Astorga 42 29N 6 8W
Astoria 46 16N 123 50W
Astrakhan .... 46 25N 48 5 E
Asturias, Reg. 43 15N 6 0W
Asunción 25 21S 57 30W
Aswân .... 24 4N 32 57 E
Aswân High Dam . 24 5N 32 54 E
Asyût .... 27 11N 31 4 E
At Ta'if .... 21 5N 40 27 E
Atacama Des. 24 0S 69 20W
Atacama, Pune de . 25 0S 67 30W
Atacama, Salar de . 24 0S 68 20W
Atakpamé .... 7 31N 1 13 E
Atami .... 35 0N 139 55 E
Atar 20 30N 13 5W
Atara .... 63 10N 129 10 E
Atasu .... 48 30N 71 0 E
Atbara .... 17 42N 33 59 E
'Atbara, Nahr, R . . 17 40N 33 56 E
Atbasar .... 51 48N 68 20 E
Atchison 39 40N 95 0W
Ath .... 50 38N 3 47 E
Athabasca 54 45N 113 20W
Athabasca, L. 59 10N 109 30W
Athabasca, R. 58 40N 110 50W
Athboy 53 37N 6 55W
Athenry 53 18N 8 45W
Athens, Ala. 34 49N 86 58W
Athens, Ga. 33 56N 83 24W
Athens, Ohio 39 52N 82 64W
Athens, Tex. 32 11N 95 48W

Athens=Athínai .. 37 58N 23 46 E
Atherton .... 17 17S 145 30 E
Athi River ...... 1 29S 36 58 E
Athíeme .... 6 37N 1 40 E
Athínai .... 37 58N 23 46 E
Athlone 53 26N 7 57W
Athol 42 36N 72 14W
Atholl, Forest of . 56 51N 3 50W
Atholville 48 5N 67 5W
Athos, Mt. ...... 40 9N 24 22 E
Athy 53 0N 7 0W
Atka .... 60 50N 151 48 E
Atka I. 52 15N 174 30W
Atlanta 33 50N 84 24W
Atlantic 41 25N 95 0W
Atlantic City 39 25N 74 25W
Atlantic Ocean 0 0 30 0W
Atlas, Anti, Mts. .. 30 0N 8 0½
Atlas, Moyen,
Mts. 37 0N 5 0W
Atlas Saharien,
Mts. .... 34 10N 3 30 E
Atlin 59 31N 133 41W
Atlit .... 32 42N 34 56 E
Atmore 31 2N 87 30W
Atocha 21 0S 66 10W
Atotonilco 20 20N 98 40W
Attawapiskat 53 0N 82 30W
Attawapiskat L. .. 52 20N 88 0W
Attawapiskat, R. .. 52 57N 82 18W
Attil .... 32 23N 35 4 E
Attleboro 41 56N 71 18W
Attock .... 33 52N 72 20 E
Attopeu .... 14 56N 106 50 E
Attu I. .... 52 55N 173 0 E
Atura .... 2 5N 32 17 E
Atwood 39 52N 101 3W
Auasberg .... 22 45S 17 22 E
Aube, R. .... 48 34N 3 43 E
Aube □ .... 48 15N 4 0 E
Auburn, Ala. 32 57N 85 30W
Auburn, Calif. ... 38 50N 121 10W
Auburn, Me. 44 6N 70 14W
Aubusson .... 45 57N 2 11 E
Auch .... 43 39N 0 36 E
Auchi .... 7 6N 6 13 E
Auckland .... 36 52S 174 46 E
Auckland Is. .... 51 0S 166 0 E
Aude, R. .... 43 13N 3 14 E
Aude □ .... 44 13N 3 15 E

Auden 50 17N 87 54W
Augathella ...... 25 48S 146 35 E
Augsburg .... 48 22N 10 54 E
Augusta,
Australia ..... 34 22S 115 10 E
Augusta, Italy ... 37 14N 15 12 E
Augusta, U.S.A. .. 33 29N 81 59W
Augusta 44 20N 69 46W
Augusto Cardoso . 12 44S 34 50 E
Augustów .... 53 51N 23 0 E
Augustus, Mt. ... 24 20S 116 50 E
Augustus Downs .. 18 35S 139 55 E
Auna .... 10 9N 4 42 E
Aunis, Reg. 46 0N 0 50W
Aurangabad,
Maharashtra ... 19 50N 75 23 E
Aurillac .... 44 55N 2 26 E
Aurora, Colo. 39 44N 104 55W
Aurora, Ill. 41 42N 88 20W
Aust-Agde □ .... 58 55N 7 40 E
Austin, Minn. 43 37N 92 59W
Austin, Nev. 39 30N 117 1W
Austin, Tex. 30 20N 97 45W
Australia ■ ...... 23 0S 135 0 E
Australian Alps,
Mts. .... 36 30S 148 8 E
Australian
Capital Terr. □ . 35 15S 149 8 E
Australian
Dependency □ .. 73 0S 90 0 E
Austria ■ .... 47 0N 14 0 E
Autlán 19 40N 104 30W
Autun .... 46 58N 4 17 E
Auvergne .... 15 39S 130 1 E
Auvergne, Mts. ... 45 20N 2 45 E
Auvergne, Reg. ... 45 30N 3 20 E
Auxerre .... 47 48N 3 32 E
Avallon .... 47 30N 3 53 E
Avalon Pen. 47 0N 53 20W
Aveiro, Brazil 3 10S 55 5W
Aveiro, Port. 40 37N 8 38W
Avellaneda 34 50S 58 10W
Avellino .... 40 54N 14 46 E
Aversa .... 40 58N 14 11 E
Aves, Is. de 12 0N 67 40W
Avesta .... 60 9N 16 10 E
Aveyron □ ...... 44 22N 2 45 E
Aviá Terai 26 45S 60 50W
Aviemore 57 11N 3 50W
Avignon .... 43 57N 4 50 E

Ávila 40 39N 4 43W
Avilés 43 35N 5 57W
Avoca .... 37 5S 143 28 E
Avoca, R. 52 48N 6 10W
Avola, Canada ... 51 45N 119 30W
Avon, R,
Australia ..... 31 40S 116 7 E
Avon, R., Avon .. 52 30N 2 43W
Avon, R., Dorset .. 50 43N 1 46W
Avon, R.,
Gloucester .. 51 59N 2 10W
Avon □ 51 30N 2 40W
Avonmouth 51 30N 2 42W
Avranches 48 40N 1 20W
Awaji-Shima, I. .. 34 30N 134 50 E
Awali .... 26 0N 50 30 E
Awash .... 9 1N 40 10 E
Awatere, R. ..... 41 37S 174 10 E
Awe, L. 56 15N 5 15W
Awgu .... 6 4N 7 24 E
Awjilah .... 29 8N 21 7 E
Awka .... 6 12N 7 5 E
Axel Heiberg
Ld. 80 0N 90 0W
Axim 4 41N 2 15W
Axminster 50 47N 3 1W
Ayabe .... 35 20N 135 20 E
Ayacucho, Arg. .. 37 5S 58 20W
Ayacucho, Peru .. 13 0S 74 0W
Ayaguz .... 48 10N 80 0 E
Ayamonte 37 12N 7 24W
Ayan .... 56 30N 138 16 E
Aykin .... 62 20N 49 56 E
Aylesbury, Canada 50 55N 105 53W
Aylesbury, U.K. .. 51 48N 0 49W
Aylmer, L. 64 0N 109 0W
Ayr, Australia ... 19 35S 147 25 E
Ayr, U.K. 55 28N 4 37W
Ayr, R. 55 29N 4 28W
Ayre, Pt. of 54 27N 4 21W
Aytos .... 42 47N 27 16 E
Ayvalik .... 39 20N 26 46 E
Az Zahiriya .... 31 25N 34 58 E
Az Zahrān ...... 26 10N 50 7 E
Az-Zarqā' ...... 32 5N 36 4 E
Az Zilfi .... 26 12N 44 52 E
Az Zubayr ...... 30 20N 47 50 E
Azamgarh ...... 26 35N 83 13 E
Āzārbāijān □ .... 37 0N 44 30 E
Azare .... 11 55N 10 10 E

Azbine=Aïr	18 0N	8 0 E
Azerbaijan S.S.R. □	40 20N	48 0 E
Azor	32 2N	34 48 E
Azores, Is.	38 44N	29 0w
Azov	47 3N	39 25 E
Azov Sea= Azovskoye More	46 0N	36 30 E
Azovskoye More	46 0N	36 30 E
Azovy	64 55N	64 35 E
Aztec	36 54N	108 0w
Azua	18 25N	70 44w
Azuaga	38 16N	5 39w
Azuero, Pen. de	7 40N	80 30w
Azul	36 42s	59 43w

B

Ba Don	17 45N	106 26 E
Baba, Koh-i-, Mts.	34 40N	67 20 E
Babahoyo	1 40s	79 30w
Babakin	32 11s	117 52 E
Babana	10 31N	5 9 E
Babati	4 13s	35 45 E
Babelthuap, I.	7 30N	134 36 E
Babinda	17 27s	146 0 E
Babo	2 30s	133 30 E
Bābol	36 40N	52 50 E
Babol Sar	36 45N	52 45 E
Babura	12 51N	8 59 E
Babuyan Chan.	18 58N	122 0 E
Babuyan Is.	19 0N	122 0 E
Babylon	32 40N	44 30 E
Bacabal	5 20s	56 45w
Bacan, I.	1 0s	127 30 E
Bachelina	57 45N	67 20 E
Back, R.	67 15N	95 15w
Bacolod	10 50N	123 0 E
Bad Ischl	47 44	13 38 E
Badagara	11 35N	75 40 E
Badagri	6 25N	2 55 E
Badajoz	38 50N	6 59w
Badakhshan □	36 30N	71 0 E
Badalona	41 26N	2 15 E
Badalzal	29 50N	65 35 E
Badanah	30 58N	41 30 E
Badas	4 20N	114 37 E

Baden	48 1N	16 13 E
Baden-Baden	48 45N	8 14 E
Baden Württemberg □	48 40N	9 0 E
Badenoch, Reg.	57 0N	4 0w
Badgastein	47 7N	13 9 E
Badghis □	35 0N	63 0 E
Badin	24 38N	68 54 E
Baeza	37 57N	3 25w
Bafang	5 9N	10 11 E
Baffin B.	72 0N	65 0w
Baffin I.	68 0N	77 0w
Bafia	4 40N	11 10 E
Bafilo	9 22N	1 22 E
Bafoussam	5 2N	10 25 E
Bafra	41 34N	35 54w
Bagamoyo	6 28s	38 55 E
Bagdarin	54 26N	113 36 E
Baghdād	32 20N	44 30 E
Baghin	30 12N	56 45 E
Baghlan	36 12N	69 0 E
Baghlan □	36 0N	68 30 E
Bagotville	48 22N	70 54w
Bagrash Kol, L.	42 0N	87 0 E
Baguio	16 26N	120 34 E
Bahamas ■	24 0N	74 0w
Bahawalpur	29 37N	71 40 E
Bahawalpur □	29 5N	71 3 E
Bahi	5 58s	35 21 E
Bahia= Salvador	13 0s	38 30w
Bahia, Is. de la	16 45N	86 15w
Bahia □	12 0N	42 0 E
Bahia Blanca	38 35s	62 13w
Bahia de Caráquez	0 40s	80 27w
Bahia Laura	48 10s	66 30w
Bahia Negra	20 5s	58 5w
Bahr el Ghazâl □	7 0N	28 0 E
Bahraich	27 38N	81 50 E
Bahrain ■	26 0N	50 35 E
Baia Mare	47 40N	23 37 E
Baião	2 50s	49 15w
Baie Comeau	49 12N	68 10w
Baie T. Paul	47 28N	70 32w
Ba 'iji	35 0N	43 30 E
Baile Atha Cliath=Dublin	53 20N	6 18w
Bainbridge	30 53N	84 34w

Baird Mts.	67 10N	160 15w
Bairnsdale	37 48s	147 36 E
Baixo-Alentejo, Reg.	38 0N	8 40w
Baja	46 12N	18 59 E
Baja California Norte □	30 0N	116 0w
Baja California Sur □	26 0N	112 0w
Bajimba, Mt.	29 17s	152 6 E
Bajoga	10 57N	11 20 E
Bajool	24 30s	150 35 E
Bakchar	57 0N	82 5 E
Baker, Calif.	36 16N	116 2w
Baker, Mont.	46 22N	104 12w
Baker I.	0 10N	176 35 E
Baker L.	64 0N	97 0w
Baker, Mt.	48 50N	121 49w
Baker Lake	64 20N	96 10w
Baker's Dozen Is.	57 30N	79 0w
Bakersfield	35 25N	119 0w
Bakhtiari □	32 0N	49 0 E
Bakinskikh Komissarov	39 20N	49 15 E
Bakony Forest= Bakony Hegyseg, Reg.	47 10N	17 30 E
Bakori	11 34N	7 0 E
Baku	40 25N	49 45 E
Bal'a	32 20N	35 6 E
Bala, L.	52 53N	3 38w
Balabac I.	8 0N	117 0 E
Balabac Str.	7 53N	117 5 E
Balaghat	21 49N	80 12 E
Balaghat Ra.	18 50N	76 30 E
Balaguer	41 50N	0 50 E
Balaklava, Australia	34 7s	138 22 E
Balaklava, U.S.S.R.	44 30N	33 30 E
Balakovo	52 4N	47 55 E
Balashov	51 30N	43 10 E
Balasore	21 35N	87 3 E
Balaton, L.	46 50N	17 40 E
Balboa	9 0N	79 30w
Balbriggan	53 35N	6 10w
Balcarce	38 0s	58 10w
Balclutha	46 15s	169 45 E
Bald, Hd.	35 6s	118 1 E
Baldy Pk.	33 55N	109 35w

Baleares, Is.	39 30N	3 0 E
Balearic Is.= Baleares, Is.	39 30N	3 0 E
Balfe's Creek	20 12s	145 55 E
Balfour	26 38s	28 35 E
Bali	5 54N	10 0 E
Bali, I.	8 20s	115 0 E
Balikesir	39 35s	27 58 E
Balikpapan	1 10s	116 55 E
Balintang Chan.	19 50N	122 0 E
Balipara	26 50N	92 45 E
Baliza	16 0s	52 20w
Balkan Pen.	42 0N	22 0 E
Balkans, Mts.	42 45N	25 0 E
Balkh □	36 30N	67 0 E
Balkhash	46 50N	74 50 E
Balkhash, Oz.	46 0N	74 50 E
Ballachulish	56 40N	5 10w
Balladonia	32 27s	123 51 E
Ballarat	37 33s	143 50 E
Ballard, L.	29 20s	120 10 E
Ballater	57 2N	3 2w
Ballidu	30 35s	116 45 E
Ballina, Australia	28 50s	153 31 E
Ballina, Mayo	54 7N	9 10w
Ballina, Tipperary	52 49N	8 27w
Ballinasloe	53 20N	8 12w
Ballinger	31 45N	99 58w
Ballinrobe	53 36N	9 13w
Ballycastle	55 12N	6 15w
Ballymena	54 53N	6 18w
Ballymena □	54 53N	6 18w
Ballymoney	55 5N	6 30w
Ballymoney □	55 5N	6 30w
Ballyshannon	54 30N	8 10w
Balmaceda	46 0s	71 50w
Balmoral	57 3N	3 13w
Balovale	13 30s	23 15 E
Balrampur	27 30N	82 20 E
Balranald	34 38s	143 33 E
Balsas, R.	17 55N	102 10w
Balta	48 2N	29 45 E
Baltic Sea	56 0N	20 0 E
Baltimore, Eire	51 29N	9 10w
Baltimore, U.S.A.	39 18N	76 37w
Baluchistan, Reg.	27 30N	65 0 E
Bam	29 7N	58 14 E
Bama	11 33N	13 33 E
Bamako	12 34N	7 55w

Bambari	5 40N	20 35 E
Bambaroo	18 50s	146 10 E
Bamberg	49 54N	10 53 E
Bamenda	5 57N	10 11 E
Bamian □	35 0N	67 0 E
Bampur	27 15N	60 21 E
Ban Kantang	7 25N	99 35 E
Banadar Daryay Oman=	25 30N	56 0 E
Banalia	1 32N	25 5 E
Banamba	13 29N	7 22w
Banana	24 32s	150 12 E
Bananal, I. de	11 30s	50 30w
Banaras=Varanasi	25 22N	83 8 E
Bânâs, Ras	23 57N	35 50 E
Banat, Reg.	45 30N	21 30 E
Banbridge	54 26N	6 16w
Banbridge □	54 21N	6 16w
Banbury	52 4N	1 21w
Banchory	57 3N	2 30w
Bancroft	45 3N	77 51w
Band-e Charak	26 45N	54 20 E
Band-e Nakhîlu	26 58s	53 30 E
Banda	25 30N	80 26 E
Banda Aceh	5 35N	95 20 E
Banda Banda, Mt.	31 10s	152 28 E
Banda Sea	6 0s	130 0 E
Bandar= Machilipatnam	16 12N	81 12 E
Bandar Abbas	27 15N	56 15 E
Bandar Maharani	2 3N	102 34 E
Bandar Seri Begawan	4 52N	115 0 E
Bandar-e Bushetir	28 55N	50 55 E
Bandar-e Lengeh	26 35N	54 58 E
Bandar-e Ma'shur	30 35N	49 10 E
Bandar-e-Pahlavi	37 30N	49 30 E
Bandar-e Rig	29 30N	50 45 E
Bandar-e Shâh	37 0N	54 10 E
Bandar-e Shahpur	30 30N	49 5 E
Bandawe	11 58s	34 5 E
Bandeira, Pico da	20 26s	41 47w
Bandera	28 55s	62 20w
Bandiagara	14 12N	3 29w
Bandirma	40 20N	28 0 E
Bandon	51 44N	8 45w
Bandon, R.	51 40N	8 35w
Bandundu	3 15s	17 22¼ E
Bandung	6 36s	107 48 E
Banes	20 58N	75 43w

Banff, Canada 51 20N 115 40W
Banff, U.K. 57 40N 2 32W
Banff Nat. Park ... 51 38N 116 22W
Bang Saphan .... 11 14N 99 28 E
Bangala Dam .... 21 7s 31 25 E
Bangalore .... 12 59N 77 40 E
Bangassou ...... 4 55N 23 55 E
Banghazi .... 32 11N 20 3 E
Bangil .... 7 36s 112 50 E
Bangka, I., Selatan 3 30s 105 30 E
Bangka, I., Utara .. 1 50N 12s 5 E
Bangkalan ...... 7 2s 112 46 E
Bangkok=Krung
  Thep......... 13 45N 100 31 E
Bangladesh ■ .... 24 0N 90 0 E
Bangor, Gwynedd . 53 13N 4 9W
Bangor, N. Down . 54 40N 5 40W
Bangor, Me. 44 48N 68 42W
Bangued .... 17 40N 120 37 E
Bangui .... 4 23N 18 35 E
Bangweulu, L. ... 11 0s 30 0 E
Bani 18 16N 70 22W
Bani Na'im ...... 31 31N 35 10 E
Baninah .... 32 0N 20 12 E
Banja Luka ...... 44 49N 17 26 E
Banjar .... 7 24s 108 30 E
Banjarmasin .... 3 20s 114 35 E
Banjarnegara .... 7 24s 109 42 E
Banjul 13 28N 16 40W
Banka Banka .... 18 50s 134 0 E
Bankipore ...... 25 35N 85 10 E
Banks I. 73 30N 120 0W
Banks, Pen...... 43 45s 173 15 E
Bankura .... 23 11N 87 18 E
Bann, R. 55 2N 6 35W
Banning 48 44N 91 56W
Bannu 33 0N 70 18s
Bannockburn 56 5N 3 55W
Banská Bystrica .. 48 46N 19 14 E
Banswara .... 23 32N 74 24 E
Banten .... 6 5s 106 8 E
Bantry 51 40N 9 28W
Bantry, B. 51 35N 9 50W
Bantul .... 7 55s 110 19 E
Bapatla .... 15 55N 80 30 E
Baqa el Gharbiya . 32 25N 35 2 E
Bar .... 42 8N 19 8 E
Barabai .... 2 32s 115 34 E
Barabinsk ...... 55 20N 78 20 E
Baraboo...,.... 43 28N 89 46W

Baracoa 20 20N 74 30W
Barahona........ 18 13N 71 7W
Barail Ra. .... 25 15N 93 20 E
Barak □......... 38 20N 140 0 E
Barakhola ...... 25 0N 92 45 E
Baramula .... 34 15N 74 20 E
Baran .... 25 9N 76 40 E
Baranof 57 0N 135 10W
Baranof I. 57 0N 135 10W
Baranovichi ...... 53 10N 26 0 E
Barat□, Java .... 7 0s 107 0 E
Barat□,
  Kalimantan ..... 0 0s 111 0 E
Barat□, Sumatera . 1 0s 101 0 E
Barat Daja,
  Kep. .... 7 30s 128 0 E
Barbacena 21 15s 43 56W
Barbacoas 1 45N 78 0w
Barbados ■ 13 0N 59 30w
Barberton,
  S. Africa ..... 25 42s 31 2 E
Barberton, U.S.A. . 41 0N 81 40W
Barbuda, I. 17 30N 61 40W
Barcaldine ...... 22 33s 145 13 E
Barce=Al Marj .. 32 25N 20 40 E
Barcelona, Sp. ... 41 21N 2 10 E
Barcelona, Ven... 10 10N 64 40W
Barcelos 1 0s 63 0w
Bardaï .... 21 25N 17 0 E
Bardera 2 20N 42 0s
Bardiyah .... 31 45N 25 0 E
Bardsey I. 52 46N 4 47W
Bareilly .... 28 22N 79 27 E
Barents Sea ..... 73 0N 39 0 E
Barfleur, Pte. de . 49 42N 1 17W
Bargal .... 11 25N 51 0 E
Bargara .... 24 50s 152 25 E
Barguzin .... 53 37N 109 37 E
Bari .... 41 6N 16 52 E
Bari Doab, Reg. .. 30 20N 73 0 E
Bari Sadri ...... 24 25N 74 29 E
Barinas 8 36N 70 15W
Baring, C. 70 0N 116 30W
Bârîs .... 24 42N 30 31 E
Barisal .... 22 30N 90 20 E
Barisan,
  Bukit, Mts. .... 3 30s 102 15 E
Barito, R. ...... 4 0s 114 50 E
Barkah .... 24 30N 58 0 E
Barkha .... 31 0N 81 45 E

Barkly East ...... 30 58s 27 33 E
Barkly Tableland .. 19 50s 138 40 E
Barkly West ..... 28 38s 24 11 E
Bar-le-Duc ...... 48 47N 5 10 E
Barlee, L. ...... 29 15s 119 30 E
Barletta .... 41 20N 16 17 E
Barmedman .... 34 9s 147 21 E
Barmer .... 25 45N 71 20 E
Barmera .... 34 15s 140 28 E
Barmouth 52 44N 4 3w
Barnard Castle ... 54 33N 1 55W
Barnaul .... 53 20N 83 40 E
Barnesville 33 6N 84 9w
Barnet 51 37N 0 15W
Barneveld ...... 52 7N 5 36 E
Barnsley 53 33N 1 29w
Barnstaple 51 5N 4 3w
Baroda=
  Vadodara ..... 22 20N 73 10 E
Barpeta .... 26 20N 91 10 E
Barqa .... 27 0N 20 0 E
Barquisimeto 9 58N 69 13w
Barra 11 5s 43 10w
Barra, I. 57 0N 7 30w
Barra de Corda .. 5 30s 45 10w
Barra do Piraí ... 22 30s 43 50w
Barraba .... 30 21s 150 35 E
Barranca 10 45s 77 50w
Barrancabermeja . 7 0N 73 50w
Barrancas 8 55N 62 5w
Barrancos 38 10N 6 58w
Barranqueras ... 27 30s 59 0w
Barranquilla 11 0N 74 50w
Barras 1 45s 73 13w
Barraute 47 30N 76 50w
Barre 44 15N 73 30w
Barreiras 12 8s 45 0w
Barreirinhas 2 30s 42 50w
Barreiro 38 40N 9 6w
Barreiros 8 49s 35 12w
Barretos 20 30s 48 35w
Barrhead 54 10N 114 30w
Barrie 44 25N 79 45w
Barrow, U.K. ... 54 8N 3 15w
Barrow, U.S.A. .. 71 16N 156 50w
Barrow, I. ..... 20 45s 115 20 E
Barrow, R. 52 46N 7 0w
Barrow Creek ... 21 30s 133 55 E
Barry 51 23N 3 19w
Barry's Bay 45 30N 77 40w

Barsaloi .... 1 20N 36 52 E
Barsi .... 18 10N 75 50 E
Barstow 34 58N 117 2w
Bartica 6 25N 58 40w
Bartlesville 36 50N 95 58w
Barton Siding ... 30 31s 132 39 E
Barton-upon-
  Humber 53 41N 0 27w
Bartow 27 53N 81 49w
Baruun Urt ..... 46 46N 113 15 E
Bas Rhin □ ..... 48 40N 7 30 E
Basel .... 47 35N 7 35 E
Bashkir
  A.S.S.R. □ .... 54 0N 57 0 E
Basilan, I. ...... 6 35N 122 0 E
Basilan City=
  Lamitan ...... 6 37N 122 0 E
Basilan Str. ..... 13 10s 122 0 E
Basildon .... 51 34N 0 29 E
Basilicata □ .... 40 30N 16 0 E
Basim .... 20 4N 77 4 E
Basingstoke 51 15N 1 5w
Baskatong Res. .. 46 46N 75 50w
Basle=Basel .... 47 35N 7 35 E
Basoka .... 1 16N 23 40 E
Basque □ 42 50N 2 45w
Basra=Al Basrah . 30 30N 47 55 E
Bass Rock 56 5N 2 40w
Bass, Str. ...... 39 15s 146 30 E
Bassano del
  Grappa ...... 45 45N 11 45 E
Bassari .... 9 19N 0 57 E
Bassas da
  India, I. ...... 22 0s 39 0 E
Basse Terre 16 0N 61 40w
Bassein, Burma .. 16 45N 94 30 E
Basseterre 17 17N 62 43w
Bassett 42 37N 99 30w
Bassigny, Reg. .. 48 0N 5 10 E
Bastak .... 27 15N 54 25 E
Basti .... 26 52N 82 55 E
Bastia .... 42 40N 9 30 E
Bastogne ...... 50 1N 5 43 E
Basutoland■=
  Lesotho ■ ... 29 40s 28 0 E
Bat Yam .... 32 2N 34 44 E
Bata .... 1 57N 9 50 E
Bataan, Pen. .... 14 38N 120 30 E
Barabanó, G. de . 22 30N 82 30w
Batagoy .... 67 38N 134 38 E

Batalha 39 40N 8 50w
Batamay .... 63 30N 129 15 E
Batan Is. .... 20 25N 121 59 E
Batang .... 6 55s 109 40 E
Batangas ...... 13 35N 121 10 E
Bataszék ...... 46 12N 18 44 E
Batavia 43 0N 78 10w
Batchelor ...... 13 4s 131 1 E
Batesville 35 48N 91 40w
Bath, U.K. 51 22N 2 22w
Bath, N.Y. 42 20N 77 17w
Bathgate 55 54N 3 38w
Bathurst=Banjul . 13 28N 16 40w
Bathurst,
  Australia ..... 33 25s 149 31 E
Bathurst, Canada . 47 37N 65 43w
Bathurst, C. 70 30N 128 30w
Bathurst, I.,
  Australia ..... 11 30s 130 10 E
Bathurst I., Canada 76 30N 130 10w
Bathurst Inlet ... 67 15N 108 30w
Bathurst Mines .. 47 30N 65 47w
Batinah, Reg. ... 24 0N 57 0 E
Batna .... 35 34N 6 15 E
Baton Rouge ... 30 30N 91 5w
Batouri .... 4 30N 14 25 E
Battambang .... 13 7N 103 12 E
Batticaloa ...... 7 43N 81 45 E
Battir .... 41 34N 35 8 E
Battle .... 50 55N 0 30 E
Battle, R. 52 45N 108 15w
Battle Creek 42 20N 85 10w
Battle Harbour .. 52 13N 55 42w
Battle Mountain . 40 45N 117 0w
Battleford 52 45N 108 15w
Batu, Kep. ..... 0 30s 98 25 E
Batu Pahat= Bandar
  Penggaram .... 1 50N 102 56 E
Batumi .... 41 30N 41 30 E
Baturadja ...... 4 11s 104 15 E
Baturité 4 28s 38 45w
Baubau .... 5 25s 123 50 E
Bauchi □ ...... 10 22N 9 48 E
Bauchi □ ...... 10 25N 10 0 E
Bauhinia Downs . 24 35s 149 18 E
Bauru 22 10s 49 0w
Baus 18 22s 5247½
Bautzen 51 11N 14 25w
Bavaria□=
  Bayern □ ..... 49 7N 11 30 E

Bawdwin . . . . 23 5N 97 50 E
Bawean, I. . . . . 5 46s 112 35 E
Bawku 11 3N 0 19w
Bawlake . . . . 19 11N 97 21 E
Bay City, Mich. . . 43 35N 83 51w
Bay City, Tex. . . . 28 59N 95 55w
Bay Shore 40 44N 73 15w
Bay View . . . . 3925w 176 50 E
Bayamón 18 24N 66 10w
Bayan . . . . .47 20N 107 55 E
Bayan Kara Shan,
  Mts. . . . . 34 0N 98 0 E
Bayan-Uul . . . . . . 49 6N 112 12 E
Bayanaul . . . . 50 45N 75 45 E
Bayantsogt . . . . . . 47 58N 105 1 E
Bayern □ . . . . 49 7N 11 30 E
Bayeux 49 17N 0 42w
Baykal, Oz. . . . . . 53 0N 108 0 E
Baykal, L.=
  Baykal, Oz. . . . . 53 0N 108 0 s
Baykir . . . . 61 50N 95 50 E
Baykonur . . . . 47 48N 65 50 E
Baynes Mts. . . . . . 22 40s 12 50 E
Bayonne . . . . 43 30N 1 28 E
Bayreuth . . . . 49 56N 11 35 E
Bayrūt . . . . 33 53N 35 31 E
Bayt Aula . . . . . . 31 37N 35 2 E
Bayt Jālā . . . . 31 43N 35 11 E
Bayt Lahm . . . . . 31 43N 35 12 E
Bayt Sāhūr . . . . . 31 42N 35 13 E
Baytin . . . . 31 56N 35 14 E
Baytown 29 42N 94 57w
Baza 37 30N 2 47w
Bazaruto, I. do . . 21 40s 35 28 E
Beach 46 57N 104 0w
Beachy Hd. . . . . . 50 44N 0 16 E
Beacon, Australia . 30 20s 117 55 E
Beacon, U.S.A. . . 41 32N 73 58w
Beagle 55 0s 68 30w
Bealey . . . . 43 2s 171 36 E
Beardmore 49 36N 87 59w
Beardstown 40 0N 90 25w
Béarn, Reg 43 28N 0 36w
Beatrice 40 20N 96 40w
Beauce, Reg. . . . . 48 10N 2 0 E
Beauceville 46 13N 70 46w
Beaudesert . . . . . 27 59s 153 0 E
Beaufort, Malaysia 5 30N 115 40 E
Beaufort,
  Australia . . . . . . 37 25s 143 25 E

Beaufort, U.S.A. . . 34 45N 76 40w
Beaufort Sea 70 30N 146 0w
Beaufort West . . . . 32 18s 22 36 E
Beauharnois 45 20N 73 20w
Beaujolais, Reg. . . 46 0N 4 25 E
Beauly 57 29N 4 27w
Beaumaris 53 16N 4 7w
Beaumont 30 5N 94 8w
Beaune . . . . 47 2N 4 50 E
Beausejour . . . . . . 50 5N 96 35 E
Beauvais . . . . 49 25N 2 8 E
Beauval 55 9N 107 35w
Beaver, U.S.A. 66 40N 147 50w
Beaver Dam 43 28N 88 50w
Beaver Falls 40 44N 80 20w
Beawar . . . . 26 3N 74 18 E
Beccles . . . . 52 27N 1 33 E
Béchar . . . . 31 38N 2 18 E
Bechuanaland■=
  Botswana ■ . . . . 23 0s 24 0 E
Bechuanaland,
  Reg.=
  Betsjoeanaland,
  Reg. . . . . 26 30s 22 30 E
Beckley 37 50N 81 8w
Bedford, Canada . . 45 10N 73 0w
Bedford,
  S. Africa . . . . . . 32 40s 26 10 E
Bedford, U.K. 52 8N 0 29w
Bedford, Ohio 41 23N 81 32w
Bedford, Ind. 38 50N 86 30w
Bedford □ 52 4N 0 28w
Bednesti 53 50N 123 10w
Bedourie . . . . 24 30s 139 30 E
Beenleigh . . . . 27 43s 153 10 E
Be'er Sheva . . . . . . 31 15N 34 48 E
Be'erotayim . . . . . . 32 19N 34 59 E
Beeston 52 55N 1 11w
Beeville 28 27N 97 44w
Bega . . . . 36 41s 149 51 E
Begoro 6 23N 0 23w
Behbehan . . . . 30 30N 50 15 E
Behshahr . . . . 36 45N 53 35 E
Beilen . . . . 52 52N 6 27 E
Beira . . . . 19 50s 34 52 E
Beira-Alta, Reg. . . 41 0N 7 20w
Beira-Baixa, Reg. . . 40 0N 7 30w
Beira Litoral,
  Reg. 40 0N 8 30w
Beirut=Bayrut . . . . 33 53N 35 31 E

Beit Hanun . . . . . . 31 32N 34 32 E
Beit'Ur et Tahta . . 31 54N 35 5 E
Beitbridge . . . . 22 12s 30 0 E
Beituniya . . . . 31 54N 35 10 E
Beja, Port. 38 2N 7 53w
Béja, Tunisia . . . . 36 10N 9 0 E
Béjaïa . . . . 36 42N 5 2 E
Békéscsaba . . . . . . 46 40N 21 10 E
Bekily . . . . 24 13s 45 19 E
Bekwai 6 25N 1 37w
Bela, India . . . . . . 25 50N 82 0 E
Bela, Pak. . . . . . . 26 12N 66 20 E
Bela Vista 17 0s 49 0w
Belawan . . . . 3 33N 98 32 E
Belaya Tserkov . . . 49 45N 30 10 E
Belcher Is. 56 20N 79 20w
Belebey . . . . 54 72N 54 7 E
Belém 1 20s 48 30w
Belén 27 40s 67 5w
Belen 34 40N 106 50w
Belet Uen . . . . 4 30N 45 5 E
Belfast, S. Afr. . . . 25 42s 30 2 E
Belfast, U.K. 54 35N 5 56w
Belfast, U.S.A. . . . 44 30N 69 0w
Belfast, L. 54 40N 5 50w
Belfast □ 54 35N 5 56w
Belfort . . . . 47 38N 6 50 E
Belfort, Terr. de □ 47 38N 6 52 E
Belgaum . . . . 15 55N 74 35 E
Belgium ■ . . . . . . 51 30N 5 0 E
Belgooly 51 44N 8 30w
Belgorod . . . . 50 35N 36 35 E
Belgorod-
  Dnestrovskiy . . . 46 11N 30 23 E
Belgrade=
  Beograd . . . . . . 44 50N 20 37 E
Belitung, Pulau, I. . 3 10s 107 50 E
Belize ■ 17 0N 88 30w
Belize City 17 25N 88 0w
Bell Ville 32 40s 62 40w
Bella Coola 52 25N 126 40w
Bella Vista 28 33s 59 0w
Bellaire 40 1N 80 46w
Bellary . . . . 15 10N 76 56 E
Bellata . . . . 29 53s 149 46 E
Belle I. 47 20N 3 10w
Belle I, Str. of . . 51 30N 56 30w
Belle Fourche 44 43N 103 52w
Belle Glade 26 43N 80 38w
Bellefontaine . . . . 40 20N 83 45 E

Belleville, Canada . 44 15N 77 37w
Belleville, U.S.A. . . 38 30N 90 0w
Bellevue 46 35N 84 10w
Bellin 60 0N 70 0w
Bellingen . . . . 30 25s 152 50 E
Bellingham 48 45N 122 27w
Bellingshausen
  Sea 66 0s 80 0w
Bellinzona . . . . . . 46 11N 9 1 E
Bellows Falls 43 10N 72 30w
Belluno . . . . 46 8N 12 6 E
Bélmez 38 17N 5 17w
Belmont . . . . 33 4s 151 42 E
Belmonte, Brazil . . 16 0s 39 0w
Belmopan 17 18N 88 30w
Belmullet 54 13N 9 58w
Belo Horizonte . . . 19 55s 43 56w
Belogorsk . . . . 51 0N 128 20 E
Beloit 42 35N 89 0w
Belomorsk . . . . . . 64 35N 34 30 E
Beloretsk . . . . 53 58N 58 24 E
Belo-sur-
  Tsiribihina . . . . . 19 40s 44 30 E
Belovo . . . . 54 30N 86 0 E
Beloye, Oz. . . . . . 60 10N 37 35 E
Beloye More . . . . 66 0N 38 0 E
Belozersk . . . . 60 0N 37 30 E
Belsty . . . . 47 48N 28 0 E
Beltana . . . . 30 48s 138 25 E
Belterra 2 45s 55 0w
Belton 31 4N 97 30w
Belturbet 54 6N 7 28w
Belvidere 42 15N 88 55w
Belyy Os. 73 30N 71 0w
Belyy Yar . . . . . . 58 26N 84 30 E
Bemidji 47 30N 94 50w
Ben Cruachan,
  Mt. 56 26N 5 8w
Ben Gardane . . . . 33 11N 11 11 E
Ben Hope, Mt. . . 58 24N 4 36w
Ben Lawers, Mt. . . 56 33N 4 13w
Ben Lomond, Mt.,
  Australia . . . . . . 30 1s 151 43 E
Ben Lomond, Mt.,
  U.K. 56 12N 4 39w
Ben Macdhui, Mt. . 57 4N 3 40w
Ben More, Mt. . . 56 26N 6 2w
Ben More Assynt,
  Mt. 58 7N 4 51w
Ben Nevis, Mt. . . 56 48N 5 0w

Ben Wyvis, Mt. . . 57 40N 4 35w
Bena . . . . 11 20N 5 50 E
Bena Dibele . . . . . 4 4s 22 50 E
Benalla . . . . 36 30s 146 0 E
Benares=Varanasi . 25 22N 83 8 E
Benbecula, I. 57 26N 7 20w
Benbonyathe Hill . 30 25s 139 11 E
Bencubbin . . . . . . 30 48s 117 52 E
Bend 44 2N 121 15w
Bendel □ . . . . 6 0N 5 40 E
Bender Beila . . . . 9 30N 50 48 E
Bendering . . . . . . 32 23s 118 18 E
Bendery . . . . 46 50N 29 50 E
Bendigo . . . . 36 40s 144 15 E
Bene Beraq . . . . . 32 5N 34 50 E
Benenitra . . . . 23 27s 45 5 E
Benevento . . . . . . 41 7N 14 45 E
Bengal, B. of . . . . 15 0N 90 0 E
Benghazi=
  Banghazi . . . . . . 32 11N 20 3 E
Bengkalis . . . . 1 30N 102 10 E
Bengkulu . . . . 3 50s 102 12 E
Bengkulu □ . . . . . 3 50s 102 10 E
Bengough 49 25N 105 10w
Benguela . . . . 12 37s 13 25 E
Beni . . . . 32 11s 148 43 E
Beni Mazar . . . . . 28 32N 30 44 E
Beni Mellal 32 21N 6 21w
Beni Suêf . . . . . . 29 5N 31 6 E
Benidorm 38 33N 0 9w
Benin, ■ . . . . 8 0N 2 0 E
Benin, B. of . . . . . 5 0N 3 0 E
Benin City . . . . . . 6 20N 5 31 E
Benjamin Constant 4 40s 70 15w
Benlidi . . . . 24 35s 144 50 E
Bennettsville 34 38N 79 39w
Bennington 42 52N 73 12w
Benoni . . . . 26 11s 28 18 E
Benson 31 59N 110 19w
Benteng . . . . 6 10s 120 30 E
Benton, Ark. 34 30N 92 35w
Benton, Ill. 38 0N 88 55w
Benton Harbor . . 42 10N 86 28w
Benue, R. . . . . . . 7 47N 6 45 E
Benue □ . . . . 7 20N 8 20 E
Beograd . . . . 44 50N 20 37 E
Beppu . . . . 33 15N 131 30 E
Ber Dagan . . . . . . 32 1N 34 49 E
Berati . . . . 40 43N 19 59 E
Berber . . . . 18 0N 34 0 E

Berbera	10 30N	45 2 E	
Berbérati	4 15N	15 40 E	
Berdicher	49 57N	28 30 E	
Berdsk	54 47N	83 2 E	
Berdyansk	46 45N	36 50 E	
Bereda	11 45N	51 0 E	
Berekum	7 29N	2 34W	
Berens River	52 25N	97 0W	
Berevo	19 44S	44 58 E	
Berezniki	59 24N	56 46 E	
Berezovo	64 0N	65 0 E	
Bérgamo	45 42N	9 40 E	
Bergen, Neth.	52 40N	4 42 E	
Bergen, Norway	60 23N	5 27 E	
Bergen-op-Zoom	51 30N	4 18 E	
Bergerac	44 51N	0 30 E	
Bergum	53 13N	5 59 E	
Berhampore	24 2N	88 27 E	
Berhampur	19 15N	84 54 E	
Bering Sea	59 0N	175 0W	
Bering Str.	66 0N	170 0W	
Beringen	51 3N	5 14 E	
Beringovskiy	63 3N	179 19 E	
Berja	36 50N	2 56W	
Berkeley	38 0N	122 20W	
Berkner I.	79 30S	50 0W	
Berkshire □	51 30N	1 20W	
Berlin, Germany	52 32N	13 24 E	
Berlin, U.S.A.	44 29N	71 10W	
Bermejo, R.	26 51S	58 23W	
Bermuda, I.	32 45N	65 0W	
Bern	46 57N	7 28 E	
Bernalilo	35 17N	106 37W	
Bernardo de Irigoyen	26 15S	53 40W	
Bernburg	51 48N	11 44 E	
Bernier, I.	24 50S	113 12 E	
Bernina, Piz	46 20N	9 54 E	
Beroun	49 57N	14 5 E	
Berowra	33 35S	151 12 E	
Berrechid	33 18N	7 36W	
Berri	34 14S	140 35 E	
Berrigan	35 38S	145 49 E	
Berry, Reg.	47 0N	2 0 E	
Bertoua	4 30N	13 45 E	
Berwick	41 4N	76 17W	
Berwick-upon-Tweed	55 47N	2 0W	
Berwyn Mts.	52 54N	3 26W	
Besalampy	16 43S	44 29 E	
Besançon	47 9N	6 0 E	
Beskids, Mts.=Vychodné Beskydy	49 30N	22 0 E	
Bessemer	46 27N	90 0W	
Bessin, Reg.	49 21N	1 0W	
Bet Ha'Emeq	32 58N	35 8 E	
Bet Ha Shitta	32 31N	35 27 E	
Bet Ha'tmeq	32 58N	35 8 E	
Bet Oren	32 43N	34 59 E	
Bet Qeshet	32 41N	35 21 E	
Be't She'an	32 30N	35 30 E	
Bet Shemesh	31 45N	35 0 E	
Bet Yosef	32 34N	35 33 E	
Betafo	19 50S	46 51 E	
Bétaré-Oya	5 40N	14 5 E	
Bethal	26 27S	29 28 E	
Bethanien	26 31S	17 8 E	
Bethany=Eizariya	31 47N	35 15 E	
Bethlehem, Jordan=Bayt Lahm	31 43N	35 12 E	
Bethlehem, S. Africa	28 14S	28 18 E	
Bethlehem, U.S.A.	40 39N	75 24W	
Bethulie	30 30S	25 29 E	
Betioky	23 48S	44 20 E	
Betoota	25 40S	140 42 E	
Betroka	23 16S	46 6 E	
Betsjoeanaland, Reg.	26 30S	22 30 E	
Bettiah	26 48N	84 33 E	
Betul	21 48N	77 59 E	
Betung	2 0S	103 10 E	
Beulah, Australia	35 58S	142 29 E	
Beulah, Canada	50 16N	101 2W	
Beverley, Australia	32 9S	116 56 E	
Beverley, U.K.	53 52N	0 26W	
Beverly	53 36N	113 21W	
Beverly Hills	34 4N	118 29W	
Beverwijk	52 28N	4 38 E	
Beyla	8 30N	8 38W	
Bexhill	50 51N	0 29 E	
Beyneu	45 10N	55 3 E	
Beypazari	40 10N	31 48 E	
Beyşehir Gólú, L.	37 40N	31 45 E	
Bezet	33 4N	35 8 E	
Bezhitsa	53 19N	34 17 E	
Béziers	43 20N	3 12 E	
Bhachau	23 10N	70 15W	
Bhadgaon	27 42N	85 27 E	
Bhadrakh	21 10N	86 30 E	
Bhagalpur	25 10N	87 0 E	
Bhamo	24 15N	97 15 E	
Bhandara	21 5N	79 42 E	
Bhanrer Ra.	23 40N	79 45 E	
Bharatpur	27 15N	77 30 E	
Bharuch	21 47N	73 0 E	
Bhatinda	30 15N	74 57 E	
Bhatpara	22 50N	88 25 E	
Bhavnagar	21 45N	72 10 E	
Bhilwara, R.	25 25N	74 38 E	
Bhima, R.	17 20N	76 30 E	
Bhimavaram	16 30N	81 30 E	
Bhind	26 30N	78 46 E	
Bhiwandi	19 15N	73 0 E	
Bhiwani	28 50N	76 9 E	
Bhopal	23 20N	77 53 E	
Bhubaneswar	20 15N	85 50 E	
Bhusaval	21 11N	75 56 E	
Bhutan ■	27 25N	89 50 E	
Biafra, B. of=Bonny, B. of	4 0N	8 0 E	
Biała Podlaska	52 4N	23 6 E	
Białystok	53 10N	23 10 E	
Biarritz	43 29N	1 33W	
Biberach	48 5N	9 49 E	
Bibiani	6 30N	2 8W	
Bic	48 20N	68 41W	
Bida	9 3N	5 58 E	
Bicester	51 53N	1 9W	
Bidar	17 55N	77 35 E	
Biddeford	43 30N	70 28 E	
Bideford	51 1N	4 13W	
Bié	12 22S	16 55 E	
Bié Plat.	12 0S	16 0 E	
Bieber	41 4N	121 6W	
Biel	47 8N	7 14 E	
Bielé Karpaty, Mts.	49 5N	18 0 E	
Bielefeld	52 2N	8 31 E	
Biella	45 33N	8 3 E	
Bielsko-Biała	49 50N	19 8 E	
Biên Hoa	10 57N	106 49 E	
Big Beaver House	52 59N	89 50W	
Big Bend Nat. Park	29 15N	103 15W	
Big Delta	64 15N	145 0W	
Big Rapids	43 42N	85 27W	
Big River	53 50N	107 0W	
Big Salmon	61 50N	136 0W	
Big Spring	32 10N	101 25W	
Big Stone Gap	36 52N	82 45W	
Big Trout L.	53 40N	90 0W	
Biggar, Canada	52 10N	108 0W	
Biggar, U.K.	55 38N	3 31W	
Bigge, I.	14 35S	125 10 E	
Biggenden	25 31S	152 4 E	
Bighorn Mts.	44 30N	107 20W	
Bigorre, Reg.	43 5N	0 2 E	
Bigtimber	45 33N	110 0W	
Bihać	44 49N	15 57 E	
Bihar	25 5N	85 40 E	
Bihar □	25 0N	86 0 E	
Biharamulo	2 25S	31 25 E	
Bijagos, Arquipélago dos	11 15N	16 10W	
Bijapur	26 2N	77 36 E	
Bijnor	29 27N	78 11 E	
Bikaner	28 2N	73 18 E	
Bikin	46 50N	134 20 E	
Bilara	26 14N	73 53 E	
Bilaspur	22 2N	82 15 E	
Bilbao	43 16N	2 56W	
Bilecik	40 5N	30 5 E	
Bilibino	68 3N	166 20 E	
Bilir	65 40N	131 20 E	
Billabalong	27 25S	115 49 E	
Billiluna	19 37S	127 41 E	
Billingham	54 36N	1 18W	
Billings	45 43N	108 29W	
Bilma	18 50N	13 30 E	
Biloela	24 34S	150 31 E	
Biloxi	30 30N	89 0W	
Biltine	14 40N	20 50 E	
Bilyana	18 5S	145 50 E	
Bima	8 22S	118 49 E	
Bina-Etawah	24 13N	78 14 E	
Binalbagan	10 12N	122 50 E	
Binatang	2 10N	111 40 E	
Binbee	20 19S	147 56 E	
Binche	50 26N	4 10 E	
Bindi Bindi	30 37S	116 22 E	
Bindura	17 18S	31 18 E	
Bingara, N.S.W.	29 40S	150 40 E	
Bingara, Queens.	28 10S	144 37 E	
Bingham Canyon	40 31N	112 10W	
Binghamton	42 9N	75 54W	
Binh Son	15 20N	104 40 E	
Binjai	3 50N	98 30 E	
Binyamina	32 32N	34 56 E	
Binzerte	37 15N	9 50 E	
Bir Atrun	18 15N	26 40 E	
Bir Nabala	31 52N	35 12 E	
Bîr Shalatein	23 5N	35 25 E	
Bir Zeit	31 59N	35 11 E	
Birch Hills	53 10N	105 10W	
Birchip	35 52S	143 0 E	
Bird, I.	22 20S	155 20 E	
Birdsville	25 51S	139 20 E	
Birdum	15 50S	133 0 E	
Bireuen	5 14N	96 39 E	
Birjand	32 57N	59 10 E	
Birkenhead	53 24N	3 1W	
Bîrlad	46 15N	27 38 E	
Birmingham, U.K.	52 30N	1 55W	
Birmingham, U.S.A.	33 31N	86 50W	
Birni Ngaouré	13 5N	2 51 E	
Birni Nkonni	13 55N	5 15 E	
Birnin Gwari	11 0N	6 45 E	
Birnin-Kebbi	12 32N	4 12 E	
Birnin Kuku	11 30N	9 29 E	
Birobidzhan	48 50N	132 50 E	
Birr	53 7N	7 55W	
Birtle	50 30N	101 5W	
Bisbee	31 30N	110 0W	
Biscay, B. of	45 0N	2 0W	
Bishop	37 20N	118 26W	
Bishop Auckland	54 40N	1 40W	
Bishop's Falls	49 2N	55 24W	
Bishop's Stortford	51 52N	0 11 E	
Biskra	34 50N	5 52 E	
Bismarck	46 49N	100 49W	
Bismark Arch.	3 30S	148 30 E	
Bispfors	63 2N	16 40 E	
Bissau	11 45N	15 45W	
Bissett	46 14N	78 4W	
Bistrita	47 9N	24 35 E	
Bistrita, R.	46 30N	26 57 E	
Bitola	41 5N	21 21 E	
Bitterfontein	31 0S	18 32 E	
Bitterroot Ra.	46 0N	114 20W	
Bittou	11 17N	0 18W	
Biu	10 40N	12 3 E	
Biwa-Ko, L.	35 15N	135 45 E	
Biysk	52 40N	85 0 E	

Bizen .... 34 44N 134 9 E
Bizerte=Binzerte .. 37 15N 9 50 E
Bjelovar .... 45 56N 16 49 E
Black Forest=
  Schwarzwald .... 48 0N 8 0 E
Black Hills, Mts ... 44 0N 103 50W
Black Mts........ 51 52N 3 3W
Black Sea .... 43 30N 35 0 E
Black Volta, R. ... 8 41N 1 33W
Blackall .... 24 26S 145 27 E
Blackbull .... 18 0S 141 7 E
Blackburn 53 44N 2 30W
Blackfoot 43 13N 112 12W
Blackheath .... 33 39S 150 17 E
Blackpool 53 48N 3 3W
Blacks Harbour ... 45 3N 66 49W
Blackville 47 5N 65 58W
Blackwater .... 23 35S 149 0 E
Blackwater, R.,
  Cork 51 51N 7 50W
Blackwater, R.,
  Dungannon 54 31N 6 34W
Blackwater, R.,
  Meath 53 39N 6 43W
Blackwell 36 55N 97 20W
Blaenau
  Ffestiniog 53 0N 3 57W
Blagodarnoye ..... 45 7N 43 37 E
Blagoveshchensk .. 50 20N 127 30 E
Blaine Lake 52 51N 106 52W
Blair Atholl,
  Australia .... 22 42S 147 31 E
Blair Atholl, U.K. . 56 46N 3 50W
Blairgowrie 56 36N 3 20W
Blairmore 49 40N 114 25W
Blanc, C.=
  Ras Nouadhibou 37 15N 9 56 E
Blanc, Mt. .... 45 50N 6 52 E
Blanca, B. 39 10S 61 30W
Blanca Pk. 37 35N 105 29W
Blanco .... 33 57S 22 24 E
Blandford 50 52N 2 10W
Blanding 37 35N 109 30W
Blantyre .... 15 45S 35 0 E
Blarney 51 57N 8 35W
Blåvands Huk .... 55 33N 8 5 E
Blaydon 54 56N 1 47W
Blayney .... 33 32S 149 14 E
Bleiburg .... 46 35N 14 49 E
Blekinge □ .... 56 15N 15 15 E

Blenheim .... 41 38S 174 5 E
Bletchley 51 59N 0 54W
Blida .... 36 30N 2 49 E
Blind River 46 15N 83 0W
Blitar .... 8 5S 112 11 E
Blitta .... 8 23N 1 6 E
Block I. 41 13N 71 35W
Bloemfontein ..... 29 6S 26 14 E
Bloemhof .... 27 38S 25 32 E
Blois .... 47 35N 1 20 E
Bloomington, Ill. .. 40 25N 89 0W
Bloomington, Ind. . 39 10N 86 30W
Bloomsburg 41 0N 76 30W
Blue Island 41 40N 87 41W
Blue Mud, B. .... 13 30S 136 0 E
Blue Mts. 45 15N 119 0W
Blue Nile, R.=
  Nîl el Azraq, R. . 10 30N 35 0 E
Blue Ridge, Mts ... 36 30N 80 15W
Bluefield 37 18N 81 14W
Bluefields 12 0N 83 50W
Bluff, Australia .. 23 40S 149 0 E
Bluff, N.Z. .... 46 36S 168 21 E
Bluff Knoll, Mt. .. 34 23S 118 20 E
Bluffton 40 43N 85 9W
Blumenau 27 0S 49 0W
Blyth 55 8N 1 32W
Blythe 33 40N 114 33W
Blytheville 35 56N 89 55W
Bo 7 55N 11 50W
Boa Vista 2 48N 60 30W
Boaco 12 29N 85 35W
Boali .... 4 48N 18 7 E
Bobadilla 36 58N 5 10W
Bobbili .... 18 35N 83 30 E
Bobcaygeon 44 33N 78 35W
Bobo-Dioulasso .. 11 8N 4 13W
Bobruysk .... 53 10N 29 15 E
Bocaiuva 17 7S 43 49W
Bocas del Toro ... 9 15N 82 20W
Bocholt .... 51 50N 6 35 E
Bochum .... 51 28N 7 12 E
Boda .... 4 19N 17 26 E
Bodaybo .... 57 50N 114 0 E
Boddington ...... 32 50S 116 30 E
Boden .... 65 50N 21 42 E
Bodensee, L. ..... 47 35N 9 25 E
Bodhan .... 18 40N 77 55 E
Bodinga .... 12 58N 5 10 E
Bodmin 50 28N 4 44W

Bodmin Moor, Reg. 50 33N 4 36W
Bodø .... 67 17N 14 27 E
Bodrog, R. .... 48 15N 21 35 E
Bogalusa 30 50N 89 55W
Bogan Gate ...... 33 6S 147 44 E
Bogantungan ..... 23 41S 147 17 E
Bogenfels .... 27 25S 15 25 E
Boggabri .... 30 45S 150 0 E
Bognor Regis 50 47N 0 40W
Bogor .... 6 36S 106 48 E
Bogorodskoye .... 52 22N 140 30 E
Bogota 4 34N 74 0W
Bogotal .... 56 15N 89 50 E
Bogra .... 24 26N 89 22 E
Boguchany .... 58 40N 97 30 E
Bohemia □ .... 49 50N 14 0 E
Bohemian Forest=
  Böhmerwald ... 14 30N 12 40 E
Böhmerwald, Mts. . 49 30N 12 40 E
Bohol, I. .... 9 58N 124 20 E
Bohotleh .... 8 20N 46 25 E
Boi .... 9 34N 9 27 E
Boiestown 46 27N 66 26W
Boise 43 43N 116 9W
Boissevain 49 15N 100 0W
Bojonegoro ...... 7 9S 111 52 E
Boju .... 7 22N 7 55 E
Boké 10 56N 14 17W
Bokkos .... 9 19N 9 1 E
Bokna, Fd. .... 59 12N 5 30 E
Bokote .... 0 12S 21 8 E
Bokpyin .... 11 18N 98 42 E
Bol, Kuh-e ...... 30 40N 52 45 E
Bolama 11 30N 15 30W
Bolan Pass ...... 29 50N 67 20 E
Bolangir .... 20 42N 83 20 E
Bolbec .... 49 30N 0 30 E
Bolgatanga 10 44N 0 53W
Bolívar, Arg. 36 2S 60 53W
Bolívar, Col. 2 0N 77 0W
Bolivia ■ 17 6S 64 0W
Bolivian Plat. 19 0S 69 0W
Bollnäs .... 61 22N 16 28 E
Bologna .... 44 30N 11 20 E
Bologoye .... 57 55N 34 0 E
Bolsena, L. di ... 42 35N 11 55 E
Bolshevik, Os. .... 78 30N 102 0 E
Bolshoi Kavkaz ... 42 50N 44 0 E
Bolshoy Atlym ... 62 25N 66 50 E
Bolshoy Shantar,Os. 55 0N 137 42 E

Bolton 53 35N 2 26W
Bolzano .... 46 30N 11 20 E
Bom Despacho ... 19 46S 45 15W
Bom Jesus da Lapa 13 10S 43 30W
Boma .... 5 50S 13 4 E
Bomaderry ...... 34 52S 150 37 E
Bomadi .... 5 9N 6 0 E
Bombala .... 36 56S 149 15 E
Bombay .... 18 55N 72 50 E
Bomboma .... 2 25N 18 55 E
Bomda .... 29 59N 96 25 E
Bon, C. .... 37 1N 11 2 E
Bonaire, I. 12 10N 68 15W
Bonaparte Arch. .. 15 0S 124 30 E
Bonaventure 48 5N 65 32W
Bonavista 48 40N 53 5W
Bonavista B. 48 58N 53 25W
Bondoukoro 9 51N 4 25W
Bondoukou 8 2N 2 47W
Bondowoso ...... 7 56S 113 49 E
Bone, Teluk, G. .. 4 10S 120 50 E
Bo'ness 56 0N 3 38W
Bongor .... 10 35N 15 20 E
Bonham 33 30N 96 10W
Bonifacio .... 41 24N 9 10 E
Bonifacio,
  Bouches de ... 41 23N 9 10 E
Bonn .... 50 43N 7 6 E
Bonners Ferry 48 38N 116 21W
Bonnie Rock ..... 30 29S 118 22 E
Bonny, R. .... 4 20N 7 10 E
Bonny, B. of .... 4 0N 8 0 E
Bonnyville 54 20N 110 45W
Bontang .... 0 10N 117 30 E
Bonthain .... 5 34S 119 56 E
Boom .... 51 6N 4 20 E
Boonah .... 28 0S 152 35 E
Boone 42 5N 93 46W
Boonville, Ind ... 38 3N 87 13W
Boonville, Mo. ... 38 57N 92 45W
Boonville, N.Y. ... 43 31N 75 20W
Boothia, G. of ... 70 0N 90 0W
Boothia Pen. 70 30N 95 0W
Bootle 53 28N 3 1W
Booué .... 0 5S 11 55 E
Bopeechee .... 29 35S 137 30 E
Borås .... 57 42N 13 1 E
Borba 4 12S 59 34W
Bordeaux 44 50N 0 36W
Borden, Australia . 34 3S 118 12 E

Borden, Canada ... 46 18N 63 47W
Borders □ 55 30N 3 0W
Bordertown ...... 36 14S 140 58 E
Borger, Neth. .... 52 54N 7 33 E
Borger, U.S.A. ... 35 40N 101 20W
Borgholm .... 56 54N 16 48 E
Borisoglebsk .... 51 27N 42 5 E
Borisov .... 54 17N 28 28 E
Borja 4 20S 77 40W
Borkou .... 18 15N 18 50 E
Borlänge .... 60 28N 14 33 E
Borneo, I. .... 1 0N 115 0 E
Bornholm, I. ..... 55 8N 14 55 E
Borno .... 12 0N 12 0 E
Bornu Yassu ..... 12 14N 12 25 E
Borogontsy ...... 62 42N 131 8 E
Boromo 11 45N 2 58W
Borovichi .... 58 25N 35 55 E
Borroloola .... 16 4S 136 17 E
Borsod-Abaúj-
  Zemplén □ .... 48 20N 21 0 E
Borujerd .... 33 55N 48 50 E
Borzya .... 50 24N 116 31 E
Bosa .... 40 17N 8 32 E
Bosanska
  Gradiška ..... 45 9N 17 15 E
Bosaso .... 11 13N 49 8 E
Boscastle 50 42N 4 42W
Boshof .... 28 31S 25 13 E
Bosna, R. .... 45 4N 18 29 E
Bosna i
  Hercegovina □ .. 44 0N 18 0 E
Bosporus, Str.=
  Karadeniz
  Boğazi .... 41 10N 29 5 E
Bossangoa .... 6 35N 17 30 E
Bossier City 32 28N 93 38W
Bosso .... 13 30N 13 15 E
Boston, U.K. 52 59N 0 2W
Boston, U.S.A. ... 42 20N 71 0W
Botany B. .... 34 2S 151 6 E
Bothaville .... 27 23S 26 34 E
Bothnia, G. ...... 63 0N 21 0 E
Bothwell 42 37N 81 54W
Botletle, R. ...... 20 10S 24 10 E
Botoșani .... 47 42N 26 41 E
Botswana ■ ..... 23 0S 24 0 E
Botucatu 22 55S 48 30W
Botwood 49 6N 55 23W
Bou Saâda .... 35 11N 4 9 E

Bouaké 7 40N 5 2w
Bouar .... 6 0N 15 40 E
Bouârfa .... 32 32N 1 58 E
Bouches-du-Rhône 43 37N 5 2 E
Bougainville, C. . 13 57 s 126 4 E
Bougouni 11 30N 7 20w
Boukombé .... 10 11N 1 6 E
Boulder 40 3N 105 10w
Boulder City 36 0N 114 58w
Boulia .... 22 52 s 139 51 E
Boulogne-sur-Mer . 50 42N 1 36 E
Boulsa 12 39N 0 34w
Bouna 9 10N 3 0N
Bountiful 40 57N 111 58w
Bourbonnais, Reg. . 46 28N 3 0 E
Bourem 17 0N 0 24w
Bourg en Bresse . 46 13N 5 12 E
Bourges .... 47 5N 2 22 E
Bourgogne, Reg. . 47 0N 4 30 E
Bourke .... 30 8 s 145 55 E
Bourlamaque 48 5N 77 56w
Bournemouth 50 43N 1 53w
Bouvet, I. .... 55 0 s 3 30 E
Bow Island 49 50N 111 23w
Bowelling .... 33 25 s 116 30 E
Bowen .... 20 0 s 148 16 E
Bowie 32 15N 109 30w
Bowland Forest ... 54 0N 2 30w
Bowling Green, Ky. 37 0N 86 25w
Bowling Green,
  Ohio 41 22N 83 40w
Bowling Green, C. 19 19 s 147 25 E
Bowman 46 12N 103 21w
Bowmanville 43 55N 78 40w
Bowmore 55 45N 6 18w
Bowness 50 55N 114 25w
Bowser .... 36 19 s 146 23 E
Bowsman 52 15N 101 12w
Boxtel .... 51 36N 5 9 E
Boyle 53 58N 8 19w
Boyne, R. 53 40N 6 34w
Boyoma, Chutes .. 0 12N 25 25 E
Boyup Brook .... 33 47 s 116 40 E
Bozeman 45 40N 111 0w
Bozoum .... 6 25N 16 35 E
Brabant □ .... 49 15N 5 20 E
Brac, I. .... 43 20N 16 40 E
Bracebridge 45 5N 79 20w
Bräcke .... 62 42N 15 32 E
Brad .... 46 10N 22 50 E

Bradenton 27 25N 82 35w
Bradford, U.K. 53 47N 1 45w
Bradford, U.S.A. .. 41 58N 78 41w
Bradore Bay 51 27N 57 18w
Brady 31 8N 99 25w
Braemar 57 2N 3 20w
Braga 41 35N 8 32w
Bragança, Brazil .. 1 0 s 47 2w
Bragança, Port. .. 41 48N 6 50w
Brahmanbaria .... 23 50N 91 15 E
Brahmani, R. .... 21 0N 85 15 E
Brahmaputra, R. .. 26 30N 93 30 E
Braich-y-Pwll, Pt. . 52 47N 4 46w
Brăila .... 45 19N 27 59 E
Brainerd 46 20N 94 10w
Braintree .... 51 53N 0 34 E
Brak, R. .... 29 35 s 22 55 E
Bralorne 50 50N 123 15w
Brampton 43 42N 79 46w
Branco, R. 1 30N 61 15w
Brandenburg ..... 52 24N 12 33 E
Brandon 49 50N 100 0w
Brandvlei .... 30 25 s 20 30 E
Braniewo .... 54 25N 19 50 E
Brańsk .... 52 45N 22 51 E
Brantford 43 15N 80 15w
Branxholme ...... 37 52 s 141 49 E
Brasília .... 15 55 s 47 45w
Brasília Legal ... 3 45 s 55 40w
Braşov .... 45 7N 25 39 E
Brasschaat ...... 51 19N 4 27 E
Bratislava ...... 48 10N 17 7 E
Bratsk .... 56 10N 101 3 E
Brattleboro 42 53N 72 37w
Braunschweig .... 52 17N 10 28 E
Braunton 51 6N 4 9w
Brava .... 1 20N 44 8 E
Brawley 32 58N 115 30w
Bray 53 12N 6 6w
Bray, Reg. ...... 49 40N 1 40 E
Brazil ■ .... 10 0 s 50 0w
Brazil 39 30N 87 8w
Brazilian
  Highlands, Mts. . 18 0 s 46 30w
Brazol, R. 30 30N 96 20w
Brazzaville ..... 4 9 s 15 12 E
Breadalbane ..... 23 48 s 139 33 E
Breadalbane, Reg. . 56 30N 4 15w
Bream, B. .... 35 56 s 174 35 E
Bream Head ..... 35 51 s 174 36 E

Brebes .... 6 52 s 109 3 E
Brechin 56 44N 2 40w
Breckenridge 32 48N 98 55w
Breckland, Reg. .. 52 30N 0 40 E
Brecon 51 57N 3 23w
Brecon Beacons,
  Mts. 51 53N 3 27w
Breda .... 51 35N 4 45 E
Bredasdorp ...... 34 33 s 20 2 E
Bredbo .... 35 58 s 149 10 E
Bregenz .... 47 30N 9 45 E
Breidafjördur 65 20N 23 0w
Brejo .... 3 41 s 42 50w
Bremen .... 53 4N 8 47 E
Bremerhaven .... 53 34N 8 35 E
Bremerton 47 30N 122 48w
Brenham 30 5N 96 27w
Brenner P. ...... 47 0N 11 30 E
Brent, Canada ... 46 0N 78 30w
Brent, U.K. 51 33N 0 18w
Brentwood 51 37N 0 19w
Bréscia .... 45 33N 10 13 E
Breslau=Wrocław . 51 5N 17 5 E
Bressanone ..... 46 43N 11 40 E
Bressay, I. 60 10N 1 5w
Bresse, Reg. .... 46 20N 5 10 E
Brest, Fr. 48 24N 4 31w
Brest, U.S.S.R. .. 52 10N 23 40 E
Bretagne, Reg. .. 48 0N 3 0w
Bretçu .... 46 7N 26 18 E
Brett, C. .... 35 10 s 174 20 E
Breves .... 1 38 s 50 20w
Brewarrina ...... 30 0 s 146 51 E
Brewer 44 43N 68 50w
Brewton 31 9N 87 2w
Breyten .... 26 16 s 30 0 E
Bria .... 6 30N 21 58 E
Briançon .... 44 54N 6 39 E
Brickaville ..... 18 49 s 49 4 E
Bridgend 51 30N 3 35w
Bridgeport 41 12N 73 12w
Bridgeton 39 29N 75 10w
Bridgetown,
  Australia ..... 33 58 s 116 7 E
Bridgetown,
  Barbados 13 0N 59 30w
Bridgetown, Can. . 44 55N 65 12w
Bridgewater,
  Australia ..... 36 36 s 143 59 E
Bridgewater, Can. . 44 25N 64 31w

Bridgnorth 52 33N 2 25w
Bridgwater 51 7N 3 0w
Bridlington 54 4N 0 10w
Bridport 50 43N 2 45w
Brie, Reg. ...... 48 35N 3 10 E
Brig .... 46 18N 7 59 E
Brigg 53 33N 0 30w
Brigham City 41 30N 112 1w
Brighton,
  Australia ..... 35 1 s 138 30 E
Brighton,
  Canada 44 3N 77 44w
Brighton, U.K. ... 50 50N 0 9w
Bríndisi .... 40 39N 17 55 E
Brisbane .... 27 25 s 152 54 E
Bristol, U.K. 51 26N 2 35w
Bristol, U.S.A. ... 41 44N 72 37w
Bristol B. 58 0N 159 0w
Bristol Chan. 51 18N 3 30w
Bristow 35 5N 96 28w
British Antarctic
  Terr. .... 66 0 s 45 0w
British
  Columbia □ ... 55 0N 125 15w
British
  Honduras■=
  Belize ■ 17 0N 88 30w
British Is. 55 0N 4 0w
Brits .... 25 37 s 27 48 E
Britstown ...... 30 37 s 23 30 E
Britt 45 46N 80 35w
Brittany, Reg.=
  Bretagne, Reg. . 48 0N 3 0w
Britton 45 50N 97 47w
Brixton .... 23 32 s 144 52 E
Brno .... 49 10N 16 35 E
Broad Arrow .... 30 23 s 121 15 E
Broad Law, Mt. .. 55 30N 3 22w
Broadford ...... 37 14 s 145 4 E
Broads, The ..... 52 30N 1 15 E
Brock 51 27N 108 42w
Brockton 42 8N 71 2w
Brockville 44 37N 75 38w
Brod .... 45 35N 21 17 E
Brodeur Pen. 72 0N 88 0w
Brodick 55 34N 5 9w
Broken Bow 41 25N 99 35w
Broken Hill ..... 31 58 s 141 29 E
Bromley .... 51 20N 0 5 E

Brönderslev ..... 57 17N 9 55 E
Brong-Ahafo □ .. 7 50N 2 0w
Bronkhorstspruit . 25 46 s 28 45 E
Bronte Pk. ..... 42 8 s 146 30 E
Brookfield 39 50N 92 50w
Brookhaven 31 40N 90 25w
Brookings 44 19N 96 48w
Brooks Ra. 68 40N 147 0w
Brookton .... 32 22N 116 57 E
Brookville 41 10N 79 6w
Broom, L. 57 55N 5 15w
Broome .... 18 0 s 122 15w
Broomehill ..... 33 40 s 117 36 E
Brora 58 0N 3 50w
Brosna, R. 53 8N 8 0w
Broughton I. 67 35N 63 50w
Broughty Ferry .. 56 29N 2 50w
Brown Willy, Mt. . 50 35N 4 34w
Brownfield 33 10N 102 15w
Browning 48 35N 113 10w
Brownlee 50 43N 105 59N
Brownsville 25 54N 97 30w
Brownwood 31 45N 99 0w
Bruce, Mt. ...... 22 31 s 118 6 E
Bruce Mines 46 20N 83 45w
Bruce Rock ..... 31 51 s 118 2 E
Bruck .... 47 24N 15 16 E
Brue, R. 51 10N 2 50w
Brugge .... 51 13N 3 13 E
Brule 53 15N 117 38w
Brumado .... 14 13 s 41 40w
Brunei ■ ...... 4 52N 115 0 E
Brunette Downs .. 18 38 s 135 57 E
Brünn=Brno .... 49 10N 16 35 E
Brunner .... 42 27 s 171 20 E
Bruno 52 20N 105 30w
Brunssum ...... 50 57N 5 59 E
Brunswick, Ga. .. 31 10N 81 30w
Brunswick, Me. .. 43 53N 69 50w
Brunswick, Pa. .. 53 30 s 71 30w
Brunswick Junction 33 15 s 115 50 E
Brusque .... 27 5 s 49 0w
Brussel .... 50 51N 4 21 E
Bruthen .... 37 43 s 147 48 E
Bruxelles=
  Brussel ...... 50 51N 4 21 E
Bryan, Ohio 41 30N 84 30w
Bryan, Tex. 30 40N 96 27w
Bryansk .... 53 13N 34 25 E
Bryne .... 58 45N 5 36 E

Brzeg .... 50 52N 17 30 E
Bucak .... 37 28N 30 36 E
Bucaramanga .. 7 0N 73 0w
Buchan, Reg. 57 32N 2 8w
Buchan Ness, Pt. .. 57 29N 1 48w
Buchanan, Canada 51 40N 102 45w
Buchanan, Liberia . 5 57N 10 2w
Buchans 49 0N 57 2w
Bucharest =
  Bucureşti .... 44 27N 26 10 E
Buckeye 33 28N 112 40w
Buckhannon 39 2N 80 10w
Buckíe 57 40N 2 58w
Buckingham, U.K.. 52 0N 0 59w
Buckingham,
  U.S.A. 45 37N 75 24w
Buckinghamshire □ 51 50N 0 55w
Buctouche 46 30N 64 45w
Bucureşti .... 44 27N 26 10 E
Bucyrus 40 48N 83 0w
Budalin .... 22 20N 95 10 E
Budapest .... 47 29N 19 5 E
Budaun .... 28 5N 79 10 E
Bude 50 49N 4 33w
Buea .... 4 10N 9 9 E
Buenaventura ... 29 15s 69 40w
Buenos Aires 34 30s 58 20w
Buenos Aires, L. .. 46 35s 72 30w
Buffalo, Canada .. 50 49N 110 42w
Buffalo, U.S.A. .. 42 55N 78 50w
Buffalo Narrows .. 55 52N 108 28w
Bug, R. .... 51 20N 23 40 E
Buga 4 0N 77 0w
Bugondo .... 1 33N 33 10 E
Bugulma .... 54 38N 52 40 E
Buguma .... 4 42N 6 55 E
Bugun Shara, Mts.. 48 30N 102 0 E
Buturuslan ..... 53 39N 52 26 E
Bui .... 58 23N 41 27 E
Builth Wells 52 10N 3 26w
Bujumbura ..... 3 16s 29 18 E
Bukachacha .... 52 55N 116 50 E
Bukavu .... 2 20s 28 52 E
Bukene .... 4 15s 32 48 E
Bukhara .... 39 50N 64 10 E
Bukit Mertajam .. 5 22N 100 28 E
Bukoba .... 1 20s 31 49 E
Bukombe .... 3 31s 32 3 E
Bukuru .... 9 42N 8 48 E

Bulak .... 45 2N 82 5 E
Bulawayo ...... 20 7s 28 32 E
Bulgaria ■ ..... 42 35N 25 30 E
Bulhar .... 10 25N 44 30 E
Bullabulling .... 31 10s 120 55 E
Bullara .... 22 30s 114 2 E
Bullaring ...... 32 28s 117 40 E
Bullock Creek .. 17 40s 144 30 E
Bulls .... 40 10s 175 24 E
Bulo Burti ..... 3 50N 45 33 E
Bulsar .... 20 40N 72 58 E
Bultfontein .... 28 18s 26 10 E
Bulun .... 70 37N 127 30 E
Bulundshahr .... 28 30N 77 45 E
Bumba .... 2 13N 22 30 E
Bumbum .... 14 0N 8 10 E
Bumhpa Bum, Mt. 26 40N 97 20 E
Bunbury .... 33 20s 115 35 E
Buncrana 55 8N 7 28w
Bundaberg ..... 24 54s 152 22 E
Bundi .... 25 30N 75 35 E
Bundooma ..... 24 54s 134 16 E
Bunia .... 1 35N 30 20 E
Bununu Dass .... 10 6N 9 25 E
Bununu Kasa .... 9 51N 9 32 E
Bunza .... 12 8N 4 0 E
Bura .... 1 6s 39 57 E
Bura Hills ..... 3 20s 38 20 E
Burdwan .... 23 16N 87 54 E
Bure, R. ...... 52 38N 1 38 E
Burgas .... 42 33N 27 29 E
Burgenland □ ... 47 20N 16 20 E
Burgeo 47 36N 57 34w
Burgersdorp .... 31 0s 26 20 E
Burgos 42 21N 3 41w
Burgsvik ...... 57 3N 18 19 E
Burias, I. ..... 13 5N 122 55 E
Burica, Pta 8 3N 82 51w
Burin .... 32 11N 35 15 E
Buriram .... 15 0N 103 0 E
Burketown ..... 17 45s 139 33 E
Burks Falls 45 37N 79 10w
Burley 42 37N 113 55w
Burlington,
  Canada 43 25N 79 45w
Burlington, Colo. . 39 21N 102 18w
Burlington, Iowa . 40 50N 91 5w
Burlington, Kans. . 38 15N 95 47w
Burlington, N.C. .. 36 7N 79 27w
Burlington, N.J. .. 40 5N 74 50w

Burlington, Vt..... 44 27N 73 14w
Burlington, Wash. . 48 29N 122 19w
Burlyu-Tyube ... 46 30N 79 10 E
Burma ■ ...... 21 0N 96 30 E
Burngup .... 33 0s 118 35 E
Burnie .... 41 4s 145 56 E
Burnley 53 47N 2 15w
Burns 43 40N 119 4w
Burns Lake 54 20N 125 45w
Burntwood, L. .. 55 35N 99 40w
Burqa .... 32 18N 35 11 E
Burra .... 33 40s 138 55 E
Burrendong Res. .. 32 45s 149 10 E
Burruyacú 26 30s 64 45w
Burry Port 51 41N 4 17w
Bursa .... 40 15N 29 5 E
Burton-on-Trent . 52 48N 1 39w
Buru, I. .... 3 30s 126 3 . E
Burundi ■ ..... 3 15s 30 0 E
Burung .... 0 21N 108 25 E
Burutu .... 5 20N 5 29 E
Bury 53 36N 2 19w
Bury St. Edmunds . 52 15N 0 42 E
Buryat A.S.S.R. □ . 53 0N 110 0 E
Busembatia .... 0 45N 33 32 E
Bushenyi ...... 0 32s 30 11 E
Busia .... 0 25N 34 6 E
Buskerud □ .... 60 20N 9 0 E
Busselton ...... 33 42s 115 15 E
Bussum .... 52 16N 5 10 E
Busto Arsizio ... 45 38N 8 50 E
Busu-Djanoa .... 1 50N 21 5 E
Busuanga, I. .... 12 10N 120 0 E
Buta .... 2 50N 24 53 E
Butare .... 2 31s 29 52 E
Bute, I. 55 48N 5 2w
Butembo .... 0 9N 29 18 E
Butere .... 0 14N 34 51 E
Butiaba .... 1 50N 31 20 E
Butler 40 52N 79 52w
Butt of Lewis,
  Pt. 58 30N 6 20w
Butte, Mont. 46 0N 112 31w
Butte, Neb. 42 56N 98 54w
Butterworth .... 5 24N 100 23 E
Butuan .... 8 52N 125 36 E
Butung, I. ..... 5 0s 122 45 E
Buturlinovka .... 50 50N 40 35 E
Buxton, S. Afr. .. 27 38s 24 42 E
Buxton, U.K. 53 16N 1 54w

Buyaga .... 59 50N 127 0 E
Buyr Nuur, L. ... 47 50N 117 35 E
Buzău .... 45 10N 26 50 E
Buzău, R. ...... 45 10N 27 20 E
Buzen .... 33 35N 131 5 E
Buzuluk .... 52 48N 52 12 E
Buzzards Bay ... 41 45N 70 38w
Bydgoszcz ..... 53 10N 18 0 E
Byelorussian
  S.S.R. □ ..... 53 30N 27 0 E
Bylas 33 11N 110 9w
Bylot I. 73 0N 78 0w
Byrd Ld. 79 30s 125 0w
Byrock .... 30 40s 146 27 E
Byron Bay ..... 28 30s 153 30 E
Byske .... 64 59N 21 17 E
Byrranga, Gory . 75 0N 100 0 E
Bytom .... 50 25N 19 0 E
Byumba .... 1 35s 30 4 E

C

Cabana 8 25s 78 5w
Cabanatuan .... 15 30N 121 5 E
Cabedelo 7 0s 34 50w
Cabimas 10 30N 71 25w
Cabinda .... 5 40s 12 11 E
Cabinet Mts. ... 48 8N 115 46w
Cabo Blanco 47 56s 65 47w
Cabo Frio 22 51s 42 3w
Cabonga Res. ... 47 35N 76 40w
Caboolture .... 27 5s 152 47 E
Cabora Bassa
  Dam .... 15 30s 32 40 E
Caborca 30 40N 112 10w
Cabot Str. 47 15N 59 40w
Cabrera, I. ..... 39 6N 2 59 E
Cabri 50 35N 108 25w
Cabriel, R. 39 14N 1 3w
Cabruta 7 50N 66 10w
Čačak .... 43 54N 20 20 E
Cáceres 39 26N 6 23w
Cache Bay 46 26N 80 0w
Cache Lake 49 55N 74 35w
Cachinal 24 59s 69 35w
Cachoeira 12 30s 39 0w
Cachoeiro de

Itapemirim 20 51s 41 7w
Cachoeira do Sul . 30 3s 52 53w
Caconda .... 13 48s 15 8 E
Cadillac, Canada .. 49 45N 108 0w
Cadillac, U.S.A. .. 44 16N 85 25w
Cadiz, Philippines . 11 30N 123 15 E
Cádiz, Sp. 36 30N 6 20w
Cádiz, G. de 36 35N 6 20w
Cadomin 52 59N 117 28½
Cadoux .... 30 47s 117 8 E
Caen 49 10N 0 22w
Caernarfon 53 8N 4 17w
Caernarfon B. ... 53 4N 4 40w
Caerphilly 51 34N 3 13w
Caesarea=Qesari . 32 30N 34 53 E
Caetité 13 50s 42 50w
Cagayan de Oro .. 8 30N 124 40 E
Cágliari .... 39 15N 9 6 E
Cágliari, G. di .. 39 8N 9 10 E
Caguas 18 14N 66 4w
Caher 52 23N 7 56w
Cahirciveen 51 57N 10 13w
Cahore Pt. 52 34N 6 11w
Cahors .... 44 27N 1 27 E
Caibarién 22 30N 79 30w
Caicara 7 50N 66 10w
Caicó 6 20s 37 0w
Caicos Is. 21 40N 71 40w
Cairn Gorm, Mt. . 57 7N 3 40w
Cairngorm Mts. .. 57 6N 3 42w
Cairns .... 16 55s 145 51 E
Cairo, Egypt=
  El Qâhira .... 30 1N 31 14 E
Cairo, Ga. 30 52N 84 12w
Cairo, Mo. 37 0N 89 10w
Cajamarca 7 5s 78 28w
Cajazeiras 7 0s 38 30w
Cala Millor .... 39 34N 3 18 E
Calabar .... 4 57N 8 20 E
Calaboza 9 0N 67 20w
Calabria □ ..... 39 4N 16 30 E
Calafate 50 25s 72 25w
Calahorra 42 18N 1 59w
Calais .... 50 57N 1 56 E
Calama 22 30s 68 55w
Calamar 10 15N 74 55w
Calamian Group,
  Is. .... 11 50N 119 55 E
Calamocha 40 50N 1 17w
Călăraşi ...... 44 14N 27 23 E

Calatayud 41 20N 1 40w
Calauag .... 13 55N 122 15 E
Calcutta .... 22 36N 88 24 E
Calder R. 53 44N 1 21w
Caldera 27 5s 70 55w
Caldwell 43 45N 116 42w
Caledon .... 34 14s 19 26 E
Caledon, R. ...... 30 31s 26 5 E
Calella .... 41 37N 2 40 E
Calf of Man, I. ... 54 4N 4 48w
Calgary 51 0N 114 10w
Cali 3 25N 76 35w
Calicut .... 11 15N 75 43 E
Caliente 37 43N 114 34w
California □ 37 25N 120 0w
California, G. de . 27 0N 111 0w
California,
  Baja, Reg. 30 0N 115 0w
Calingasta 31 15s 69 30w
Calipatria 33 8N 115 30w
Calitzdorp .... 33 30s 21 41 E
Callan 52 33N 7 25w
Callao 12 0s 77 0w
Callide .... 24 23s 150 33 E
Calliope .... 24 0s 151 16 E
Calo .... 31 37s 27 33 E
Caloundra .... 26 45s 153 10 E
Calatagirone ..... 37 13N 14 30 E
Caltanissetta ..... 37 30N 14 3 E
Calvados □ 49 5N 0 15w
Calvi .... 42 34N 8 45 E
Calvinia .... 31 28s 19 45 E
Cam, R. .... 52 21N 0 15 E
Camagüey 21 20N 78 0w
Camarones 44 50s 66 0w
Cambay .... 22 23N 72 33 E
Cambay, G. of ... 20 45N 72 30 E
Cambodia ■ ...... 12 15N 105 0 E
Camborne 50 13N 5 18w
Cambrai .... 50 11N 3 14 E
Cambrian Mts. ... 52 10N 3 52w
Cambridge, Canada 43 23N 80 19w
Cambridge, N.Z. .. 37 54s 175 29 E
Cambridge, U.K. .. 52 13N 0 8 E
Cambridge, Mass. . 42 20N 71 8w
Cambridge, Ohio .. 40 1N 81 22w
Cambridge □ ..... 52 21N 0 5 E
Cambridge B. 69 10N 105 0w
Cambridge, G. .... 14 45s 128 0 E
Camden, Australia 34 5s 150 38 E

Camden, Ala. 31 59N 87 15w
Camden, Ark. 33 30N 92 50w
Camden, S.C. 34 17N 80 34w
Cameron 30 53N 97 0w
Cameroon ■ ...... 3 30N 12 30 E
Cameroun, Mt. ... 4 45N 8 55 E
Cametá 2 0s 49 30w
Caminha 41 50N 8 50w
Camira Creek .... 29 15s 153 10 E
Camocim 2 55s 40 50w
Camooweal .... 19 56s 138 7 E
Camopi 3 45N 52 50w
Campania □ ...... 40 50N 14 45 E
Campana, I. 48 20s 75 10w
Campbell I. .... 52 30s 169 0 E
Campbell River ... 50 1N 125 15w
Campbell Town ... 41 52s 147 30 E
Campbelltown,
  Australia .... 34 5s 150 48 E
Campbellton, N.B. 47 57N 66 43w
Campbellton, Alta. 53 32N 113 15w
Campbeltown 55 25N 5 36w
Camperdown ...... 38 4s 143 12 E
Campino Grande .. 7 20s 35 47w
Campinas 22 50s 47 0w
Campo Formoso .. 10 30s 40 20w
Campo Gallo 26 35s 62 50w
Campo Grande ... 20 25s 54 40w
Campo Maior,
  Brazil 4 50s 42 12w
Campo Maior 2 48N 75 20w
Campobasso ...... 41 34N 14 40 E
Campos 21 50s 41 20w
Campos Belos 13 10s 46 45w
Camrose 53 0N 112 50w
Can Tho .... 10 2N 105 46 E
Canada ■ 60 0N 100 0w
Cañada de
  Gómez 32 55s 61 30w
Canadian, R. 35 27N 95 3w
Canal Zone 9 10N 79 48w
Cananea 31 0N 110 20w
Canarias, Is. 29 30N 17 0w
Canary Is.=
  Canarias, Is. 29 30N 17 0w

Canaveral, C. 28 28N 80 31w
Canavieiras 15 45s 39 0w
Canberra .... 35 15s 149 8 E
Candia=Iráklion .. 35 20N 25 12 E
Candle 65 55N 161 56w
Canelones 34 32s 56 10w
Cañete 37 50s 73 10w
Cangamba 13 40s 19 54w
Cangas de Narcea . 43 10N 6 32w
Canguaretama ... 6 20s 35 5w
Canguçu 31 22s 52 43w
Canipaan .... 8 33N 117 15 E
Canmore 51 7N 115 18w
Cann River ...... 37 35s 149 6 E
Canna, I. 57 3N 6 33w
Cannakale=
  Dardenelles, Str. 40 10N 27 20 E
Cannanore .... 11 53N 75 27 E
Cannes .... 43 32N 7 0 E
Cannock 52 42N 2 2w
Canon City 39 30N 105 20w
Canora 51 40N 102 30w
Canso 45 20N 61 0w
Cantabrian Mts.=
  Cantábrica, Cord. 43 0N 5 10w
Cantábrica, Cord. . 43 0N 5 10w
Cantal □ .... 45 4N 2 45 E
Canterbury □ ..... 43 45N 171 19 E
Canterbury,
  Australia .... 33 55s 151 7 E
Canterbury, U.K. . 51 17N 1 5 E
Canterbury Bight . 44 16s 171 55 E
Canterbury Plain . 43 55s 171 22 E
Canton, China=
  Kwangchow .... 23 10N 133 10 E
Canton, Mo. 40 10N 91 33w
Canton, N.Y. 44 32N 75 3w
Canton, Ohio 40 47N 81 22w
Canton I. 36 12N 98 40w
Canutillo 31 55N 106 36w
Canyon 44 43N 110 36w
Canyonlands
  Nat. Park 38 25N 109 30w
Cap Breton, I. ... 46 0N 61 0w
Cap Chat 49 6N 66 40w
Cap Haïtien 19 40N 72 20w
Cape Barren, I. .. 40 25s 184 15 E
Cape Coast 5 5N 1 15w
Cape Dorset 64 30N 77 0w

Cape Dyer 66 30N 61 0w
Cape Girardeau ... 37 20N 89 30w
Cape Province □ .. 32 0s 23 0 E
Cape Town .... 33 55s 18 22 E
Cape Verde Is. 17 10N 25 20w
Cape York Pen. ... 13 30s 142 30 E
Capela 10 15s 37 0w
Capella .... 23 2s 148 1 E
Capraia, I. .... 43 2N 9 50 E
Capreol 46 40N 80 50w
Caprera, I. .... 41 12N 9 28 E
Capri, I. .... 40 34N 14 15 E
Caprivi Strip, Reg. 18 0s 23 0 E
Caquetá, R. 3 8s 64 46w
Caracal .... 44 8N 24 22 E
Caracas 10 30N 66 50w
Caracol 9 15s 64 20w
Caragabal .... 33 54s 147 50 E
Carangola 20 50s 42 5w
Carani .... 30 57s 116 28 E
Caransebeş ...... 45 28N 22 18 E
Caratasca, L. 15 30N 83 40w
Caratinga 19 50s 42 10w
Caraúbas 5 50s 37 25w
Caravaca 38 8N 1 52w
Caravelas 17 50s 39 20w
Carballo 43 13N 8 41w
Carberry 49 50N 99 25w
Carbonara, C. .... 39 8N 9 30 E
Carbondale, Colo. . 39 30N 107 10w
Carbondale, Ill. ... 37 45N 89 10w
Carbondale, Pa. .. 41 37N 75 30w
Carbonear 47 42N 53 13w
Carcassonne ..... 43 13N 2 20 E
Carcross 60 20N 134 40w
Cardabia .... 23 2s 113 55 E
Cardamon Hills .. 9 30N 77 15 E
Cárdenas, Cuba .. 23 0N 81 30w
Cárdenas, Mexico . 22 0N 99 41w
Cardiff 51 28N 3 11w
Cardigan 52 6N 4 41w
Cardigan Bay 52 30N 4 30w
Cardross 49 50N 105 40w
Cardston 49 15N 113 20w
Cardwell .... 18 14s 146 2 E
Carei .... 47 40N 22 29 E
Carey, L. .... 29 0s 122 15 E
Cargados
  Garajos, Is. .....
Carhué 37 10s 62 50w

Caribbean Sea 15 0N 75 0w
Cariboo Mts. 53 0N 121 0w
Carinhanha 14 15s 44 0w
Carinthia□=
  Kärnten .... 46 52N 13 30 E
Caripito 10 2N 63 0w
Carleton Place ... 45 8N 76 11w
Carletonville ..... 26 23s 27 22 E
Carlin 40 50N 116 5w
Carlingford L. 54 0N 6 5w
Carlinville 39 20N 89 55w
Carlisle, U.K. 54 54N 2 55w
Carlisle, U.S.A. ... 40 12N 77 10w
Carlow 52 50N 6 58w
Carlow □ 52 43N 6 50w
Carlsbad 32 20N 104 7w
Carlsruhe=
  Karlsruhe ...... 49 3N 8 23 E
Carmacks 62 0N 136 0w
Carman 49 30N 98 0w
Carmarthen 51 52N 4 20w
Carmel, Mt. ..... 32 45N 35 3 E
Carmelo 34 0s 58 10w
Carmen, Col. 9 43N 75 6w
Carmen de
  Patagones 40 50s 63 0w
Carmila .... 21 53s 149 5 E
Carmona 37 28N 5 42w
Carnac 47 13N 3 10w
Carnarvon,
  Australia .... 24 51s 113 42 E
Carnarvon,
  S. Africa ...... 30 56s 22 8 E
Carnatic, Reg. ... 12 0N 79 0 E
Carndonagh 55 15N 7 16w
Carnegie, L. ..... 26 5s 122 30 E
Carnsore Pt. 52 10N 6 20w
Carolina, Brazil ... 7 10s 47 30w
Carolina, S. Afr. .. 26 5s 30 6 E
Caroline Is. ...... 8 0N 150 0 E
Caron 50 30N 105 50w
Carpathians, Mts. . 46 20N 26 0 E
Carpatii
  Meridionali, Mts. 45 30N 25 0 E
Carpentaria, G. of . 14 0s 139 0 E
Carpentaria Downs 18 44s 144 20 E
Carrara .... 44 5N 10 7 E
Carrick-on-
  Shannon 53 57N 8 7w
Carrick-on-Suir ... 52 22N 7 30w

Carrickfergus 54 43N 5 50W
Carrickfergus □ ... 54 43N 5 50W
Carrickmacross ... 54 0N 6 43W
Carrieton .... 32 27s 138 27 E
Carrizal Bajo 28 5s 71 20W
Carrizozo 33 40N 105 57W
Carroll 42 2N 94 55W
Carrollton 33 36N 85 5W
Carrot River 53 50N 101 17W
Carson City 39 12N 119 52W
Carson Sink 39 50N 118 40W
Carstairs 55 42N 3 41W
Cartagena, Col. ... 10 25N 75 33W
Cartagena, Sp. 37 38N 0 59W
Cartago, Col. 4 45N 75 55W
Cartago, Costa Rica 9 50N 84 0W
Cartersville 34 11N 84 48W
Carterton .... 41 2s 175 31 E
Carthage, Mo. 37 10N 94 20W
Carthage, N.Y. 43 59N 75 37W
Cartwright 53 41N 56 58W
Caruaru 8 15s 35 55W
Carúpano 10 45N 63 15W
Caruthersville 36 10N 89 40W
Casa Grande 32 53N 111 51W
Casa Nova 9 10s 41 5W
Casablanca 33 43N 7 24W
Casale
  Monferrato ...... 45 8N 8 28 E
Casas Grandes 30 22N 108 0W
Cascade Ra. 44 0N 122 10W
Caserta .... 41 5N 14 20 E
Cashel 52 31N 7 53W
Casilda 33 10s 61 10W
Casino .... 28 52s 153 3 E
Casiquiare, R. 2 1N 67 7W
Caspe 41 14N 0 1W
Casper 42 52N 106 27W
Caspian Sea .... 42 30N 51 0 E
Cassel=Kassel ..... 51 19N 9 32 E
Cassiar Mts. 39 30N 130 30W
Cassinga .... 15 5s 16 23 E
Castellammare del
  Golfo .... 38 2N 12 53 E
Castellammare di
  Stábia .... 40 47N 14 29 E
Castellón de la
  Plana 39 58N 0 3W
Castelo Branco 39 50N 7 31W
Castelvetrano ..... 37 40N 12 46 E

Casterton .... 37 30s 141 30 E
Castilla la Nueva,
  Reg. 39 45N 3 20W
Castilla la
  Vieja, Reg. 41 55N 4 0W
Castle Douglas 54 57N 3 57W
Castle Harbour 32 17N 64 44W
Castle Rock 46 20N 122 58W
Castlebar 53 52N 9 17W
Castleblayney 54 7N 6 44W
Castleford 53 43N 1 21W
Castlegar 49 20N 117 40W
Castlemaine .... 37 2s 144 12 E
Castlereagh 53 47N 8 30W
Castlereagh □ 53 47N 8 30W
Castletown 54 4N 4 40W
Castletown
  Bearhaven 51 40N 9 54W
Castlevale .... 24 30s 146 48 E
Castor 52 15N 111 50W
Castres .... 43 37N 2 13 E
Castries 14 0N 60 50W
Castro, Brazil 24 45s 50 0W
Castro, Chile 42 30s 73 50W
Castro Alves 12 46s 39 33W
Castro del Rio 37 41N 4 29W
Cat I. 24 30N 75 30W
Catalão 18 5s 47 52W
Catalina 25 13s 69 43W
Cataluña, Reg. .... 41 40N 1 15 E
Catamarca 28 30s 65 50W
Catánia .... 37 31N 15 4 E
Catanzaro .... 38 54N 16 38 E
Catarman .... 12 28N 124 1 E
Cathcart .... 32 18s 27 10 E
Catine, Reg. 46 30N 0 15W
Cato, I. .... 23 15s 155 32 E
Catoche, C. 21 40N 87 0W
Catrilό 36 23s 63 24W
Catrimani 0 27N 61 41W
Catskill 42 14N 73 52W
Catskill Mts. 42 15N 74 10W
Caucasus Mts.=
  Bolshoi Kavkaz .. 42 50N 44 0 E
Caucia 3 40s 38 55W
Cauquenes 36 0s 72 30W
Causapscal 48 19N 67 12W
Cauvery, R. .... 11 10N 79 51 E
Caux, Reg. .... 49 38N 0 35 E
Cavan 54 0N 7 22W
Cavan □ 53 58N 7 10W

Cavan 54 0N 7 22W
Cavendish .... 37 31s 142 2 E
Caviana, I. 0 15N 50 0W
Cavite .... 14 20N 120 55 E
Caxias 5 0s 43 27W
Caxias do Sul 29 10s 51 10W
Caxito .... 8 30s 13 30 E
Cayambe 0 3N 78 22W
Cayenne 5 0N 52 18W
Cayman Is. 19 40N 79 50W
Cayo 17 10N 89 0W
Cazombo .... 12 0s 22 48 E
Ceanannas Mor 53 42N 6 53W
Ceara □ 5 0s 40 0W
Ceará=Fortaleza .. 3 35s 38 35W
Cebollar 29 10s 66 35W
Cebu .... 10 30N 124 0 E
Cebu, I. .... 10 23N 123 58 E
Cedar City 37 41N 113 3w
Cedar Creek Res. .. 32 15N 96 0w
Cedar Falls 42 39N 92 29W
Cedar L. 53 30N 100 30W
Cedar Rapids 42 0N 91 38W
Cedartown 34 1N 85 15W
Cedarvale 55 1N 128 22W
Cedarville 41 37N 120 13W
Cedro 6 34s 39 3W
Cedros, I. de 28 10N 115 20W
Ceduna .... 32 7s 133 46 E
Cefalù .... 38 3N 14 1 E
Cegléd .... 47 11N 19 47 E
Celaya 20 31N 100 37W
Celbridge 53 20N 6 33W
Celebes, I.=
  Sulawesi, I. .... 2 0s 120 0 E
Celebes Sea .... 3 0N 123 0 E
Celje .... 46 16N 15 18 E
Celle .... 52 37N 10 4 E
Centerville 31 15N 95 56W
Central 32 46N 108 9w
Central □, Ghana .. 5 40N 1 20W
Central □, U.K. ... 56 12N 4 25W
Central Africa ■ .. 7 0N 20 0 E
Central Makan Ra. . 26 30N 64 15 E
Central Russian
  Uplands .... 54 0N 36 0 E
Central Siberian
  Plat. .... 65 0N 105 0 E
Centralia, Ill. ... 38 32N 89 5w
Centralia, Wash. .. 46 46N 122 59W

Cephalonia, I.=
  Kefallinía, I. ... 38 28N 20 30 E
Ceram, I.=
  Seram, I. .... 3 10s 129 0 E
Ceres, Arg. 29 55s 61 55W
Ceres, S. Africa .. 33 21s 19 18 E
Cerignola .... 41 17N 15 53 E
Çerkeş .... 40 40N 32 58 E
Cernavodă .... 44 22N 28 3 E
Cerralvo, I. ...... 24 20N 109 45 E
Cerritos 22 20N 100 20W
Cervera .... 41 40N 1 16 E
Cesena .... 44 9N 12 14 E
České Budějovice .. 48 55N 14 25 E
Ceskomoravská
  Vrchovina .... 49 20N 15 30 E
Český Těšín .... 49 45N 18 39 E
Cessnock .... 33 0s 151 15 E
Cetinje .... 42 23N 18 59 E
Ceuta 35 52N 5 26W
Cevennes, Mts. .... 44 10N 3 50 E
Ceyhan .... 37 4N 35 47 E
Ceylon=
  Sri Lanka ■ ..... 7 30N 80 50 E
Chablais, Reg. .... 46 20N 6 45 E
Chachran .... 28 55N 70 28 E
Chaco Austral, Reg. 27 30s 61 40W
Chaco Boreal, Reg. 22 30s 60 10W
Chaco Central, Reg. 24 0s 61 0W
Chad ■ .... 12 30N 17 15 E
Chad, L. .... 13 30N 14 30 E
Chadron 42 50N 103 0w
Chafe .... 11 56N 6 55 E
Chagai Hills ...... 29 30N 63 0 E
Chagos Arch. ...... 6 0s 72 0 E
Chah Bahar .... 25 20N 60 40 E
Chake Chake .... 5 15s 39 45 E
Chakhansur .... 31 10N 62 0 E
Chakhansur .... 30 25N 62 0 E
Chakradharpur ..... 22 45N 85 40 E
Chakwal .... 32 50N 72 45 E
Chaling .... 26 55N 113 30 E
Chalisgaon .... 20 30N 75 10 E
Challapata 19 0s 66 50W
Chalon-sur-Saône . 46 48N 4 50 E
Châlons-sur-
  Marne .... 48 58N 4 20 E
Chaman .... 30 55N 66 22 E
Chamba, India ..... 32 35N 76 10 E
Chamba, Tanz. ..... 11 35s 36 58 E

Chambersburg 39 53N 77 41W
Chambéry .... 45 34N 5 55 E
Chambeshi .... 10 58s 31 5 E
Chambord 48 25N 72 6W
Chamdo .... 31 21N 97 2 E
Chamical 30 22s 66 19W
Chamonix .... 45 55N 6 51 E
Champagne, Reg. .. 49 0N 4 40 E
Champaign 40 8N 88 14W
Champlain, L. 44 30N 73 20W
Champotón 19 20N 90 50W
Chañaral 26 15s 70 50W
Chanchiang=
  Chankiang ...... 21 7N 110 21 E
Chanda .... 19 57N 79 25 E
Chandalar 67 30N 148 30W
Chandeleur Sd. ... 29 58N 88 40W
Chandigarh .... 30 30N 76 58 E
Chandler, Canada . 48 18N 64 46W
Chandler, U.S.A. . 33 20N 111 56W
Chandpur .... 29 8N 78 19 E
Changane, R. ..... 24 45s 33 37 E
Changchih .... 36 7N 113 0 E
Changchow,
  Fukien .... 24 32N 117 44 E
Changchow,
  Kiangsu .... 31 45N 120 0 E
Changchow,
  Shantung .... 36 55N 118 3 E
Changchun .... 43 58N 125 9 E
Changhua .... 24 2N 120 30 E
Changkiakow ...... 40 52N 114 45 E
Changkiang .... 21 7N 110 21 E
Changli .... 39 40N 119 19 E
Changpai .... 41 26N 128 0 E
Changpai
  Shan, Mts. ..... 42 0N 128 0 E
Changping, Fukien 25 30N 117 33 E
Changping, Peiping 40 15N 116 15 E
Changpu .... 24 2N 117 31 E
Changsha .... 28 5N 113 1 E
Changshu .... 31 33N 120 45 E
Changtai .... 24 34N 117 50 E
Changteh .... 29 12N 111 43 E
Changting .... 25 46N 116 30 E
Changwu .... 42 21N 122 45 E
Changyeh .... 39 0N 100 59 E
Channapatna ...... 12 40N 77 15 E
Channel Is. 49 30N 2 40W
Chantada 42 37N 7 46W

Chanthaburi ...... 12 38N 102 12 E
Chanute 37 45N 95 25W
Chanyi .... 25 56N 104 1 E
Chao Phraya, R. . 13 32N 100 36 E
Chaoan .... 23 45N 117 11 E
Chaochow .... 23 45N 116 32 E
Chaohwa .... 32 16N 105 41 E
Chaotung .... 27 30N 103 40 E
Chaoyang .... 41 46N 120 16 E
Chapata, L. 20 10N 103 20W
Chapayevo ...... 50 25N 51 10 E
Chapayevsk ..... 53 0N 49 40 E
Chapel Hill 35 53N 79 3W
Chapleau 47 45N 83 30W
Chapra .... 25 48N 84 50 E
Charadai 27 40s 59 55W
Charagua 19 45s 63 10W
Charambira, Pta. .. 4 20N 77 30W
Charaña 17 30s 69 35W
Charchan .... 38 4N 85 16 E
Charchan, R. .... 39 0N 86 0 E
Chard, U.K. 50 52N 2 59W
Chard, U.S.A. ... 55 55N 111 10W
Chardara .... 41 16N 67 59 E
Chardzhou ...... 39 0N 63 20 E
Charente □ 45 50N 0 36W
Charente-
 Maritime □ ... 45 50N 0 35W
Chari, R. .... 12 58N 14 31 E
Charikar .... 35 0N 69 10 E
Charkhlikh ...... 39 16N 88 17 E
Charleroi .... 50 24N 4 27 E
Charles, C. 37 10N 75 52W
Charles City 43 2N 92 41W
Charleston, Mass. 34 2N 90 3W
Charleston, S.C. . 32 47N 79 56W
Charleston, W.Va. 38 24N 81 36W
Charlestown, Nevis 17 8N 62 37W
Charlestown, S. Afr. 27 30s 29 55 E
Charleville,
 Australia ..... 26 24s 146 15 E
Charleville, Eire=
 Rath Luire 52 21N 8 40W
Charleville ..... 26 24s 146 15 E
Charleville-
 Mézières ..... 49 44N 4 40 E
Charlotte 35 16N 80 46W
Charlotte Amalie . 18 22N 64 56W
Charlottenburg .. 52 31N 13 16 E
Charlottesville ... 38 1N 78 30W

Charlottetown 46 19N 63 3W
Charlton .... 36 16s 143 24 E
Charlton 40 59N 93 20W
Charlton I. 52 0N 79 20W
Charny 46 43N 71 15W
Charolles .... 46 27N 4 16 E
Charters Towers .. 20 5s 146 13 E
Chartres .... 48 29N 1 30 E
Chascomús 35 30s 58 0W
Chatanika 65 7N 147 31W
Château Salins .. 48 49N 6 30 E
Châteaubriant ... 47 43N 1 23W
Châteauroux .... 46 50N 1 40 E
Châtellerault .... 46 50N 0 30 E
Chatham, U.K. ... 51 22N 0 32 E
Chatham, N.B. ... 47 2N 65 28W
Chatham, Ont. ... 42 23N 82 15W
Chatham, Alas. .. 57 30N 135 0W
Chatham Is. 44 0s 176 40W
Chatham Str. 57 0N 134 40W
Chatrapur ...... 19 21N 85 0 E
Chattahoochee ... 30 43N 84 51W
Chattanooga 35 2N 85 17W
Chaumont ...... 48 7N 5 8 E
Chaves, Brazil ... 0 15s 49 55W
Chaves, Port. 41 45N 7 32W
Cheb .... 50 9N 12 20 E
Cheboksary ..... 56 8N 47 30 E
Cheboygan 45 38N 84 29W
Chefoo=Yentai .. 37 30N 121 21 E
Chegdomyn .... 51 7N 132 52 E
Chehallis 46 44N 122 59W
Cheju .... 33 28N 126 30 E
Cheju Do, I. ..... 33 29N 126 34 E
Chekiang □ ..... 29 30N 120 0 E
Chelforó 39 0s 66 40W
Chelkar .... 47 40N 59 32 E
Chelkar Tengiz
 Solonchak .... 48 0N 62 30 E
Chełm .... 51 8N 23 30 E
Chełmno .... 53 20N 18 30 E
Chelmsford ..... 51 44N 0 29 E
Chełmza .... 53 10N 18 39 E
Chelsea .... 38 5s 145 8 E
Chelyabinsk .... 55 10N 61 35 E
Chemainus 48 54N 123 41W
Chemba .... 17 11s 34 53 E
Chemikovsk 54 58N 56 0W

Karl Marx Stadt . 50 50N 12 55 E
Chemult 43 14N 121 54W
Chenab, R. ...... 29 23N 71 2 E
Chengchou=
 Chengchow ... 34 47N 113 46 E
Chengchow ..... 34 47N 113 46 E
Chengkiang ..... 24 58N 102 59 E
Chengteh .... 41 0N 117 55 E
Chengting ...... 38 8N 114 37 E
Chengtu .... 30 45N 104 0 E
Chengyang ..... 36 20N 120 16 E
Chenhsien ...... 25 45N 112 37 E
Chenning .... 25 57N 105 51 E
Chentung .... 46 2N 123 1 E
Chenyuan ...... 27 0N 108 20 E
Chepo 9 10N 79 6W
Chepstow 51 39N 2 41W
Chequamegon B. . 46 40N 90 30W
Cher, R. .... 47 21N 0 29 E
Cher □ .... 47 10N 2 30 E
Cherbourg 49 39N 1 40W
Cherchell .... 36 35N 21 63 E
Cherdyn .... 60 20N 56 20 E
Cheremkhovo ... 53 32N 102 40 E
Cherepanovo .... 54 15N 83 30 E
Cherepovets .... 59 5N 37 55 E
Cherkassy ...... 49 30N 32 0 E
Chernigov ...... 51 28N 31 20 E
Chernovtsy ..... 48 0N 26 0 E
Chernoye .... 70 30N 89 10 E
Cherokee 42 40N 95 30W
Cheropovets .... 59 5N 37 55 E
Cherquenco 38 35s 72 0W
Cherrapunji .... 25 17N 91 47 E
Cherskogo
 Khrebet ...... 65 0N 143 0 E
Cherwell, R. 51 44N 1 15W
Chesapeake B. .. 38 0N 76 12W
Cheshire □ 53 14N 2 30W
Chester, U.K. ... 53 12N 2 53W
Chester, Pa. 39 54N 75 20W
Chester, S.C. ... 34 44N 81 13W
Chesterfield 53 14N 1 26W
Chesterfield Inlet . 63 30N 91 0W
Chesterfield Is. .. 19 52s 158 15 E
Chetumal 18 30N 88 20W
Chetumal, B. de . 18 40N 88 10W
Cheviot, The, Mt. 55 28N 2 8W
Cheviot Hills 55 20N 2 30W
Chew Bahir, L. .. 4 40N 30 50 E

Chewelah 48 25N 117 56W
Cheyenne 41 9N 104 49W
Cheyenne, R. 44 40N 101 15W
Chhindwara .... 22 2N 78 59 E
Chi, R. .... 15 13N 104 45 E
Chiai .... 23 29N 120 25 E
Chianje .... 15 35s 13 40 E
Chiapas □ 17 0N 92 45W
Chiávari .... 44 20N 9 20 E
Chiavenna ...... 46 18N 9 23 E
Chiba .... 35 30N 140 7 E
Chiba □ .... 35 30N 140 20 E
Chibemba ...... 15 48s 14 8 E
Chibougamau ... 49 56N 74 24W
Chibuk .... 10 52N 12 50 E
Chicago 41 45N 87 40W
Chicago Heights . 41 29N 87 37W
Chicagof I. 58 0N 136 0W
Chichester 50 50N 0 47W
Chichén Itzá 20 40N 88 34W
Chichibu .... 36 5N 139 10 E
Chichirin .... 50 35N 123 45 E
Chickasha 35 0N 98 0W
Chiclana de la
 Frontera 36 26N 6 9W
Chiclayo 6 42s 79 50W
Chico 39 45N 121 54W
Chico, R. 43 50s 66 25W
Chicopee 42 6N 72 37W
Chicoutimi 48 28N 71 5W
Chidley, C. 60 30N 64 15W
Chiengi .... 8 38s 29 10 E
Chiengmai ..... 18 55N 98 55 E
Chieti .... 42 22N 14 10 E
Chiguana 21 0s 67 50W
Chihfeng ...... 42 10N 118 56 E
Chihing .... 25 2N 113 45 E
Chihkiang ..... 27 21N 109 45 E
Chihli, G. of=
 Po Hai, G. ... 38 30N 119 0 E
Chihsien ...... 35 29N 114 1 E
Chihuahua 28 40N 106 3W
Chihuahua □ ... 28 40N 106 3W
Chiili .... 44 10N 66 55 E
Chilas .... 35 25N 74 5 E
Childers .... 25 15s 152 17 E
Childress 34 30N 100 50W
Chile ■ 35 0s 71 15W
Chilete 7 10s 78 50W

Chililabombwe ... 12 18s 27 43 E
Chilin=Kirin ..... 43 58N 126 31 E
Chilka .... 19 40N 85 25 E
Chillán 36 40s 72 10W
Chillicothe, Mo. .. 39 45N 93 30W
Chillicothe, Ohio. . 39 53N 82 58W
Chilliwack 49 10N 122 0W
Chiloé, I. de 42 50s 73 45W
Chilpancingo ... 17 30N 99 40W
Chiltern .... 36 10s 146 36 E
Chiltern Hills ... 51 44N 0 42W
Chilumba ...... 10 28N 34 12 E
Chilung .... 25 3N 121 45 E
Chilwa, L. ..... 15 15s 35 40 E
Chimai .... 34 0N 101 39 E
Chimala .... 8 55s 34 4 E
Chimborazo, Mt. . 1 20s 78 55W
Chimbote 9 0s 78 35W
Chimkent ...... 42 40N 69 25 E
Chin □ .... 22 0N 93 0 E
China ■ .... 35 0N 100 0 E
Chinan=Tsinan .. 34 50N 105 40 E
Chinandega 12 30N 87 0W
Chincha Alta ... 13 20s 76 0W
Chinchilla ..... 26 45s 150 38 E
Chinchow ..... 41 10N 121 2 E
Chinde .... 18 45s 36 30 E
Chindwin, R. ... 21 26N 95 15 E
Ching Ho, R. ... 34 20N 109 0 E
Chingola ...... 12 31s 27 53 E
Chingole ...... 13 4s 34 17 E
Ch'ingtao=
 Tsingtao .... 36 0N 120 25 E
Chinhae ...... 35 9N 128 58 E
Chiniot .... 31 45N 73 0 E
Chinju .... 35 12N 128 2 E
Chinkiang .... 32 2N 119 29 E
Chino Valley ... 34 54N 112 28W
Chinon .... 47 10N 0 15 E
Chinook, Canada . 51 28N 110 59W
Chinook, U.S.A. . 48 35N 109 19W
Chintheche .... 11 50s 34 5 E
Chinwangtao ... 40 0N 119 31 E
Chióggia ...... 45 13N 12 15 E
Chios, I.=
 Khíos, I. .... 38 20N 26 0 E
Chip Lake 53 35N 115 35W
Chipata .... 13 38s 32 28 E
Chipinga ...... 20 13s 32 36 E
Chippenham ... 51 27N 2 7W

Chippewa, R. 44 25N 92 10W
Chippewa Falls 44 56N 91 24W
Chiquimula 14 51N 89 37W
Chiquinquira 5 37N 73 50W
Chirala .... 15 50N 80 20 E
Chirchik .... 81 58N 69 15 E
Chirikof I. 55 50N 155 35W
Chiriquí, G. de ... 8 0N 82 10W
Chiriquí, L. de ... 9 10N 82 0W
Chiriqui, Mt. 8 55N 82 35W
Chiromo .... 16 30S 35 7 E
Chisamba .... 14 55S 28 20 E
Chita .... 52 0N 113 25 E
Chitembo .... 13 30S 16 50 E
Chitorgarh ...... 24 52N 74 43 E
Chitré 7 59N 80 27W
Chittagong ...... 22 19N 91 55 E
Chittagong □ .... 24 5N 91 25 E
Chittoor .... 13 15N 79 5 E
Chiusi .... 43 1N. 11 58 E
Chivasso .... 45 10N 7 52 E
Chivilcoy 35 0S 60 0W
Chiwanda .... 11 22S 34 54 E
Chobe Nat. Park . 18 25S 24 15 E
Choele Choel 39 11S 65 40W
Choinice .... 53 42N 17 40 E
Cholet 47 4N 0 52W
Choluteca 13 20N 87 14W
Choma .... 16 48S 26 59 E
Chomutov .... 50 28N 13 23 E
Chon Buri ...... 13 21N 101 1 E
Chorley 53 39N 2 39W
Chorzow .... 50 18N 19 0 E
Chos-Malal 37 20S 70 15W
Chóshi .... 35 45N 140 45 E
Choszczno ...... 53 7N 15 25 E
Choteau 47 50N 112 10W
Chotila .... 22 25N 71 11 E
Choybalsan ...... 48 3N 114 28 E
Christchurch, N.Z. 43 33S 172 47W
Christchurch, U.K. 50 44N 1 47W
Christiana ...... 27 52S 25 8 E

Christmas Creek .. 18 29S 125 23 E
Christmas I.
  Indian Oc....... 10 0S 105 40 E
Christmas I.
  Pacific Oc....... 1 58N 157 27W
Chu .... 43 36N 73 42 E
Chu Kiang, R. .... 24 50N 113 37 E
Chuanchow ...... 24 57N 118 31 E
Chuanhsien ..... 25 50N 111 12 E
Chúbu □ .... 36 45N 137 0 E
Chubut, R. 43 20S 65 5W
Chucheng .... 36 0N 119 16 E
Chuchow .... 27 56N 113 3 E
Chudskoye, Oz. ... 58 13N 27 30 E
Chugiak 61 25N 149 30W
Chúgoku □ ..... 35 0N 133 0 E
Chúgoku-Sanchi,
  Mts. .... 35 0N 133 0 E
Chuhsien .... 30 51N 107 1 E
Chuka .... 0 23S 37 38 E
Chukai .... 4 13N 103 25 E
Chukotskiy Khrebet 68 0N 175 0 E
Chukotskoye More 68 0N 175 0 E
Chula Vista 33 44N 117 8W
Chumatien ...... 33 0N 114 4 E
Chumbicha 29 0S 66 10W
Chumikan .... 54 40N 135 10 E
Chumphon ...... 10 35N 99 14 E
Chunchón .... 37 58N 127 44 E
Ch'ungch'ing=
  Chungking .... 29 30N 106 30 E
Chunghsien ..... 30 17N 108 4 E
Chungking ...... 29 30N 106 30 E
Chungtien ...... 28 0N 99 30 E
Chungwei .... 37 35N 105 10 E
Chunya .... 8 30S 33 27 E
Chur .... 46 52N 9 32 E
Churchill 58 45N 94 5W
Churchill, R.,
  Man. 58 47N 94 12W
Churchill, R.,
  Newf. 53 30N 60 10W
Churchill Pk. 58 10N 125 10W
Churu .... 28 20N 75 0 E
Chusan, I. ...... 30 0N 122 20 E
Chuvash
  A.S.S.R. □ .... 53 30N 48 0 E
Chuvovoy ...... 58 15N 57 40 E
Cianjur .... 6 81S 107 7 E
Cibatu .... 7 8S 107 59 E

Cicero 41 48N 87 48W
Ciechanów □ .... 53 0N 20 0 E
Ciego de Avila .. 21 50N 78 50W
Ciénaga 11 0N 74 10W
Cienfuegos 22 10N 80 30W
Cieszyn .... 49 45N 18 35 E
Cieza 38 17N 1 23W
Cilacap .... 7 43S 109 0 E
Cimarron, R. 36 10N 96 17W
Cimahi .... 6 53S 107 33 E
Cimpina .... 45 10N 25 45 E
Cimpulung ...... 45 17N 25 3 E
Cinca, R. .... 41 26N 0 21 E
Cincinnati 39 10N 84 26W
Cinto, Mt. ...... 42 24N 8 54 E
Circle 47 26N 105 35W
Circleville, Ohio . 39 35N 82 57W
Circleville, Utah .. 38 12N 112 24W
Cirebon .... 6 45S 108 32 E
Cirencester 51 43N 1 59W
Cisco 32 25N 99 0W
Citlaltepetl, Mt. .. 19 0N 97 20W
Citrusdal .... 32 35S 19 0 E
Ciudad Acuña ... 29 20N 101 10W
Ciudad Bolívar .. 8 5N 63 30W
Ciudad Camargo . 27 41N 105 10W
Ciudad de Valles . 22 0N 98 30W
Ciudad del
  Carmen 18 20N 97 50W
Ciudad Guayana . 8 20N 62 35W
Ciudad Guzmán .. 19 40N 103 30W
Ciudad Juárez ... 31 40N 106 28W
Ciudad Madero .. 22 19N 97 50W
Ciudad Mante ... 22 50N 99 0W
Ciudad Obregón . 27 28N 109 59W
Ciudad Piar 7 27N 63 19W
Ciudad Real 38 59N 3 55W
Ciudad Rodrigo .. 40 35N 6 32W
Ciudad Victoria .. 23 41N 99 9W
Civitanova
  Marche .... 43 18N 13 41 E
Civitavécchia .... 42 6N 11 46 E
Çivril .... 38 20N 29 55 E
Clackline .... 31 40S 116 32 E
Clacton .... 51 47N 1 10 E
Clanwilliam ..... 32 11S 18 52 E
Clara 53 20N 7 38W
Clare .... 33 20S 143 50 E
Clare □ 52 52N 8 55W
Clare, R. 53 20N 9 3W

Claremont 43 23N 72 20W
Claremore 36 20N 95 20W
Claremorris 53 45N 9 0W
Clarence, I. 54 0S 72 0W
Clarence, Str. ... 12 0S 131 0 E
Clarence, R. .... 42 10S 173 56 E
Clarendon 34 41N 91 20W
Clarenville 48 10N 54 1W
Claresholm 50 0N 113 45W
Clarinda 40 45N 95 0W
Clark Fork, R. ... 48 9N 116 15W
Clarkdale 34 53N 112 3W
Clarke City 50 12N 66 38W
Clarkes Harbour . 43 25N 65 38W
Clarksburg 39 18N 80 21W
Clarksdale 34 12N 90 33W
Clarkston 46 28N 117 2W
Clarksville 36 32N 87 20W
Clayton 44 14N 76 5W
Clear, L. 51 26N 9 30W
Clearfield 41 0N 78 27W
Clearwater,
  Canada 51 38N 120 2W
Clearwater, U.S.A. 27 58N 82 45W
Clearwater L. 56 10N 75 0W
Cleburne 32 18N 97 25W
Clee Hills 55 25N 2 35W
Cleethorpes 53 33N 0 2W
Clermont,
  Australia ...... 22 46S 147 38 E
Clermont-Ferrand . 45 46N 3 4 E
Clevedon 51 27N 2 51W
Cleveland,
  Australia ...... 27 31S 153 3 E
Cleveland, Miss. . 33 34N 90 43W
Cleveland, Ohio. . 41 28N 81 43W
Cleveland, Tenn. . 35 9N 84 52W
Cleveland, Tex. .. 30 18N 95 0W
Cleveland □ 54 30N 1 12W
Cleveland, Mt. .. 48 56N 113 51W
Cleveleys 53 53N 3 3W
Clew B. 53 54N 9 50W
Clifden, Eire 53 30N 10 2W
Clifden, N.Z. .... 46 1S 167 42 E
Clifton 33 8N 109 23W
Clifton Forge 37 49N 79 51W
Clingmans Dome,
  Mt. 35 35N 83 30W
Clinton, B.C. 51 0N 121 40W
Clinton, Ont. 43 38N 81 33W

Clinton, N.Z. .... 46 12S 169 23 E
Clinton, Ark. 35 37N 92 30W
Clinton, Ill. 40 8N 89 0W
Clinton, Iowa ... 41 50N 90 18W
Clinton, Mass. .. 42 26N 71 40W
Clinton, Mo. 38 20N 93 40W
Clinton, N.C. ... 35 5N 78 15W
Clinton Colden L. . 64 0N 107 0W
Clipperton I. 10 18N 109 13W
Clocolan .... 28 55S 27 34 E
Clonakilty 51 37N 8 53W
Cloncurry ...... 20 40S 140 28 E
Clones 54 10N 7 13W
Clonmel 52 22N 7 42W
Cloquet 46 40N 92 30W
Clovis, Calif. ... 36 54N 119 45W
Clovis, N.Mex. .. 34 20N 103 10W
Cluj .... 46 47N 23 38 E
Clutha, R. ...... 46 20S 169 49 E
Clwyd □ 53 0N 3 15W
Clwyd, R. 53 20N 3 30W
Clyde, Canada ... 70 30N 68 30W
Clyde, N.Z. ..... 45 12S 169 20 E
Clyde, R. 55 56N 4 29W
Clyde, Firth of .. 55 42N 5 0W
Clydebank 55 54N 4 25W
Coachella 33 44N 116 13W
Coachman's Cove . 50 6N 56 20W
Coahuila □ 27 0N 112 30W
Coaldale,
  Canada 49 45N 112 35W
Coalinga 36 10N 120 21W
Coalville 52 43N 1 21W
Coast Mts. 52 0N 126 0W
Coast Ra. 40 0N 124 0W
Coastal Plains
  Basin .... 30 10S 115 30 E
Coatbridge 55 52N 4 2W
Coatepeque 14 46N 91 55W
Coaticook 45 10N 71 46W
Coats I. 62 30N 82 0W
Coatzacoalcos .. 18 7N 94 35W
Coazapá 26 0S 56 35W
Cobalt 47 25N 79 42W
Coban 15 30N 90 21W
Cobar .... 31 27S 145 48 E
Cobh 51 50N 8 18W
Cobham .... 30 10S 142 0 E
Cobourg 44 0N 78 20W
Coburg .... 50 15N 10 58 E

Cocanada=
  Kakinada .... 16 55N 82 20 E
Cochabamba 17 15s 66 20w
Cochin-China,
  Reg.=Nam-
  Phan, Reg. ..... 10 30N 106 0 E
Cochrane, Alta. ... 51 20N 114 30w
Cochrane, Ont. ... 49 0N 81 0w
Cochrane, L. 47 10s 72 0w
Cockburn,
  Australia .... 32 5s 141 2 E
Cockburn,
  Canada 54 30s 72 0w
Coco, R. 15 0N 83 8w
Cocos Is. .... 12 12s 96 54 E
Cod, C. 42 8N 70 10w
Codajás 3 40s 62 0w
Codó, R. 4 30s 43 55w
Codrington 17 43N 61 49w
Cody 44 35N 109 0w
Coen .... 13 52s 143 12 E
Coeur d'Alene ... 47 45N 116 51w
Coffeyville 37 0N 95 40w
Coffs Harbour ... 30 16s 153 5 E
Cognac 45 41N 0 20w
Cohoes 42 47N 73 42w
Cohuna .... 35 45s 144 15 E
Coiba, I. 7 30N 81 40w
Coig, R. 51 0s 69 10w
Coihaique 45 35s 72 8w
Coimbatore ..... 11 2N 76 59 E
Coimbra 40 15N 8 27w
Coín 36 40N 4 48w
Cojimies 0 20N 80 0w
Cojutepeque 13 41N 88 54w
Colac .... 38 10s 143 30 E
Colby 39 27N 101 20w
Colchester ...... 51 54N 0 55 E
Cold Lake· 54 27N 110 10w
Coldstream 55 39N 2 14w
Coldwell 48 45N 86 30w
Colebrook 44 54N 71 29w
Coleman 31 52N 99 30w
Colenso .... 28 44s 29 50 E
Coleraine,
  Australia ...... 37 36s 141 40 E
Coleraine, U.K. ... 55 8N 6 40w
Coleraine □ 55 8N 6 40w
Colesburg ...... 30 45s 25 5 E
Colhué Huapí, L.. 45 30s 69 0w

Coligny .... 26 17s 26 18 E
Colima 19 10N 103 50w
Colima □ 19 10N 103 40w
Colinas 6 0s 44 10w
Colinton .... 35 50s 149 10 E
Coll, I. 56 40N 6 35w
College Park 33 42N 84 27w
Collie .... 33 25s 116 30 E
Collier, B. .... 16 0s 124 0 E
Collingwood,
  Australia .... 22 20s 142 31 E
Collingwood,
  Canada 44 30N 80 20w
Collingwood, N.Z. . 40 42s 172 40 E
Collinsville ...... 20 30s 147 56 E
Collooney 54 11N 8 28w
Colmar .... 48 5N 7 20 E
Colne 53 51N 2 11w
Colo, R. .... 33 20s 150 40 E
Cologne=Köln ... 50 56N 9 58 E
Colombia ■ 3 45N 73 0w
Colombia 3 24N 79 49w
Colombo .... 6 56N 79 58 E
Colón, R. 9 20N 80 0w
Colona .... 31 38s 132 5 E
Colonia del
  Sacramento 34 25s 57 50w
Colonia 25 de
  Mayo 38 0s 67 32w
Colonsay, I. 56 4N 6 12w
Colorado □ 37 40N 106 0w
Colorado, R., Arg. . 39 50s 62 8w
Colorado, R.
  Mex.–U.S.A. .. 31 45N 114 40w
Colorado, R.,
  U.S.A. 28 36N 95 58w
Colorado Aqueduct 34 0N 115 20w
Colorado City ... 32 25N 100 50w
Colorado Plat. ... 36 40N 110 30w
Colorado Springs . 38 55N 104 50w
Columbia, La. ... 32 7N 92 5w
Columbia, Mo. ... 38 58N 92 20w
Columbia, S.C. ... 34 0N 81 0w
Columbia, Tenn. . 35 40N 87 0w
Columbia,
  District of □ 38 55N 77 0w
Columbia, Mt. ... 52 20N 117 30w
Columbia, R. 45 49N 120 0w
Columbia Falls .. 48 25N 114 16w
Columbia Heights . 45 5N 93 10w

Columbia Plat. 47 30N 118 30w
Columbus, Ga. 32 30N 84 58w
Columbus, Ind. ... 39 14N 85 55w
Columbus, Miss. .. 33 30N 88 26w
Columbus, N.D. ... 48 52N 102 48w
Columbus, Ohio .. 39 57N 83 1w
Colville, C. ...... 36 29s 175 21 E
Colville, R. 70 25N 150 30w
Colwyn Bay 53 17N 3 44w
Comácchio ..... 44 41N 12 10 E
Comallo 41 0s 70 5w
Comet .... 23 36s 148 38 E
Comilla .... 23 22N 91 18 E
Comino, I. ...... 36 0N 14 22 E
Comitán 16 18N 92 9w
Committee B. 68 0N 37 0w
Commerce 33 15N 95 50w
Como .... 45 48N 9 5 E
Como, L. di .... 46 5N 9 17 E
Comodoro
  Rivadavia 45 50s 67 40w
Comorin, C. ..... 8 3N 77 40 E
Comoro Is. ..... 12 10s 44 15 E
Comox 49 42N 125 0w
Compiègne ..... 49 24N 2 50 E
Conakry 9 29N 13 49w
Conard Junction .. 41 48s 143 70 E
Concarneau 47 52N 3 56w
Conceição do
  Araguaia 8 0s 49 2w
Conceiçao do
  Barra 18 50s 39 50w
Concepción, Chile . 36 50s 73 0w
Concepción,
  Paraguay 23 30s 57 20w
Concepción, Canal. 50 30s 75 0w
Concepción, Pt. ... 34 30N 120 34w
Concepción del Oro 24 40N 101 30w
Concepción del
  Uruguay 32 35s 58 20w
Concord, N.C. ... 35 28N 80 35w
Concord, N.H. ... 43 5N 71 30w
Concordia, Arg. ... 31 20s 58 2w
Concordia, U.S.A. . 39 35N 97 40w
Condamine ..... 26 55s 150 3 E
Condobolin ..... 33 4s 147 6 E
Congleton 53 10N 2 12w
Congo ■ .... 1 0s 16 0 E
Congo (Kinshasa)■
  =Zaïre ■ ...... 3 0s 22 0 E

Congo, R.=
  Zaïre, R. ...... 6 4s 12 24 E
Congo Basin .... 1 0s 23 0 E
Congress 34 11N 112 56w
Coniston 46 32N 80 51w
Conjeeveram=
  Kanchipuram .. 12 52N 79 45 E
Conjuboy ...... 18 35s 144 45 E
Connacht □ 53 23N 8 40w
Conneaut 41 55N 80 32w
Connecticut □ ... 41 40N 72 40w
Connecticut, R. .. 41 17N 72 21w
Connemara 53 29N 9 45w
Connersville 39 40N 85 10w
Conquest 51 35N 107 0w
Conroe 30 15N 95 28w
Conselheiro 20 40s 43 8w
Consett 54 51N 1 49w
Consort 52 1N 110 46w
Constance, L.=
  Bodensee ..... 47 35N 9 25 E
Constanța ..... 44 14N 28 38 E
Constantine .... 36 25N 6 42 E
Constitución ... 35 20s 72 30w
Conway, Ark. ... 35 5N 92 30w
Conway, N.H. ... 43 58N 71 8w
Conway, S.C. ... 33 49N 79 2w
Conwy 53 17N 3 50w
Conwy R. 53 17N 3 50w
Cooch Behar ... 26 22N 89 29 E
Cook .... 30 42s 130 48 E
Cook, B. 55 10s 70 0w
Cook Inlet 59 0N 151 0w
Cook Is. 22 0s 157 0w
Cook, Mt. ..... 43 36s 170 9 E
Cook, Str. ..... 41 15s 174 29 E
Cookeville 36 12N 85 30w
Cookhouse .... 32 44s 25 47 E
Cooktown .... 15 30s 145 16 E
Cookstown □ ... 54 40N 6 43w
Coolabah ..... 31 0s 146 15 E
Coolangatta ... 28 11s 153 29 E
Coolgardie .... 30 55s 121 8 E
Coolidge 33 1N 111 35w
Coolidge Dam .. 33 10N 110 30w
Cooma .... 36 12s 149 8 E
Coonabarabran . 31 14s 149 18 E
Coonamble .... 30 56s 148 27 E
Coonana ..... 31 0s 123 0 E
Coongoola .... 27 43s 145 47 E

Cooper. 39 57N 75 7w
Cooper
  Creek, R., L. ... 28 0s 139 0 E
Coorong, The .. 35 50s 139 20 E
Coorow ...... 29 50s 115 59 E
Cooroy ...... 26 22s 152 54 E
Coos Bay 43 26N 124 7w
Cootamundra .. 34 36s 148 1 E
Cootehill 54 5N 7 5w
Copenhagen=
  København .. 55 41N 12 34 E
Copiapó ...... 27 15s 70 20 E
Copper Center .. 62 10N 145 25w
Copper Cliff ... 46 30N 81 4w
Copper Mountain 49 20N 120 30w
Coppermine ... 68 0N 116 0w
Coquet, R. 55 22N 1 37w
Coquilhatville=
  Mbandaka .... 0 1N 18 18 E
Coquimbo 30 0s 71 20w
Corabia ...... 43 48N 24 30 E
Coracora 15 5s 73 45w
Coral Harbour . 64 0N 83 0w
Coral Rapids .. 50 20N 81 40w
Coral Sea .... 15 0s 150 0 E
Corbin 37 0N 84 3w
Corby 52 29N 0 41w
Corcoran 36 6N 119 35w
Corcubión ... 42 56N 9 12w
Cordele 31 55N 83 49w
Córdoba, Arg. . 31 20s 64 10w
Córdoba, Mexico . 26 20N 103 20w
Córdoba, Sp. .. 37 50N 4 50w
Córdoba, Sa. de . 31 10s 64 25w
Cordon ..... 16 42N 121 32 E
Cordova 60 36N 145 45w
Corfield .... 21 40s 143 21 E
Corfu, I.=
  Kérkira, I. .... 39 38N 19 50 E
Corigliano
  Cálabro .... 39 36N 16 31 E
Corinth 34 54N 88 30w
Corinto, Nic. .. 12 30N 87 10w
Corinto,
  Brazil 18 20s 44 30w
Cork 51 54N 8 30w
Cork □ 51 54N 8 30w
Çorlu .... 41 11N 27 49 E
Cormorant ... 54 5N 100 45w
Corn Is. 12 0N 83 0w

Corner Brook 49 0N 58 0W
Corning, Calif. 39 56N 122 9W
Corning, N.Y..... 42 10N 77 3W
Cornwall 45 5N 74 45W
Cornwall □ 50 26N 4 40W
Coro 11 30N 69 45W
Coroatá 4 20S 44 0W
Corocoro 17 15S 69 19W
Coromandel .... 36 45S 175 31 E
Coromandel Coast
  Reg. .... 12 30N 81 0 E
Corona 33 49N 117 36W
Coronado 32 45N 117 9W
Coronado, B. de . 9 0N 83 40W
Coronation G. .. 68 0N 114 0W
Coronel 37 0S 73 10W
Coronel Dorrego . 38 40S 61 10W
Coronel Pringles . 38 0S 61 30W
Coronel Suárez .. 37 30S 62 0W
Corpus Christi .. 27 50N 97 28W
Correntes, C. das . 24 11S 35 34 E
Corrèze □ .... 45 20N 1 50 E
Corrib, L. 53 25N 9 10W
Corrientes 27 30S 58 45W
Corrientes, C.,
  Cuba 21 43N 84 30N
Corrientes, C.,
  Col. 5 30N 77 34W
Corrigin .... 32 18S 117 45 E
Corry 41 55N 79 39W
Corse, C. .... 43 1N 9 25 E
Corse, I. .... 42 0N 9 0 E
Corse du Sud □ .. 41 40N 9 0 E
Corsica, I.=
  Corse, I. ..... 42 0N 9 0 E
Corsicana 32 5N 96 30W
Cortez 37 24N 108 35W
Cortland 42 35N 76 11W
Cortona .... 43 16N 12 0 E
Çorum .... 40 30N 35 5 E
Corumbá 19 0S 57 30W
Corunna=
  La Coruña 43 20N 8 25W
Corvallis 44 36N 123 15W
Cosamaloapan .. 18 23N 95 50W
Cosenza .... 39 17N 16 14 E
Coshocton 40 17N 81 51W
Costa, Cord. de la . 30 0S 71 0W
Costa Blanca, Reg. 38 25N 0 10W
Costa Brava, Reg. . 41 30N 3 0 E

Costa del Sol, Reg. 36 30N 4 30W
Costa Dorada, Reg. 40 45N 1 15 E
Costa Rica ■ 10 0N 84 0W
Cotabato .... 7 8N 124 13 E
Côte d'Or □ ..... 47 30N 4 50 E
Côte d'Or, Reg. ... 47 10N 4 50 E
Cotentin, Reg. ... 49 30N 1 30W
Cotonou .... 6 20N 2 25 E
Cotopaxi, Mt. 0 30S 78 30W
Cotswold Hills ... 51 42N 2 10W
Cottage Grove ... 43 48N 123 2W
Cottbus .... 51 44N 14 20 E
Cottonwood 34 48N 112 1W
Coulee City 47 44N 119 12W
Council, Alas. 64 55N 163 45W
Council, Id. 44 45N 116 30W
Council Bluffs ... 41 20N 95 50W
Courtenay 49 45N 125 0W
Coventry 52 25N 1 32W
Covilhã 40 17N 7 31W
Covington, Ga. ... 33 36N 83 50W
Covington, Ky. ... 39 5N 84 30W
Cowan 52 5N 100 45W
Cowan, L. ...... 31 45S 121 45 E
Cowangie ...... 35 12S 141 26 E
Cowansville 45 14N 72 46W
Cowdenbeath ... 56 7N 3 20W
Cowell .... 33 38S 136 40 E
Cowes 50 45N 1 18W
Cowra .... 33 49S 148 42 E
Coxim 18 30S 54 55W
Cox's Bazar ..... 21 25N 92 3 E
Cozumel, I. de .. 20 30N 86 40W
Cracow=
  Kraków ...... 50 4N 19 57 E
Cradock .... 32 8S 25 36 E
Craig 40 32N 107 44W
Craigavon □ 54 27N 6 26W
Craiova .... 44 21N 23 48 E
Crampel .... 7 8N 19 8 E
Cranberry Portage 54 36N 101 22W
Cranbrook,
  Tas. .... 42 0S 148 5 E
Cranbrook,
  W. Australia .... 34 20S 117 35 E
Cranbrook
  Canada 49 30N 115 55W
Crateús 5 10S 40 50W
Crato, Brazil 7 10S 39 25W

Crawfordsville 40 2N 86 51W
Crawley 51 7N 0 10W
Crécy .... 48 50N 2 53 E
Cree L. 57 30N 107 0W
Cremona .... 45 8N 10 2 E
Cres, I. .... 44 58N 14 25 E
Crescent City 41 45N 124 12W
Cressman 47 40N 72 55W
Creston, Canada . 49 10N 116 40W
Creston, U.S.A. ... 41 0N 94 20W
Crestview 30 45N 86 35W
Crete, I. .... 35 10N 25 0 E
Creus, C. .... 42 20N 3 19 E
Creuse □ .... 46 0N 2 0 E
Creuse, R. ...... 47 0N 0 34 E
Crewe 53 6N 2 28W
Criciúma 28 40S 49 23W
Crieff 56 22N 3 50W
Crimea=
  Krymskaya, Reg. 45 0N 34 0 E
Crinan 56 4N 5 30W
Cristóbal 9 10N 80 0W
Crişul Alb, R..... 46 42N 21 17 E
Crişul Negru, R. .. 46 42N 21 16 E
Crna, R. .... 41 35N 21 59 E
Crna Gora □ .... 42 40N 19 20 E
Crna Gora, Mts. .. 42 20N 21 30 E
Crockett 31 20N 95 30W
Croker, I. ...... 11 12S 132 32 E
Cromarty 57 40N 4 2W
Cromer .... 52 56N 1 18 E
Cromwell ...... 45 3S 169 14 E
Cronulla .... 34 3S 151 8 E
Crooked I. 22 50N 74 10W
Crookston 47 50N 96 40W
Cross Fell, Mt. ... 54 44N 2 29W
Cross River □ .... 6 20N 8 20 E
Crosshaven 51 48N 8 19W
Crotone .... 39 5N 17 6 E
Crow Agency 45 40N 107 30W
Crow Hd. 51 34N 10 9W
Crowley 30 15N 92 20W
Crowsnest P. 49 40N 114 40W
Croydon,
  Australia ..... 18 15S 142 14 E
Croydon, U.K. ... 51 18N 0 5W
Crozet Is. ...... 46 27S 52 0 E
Cruz Alta 28 40S 53 32W
Cruz del Eje 30 45S 64 50W
Cruzeiro 22 50S 45 0W

Cruzeiro do Sul ... 7 35S 72 35W
Crystal Brook .... 33 21S 138 13 E
Crystal City 38 15N 90 23W
Csongrád .... 46 43N 20 12 E
Cuamba .... 14 45S 36 22 E
Cuando, R. ..... 14 0S 19 30 E
Cuba ■ 22 0N 79 0W
Cuballing ...... 32 50S 117 15 E
Cubango, R. ..... 18 50S 22 25 E
Cucui 1 10N 66 50W
Cúcuta 7 54N 72 31W
Cuddalore ...... 11 46N 79 45 E
Cuddapah ...... 14 30N 78 47 E
Cue .... 27 20S 117 55 E
Cuenca, Ecuador . 2 50S 79 9W
Cuenca, Sa. de .. 39 55N 1 50W
Cuernavaca 18 50N 99 20W
Cuero 29 5N 97 17W
Cuevas de
  Almanzora 37 18N 1 58W
Cuiabá 15 30S 56 0W
Cuillin Hills 57 14N 6 15W
Cuito, R. .... 18 1S 20 48 E
Cuitzeo, L. 19 55N 101 5W
Culcairn .... 35 41S 147 3 E
Culebra, Sa. de la . 41 55N 6 20W
Culiacán 24 50N 107 40W
Cullen 57 45N 2 50W
Cullen, Pt. ...... 11 50S 141 47 E
Cullera 39 9N 0 17W
Culloden Moor ... 57 29N 4 7W
Culverden ...... 42 47S 172 49 E
Cumaná 10 30N 64 5W
Cumberland,
  Canada 49 40N 125 0W
Cumberland,
  U.S.A. 39 40N 78 43W
Cumberland Pen.. 67 0N 65 0W
Cumberland Plat.. 36 0N 84 30W
Cumberland Sd. .. 65 30N 66 0W
Cumbria □ 54 44N 3 0W
Cumbrian, Mts. .. 54 30N 3 0W
Cumbum .... 15 40N 79 10 E
Cunderdin ...... 31 39S 117 15 E
Cunene, R. ..... 17 20S 11 50 E
Cúneo .... 44 23N 7 32 E
Cunnamulla .... 28 4S 145 41 E
Cupar, Canada .. 51 0N 104 10W
Cupar, U.K. 56 20N 3 0W
Cupica, G. de 6 25N 77 30W

Curaçao 12 10N 69 0W
Curiapo 8 33N 61 5W
Curicó 34 55S 71 20W
Curitiba 25 20S 49 10W
Currais Novos ... 6 13S 36 30W
Curralinho 1 35S 49 30W
Currawilla ...... 25 10S 141 20 E
Currie 40 16N 114 45W
Curtis, I. .... 23 40S 151 15 E
Curuçá 0 35S 47 50W
Cururupu 1 50S 44 50W
Curuzú Cuatiá ... 29 50S 58 5W
Curvelo 18 45S 44 27W
Curya .... 35 53S 142 54 E
Cushing 31 43N 94 50W
Custer 43 45N 103 38W
Cut Bank 48 40N 112 15W
Cuttack .... 20 25N 85 57 E
Cuvier, C. ...... 23 14S 113 22 E
Cuxhaven ...... 53 52N 8 42 E
Cuyahoga Falls .. 41 8N 81 30W
Cuzco, Mt. 20 0S 66 50W
Cuzco 13 32S 72 0W
Cyclades, Is.=
  Kikládhes, Is. .. 37 20N 24 30 E
Cygnet .... 43 8S 147 1 E
Cyprus ■ .... 35 0N 33 0 E
Cyrenaica=Barqa
  Reg. .... 27 0N 20 0 E
Cyrene=Shahhat . 32 39N 21 18 E
Czechoslovakia ■ . 49 0N 17 0 E
Częstochowa .... 50 49N 19 7 E

D

Da, R. .... 16 0N 107 0 E
Da Lat .... 12 3N 108 32 E
Da Nang .... 16 10N 108 7 E
Dabai .... 11 25N 5 15 E
Dabakala 8 15N 4 20W
Dąbie .... 53 27N 14 45 E
Dabola 10 50N 11 5W
Dacca .... 23 43N 90 26 E
Dacca □ .... 24 0N 90 0 E
Dadanawa 3 0N 59 30W
Dadiya .... 9 35N 11 24 E
Dadu .... 26 45N 67 45 E

Dagesta
  A.S.S.R. □ ..... 42 30N 47 0 E
Dagupan .... 16 3N 120 33 E
Dahomey ■=
  Benin ■ .... 8 0N 2 0 E
Daingean 53 18N 7 15W
Dairen=Talien ... 39 0N 121 31 E
Dairût .... 27 34N 30 43 E
Dairy Creek ..... 25 12s 115 48 E
Daisetsu-Zan, Mt. . 43 30N 142 57 E
Dajarra .... 21 42s 139 30 E
Dakar 14 34N 17 29W
Dakhla 23 50N 15 53W
Dakhovskaya ..... 44 13N 40 13 E
Dakingari .... 11 37N 4 1 E
Dalai Nor, L. .... 49 0N 117 50 E
Dalälven, R. ..... 60 38N 17 27 E
Dalandzadgad .... 43 35N 104 30 E
Dalarö .... 59 8N 18 24 E
Dalbandin .... 28 53N 64 25 E
Dalbeattie 54 56N 3 49W
Dalby .... 27 11s 151 16 E
Dalhart 36 4N 102 31W
Dalhousie 48 0N 66 26W
Daliyat el Karmel . 32 41N 35 3 E
Dalkeith 55 54N 3 4W
Dallas 32 47N 96 48W
Dalma, I. .... 24 30N 52 20 E
Dalmacija, Reg. .. 43 0N 17 0 E
Dalmatia, Reg.=
  Dalmacija, Reg. .. 43 0N 17 0 E
Dalmellington ... 55 20N 4 25W
Dalnerechensk ... 45 50N 133 40 E
Daloa 6 53N 6 27W
Dalton, Canada .. 60 10N 137 0W
Dalton, Neb..... 41 27N 103 0W
Daly, R. .... 13 20s 130 19 E
Daly Waters .... 16 15s 133 22 E
Daman .... 20 25N 72 57 E
Daman, Dadra &
  Nagar Haveli □ . 20 25N 72 58 E
Damanhûr .... 31 2N 30 28 E
Damaraland, Reg. . 22 33s 17 6 E
Damascus=
  Dimashq .... 33 30N 36 18 E
Damataru .... 11 45N 11 55 E
Damâvand .... 35 45N 52 10 E
Damâvand,
  Qolleh-ye, Mt. . 35 56N 52 8 E
Dâmbovița, R. ... 44 40N 26 0 E

Dâmäghan .... 36 10N 54 17 E
Damietta=
  Dumyât .... 31 24N 31 48 E
Damiya .... 32 6N 35 34 E
Damoh .... 23 50N 79 28 E
Dampier .... 20 39s 116 45 E
Dampier, Selat .. 0 40s 130 40 E
Dan .... 33 13N 35 39 E
Dan Dume .... 11 28N 7 8 E
Dan Gulbi .... 11 40N 6 15 E
Dan Yashi .... 12 0N 8 5 E
Danané 7 16N 8 9W
Danbury 41 23N 73 29W
Dandenong ...... 37 52s 145 12 E
Dangora .... 11 25N 8 7 E
Daniel's Harbour . 50 13N 57 35W
Danilov .... 58 16N 40 13 E
Danja .... 11 29N 7 30 E
Dankama .... 13 20N 7 44 E
Dankhar Gompa .. 32 9N 78 10 E
Dannemora ...... 60 11N 16 49 E
Dannevirke ...... 40 12s 176 8 E
Dannhauser ..... 28 0s 30 3 E
Dansville 42 32N 77 41W
Danube,
  R. (Donau)
  =Dunárea, R. .. 45 20N 29 40 E
Danville, Ill. 40 10N 87 45W
Danville, Ky. 37 40N 84 45W
Danville, Va. 36 40N 79 20W
Danzig=
  Gdánsk .... 54 22N 18 40 E
Dapango .... 10 52N 0 12 E
Dapto .... 34 30s 150 47 E
Dar'a .... 32 37N 36 6 E
Dar-es-Salaam ... 6 50s 39 12 E
Dárāb .... 28 50N 54 30 E
Darazo .... 11 1N 10 24 E
Darband .... 34 30N 72 50 E
Darbhanga ...... 26 15N 86 3 E
D'Arcy 50 35N 122 30W
Dardanelles=
  Cannakale
  Boğazı, Str. ... 40 0N 26 20 E
Dârfûr .... 15 35N 25 0 E
Dârfûr, Reg. .... 12 35N 25 0 E
Dargai .... 34 25N 71 45 E
Dargan Ata ..... 40 40N 62 20 E
Dargaville ...... 35 57s 173 52 E
Darhan .... 49 27N 105 57 E

Darién, G. del ... 9 0N 77 0W
Darmstadt ...... 49 51N 8 40 E
Darnall .... 29 23s 31 18 E
Darnley, B. 69 30N 124 30W
Darr .... 24 34s 144 52 E
Dart, R. 50 34N 3 56W
Dartmoor .... 37 56s 141 19 E
Dartmoor, Reg. . 50 36N 4 0W
Dartmouth,
  Australia ...... 23 30s 144 40 E
Dartmouth
  Canada 44 40N 63 30W
Dartmouth, U.K. . 50 21N 3 35W
Darjeeling ...... 27 3N 88 18 E
Dark Cove 49 54N 54 5W
Darkan .... 33 19s 116 37 E
Darling, R. ..... 34 4s 141 54 E
Darling Downs .. 27 30s 150 30 E
Darling Ra...... 32 0s 116 30 E
Darlington 54 33N 1 33W
Darłowo .... 54 26N 16 23 E
Darvaza .... 40 12N 58 24 E
Darwin .... 12 20s 130 50 E
Darwin River ... 12 49s 130 58 E
Daryācheh-ye
  Reza'iyeh, L. .. 37 30N 45 30 E
Das .... 35 5N 75 4 E
Dashen, Ras, Mt.. 13 10N 38 26 E
Dashinchilen .... 47 50N 103 60 E
Dasht, R........ 25 10N 61 40 E
Dasht-e Kavir,
  Des. .... 34 30N 55 0 E
Dasht-e Lút,
  Des. .... 31 30N 58 0 E
Datia .... 25 39N 78 27 E
Daugavpils ..... 55 53N 26 32 E
Daulat Yar ..... 34 33N 65 46 E
Dauphin 51 15N 100 5W
Dauphiné, Reg. . 45 15N 5 25 E
Daura .... 13 2N 8 21 E
Davangere ...... 14 25N 75 50 E
Davao .... 7 0N 125 40 E
Davao G. .... 6 30N 125 48 E
Davenport,
  Iowa 41 30N 90 40W
Davenport,
  Wash. 47 40N 118 5W
Daventry 52 16N 1 10W
David 8 30N 82 30W
Davis, Alas. 51 52N 176 39W

Davis, Calif. 38 39N 121 45W
Davis Inlet 55 50N 60 45W
Davis Str. 68 0N 58 0W
Davos .... 46 48N 9 50 E
Dawson 64 4N 139 25W
Dawson Creek ... 55 46N 120 14W
Dawson, I. 53 50s 70 50W
Dayr al-Ghusūn .. 32 21N 35 5 E
Dayr az Zawr ... 35 20N 40 9 E
Dayral Balah ... 31 25N 34 21 E
Dayton, Ohio ... 39 45N 84 10W
Dayton, Wash. .. 46 20N 118 0W
Daytona Beach .. 29 14N 81 0W
D'Entrecasteaux,
  Pt. .... 34 50s 116 0 E
De Aar .... 30 39s 24 0 E
De Grey .... 20 30s 120 0 E
De Grey, R. ..... 20 12s 119 11 E
De Kalb 41 55N 88 45W
De Land 29 1N 81 19W
De Ridder 30 48N 93 15W
De Soto 38 8N 90 34W
Dead Sea=
  Miyet, Bahr el . 31 30N 35 30 E
Deadwood 44 25N 103 43W
Deakin .... 30 46s 129 0 E
Deal .... 51 13N 1 25 E
Dean, Forest of . 51 50N 2 35W
Deán Funes 30 20s 64 20W
Dease Arm, B.... 66 45N 120 0W
Dease Lake 58 40N 130 5W
Death Valley ... 36 0N 116 40W
Death Valley
  Nat. Mon. 36 30N 117 0W
Death Valley
  Junction 36 15N 116 30W
Deba Habe ..... 10 14N 11 20 E
Debre Markos ... 10 20N 37 40 E
Debre Tabor .... 11 50N 38 5 E
Debrecen .... 47 33N 21 42 E
Decatur, Ala. ... 34 35N 87 0W
Decatur, Ga. 33 47N 84 17W
Decatur, Ill. 39 50N 89 0W
Decatur, Ind. ... 40 52N 85 28W
Deccan, Reg. ... 18 0N 77 0 E
Decorah 43 20N 91 50W
Dédougou 12 30N 3 35W
Dee, R., Scot. .. 57 4N 3 7W
Dee, R., Wales .. 53 15N 3 7W
Deep Well ...... 24 25s 134 5 E

Deepwater ...... 29 25s 151 51 E
Deer Lake....... 49 11N 57 27W
Deer Lodge 46 25N 112 40W
Deesa .... 24 18N 72 10 E
Defiance 41 20N 84 20W
Deganya .... 32 43N 35 34 E
Degeh Bur ..... 8 14N 43 35 E
Degema .... 4 50N 6 48 E
Deggendorf .... 48 49N 12 59 E
Deh Bǐd .... 30 39N 53 11 E
Dehra Dun .... 30 20N 78 4 E
Deir Dibwan ... 31 55N 35 15 E
Dej .... 47 10N 23 52 E
Del Norte 37 47N 106 27W
Del Rio 29 15N 100 50W
Delagoa B. ..... 25 50s 32 45 E
Delano 35 48N 119 13W
Delareyville .... 26 41s 25 26 E
Delaware 40 20N 83 0W
Delaware □ 39 0N 75 40W
Delaware, R. ... 41 50N 75 15W
Delft .... 52 1N 4 22 E
Delfzijl .... 53 20N 6 55 E
Delgado, C. .... 10 45s 40 40 E
Delgo .... 20 6N 30 40 E
Delhi .... 28 38N 77 17 E
Delicias 28 10N 105 30W
Delmiro Gonveia . 9 24s 38 6W
Delong, Os. .... 76 30N 153 0 E
Deloraine ...... 41 30s 146 40 E
Delphos 40 51N 84 17W
Delray Beach ... 26 27N 80 4W
Delta 38 44N 108 5W
Delungra .... 29 40s 150 45 E
Demanda, Sa. de . 42 15N 3 0W
Deming .... 48 49N 122 13 E
Demmit 55 26N 119 54W
Demopolis 32 31N 87 50W
Dempo, Mt. .... 4 2s 103 9 E
Den Helder .... 52 54N 4 45 E
Denau .... 38 16N 67 54 E
Denbigh 53 11N 3 25W
Dendang .... 3 5s 107 54 E
Dendermonde ... 51 2N 4 7 E
Denge .... 12 52N 5 21 E
Dengi .... 9 25N 9 55 E
Denham .... 25 55s 113 32 E
Denholm 52 40N 108 0W
Denia .... 38 49N 0 8 E
Deniliquin ..... 35 32s 144 58 E

Denison 33 45N 96 33w
Denizli .... 37 46N 29 6 E
Denmark .... 34 57s 117 21 E
Denmark ■ ...... 56 0N 10 0 E
Denmark Str. 67 0N 25 0w
Denpasar .... 8 39s 115 13 E
Denton 33 13N 97 8w
Denver 39 43N 105 1w
Deoghar .... 24 30N 86 59 E
Deolali .... 19 56N 73 50 E
Deosai Mts. ..... 35 10N 75 20 E
Depot Springs ... 27 55s 120 3 E
Deputatskiy ..... 69 18N 139 54 E
Dera Ghazi Khan . 30 3N 70 38 E
Dera Ismail Khan . 31 50N 70 50 E
Dera Ismail Khan □ 31 50N 70 54 E
Derbent .... 42 3N 48 18 E
Derby, Australia .. 17 18s 123 38 E
Derby, U.K. 52 55N   1 29w
Derby □ 52 55N   1 29w
Derg, L. 53 0N   8 20w
Derna .... 32 40N 22 35 E
Derrinallum ..... 37 57s 143 13 E
Derriwong ...... 33 6s 147 21 E
Derry=
   Londonderry ... 55 0N   7 20w
Derryveagh Mts. .. 55 0N   8 40w
Derudub .... 17 31N 36 7 E
Derwent R.
   Cumbria 54 42N   3 22w
Derwent, R.
   Derby 53 26N   1 44w
Derwent, R.
   Yorks 54 13N   0 35w
Derwentwater, L. . 53 34N   3 9w
Des Moines 41 35N 93 37w
Des Moines, R. ... 41 15N 93 0w
Deseado, R. 40 0s 69 0w
Desert Center ... 33 45N 115 27w
Desna, R. .... 52 0N 33 15 E
Desolación, I. ... 53 0s 74 10w
Dessau .... 51 50N 12 14 E
Detmold .... 51 56N   8 52 E
Detroit 42 20N 83 3w
Detroit Lakes ... 46 49N 95 57w
Deurne, Belgium .. 51 13N   4 28 E
Deurne, Neth. .... 51 28N   5 47 E
Deutsche, B. .... 54 30N   7 30 E
Deux-Sèvres □ ... 46 30N   0 20w
Deva .... 45 53N 22 55 E

Deventer .... 52 15N   6 10 E
Deveron, R. 57 22N   3 0w
Devils Lake 48 7N 98 59w
Devizes 51 22N   1 59w
Devon 53 22N 113 44w
Devon □ 50 45N   3 50w
Devon I. 75 0N 87 0w
Devonport,
   Australia ..... 41 11s 146 21 E
Devonport, N.Z. .. 36 49s 174 48 E
Devonport, U.K. .. 50 22N   4 10w
Dewas .... 22 57N 76 4 E
Dewsbury 53 42N   1 37w
Deyhūk .... 33 17N 57 30 E
Deyyer .... 27 50N 51 55 E
Dezfūl .... 32 23N 48 24 E
Dezh Shāhpūr .... 35 31N 46 10 E
Dhahaban .... 21 58N 39 3 E
Dhahran=
   Az Zahrān .... 26 10N 50 7 E
Dhamar .... 14 46N 44 23 E
Dhamtari .... 20 42N 81 33 E
Dhanbad .... 23 47N 86 26 E
Dhar .... 22 36N 75 18 E
Dharmapuri ..... 12 8N 78 10 E
Dharwar .... 15 28N 75 1 E
Dhaulagiri, Mt. ... 28 42N 83 31 E
Dhenkanal ...... 20 45N 85 35 E
Dhidhimotikhon .. 41 21N 26 30 E
Dhodhekánisos, Is. 36 35N 27 10 E
Dholpur .... 26 42N 77 54 E
Dhrol .... 22 34N 70 25 E
Dhubri .... 26 1N 89 59 E
Dhula .... 15 5N 48 5 E
Dhulia .... 20 54N 74 47 E
Diamante 32 5s 60 35w
Diamantina 18 5s 43 40w
Diamantina, R. ... 26 45s 139 10 E
Diamantino 14 25s 56 27w
Diamond Harbour . 22 11N 88 14 E
Diapangou ...... 12 5N   0 10 E
Dibaya Lubue .... 4 12s 19 54 E
Dibba .... 25 45N 56 16 E
Dibi .... 4 12N 41 58 E
Dibrugarh ...... 27 29N 94 55 E
Dickinson 46 53N 102 47w
Didsbury 51 40N 114 8w
Diefenbaker L. ... 51 0N 106 55w
Diego Garcia, I. .. 7 20s 72 25 E
Diego Ramirez,

Is. 56 30s 68 44w
Diégo-Suarez ... 12 16s 49 17 E
Diégo-Suarez □ ... 14 0s 49 0 E
Dieppe .... 49 56N   1 5 E
Differdange ..... 49 32s   5 32 E
Digby 44 41N 65 50w
Dighinala .... 23 15N 92 5 E
Digne .... 44 6N   6 14 E
Dihang, R. ...... 27 30N 96 30 E
Dijlah, Nahr .... 30 90N 47 50 E
Dijon .... 47 19N   5 1 E
Dikson .... 73 30N 80 35 E
Dikwa .... 12 2N 13 56 E
Dili .... 8 33s 125 35 E
Dillon, Mont. 45 13N 112 38w
Dillon, S.C. 34 25N 79 22w
Dimashq .... 33 30N 36 18 E
Dimbokro 6 39N   4 42w
Dimboola .... 36 27s 142 2 E
Dimitrovgrad,
   Bulgaria ...... 42 3N 25 36 E
Dimitrovgrad,
   U.S.S.R. ...... 54 25N 49 33 E
Dinagat, I. ...... 10 10N 125 35 E
Dinajpur .... 35 38N 88 38 E
Dinan 48 27N   2 2w
Dinant .... 50 16N   4 55 E
Dinar .... 38 4N 30 10 E
Dinar, Kuh-e,
   Mt. .... 30 48N 51 40 E
Dinara Planina,
   Mts. .... 43 50N 16 35 E
Dinard 48 38N   2 4w
Dinaric Alps,
   Mts. 43 50N 16 35w
Dindigul .... 10 21N 77 58 E
Dingle 52 8N 10 15w
Dingle, B. 52 5N 10 15w
Dingo .... 23 39s 149 20 E
Dinguiraye 11 18N 10 43w
Dingwall 57 35N   4 29w
Dinosaur Nat.
   Mon. 40 32N 108 58w
Dinuba 36 32N 119 23w
Diourbel 14 40N 16 15w
Dipolog .... 8 36N 123 20 E
Dire Dawa ..... 9 37N 41 52 E
Diriamba .... 11 53N 86 15 E
Dirico .... 17 50s 20 42 E
Dirk Hartog, I. .... 25 48s 113 0 E

Dirranbandi ..... 28 35s 148 14 E
Disappointment.C. 46 18N 124 3w
Disappointment, L. 23 30s 122 50 E
Discovery 63 0N 115 0w
Discovery, B. .... 38 12s 141 7 E
Disina .... 11 35N   9 50 E
Disko, I. 69 50N 53 30w
Diss .... 52 23N   1 6 E
Disteghil Sar, Mt. . 36 22N 75 12 E
Districto Federal □ 15 45s 47 45w
Distrito
   Federal □ 19 15N 99 10w
Diu .... 20 43N 70 69 E
Divnoye .... 45 55N 43 27 E
Dixon 41 50N 89 29w
Dixon Entrance .. 54 25N 132 30w
Diyarbakir ...... 37 55N 40 14 E
Djajapura=
   Jayapura ..... 2 28s 140 38 E
Djakarta=
   Jakarta ...... 6 9s 106 49 E
Djambala .... 2 33s 14 45 E
Djangeru .... 2 20s 116 29 E
Djawa, I.=
   Java, I. ...... 7 0s 110 0 E
Djelfa .... 34 30N   3 20 E
Djema .... 6 3N 25 19 E
Djerba, I. de ... 33 56N 11 0 E
Djerid, Chott el,
   Reg. .... 33 50N   8 30 E
Djibouti .... 11 36N 43 9 E
Djibouti ■ ...... 11 30N 42 15 E
Djidjelli .... 36 52N   5 50 E
Djirlagne .... 11 44N 108 15 E
Djolu .... 0 37N 22 21 E
Djougou .... 9 42N   1 40 E
Djourab, Erg du . 16 40N 18 50 E
Djugu .... 1 55N 30 30 E
Djúpivogur 64 40N 14 10w
Dnepr, R. ...... 46 30N 32 18 E
Dneprodzerzhinsk . 48 30N 34 37 E
Dnepropetrovsk ... 48 30N 35 0 E
Dnestr, R. ...... 46 18N 30 17 E
Dnieper, R.=
   Dnepr, R. ..... 46 30N 32 18 E
Dniester, R.=
   Dnestr, R. ..... 46 18N 30 17 E
Doba .... 8 40N 16 51 E
Doberai, Jazirah .. 1 25s 133 0 E
Doblas 37 5s 64 0w

Dobo .... 5 46s 134 13 E
Dobruja, Reg. .... 44 30N 28 30 E
Dodecanese Is.=
   Dhodhekánisos,
   Is. .... 36 35N 27 10 E
Dodge City 37 45N 100 1w
Dodoma .... 6 11s 35 45 E
Dodsland 51 48N 108 49w
Doetinchem .... 51 58N   6 17 E
Dog Creek 51 35N 122 18w
Dogondoutchi ... 13 38N   4 2 E
Doha .... 25 15N 51 36 E
Dohad .... 22 50N 74 15 E
Dohazari .... 22 10N 92 5 E
Dolbeau 48 53N 72 14w
Dôle .... 47 6N   5 30 E
Dolgellau 52 44N   3 53w
Dolisie .... 4 12s 12 41 E
Dolo, Somali Rep. . 4 13N 42 8 E
Dolomiti, Mts. ... 46 25N 11 50 E
Dolores, Arg. 36 19s 57 40w
Dolores, Uruguay . 33 33s 58 13w
Dolphin, C. 51 15s 58 58w
Dolphin &
   Union Str. ... 69 5N 114 45w
Doma .... 8 25N   8 18 E
Dombarovskiy ... 50 46N 59 39 E
Dombås .... 62 5N   9 8 E
Dombes, Reg. ... 46 0N   5 3 E
Dominica, I. 15 30N 61 20w
Dominica Pass .. 15 10N 61 20w
Dominican Rep. ■ 19 0N 70 40w
Domodossola ... 46 7N   8 17 E
Don, R., Eng. 53 39N   0 59w
Don, R., Scot. ... 57 10N   2 4w
Don, R., U.S.S.R. . 47 4N 39 18 E
Donaghadee ... 54 39N   5 33w
Donalda 52 35N 112 34w
Donau, R.=
   Dunárea, R. ... 45 20N 29 40 E
Donauwörth .... 48 43N 10 46 E
Doncaster 53 32N   1 7w
Dondra Hd. .... 5 55N 80 35 E
Donegal 54 39N   8 7w
Donegal □ 54 50N   8 8w
Donegal, B. 54 30N   8 30w
Donetsk .... 48 0N 37 48 E
Dong Hoi ...... 17 18N 106 36 E
Dongara .... 29 15s 114 56 E
Dongola .... 19 9N 30 22 E

Donnacona 46 40N 71 47W
Donnelly's Crossing 35 43S 173 33 E
Donnybrook ...... 33 35S 115 48 E
Donor's Hills ..... 18 42S 140 33 E
Doodlakine .....¡,. 31 35S 117 28 E
Doon, R. 55 26N 4 38W
Dor .... 32 37N 34 55 E
Dora Báltea, R. .. 45 11N 8 5 E
Dorchester 50 43N 2 26W
Dorchester, C. 65 29N 77 30W
Dordogne □ ...... 45 10N 0 45 E
Dordogne, R. 45 2N 0 35W
Dordrecht, Neth. .. 51 49N 107 45W
Dordrecht, S. Afr. . 31 20S 27 3 E
Dore, Mt. .... 45 32N 2 50 E
Dore Lake 54 56N 107 45W
Dori 14 3N 0 2W
Dorion 45 23N 74 3W
Dornie 57 17N 5 30W
Dornoch 57 52N 4 2W
Dornoch Firth ... 57 52N 4 2W
Döröö Nuur, L. .. 47 40N 93 30 E
Dorre, I. .... 25 9S 113 7 E
Dorrigo .... 30 21S 152 43 E
Dorset □ 50 47N 2 20W
Dortmund .... 51 31N 7 28 E
Dos Bahias, C. .. 44 55S 65 32W
Doshi .... 35 37N 68 41 E
Dosso .... 13 3N 3 12 E
Dot 50 12N 121 25W
Dothan 31 13N 85 24W
Douai........... 50 22N 3 4 E
Douala .... 4 3N 9 42 E
Douarnenez 48 6N 4 20W
Doubs □ .... 47 10N 6 25 E
Doubtless, B. .... 34 55S 173 27 E
Doucet 48 15N 76 35W
Douentza 14 58N 2 48W
Douglas, S. Afr. ... 29 4S 23 46 E
Douglas, U.K. 54 9N 4 25W
Douglas, Ariz. ... 31 21N 109 33W
Douglas, Ga. 31 31N 82 51W
Douglas, Wyo. ... 42 45N 105 24W
Dounreay 58 40N 3 28W
Dourada, Sa. ... 13 10S 48 45W
Douro, R. 41 8N 8 40W
Douro
  Litoral, Reg. 41 5N 8 20W
Dove, R. 54 20N 0 55W
Dover, Australia . 43 19S 147 1 E

Dover, U.K. ...... 51 8N 1 19 E
Dover, Del. 39 10N 75 32W
Dover, N.H. 43 12N 70 56W
Dover, Ohio 40 32N 81 30W
Dover, Str. of ..... 51 0N 1 30 E
Dovey, R. 52 32N 4 0W
Dovrefjell, Mts. .. 62 6N 9 25 E
Dowagiac 41 59N 86 6W
Dowlátábád ..... 28 18N 56 40 E
Downham Market . 52 36N 0 23 E
Downpatrick 54 20N 5 43W
Draguignan ..... 43 32N 6 28 E
Drake Pass....... 58 0S 70 0W
Drakensberg, Mts.. 27 0S 30 0 E
Dráma .... 41 9N 24 8 E
Drammen .... 59 44N 10 15 E
Drava, R. .... 45 33N 18 55 E
Drayton Valley ... 53 13N 114 59W
Drenthe □ .... 52 45N 6 30 E
Dresden .... 51 3N 13 44 E
Dreux .... 48 44N 1 22 E
Driffield 54 0N 0 27W
Drina, R. .... 44 53N 19 21 E
Drini, R. .... 41 17N 20 2 E
Drøbak .... 59 39N 10 48 E
Drogheda 53 43N 6 21W
Drogobych ...... 49 20N 23 30 E
Droitwich 52 16N 2 9W
Dróme □ .... 44 35N 5 10 E
Dromedary, C. ... 36 17S 150 10 E
Dronfield 53 19S 1 27W
Dronning Maud
  Ld. .... 75 0S 10 0 E
Drouin .... 38 8S 145 51 E
Drumheller 51 28N 112 42W
Drummondville ... 45 53N 72 30W
Druzhina .... 68 11N 145 5 E
Dryden 49 47N 92 50W
Drysdale, R. ..... 13 59S 126 51 E
Dschang .... 5 27N 10 4 E
Du Bois 41 7N 78 46W
Du Quoin 38 0N 89 10W
Duaringa .... 23 42S 149 42 E
Dubá .... 27 10N 35 40 E
Dubawnt L. 63 0N 102 0W
Dubayy .... 25 18N 55 18 E
Dubbo .... 32 15S 148 36 E
Dublin, Eire 53 20N 6 15W
Dublin, U.S.A. 32 32N 82 54W

Dublin □ 53 20N 6 15W
Dubois 44 10N 112 14W
Dubovka .... 49 5N 44 50 E
Dubreka 9 48N 13 31W
Dubrovnik ...... 42 38N 18 7 E
Dubrovskoye .... 47 28N 42 40 E
Dubuque 42 30N 90 41W
Duchesne 40 10N 110 24W
Duchess .... 21 22S 139 52 E
Ducie I. 24 47S 124 50W
Duck Lake 52 47N 106 13W
Duck Mt. Prov.
  Park 51 36N 100 55W
Dudinka .... 69 25N 86 15 E
Dudley 52 30N 2 5W
Duero, R. 41 37N 4 25W
Dufftown 57 26N 3 9W
Dugi Otok, I. .... 44 0N 15 0 E
Duisburg .... 51 27N 6 42 E
Duiwelskloof .... 23 42S 30 10 E
Dukhan .... 25 25N 50 50 E
Duku .... 10 43N 10 43 E
Dulce, G. 8 40N 83 20W
Dullstroom ..... 25 24S 30 7 E
Dululu .... 23 48S 150 15 E
Duluth 46 48N 92 10W
Dum Duma ..... 27 40N 95 40 E
Dumai .... 1 35N 101 20 E
Dumas 35 50N 101 58W
Dumbarton 55 58N 4 35W
Dumbleyung .... 33 17S 117 42 E
Dumfries 55 4N 3 37W
Dumfries-
  Galloway □ 55 12N 3 30W
Dumosa .... 35 52S 143 6 E
Dumyát .... 31 25N 31 48 E
Dun Laoghaire ... 53 17N 6 9W
Dun Leary=
  Dun Laoghaire .. 53 17N 6 9W
Dunaföldvár .... 46 50N 18 57 E
Dunárea, R. ..... 45 20N 29 40 E
Dunaújváros .... 47 0N 18 57 E
Dunback .... 42 23S 170 36 E
Dunbar 56 0N 2 32W
Dunblane, Canada . 51 11N 106 52W
Dunblane, U.K. ... 56 10N 3 58W
Duncan, Canada .. 48 45N 123 40W
Duncan, U.S.A. ... 34 25N 98 0W
Duncan Town 22 20N 75 80W
Dundalk, U.K. ... 53 55N 6 45W

Dundas 43 17N 79 59W
Dundas, L. ...... 32 35S 121 50 E
Dundas, Str. .... 11 15S 131 35 E
Dundee,
  S. Africa ...... 28 11S 30 15 E
Dundee, U.K. 56 29N 3 0W
Dundrum 54 17N 5 50W
Dundrum, B. 54 12N 5 40W
Dunedin .... 45 50S 170 33 E
Dunfermline 56 5N 3 28W
Dungannon 54 30N 6 47W
Dungannon □ 54 30N 6 47W
Dungarvan 52 6N 7 40W
Dunbure Shan,
  Mts. .... 35 0N 90 0 E
Dungeness, Pt. ... 50 54N 0 59 E
Dungu .... 3 42N 28 32 E
Dunkeld, Australia 37 40S 142 22 E
Dunkeld, U.K. 56 34N 3 36W
Dunkerque ...... 51 2N 2 20 E
Dunkery Beacon .. 51 15N 3 37W
Dunkirk 42 30N 79 18W
Dunkwa, Ghana .. 6 0N 1 47W
Dunkwa, Ghana ... 5 30N 1 0W
Dunmara .... 16 42S 133 25 E
Dunmore 41 27N 75 38W
Dunmore Hd. 53 37N 8 44W
Dunn 35 18N 78 36W
Dunnet Hd. 58 38N 3 22W
Dunoon 55 57N 4 56W
Duns 55 47N 2 20W
Dunsmuir 41 0N 122 10W
Dunstable 51 53N 0 31W
D'Urville, I. ..... 40 50S 173 55 E
Dúra .... 31 30N 35 2 E
Durack, R. ...... 15 33S 127 52 E
Durance, R. ..... 43 55N 4 44 E
Durango, Mexico .. 24 3N 104 39W
Durango, Sp. 43 13N 2 40W
Durango, U.S.A. ... 37 10N 107 50W
Durango □ 25 0N 105 0W
Duranillin ...... 33 30S 116 45 E
Durant 34 0N 96 25W
Durazno 33 25S 56 38W
Durban .... 29 49S 31 1 E
Durg .... 21 15N 81 22 E
Durham, Canada .. 44 10N 80 48W
Durham, U.K. 54 47N 1 34W
Durham, U.S.A. ... 36 0N 78 55W
Durham □ 54 42N 1 45W

Durrësi .... 41 19N 19 28 E
Dushak .... 37 20N 60 10 E
Dushanbe .... 38 40N 68 50 E
Dusky, Sd. ...... 45 47S 166 29 E
Düsseldorf ...... 51 15N 6 46 E
Dutch Harbor 53 54N 166 35W
Duzce .... 40 50N 31 10 E
Dwarka .... 22 18N 69 8 E
Dwellingup ..... 32 38S 115 58 E
Dyersburg 36 2N 89 20W
Dyfed □ 52 0N 4 30W
Dzerzhinsk ..... 56 15N 43 15 E
Dzhalal Abad .... 41 0N 73 0 E
Dzhalinda ...... 53 50N 124 0 E
Dzhambul ...... 43 10N 71 0 E
Dzhankoi .... 45 40N 34 30 E
Dzhardzhan .... 68 43N 124 2 E
Dzhelinde ...... 70 0N 114 20 E
Dzhezkazgan ... 47 10N 67 40 E
Dzhizak .... 40 20N 68 0 E
Dzhugdzhur
  Khrebet, Ra.... 57 30N 138 0 E
Dzungaria, Reg... 44 10N 88 0 E
Dzungarian Gate=
  Dzungarskiye
  Vorota .... 45 25N 82 25 E
Dzungarskiye
  Vorota .... 45 25N 82 25 E
Dzuunbulag ..... 46 58N 115 30 E
Dzuunmod ...... 47 45N 106 58 E

E

Eagle 64 44N 141 29W
Eagle Pass 28 45N 100 35W
Eaglehawk ...... 36 43S 144 16 E
Ealing 51 30N 0 19W
Earlimart 35 57N 119 14W
Earn, L. 56 23N 4 14W
Earnslaw, Mt. ... 44 32S 168 27 E
Easley 34 52N 82 35W
East, C. .... 37 42S 178 35 E
East Angus 45 30N 71 40W
East Bengal, Reg. .. 23 0N 90 0 E
East C. 65 50N 168 0W
East Chicago 41 40N 87 30W

East China Sea.... 30 0N 126 0 E
East Cleveland ... 41 32N 81 35W
East Falkland . 51 30s 58 30W
East Germany ■ . 52 0N 12 30 E
East Grand
  Forks 47 55N 97 5W
East Indies, Is. .... 0 0 120 0 E
East Kilbride ... 55 48N 4 12W
East Lansing 42 44N 84 37W
East Liverpool .. 40 39N 80 35W
East London .... 33 0s 27 55 E
East Main 52 20N 78 30W
East Orange 40 45N 74 15W
East Pine 55 48N 120 5W
East Point 33 40N 84 28W
East Retford 53 19N 0 55W
East St. Lovis ... 38 36N 90 10W
East Siberian
  Sea .... 73 0N 160 0 E
East Sussex □ ... 50 55N 0 20 E
Eastbourne, N.Z. . 41 19s 174 55 E
Eastbourne, U.K. . 50 46N 0 18 E
Eastend 49 32N 108 50W
Easter Is......... 27 0s 109 0w
Eastern Ghats, Mts. 15 0N 80 0 E
Eastern □, Ghana . 6 20N 1 0W
Eastern
  Malaysia □ ..... 3 0N 112 30 E
Eastleigh 50 58N 1 21W
Eastmain, R. 52 20N 78 30W
Easton 40 41N 75 15W
Eastport 44 57N 67 0W
Eastview 45 27N 75 40W
Eatonia 51 20N 109 25W
Eau Claire 44 46N 91 30W
Ebbw Vale 51 47N 3 12W
Ebden .... 36 10s 147 1 E
Ebeltoft .... 56 12N 10 41 E
Eberswalde .... 52 49N 13 50 E
Eboli .... 40 39N 15 2 E
Ebro, R. .... 40 43N 0 54 E
Echuca .... 36 3s 144 46 E
Ecija 37 30N 5 10W
Ecuador ■ 2 0s 78 0W
Ed Dâmer .... 17 27N 34 0 E
Ed Debba .... 18 0N 30 51 E
Ed Dueim .... 10 10N 28 20 E
Edah .... 28 16s 117 10 E
Edam .... 52 31N 5 3 E
Eday, I. 59 11N 2 47W

Eddystone Rock .. 50 11N 4 16W
Ede, Neth. ...... 52 4N 5 40 E
Ede, Nigeria .... 7 45N 4 29 E
Edea .... 3 51N 10 9 E
Eden, R. 54 57N 3 1W
Edenburg .... 29 43s 25 58 E
Edenderry 53 21N 7 3W
Edenville .... 27 37s 27 34 E
Eder, R. .... 51 13N 9 27 E
Edge Hill 52 7N 1 28W
Edgeley 46 27N 98 41W
Edgemont 43 15N 103 53W
Edhessa .... 40 48N 22 5 E
Edievale .... 45 49s 169 22 E
Edinburg 26 22N 98 10W
Edinburgh 55 57N 3 12W
Edirne .... 41 40N 26 45 E
Edith River .... 14 12s 132 2 E
Edmond 35 37N 97 30W
Edmonton,
  Australia ..... 17 2s 145 45 E
Edmonton, Canada 53 30N 113 30W
Edmundston 47 23N 68 20W
Edremit .... 39 40N 27 0 E
Edson 53 40N 116 28W
Edward, L.=Idi
  Amin Dada, L. ... 0 25s 29 40 E
Edwards Plat. ... 30 30N 101 5W
Eekloo .... 51 11N 3 33 E
Eersterus .... 25 45s 28 20 E
Effingham 39 8N 88 30W
Égadi, Is. .... 37 55N 12 10 E
Eganville 45 32N 77 5W
Eger .... 47 53N 20 27 E
Egersund=
  Eigersund ..... 58 2N 6 1 E
Eginbah .... 20 53s 119 47 E
Egmont, Mt. .... 39 17s 174 5 E
Egume .... 7 30N 7 14 E
Egvekind 66 19N 179 10W
Egypt ■ .... 28 0N 31 0 E
Eha Amufu .... 6 30N 7 40 E
Ehime □ .... 33 30N 132 40 E
Eidsvold .... 25 25s 151 12 E
Eidsvoll .... 60 19N 11 14 E
Eifel, Mts. .... 50 10N 6 45 E
Eiffel Flats .... 18 20s 30 0 E
Eigersund .... 58 2N 6 1 E
Eigg, I........... 56 54N 6 10W
Eighty Mile
  Beach .... 19 30s 120 40 E

Eil, L. .... 56 50N 5 15 E
Eildon, L. .... 37 10s 146 0 E
Einasleigh .... 18 32s 144 5 E
Eindhoven .... 51 26N 5 30 E
Eire ■=
  Irish Rep. ■ ... 53 0N 8 0W
Eisenerz .... 47 32N 15 54 E
Eizariya .... 31 47N 35 15 E
Ejura .... 7 25N 1 25 E
Ekenäs .... 59 58N 23 26 E
Eket 4 38N 7 56W
Eketahuna .... 40 38s 175 43 E
Ekibastuz .... 51 40N 75 22 E
Ekimchan 53 0N 133 0W
El Aaiun 27 0N 12 0W
El Alamein .... 30 48N 28 58 E
El Aricha 34 13N 1 16W
El Ariha .... 31 52N 35 27 E
El Arish .... 17 49s 146 1 E
El'Arîsh .... 31 8N 33 50 E
El Asnam .... 36 10N 1 20 E
El Bawiti .... 28 25N 28 45 E
El Bayadh .... 33 40N 1 1 E
El Cajon 32 49N 117 0W
El Campo 29 10N 96 20W
El Centro 32 50N 115 40W
El Cuy 39 55s 68 25W
El Dere .... 3 50N 47 8 E
El Diviso 1 22N 78 14W
El Djouf .... 20 0N 11 30 E
El Dorado, Ark. .. 33 10N 92 40W
El Dorado, Kans. . 37 55N 96 56W
El Dorado,
  Venezuela 6 55N 61 30W
El Escorial 40 35N 4 7W
El Faiyûm .... 29 19N 30 50 E
El Fâsher .... 13 33N 25 26 E
El Ferrol 43 29N 3 14W
El Geneina .... 13 27N 22 45 E
El Geteina .... 14 50N 32 27 E
El Gezira .... 14 0N 33 0 E
El Gîza .... 30 0N 31 10 E
El Goléa .... 30 30N 2 50 E
El Harrach .... 36 45N 3 5 E
El Iskandarîya .. 31 0N 30 0 E
El Istwa'ya □ .... 5 0N 32 0 E
El Jadida 33 16N 9 31W
El Jebelein .... 12 30N 32 45 E
El Kef .... 36 12N 8 47 E

El Khandaq .... 18 30N 30 30 E
El Khârga .... 25 30N 30 33 E
El Khartûm .... 15 31N 32 35 E
El Khartum
  Bahrî .... 15 40N 32 31 E
El Mafâza .... 13 38N 34 30 E
El Mahalla el
  Kubra .... 31 0N 31 0 E
El Mansura .... 31 0N 31 19 E
El Minyâ .... 28 7N 30 33 E
El Niybo .... 4 32N 39 59 E
El Obeid .... 13 8N 30 18 E
El Oro 3 30s 79 50W
El Oued .... 33 20N 6 58 E
El Paso 31 50N 106 30W
El Progreso 15 26N 87 51W
El Qâhira .... 30 1N 31 14 E
El Qantara .... 30 51N 32 20 E
El Qasr .... 25 44N 28 42 E
El Qubba .... 11 10N 27 5 E
El Reno 35 30N 98 0W
El Suweis .... 29 58N 32 31 E
El Tigre 8 55N 64 15W
El Tocuyo 9 47N 69 48W
El Turbio 51 30s 72 40W
El Uqsur .... 25 41N 32 38 E
El Vigia 8 38N 71 39W
El Wâhat el-
  Dakhla .... 26 0N 27 50 E
El Wâhât el
  Khârga .... 24 0N 23 0 E
El Wak .... 2 49N 40 56 E
Elaine .... 37 44s 144 2 E
Elat .... 5 40s 133 5 E
Elazig .... 38 37N 39 22 E
Elba, I. .... 42 48N 10 15 E
Elbasani .... 41 9N 20 9 E
Elbe, R. .... 53 50N 9 0 E
Elbert, Mt. 39 12N 106 36W
Elberton 34 7N 82 51W
Elbeuf .... 49 17N 1 2 E
Elbląg .... 54 10N 19 25 E
Elbrus, Mt. .... 43 30N 42 30 E
Elburz Mts.=
  Alberz, Reshteh-
  Ye-Kakha-Ye ... 36 0N 52 0 E
Elche de la
  Sierra 38 27N 2 3W
Eldama .... 0 3N 35 43 E
Elde, R. .... 53 17N 12 40 E

Eldorado 59 35N 108 30W
Eldoret .... 0 30N 35 5 E
Elefantes, R. .... 24 10s 32 40 E
Elele .... 5 5N 6 50 E
Elephant Butte
  Res. 33 45N 107 30W
Eleuthera I. 25 0N 76 20W
Elgin, U.K. 57 39N 3 20W
Elgin, Ill. 42 0N 88 20W
Elgin, Ore. 45 37N 118 0W
Elgin, Tex. 30 21N 97 22W
Elgon, Mt. .... 1 10N 34 30 E
Eliase .... 8 10s 130 55 E
Elisabethville=
  Lubumbashi .... 11 32s 27 38 E
Elista .... 46 16N 44 14 E
Elizabeth,
  Australia .... 34 45s 138 39 E
Elizabeth, U.S.A. . 40 37N 74 12W
Elizabeth City .. 36 18N 76 16W
Elizabethton 36 20N 82 13W
Elizabethtown .. 37 40N 85 54W
Elk City 35 25N 99 25W
Elk Lake 47 40N 80 25W
Elk Point 54 10N 110 55W
Elkhart 41 42N 85 55W
Elkhorn 50 0N 101 11W
Elkhovo .... 42 10N 26 40 E
Elkins 38 53N 79 53W
Elko, Canada .. 49 20N 115 10W
Elko, U.S.A. .. 40 40N 115 50W
Ellen Mt. 38 4N 110 56W
Ellendale,
  Australia .... 17 56s 124 48 E
Ellendale, U.S.A. . 46 3N 98 30W
Ellensburg 47 0N 120 30W
Ellesmere I. .. 79 30N 80 0W
Ellesmere Port .. 53 17N 2 55W
Ellice Is=
  Tuvalu ■ .... 8 0s 176 0 E
Elliot .... 31 22s 27 48 E
Elliot Lake .. 46 35N 82 35W
Elliott .... 41 5s 145 38 E
Elliston .... 33 39s 134 55 E
Ellon 57 21N 2 5W
Ellore=Eluru .. 16 48N 81 8 E
Ellsworth 38 47N 98 15W
Ellsworth Ld. .. 75 30s 80 0W
Ellwood City .. 40 52N 80 19W
Elma .... 47 0N 123 30 E

Elmali .... 36 44N 29 56 E
Elmenteita .... 0 32 s 36 14 E
Elmhurst 41 52N 87 58w
Elmina 5 5N 1 21w
Elmira 42 8N 76 49w
Elmore .... 36 30 s 144 37 E
Elrose 51 20N 108 0w
Elsinore 33 40N 117 15w
Eltham .... 39 26 s 174 19 E
Eluru .... 16 48N 81 8 E
Elvas 38 50N 7 17w
Elverum .... 60 55N 11 34 E
Elwood 40 20N 85 50w
Ely, U.K. .... 52 24N 0 16 E
Ely, U.S.A. 47 54N 91 52w
Elyashiv .... 32 23N 34 55 E
Elyria 41 22N 82 8w
Emba .... 48 50N 58 8 E
Embarcación ..... 23 10 s 64 0w
Embu .... 0 32 s 37 38 E
Emden .... 53 22N 7 12 E
Emerald .... 23 30 s 148 11 E
Emerson 49 0N 97 10w
Emilia Romagna □ 44 33N 10 40 E
Emmen .... 52 48N 6 57 E
Emmett .... 24 45 s 144 30w
Empalme 28 1N 110 49w
Empangeni ...... 28 50 s 31 52 E
Empédrado ...... 28 0 s 58 46w
Emporia, Kans. ... 38 25N 96 16w
Emporia, Va. 36 41N 77 32w
Emporium 41 30N 78 17w
Ems, R. .... 51 9N 9 26 E
'En Kerem ...... 31 47N 35 6 E
En Nahud .... 12 45N 28 25 E
'En Yahav ...... 30 37N 35 11 E
Ena .... 35 25N 137 25 E
Encarnación ..... 27 15 s 56 0w
Encarnación de
   Diaz 21 30N 102 20w
Enchi 5 53N 2 48w
Encontrados 9 3N 72 14w
Ende .... 8 45 s 121 30 E
Endeavour, Str. ... 10 45 s 142 0 E
Enderby 50 35N 119 10w
Enderby, I. ..... 20 35 s 116 30 E
Enderby Ld. ..... 66 0 s 53 0 E
Endicott 42 6N 76 2w
Enfield 51 38N 0 4w
Engaño, C.,

Dom. Rep. 18 30N 68 20w
Engaño, C.,
   Philippines ... 18 35N 122 23 E
Engcobo .... 31 39 s 28 1 E
Engels .... 51 28N 46 6 E
Enggano .... 5 20 s 102 40 E
England ■ 53 0N 2 0w
Englee 50 45N 56 5w
Englehart 47 49N 79 52w
Englewood, Colo. . 39 39N 104 59w
English, R. 50 12N 95 0w
English Bazar .... 24 58N 88 21 E
English Chan. 50 0N 2 30w
Enid 36 26N 97 52w
Enkeldoorn ...... 19 2 s 30 52 E
Enkhuizen ...... 52 42N 5 17 E
Enna .... 37 34N 14 15 E
Ennedi .... 17 15N 22 0 E
Ennis, Eire 52 51N 8 59w
Ennis, U.S.A. 32 15N 96 40w
Enniscorthy 52 30N 6 35w
Enniskillen 54 20N 7 40w
Ennistymon 52 56N 9 18w
Enontekio ...... 68 23 s 23 38 E
Enschede .... 52 13N 6 53 E
Entebbe .... 0 4N 32 28 E
Enterprise 45 25N 117 17w
Entre Rios ...... 14 57 s 37 20 E
Entre Rios, Reg. .. 30 0 s 58 30w
Enugu .... 6 30N 7 30 E
Enugu Ezike ..... 7 0N 7 29 E
Eólie o
   Lípari, I. ..... 38 30N 14 50 E
Epe, Neth. ...... 52 21N 5 59 E
Epe, Nigeria ..... 6 36N 3 59 E
Épernay .... 49 3N 3 56 E
Ephraim 39 30N 111 37w
Épinal .... 48 19N 6 27 E
Epping .... 51 42N 0 8 E
Equatorial
   Guinea ■ ..... 2 0N 8 0 E
Er Rahad .... 12 45N 30 32 E
Er Rif 35 1N 4 1w
Er Roseires ..... 11 55N 34 30 E
Eradu .... 28 40 s 115 2 E
Ercha .... 69 45N 147 20 E
Erdene .... 44 30N 111 10 E
Erdenedalay ..... 46 3N 105 1 E
Erechim .... 27 35 s 52 15w
Ereğli .... 41 15N 31 30 E

Erfurt .... 50 58N 11 2 E
Ergani .... 38 26N 39 49 E
Ergeni
   Vozvyshennost . 47 0N 44 0 E
Erhlien .... 43 42N 112 2 E
Eriboll, I. 58 28N 4 41w
Erie 42 10N 80 7w
Erie, L. 42 30N 82 0w
Erigavo .... 10 35N 47 35 E
Eriksdale 50 52N 98 5w
Erimanthos, Mt... 37 57N 21 50 E
Erith 53 25N 116 46w
Eritrea □ .... 14 0N 41 0 E
Erlangen .... 49 35N 11 2 E
Erldunda .... 25 14 s 133 12 E
Ermelo, Neth. ... 52 35N 5 35 E
Ermelo, S. Afr. ... 26 31 s 29 59 E
Ernakulam ...... 9 59N 76 19 E
Erne, L. 54 14N 7 30w
Erne, R. 54 30N 8 16w
Erode .... 11 24N 77 45 E
Erramala Hills ... 15 30N 78 15 E
Eruwa .... 7 33N 3 26 E
Erzgebirge Mts... 50 25N 13 0 E
Erzurum .... 39 57N 41 15 E
Es Sider .... 30 50N 18 21 E
Esbjerg .... 55 29N 8 29 E
Escanaba 45 44N 87 5w
Esch .... 49 32N 6 0 E
Escondido 33 9N 117 4w
Escuintla 14 20N 90 48w
Eshowe .... 28 50 s 31 30 E
Eshta'ol .... 31 47N 35 0 E
Esk, R., Eng. 54 29N 0 37w
Esk, R., Scot. 54 58N 3 2w
Eskilstuna ...... 59 22N 16 32 E
Eskimo Point 61 10N 94 15w
Eskişehir .... 39 50N 30 35 E
Esla, R. 41 29N 6 3w
Esmeraldas 1 0N 79 40w
Espanola 46 15N 81 46w
Espe .... 44 0N 74 5 E
Esperance ...... 33 51 s 121 53 E
Esperance, B. .... 33 48 s 121 51 E
Esperanza ...... 31 29 s 61 3w
Espichel, C. 38 22N 9 16w
Espinal 4 9N 74 53w

Espinhaço, Sa. do . 17 30 s 43 30w
Espíritu Santo,
   B. del 19 15N 79 40w
Espíritu Santo □ .. 19 30 s 40 30w
Esquel .... 42 40 s 71 20w
Essaouira 31 32N 9 42w
Essen, Belgium ... 51 28N 4 28 E
Essen,
   W. Germany .. 51 28N 6 59 E
Essex □ .... 51 48N 0 30 E
Esslingen .... 48 43N 9 19 E
Essonne □ ...... 48 30N 2 20 E
Estados,
   I. de los ..... 54 40 s 64 30w
Estância, Brazil .. 11 15 s 37 30w
Estancia, U.S.A. .. 34 50N 106 1w
Estcourt .... 28 58 s 29 53 E
Estelí 13 9N 86 22w
Esterhazy 50 37N 102 5w
Estevan 49 10N 103 0w
Estheville 43 25N 94 50w
Estonian S.S.R. □ . 48 30N 25 30 E
Estoril 38 42N 9 23w
Estrêla, Sa. da ... 40 10N 7 45w
Estremadura, Reg. 39 0N 9 0w
Estrondo, Sa. de .. 7 20 s 48 0w
Esztergom ...... 47 47N 18 44 E
Etawah .... 26 48N 79 6 E
Ethel Creek ..... 22 55 s 120 11 E
Ethelbert 51 32N 100 25w
Ethiopia ■ ...... 8 0N 40 0 E
Ethiopian
   Highlands, Mts. 10 0N 37 0 E
Etive, L. 56 30N 5 12w
Etna, Mt. .... 37 45N 15 0 E
Etoshapan ...... 18 40 s 16 30 E
Ettrick, R. 55 31N 2 55w
Etzatlán 20 48N 104 5w
Euclid 41 32N 81 31w
Eucumbene, L. ... 36 2 s 148 40 E
Eufaula 31 55N 85 11w
Eugene 44 0N 123 8w
Eunice 30 35N 92 28w
Eupen .... 50 37N 6 3 E
Euphrates, R.=
   Furat, Nahr al .. 33 30N 43 0 E
Eure □ .... 49 6N 1 0 E
Eureka, Calif. 40 50N 124 0w
Eureka, Nev. 39 32N 116 2w
Eureka, Utah 40 0N 112 0w

Eure-et-Loir □ .... 48 22N 1 30 E
Euroa .... 36 44 s 145 35 E
Europa, Île ...... 22 20 s 40 22 E
Europa, Picos de .. 43 10N 5 0w
Europa, Pta. de ... 36 3N 5 21w
Europe .... 50 0N 20 0 E
Europoort ...... 51 57N 4 10 E
Evans Head ..... 29 7 s 153 27 E
Evanston, Ill. 42 0N 87 40w
Evanston, Wyo. ... 41 10N 111 0w
Evansville 38 0N 87 35w
Eveleth 47 35N 92 40w
Even Yehuda ..... 32 16N 34 53 E
Everest, Mt. ..... 28 5N 86 58 E
Everett 48 0N 122 10w
Everglades
   Nat. Park 25 50N 80 40w
Evesham 52 6N 1 57w
Evora 38 33N 7 57w
Évreux .... 49 0N 1 8 E
Evron .... 32 59N 35 6 E
Evvoia □ .... 38 40N 23 40 E
Ewe, L. 57 49N 5 38w
Excellsior Springs . 39 20N 94 10w
Exe, R. 50 37N 3 25w
Exeter 50 43N 3 31w
Exmoor, Reg. 51 10N 3 55w
Exmouth,
   Australia ..... 22 6 s 114 0 E
Exmouth, U.K. ... 50 37N 3 24w
Exmouth, G. ..... 22 15 s 114 15 E
Extremadura, Reg. 39 30N 6 0w
Exuma Sd. 24 30N 76 20w
Eyasi, L. .... 3 30 s 35 0 E
Eye Pen. .... 58 20N 0 51 E
Eyemouth 55 53N 2 5w
Eyre, L. .... 28 30 s 136 45 E
Eyre, Pen. ...... 33 30 s 137 17 E

F

Fabens 31 30N 106 8w
Fabriano .... 43 20N 12 52 E
Facatativa 4 49N 74 22w
Fada N'Gourma ... 12 10N 0 30 E
Faenza .... 44 17N 11 53 E
Fafa .... 15 22N 0 48 E

Fagam .... 11 1N 10 1 E
Fagaraş .... 45 48N 24 58 E
Fagernes .... 61 0N   9 16 E
Fagersta .... 61 1N 15 46 E
Fagnano, L. ..... 54 30 s 68 0w
Fahraj .... 29 0N 59 0 E
Fahsien .... 21 19N 110 33 E
Fahud .... 22 18N 56 28 E
Fair Haven 43 36N 76 16w
Fairbank 31 44N 110 12w
Fairbanks 64 59N 147 40w
Fairbury 40 5N 97 5w
Fairfield,
   Australia ...... 37 45 s 175 17 E
Fairfield, Ala. 33 30N 87 0w
Fairfield, Calif. .. 38 14N 122 1w
Fairfield, Ill. 38 20N 88 20w
Fairfield, Iowa .. 41 0N 91 58w
Fairfield, Tex. 31 40N 96 0w
Fairlie .... 44 5 s 170 49 E
Fairmont, Minn. .. 43 37N 94 30w
Fairmont, W. Va. . 39 29N 80 10w
Fairport 43 8N 77 29w
Fairview,
   Australia ...... 15 31 s 144 17 E
Fairview, Canada .. 56 5N 118 25w
Fairweather, Mt. . 58 55N 137 45w
Faizabad,
   Afghanistan .... 37 7N 70 33 E
Faizabad, India .. 26 45N 82 10 E
Fajardo 18 20N 65 39w
Fakenham .... 52 50N   0 51 E
Fakfak .... 3 0 s 132 15 E
Faku .... 42 31N 123 26 E
Falaise 48 54N   0 12w
Falam .... 23 0N 93 45 E
Falcone, C. ...... 41 0N   8 10 E
Falfurrias .... 27 8N 98 8 E
Falkenberg ...... 56 54N 12 30 E
Falkirk 56 0N   3 47w
Falkland, Sd. .... 52 0 s 60 0w
Falkland Is. □ ... 51 30 s 59 0w
Falkland Is.
   Dependencies □ . 57 0 s 40 0N
Falköping .... 58 12N 13 33 E
Fall River 41 45N 71 5w
Fallon 39 31N 118 51w
Falls City 40 0N 95 40w
Falmouth, Jamaica 18 30N 77 40w
Falmouth, U.K. ... 50 9N   5 5w

Falso, C. 17 45N 71 40w
Falster, I. .... 54 48N 11 58 E
Falsterbo .... 55 23N 12 50 E
Falun .... 60 37N 15 37 E
Famagusta .... 35 8N 33 55 E
Fandriana .... 20 14 s 47 21 E
Fangcheng .... 31 2N 118 13 E
Fanning I. 3 51N 159 22w
Fano .... 43 50N 13 0 E
Fanshaw 57 11N 133 30w
Faradje .... 3 50N 29 45 E
Farafangana ...... 22 49 s 47 50 E
Faranah 10 2N 10 45w
Farar □ .... 32 30N 62 17 E
Farar □ .... 32 25N 62 10 E
Farasān, Jazā'ir, I. 16 45N 41 55 E
Faratsiho .... 19 24 s 46 57 E
Fareham 50 52N   1 11w
Farewell, C.,
   Greenland=
   Farvel, K. 66 0N 44 0w
Farewell, C., N.Z. . 40 29 s 172 43 E
Fargo 47 0N 97 0w
Faribault 44 15N 93 19w
Faridpur .... 23 36N 89 53 E
Farina .... 30 3 s 138 15 E
Farmington,N. Mex. 36 45N 108 28w
Farmington, Utah . 41 0N 111 58w
Farnborough 51 17N   0 46w
Farne Is. 55 38N   1 37w
Faro, Brazil ..... 2 0 s 56 45w
Faro, Port. 37 2N   7 55w
Faroe Is. 62 0N   7 0w
Farquhar, C. ..... 23 38 s 113 36 E
Farrāshband ...... 28 57N 52 5 E
Farrell 41 13N 80 29w
Farrell Flat ...... 33 48 s 138 48 E
Fars □ .... 29 30N 55 0 E
Farsund .... 58 5N   6 55 E
Faru .... 12 48N   6 12 E
Farvel, K. 60 0N 44 0w
Faryab □ .... 36 0N 65 0 E
Fastnet Rock 51 22N   9 27w
Fatehgarh .... 27 25N 79 35 E
Fatehpur,
   Rajasthan ..... 28 0N 75 4 E
Fatehpur, Ut.P. .. 27 8N 81 7 E
Fatshan .... 23 0N 113 4 E
Faulkton 45 4N 99 8w
Faure, I. .... 25 52 s 113 50 E

Fauresmith ...... 29 44 s 25 17 E
Fauske .... 67 17N 15 25 E
Favara .... 37 19N 13 39 E
Favignana, I. ..... 37 56N 12 18 E
Faxaflói, B. 64 29N 23 0w
Fayetteville, Ark. . 36 0N 94 5w
Fayetteville, N.C. . 35 0N 78 58w
Fazilka .... 30 27N 74 2 E
F'Dérik .... 22 40N 12 45 E
Feale, R. 52 26N   9 28w
Fear, C. 33 45N 78 0w
Featherston ...... 41 6 s 175 20 E
Fécamp .... 49 45N   0 22 E
Fehmarn, I. ...... 54 26N 11 10 E
Fehmarn Bælt .... 54 35N 11 20 E
Feilding .... 40 13 s 175 35 E
Feira de
   Santana .... 12 15 s 38 57w
Feldkirch .... 47 15N   9 37 E
Felipe
   Carillo Puerto ... 19 38N 88 3w
Felixstowe 51 58N   1 22w
Femund, L. ...... 62 5N 11 55 E
Fen Ho, R. ...... 35 36N 110 42 E
Fénérive .... 17 22 s 49 25 E
Fencheng .... 28 2N 115 46 E
Fengcheng,
   Heilungkiang .. 45 41N 128 54 E
Fengcheng,
   Liaoning ...... 40 28N 124 4 E
Fenghsien .... 33 56N 106 41 E
Fengkieh .... 31 0N 109 33 E
Fengtai .... 39 57N 116 21 E
Fengyuan .... 24 10N 120 45 E
Fenoarivo .... 18 26 s 46 34 E
Fenyang .... 37 19N 111 46 E
Feodosia .... 45 2N 35 28 E
Fergana .... 40 23N 71 46 E
Fergus 43 43N 80 24w
Fergus Falls 46 25N 96 0w
Ferland 50 19N 88 27w
Fermanagh □ 54 21N   7 40w
Fermoy 52 4N   8 18w
Fernando de
   Noronha, Is. ... 4 0 s 33 10w
Fernando Póo, I.=
   Macias Nguema
   Biyoga .... 3 30N   8 4 E
Fernie 49 30N 115 5w

Fernlees .... 23 51 s 148 7 E
Ferozepore ...... 30 55N 74 40 E
Ferrara .... 44 50N 11 36 E
Fès 34 0N   5 0½
Fetlar, I. 60 36N   0 52w
Fezzan .... 27 0N 15 0 E
Fianarantsoa ..... 21 26 s 47 5 E
Fianarantsoa □ ... 21 30 s 47 0 E
Fichtelgebirge, Mts. 50 10N 12 0 E
Ficksburg .... 28 51 s 27 53 E
Fiditi .... 7 45N   3 53 E
Fier, Portile de .. 44 42N 22 30 E
Fife □ 56 13N   3 2w
Figeac .... 44 37N   2 2 E
Figtree .... 20 22 s 28 20 E
Figueira da
   Foz 40 7N   8 54w
Figueras .... 42 18N   2 58 E
Figuig 32 5N   1 11w
Fihaonana .... 18 36 s 47 12 E
Fiji ■ .... 17 20 s 179 0 E
Filey 54 13N   0 18w
Filiatrá .... 37 9N 21 35 E
Filingué .... 14 21N   3 19 E
Filipstad .... 59 43N 14 9 E
Fillmore 34 23N 118 58w
Findhorn 57 30N   3 45w
Findlay 41 0N 83 41w
Finistère □ 48 20N   4 20w
Finisterre, C. 42 50N   9 19w
Finke .... 25 34 s 134 35 E
Finland ■ .... 70 0N 27 0 E
Finland, G. of ... 60 0N 26 0¼
Finley .... 35 38 s 145 35 E
Finnegan 51 7N 112 5w
Finnigan, Mt. .... 15 49 s 145 17 E
Finniss, C. ...... 33 38 s 134 51 E
Finnmark □ ..... 69 30N 25 0 E
Firenze .... 43 47N 11 15 E
Firozabad .... 27 10N 78 25 E
Firūzābād .... 28 52N 52 35 E
Firūzkūh .... 35 50N 52 40 E
Fisher .... 30 30 s 131 0 E
Fishguard 51 59N   4 59w
Fitchburg 42 35N 71 47w
Fitz Roy .... 47 10 s 67 0w
Fitzgerald 31 45N 83 10w
Fitzroy, R., Queens. 23 32 s 150 52 E
Fitzroy, R.,
   W. Australia ... 17 31 s 138 35 E

Fitzroy Crossing ... 18 9 s 125 38 E
Fizi .... 4 17 s 28 55 E
Flagstaff 35 10N 111 40w
Flåm .... 60 52N   7 14 E
Flamborough Hd. . 54 8N   0 4w
Flaming Gorge L. . 41 15N 109 30w
Flanders=
   Flandres,
   Plaines des ..... 51 10N   3 15 E
Flandre
   Occidentale □ .. 51 0N   3 0 E
Flandre
   Orientale □ ..... 51 0N   4 0 E
Flandres, Plaines
   des .... 51 10N   3 15 E
Flannan Is. 58 9N   7 52w
Flathead L. 47 50N 114 0w
Flattery, C.,
   Australia ...... 14 58 s 145 21 E
Flattery, C.,
   U.S.A. 48 21N 124 31w
Fleetwood .... 53 55N   3 .1w
Flekkefjord ...... 58 18N   6 39 E
Flensburg .... 54 46N   9 28 E
Fletton 52 34N   0 13w
Flin Flon 54 46N 101 53w
Flinders, B. ...... 34 19 s 114 9 E
Flinders, I. ...... 40 0 s 148 0 E
Flinders, Ras. .... 31 30 s 138 30 E
Flint, U.K. 53 15N   3 7w
Flint, U.S.A. 43 0N 83 40w
Flint I. .... 11 26 s 151 48w
Flodden 55 37N   2 8w
Flora 38 40N 88 30w
Florence, Italy=
   Firenze .... 43 47N 11 15 E
Florence, Ala. 34 50N 87 50w
Florence, Ariz. ... 33 0N 111 25w
Florence, Oreg. .. 44 0N 124 3w
Florence, S.C. 34 5N 79 50w
Florencia 1 36N 75 36w
Flores 16 50N 89 40w
Flores, I. .... 8 35 s 121 0¼
Flores Sea ...... 6 30 s 124 0 E
Floriano .... 6 50 s 43 0w
Florianópolis ..... 27 30 s 48 30w
Florida .... 34 7 s 56 10w
Florida □ 28 30N 82 0w
Florida Str. 25 0N 80 0w
Flórina .... 40 48N 21 26 E

Florø 61 35N 5 1E
Flushing=
  Vlissingen 51 26N 3 34E
Fly, R. 7 50s 141 20E
Foam Lake 51 40N 103 15w
Focşani 45 41N 27 15E
Fóggia 41 28N 15 31E
Foggo 11 21N 9 57E
Fogo 49 43N 54 17w
Foix, Reg. 43 0N 1 30E
Foleyet 48 15N 82 25w
Foligno 42 58N 12 40E
Folkestone 51 5N 1 11E
Fond du Lac,
  Canada 59 20N 107 10w
Fond-du-Lac,
  U.S.A. 43 46N 88 26w
Fondi 41 21N 13 25E
Fonsagrada 43 8N 7 4w
Fonseca, G. de ... 13 10N 87 40w
Fontainebleau ... 48 24N 2 40E
Fonte Boa 2 25s 66 0w
Fontem 5 32N 9 52E
Fontenay-le-
  Comte 46 28N 0 48w
Foochow 26 5N 119 18E
Forbes 33 22s 148 0E
Forest Lawn 51 4N 114 0w
Forestburg 52 35N 112 1w
Forestville 48 48N 69 20w
Forez, Mts. du ... 45 40N 3 50E
Formby Pt. 53 33N 3 7w
Formentera, I. ... 38 40N 1 30E
Formiga 20 27s 45 25w
Formosa, Arg. ... 26 15s 58 10w
Formosa, Brazil ... 15 32s 47 20w
Formosa=
  Taiwan ■ 24 0N 121 0E
Formosa, Sa. 12 0s 55 0w
Formosa Str. 24 40N 124 0E
Forres 57 37N 3 38w
Forrest 38 22s 143 40E
Forrest City 35 1N 90 47w
Forsayth 18 33s 143 34E
Forst 51 43N 15 37E
Forsyth 46 14N 106 37w
Fort Albany 52 15N 81 35w
Fort-Archambault

=Sarh 9 5N 18 23E
Fort Assinboine ... 54 20N 114 45w
Fort Augustus ... 57 9N 4 40w
Fort Beaufort ... 32 46s 26 40E
Fort Benton 47 50N 110 40w
Fort Bragg 39 28N 123 50w
Fort Bridger 41 22N 110 20w
Fort Chimo 58 9N 68 12w
Fort Chipewyan ... 58 46N 111 9w
Fort Collins 40 30N 105 4w
Fort Coulonge ... 45 50N 76 45w
Fort-Dauphin 25 2s 47 0E
Fort Dodge 42 29N 94 10w
Fort Frances 48 35N 93 25w
Fort Franklin ... 65 30N 123 45w
Fort George 53 40N 79 0w
Fort George, R. ... 53 50N 77 0w
Fort Good Hope ... 66 14N 128 40w
Fort Graham 56 38N 124 35w
Fort Hancock 31 19N 105 56w
Fort Hope 51 30N 88 10w
Fort Kent 47 12N 68 30w
Fort-Lamy=
  Ndjamena 12 4N 15 8E
Fort Laramie 42 15N 104 30w
Fort Lauderdale ... 26 10N 80 5w
Fort Liard 60 20N 123 30w
Fort Mackay 57 12N 111 41w
Fort McKenzie ... 56 50N 69 0w
Fort Macleod 49 45N 113 30w
Fort MacMahon ... 29 31N 2 55E
Fort McPherson ... 67 30N 134 55w
Fort Madison 40 39N 91 20w
Fort Mirabel 29 31N 2 55E
Fort Morgan 40 10N 103 50w
Fort Munro 30 0N 69 55E
Fort Myers 26 30N 82 0w
Fort Nelson 58 50N 122 30w
Fort Norman 64 57N 125 30w
Fort Payne 34 25N 85 44w
Fort Peck 47 1N 105 30w
Fort Peck Res. ... 47 40N 107 0w
Fort Pierce 27 29N 80 19w
Fort Portal 0 40N 30 20E
Fort Providence ... 61 20N 117 30w
Fort Qu'Appelle ... 50 45N 103 50w
Fort Resolution ... 61 10N 114 40w
Fort-Rousset 0 29s 15 55E
Fort Rupert 51 30N 78 40w
Fort St. James ... 54 30N 124 10w

Fort St. John 56 15N 120 50w
Fort Sandeman ... 31 20N 69 25E
Fort Saskatchewan 53 40N 113 15w
Fort Scott 38 0N 94 40w
Fort Selkirk 62 43N 137 22w
Fort Severn 56 0N 87 40w
Fort Simpson 61 45N 121 30w
Fort Shevchenko .. 44 30N 50 10E
Fort Smith 35 25N 94 25w
Fort Stockton ... 30 48N 103 2w
Fort Sumner 34 24N 104 8w
Fort Valley 32 33N 83 52w
Fort Vermilion ... 58 30N 115 57w
Fort Victoria ... 20 8s 30 55E
Fort Wayne 41 5N 85 10w
Fort William,
  Canada=
  Thunder Bay ... 48 20N 89 10w
Fort William, U.K. 56 48N 5 8w
Fort Worth 32 45N 97 25w
Fort Yukon 66 35N 145 12w
Fortaleza 3 35s 38 35w
Fort-de-France ... 14 36N 61 5w
Fortescue, R. ... 21 20s 116 5E
Forth, Firth of ... 56 5N 2 55w
Fortrose 57 35N 4 10w
Fortuna 48 38N 124 8w
Forty Mile 64 20N 140 30w
Fostoria 41 8N 83 25w
Fougères 48 21N 1 14w
Foula, I. 60 10N 2 5w
Foulness 51 26N 0 55E
Foumban 5 45N 10 50E
Fourcroy, C. 11 45s 130 2E
Fouriesburg 28 38s 28 14E
Foveaux, Str. ... 46 42s 168 10E
Fowey 50 20N 4 39w
Fowlers, B. 31 59s 132 34E
Fowning 33 30N 119 40E
Fox Valley 50 30N 109 25w
Foxe Basin 68 30N 77 0w
Foxe Chan. 66 0N 80 0w
Foxe Pen. 65 0N 76 0w
Foxton 40 29s 175 18E
Foyle, L. 55 6N 7 18w
Foynes 52 37N 9 6w
Foz do Iguaçu ... 25 30s 54 30w
Franca 20 25s 47 30w
Francavilla

Fontana 40 32N 17 35E
France ■ 47 0N 3 0E
Franceville 1 38s 13 35E
Franche Comté,
  Reg. 46 30N 5 50E
Francis Harbour ... 52 34N 55 44w
Francistown 21 11s 27 32E
François 47 34N 56 44w
Franconia 50 0N 9 0E
Frankfort, S. Afr. ... 27 16s 28 30E
Frankfort, Ind. ... 40 20N 86 33w
Frankfort, Ky. ... 38 12N 85 44w
Frankfurt am Main . 50 7N 8 40E
Frankfurt an der
  Oder 52 50N 14 31E
Fränkische Alb. ... 49 20N 11 30E
Franklin, Nebr. ... 40 9N 98 55w
Franklin, N.H. ... 43 28N 71 39w
Franklin, Pa. ... 41 22N 79 45w
Franklin, Tenn. ... 35 54N 86 53w
Franklin, W. Va. ... 38 38N 79 21w
Franklin, Reg. ... 71 0N 99 0w
Franklin D.
  Roosevelt L. ... 48 30N 118 16w
Franklin Mts. ... 66 0N 125 0w
Franklin Str. ... 72 0N 96 0w
Frankston 38 8s 145 8E
Frantsa Iosifa,
  Zemlya, Is. ... 76 0N 62 0E
Franz 48 25N 85 30w
Fraser, I. 25 15s 153 10E
Fraser, R. 49 9N 123 12w
Fraser Lake 54 0N 124 50w
Fraserburg 31 55s 21 30E
Fraserburgh 47 41N 2 0½
Fray Bentos 33 10s 58 15w
Frazier Downs ... 18 48s 121 42E
Fredericia 55 34N 9 45E
Frederick, Md. ... 39 25N 77 23w
Frederick, Okla. ... 34 22N 99 0w
Fredericksburg ... 38 16N 77 29w
Fredericton 45 57N 66 40w
Frederikshavn ... 57 28N 10 31E
Fredonia 42 26N 79 20w
Fredrikstad 59 13N 10 57E
Freeport, Bahamas 26 30N 78 35w
Freeport, Ill. ... 42 18N 89 40w
Freeport, N.Y. ... 40 39N 73 35w
Freeport, Tex. ... 28 55N 95 22w
Freetown 8 30N 13 10w

Freiburg 48 0N 7 50E
Freire 39 0s 72 50w
Freising 48 24N 11 27E
Freistadt 48 30N 14 30E
Fréjus 43 25N 6 44E
Fremantle 32 1s 115 47E
Fremont, Nebr. ... 41 30N 96 30w
Fremont, Ohio ... 41 20N 83 5w
French, I. 38 20s 145 22E
French Guiana ■ . 4 0N 53 0w
French Terr. of the
  Afars & Issas■=
  Djibouti ■ 11 30N 42 15E
Fresco, R. 6 39s 51 59w
Fresnillo 23 10N 103 0w
Fresno 36 47N 119 50w
Frewena 19 50s 135 50E
Frías 28 40s 65 5w
Fribourg 46 49N 7 9E
Friedrichshafen ... 47 39N 9 29E
Friendly Is.=
  Tonga Is. 20 0s 173 0w
Friesian Is.=
  Waddeniladen .. 53 30N 5 30E
Friesland □ 53 5N 5 50E
Frio, C. 18 0s 12 0E
Friuli Venezia
  Giulia □ 46 0N 13 0E
Frobisher B. 63 0N 67 0w
Frome 51 16N 2 17w
Front Royal 38 55N 78 10w
Frontera 18 30N 92 40w
Frosinone 41 38N 13 20E
Frostburg 39 43N 78 57w
Frunze 42 54N 74 36E
Frutal 20 0s 49 0w
Frýdek Místek ... 49 40N 18 20E
Fuchin 47 10N 132 0E
Fuchou=Foochow .. 26 5N 119 18E
Fuchow 27 50N 116 14E
Fuchun Kiang, R. .. 30 10N 120 9E
Fuente Ovejuna ... 38 15N 5 25w
Fuentes de Oñoro .. 40 33N 6 52w
Fuerteventura, I. ... 28 30N 14 0w
Fujairah 25 7N 56 18E
Fuji 35 9N 138 39E
Fuji-san, Mt. ... 35 22N 138 44E
Fuji-no-miya 35 20N 138 40E
Fujisawa 35 22N 139 29E

Fukien □ .... 26 0N 117 30 E
Fukuchiyama ... 35 25N 135 9 E
Fukui .... 36 0N 136 10 E
Fukui □ .... 36 0N 136 12 E
Fukuoka .... 33 30N 130 30 E
Fukuoka □ ...... 33 30N 131 0 E
Fukushima ..... 37 30N 140 15 E
Fukushima □ .... 37 30N 140 15 E
Fukuyama ...... 34 35N 133 20 E
Fulda .... 50 32N 9 41 E
Fullerton 33 52N 117 58W
Fulton, Mo. 38 50N 91 55W
Fulton, N.Y. 43 20N 76 22W
Funabashi ...... 35 45N 140 0 E
Funafuti, I. ..... 8 30S 179 0 E
Funchal 32 45N 16 55W
Fundación 10 31N 74 11W
Fundão 40 8N 7 30W
Fundy, B. of 45 0N 66 0W
Funtua .... 11 31N 7 17 E
Furat, Nahr al, R. 33 30N 43 0 E
Furness 54 14N 3 8W
Fürth .... 49 29N 11 0 E
Fury & Hecla Str. . 69 40N 81 0W
Fusagasugá 4 21N 74 22W
Fushan .... 37 30N 121 5 E
Fushun .... 42 0N 123 59 E
Fusin .... 42 12N 121 33 E
Futing .... 27 15N 120 10 E
Futsing .... 25 46N 119 29 E
Fuyang .... 30 5N 119 56 E
Fuyu .... 45 10N 124 50 E
Fyen, I.=Fyn, I. .. 55 20N 10 30 E
Fylde, R. 53 47N 2 56W
Fyn, I. .... 55 20N 10 30 E
Fyne, L. 56 0N 5 20W

G

Gaanda .... 10 10N 12 27 E
Gabès .... 33 53N 10 2 E
Gabès, G. de .... 34 0N 10 30 E
Gabon ■ .... 0 10S 10 0 E
Gaborone .... 24 37S 25 57 E
Gabrovo .... 42 52N 25 27 E
Gach-Sarán ..... 30 15N 50 45 E
Gada .... 13 38N 5 36 E

Gadag .... 15 30N 75 45 E
Gadarwara ...... 22 50N 78 50 E
Gadhada .... 22 0N 71 35 E
Gadsden, Ala. ... 34 1N 86 0W
Gadsden, Ariz. ... 32 35N 114 47W
Gadwal .... 16 10N 77 50 E
Gaeta .... 41 12N 13 35 E
Gaffney 35 10N 81 31W
Gafsa .... 34 24N 8 51 E
Gagetown 45 46N 66 29W
Gagnoa 6 4N 5 55W
Gagnon 51 50N 68 5W
Gainesville, Fla. ... 29 38N 82 20W
Gainesville, Ga. ... 34 17N 83 47W
Gainesville, Tex. ... 33 40N 97 10W
Gainsborough ... 53 23N 0 46W
Gairdner, L. .... 32 0S 136 0 E
Gairloch, L. 57 43N 5 45W
Gajiram .... 12 29N 13 9 E
Galangue .... 13 48S 16 3 E
Galápagos, Is. ... 0 0N 89 0W
Galashiels 55 37N 2 50W
Galaţi .... 45 27N 28 2 E
Galatina .... 40 10N 18 10 E
Galax 36 42N 80 57W
Galdhøpiggen, Mt. 61 45N 8 40 E
Galena .... 27 50S 114 41 E
Galesburg 40 57N 90 23W
Galich .... 58 23N 42 18 E
Galicia, Reg. 42 43N 8 0W
Galilee=
 Hagalil, Reg. .. 32 53N 35 18 E
Galilee, Sea of=
 Kinneret, Yam . 32 49N 35 36 E
Gallatin 36 24N 86 27W
Galle .... 6 5N 80 10 E
Gállego, R. 41 39N 0 51W
Gallegos, R. 51 35S 69 0W
Gallinas, Pta. ... 12 28N 71 40W
Gallipoli .... 40 8N 18 0 E
Gallipolis 38 50N 82 10W
Gällivare .... 67 7N 20 32 E
Galloway, Reg. ... 55 0N 4 25W
Galloway, Mull of . 54 38N 4 50W
Gallup 35 30N 108 54W
Galt=
 Cambridge 43 23N 80 19W
Galty Mts. 52 20N 8 10W
Galveston 29 15N 94 48W
Galveston B. 29 30N 94 50W

Gálvez 32 0S 61 20W
Galway 53 16N 9 4W
Galway, B. 53 10N 9 20W
Galway □ 53 16N 9 3W
Gamagori .... 34 50N 137 14 E
Gamawa .... 12 10N 10 31 E
Gambaga 10 30N 0 28W
Gambia ■ 13 20N 15 45W
Gambia, R. 13 28N 16 34W
Gambier, C. ..... 11 56S 130 57 E
Gamboa 9 8N 79 42W
Gamerco 35 33N 108 56W
Gamtoos, R. .... 33 58S 25 1 E
Gan Shamu'el ... 32 28N 34 56 E
Gan Yavne ..... 31 48N 34 42 E
Gananoque 44 20N 76 10W
Gand=Gent ..... 51 2N 3 37 E
Gandak, R. ..... 25 32N 85 5 E
Gander 49 1N 54 33W
Gandi .... 12 55N 5 49 E
Ganga, R. ...... 23 22N 90 32 E
Ganganagar .... 29 56N 73 56 E
Gangaw .... 22 5N 94 15 E
Ganges, R.=
 Ganga, R. .... 23 22N 90 32 E
Gangtok .... 27 20N 88 40 E
Gao .... 18 0N 1 0 E
Gaoua 10 20N 3 8W
Gaoual 11 45N 13 25W
Gap .... 44 33N 6 5 E
Garanhuns 8 50S 36 30W
Garberville 40 11N 123 50W
Garcia .... 25 32S 32 13 E
Gard □ .... 44 2N 4 10 E
Garda, L. di .... 45 40N 10 40 E
Garden City 38 0N 100 45W
Gardez .... 33 31N 68 59 E
Gardiner 45 3N 110 53W
Gardner 42 35N 72 0W
Gardo .... 9 18N 49 20 E
Garfield 47 3N 117 8W
Gargano, Mte. ... 41 43N 15 40 E
Garissa .... 0 25S 39 40 E
Garkida .... 10 27N 12 36 E
Garko .... 11 45N 8 53 E
Garland 41 47N 112 10W
Garm .... 39 0N 70 20 E
Garmsar .... 35 20N 52 25 E
Garoe .... 8 35N 48 40 E
Garonne, R. 45 2N 0 36W

Garoua .... 9 19N 13 21 E
Garrison 46 37N 112 56W
Garrison Res. 47 30N 102 0W
Garry, L. 65 40N 100 0W
Garson 50 5N 96 50W
Gartok .... 31 59N 80 30 E
Garut .... 7 14S 107 53 E
Garvie, Mts. .... 45 27S 169 59 E
Gary 41 35N 87 20W
Garzón 2 10N 75 40W
Gascogne, Reg. .. 43 45N 0 20 E
Gascogne, G. de .. 44 0N 2 0W
Gascony, Reg.=
 Gascogne, Reg. . 43 45N 0 20 E
Gascoyne, R. .... 24 52S 113 37 E
Gascoyne Junction 25 3S 115 12 E
Gashaka .... 7 20N 11 29 E
Gashua .... 12 54N 11 0 E
Gaspé 48 52N 64 30W
Gaspé, C. 48 48N 64 7W
Gaspé Pass. 49 10N 64 0W
Gaspé Pen. 48 45N 65 40W
Gaspesian Prov.
 Park 49 0N 66 45W
Gastonia 35 17N 81 10W
Gastre 42 10S 69 15W
Gata, C. de 36 41N 2 13W
Gata, Sa. de 40 20N 6 20W
Gatehouse of
 Fleet 54 53N 4 10W
Gateshead 54 57N 1 37W
Gaths .... 26 2S 30 32 E
Gatineau Nat.
 Park 45 30N 75 52W
Gatooma .... 18 21S 29 55 E
Gatun 9 16N 79 55W
Gatun L. 9 7N 79 56W
Gauhati .... 26 5N 91 55 E
Gaula, R. .... 63 21N 10 14 E
Gavater .... 25 10N 61 23 E
Gavle .... 60 41N 17 13 E
Gävleborg □ .... 61 20N 16 15 E
Gawilgarh Hills .. 21 15N 76 45 E
Gawler .... 34 30S 138 42 E
Gaya, India ..... 24 47N 85 4 E
Gaya, Nigeria .... 11 57N 9 0 E
Gayndah .... 25 35S 151 39 E
Gaza .... 31 30N 34 28 E
Gaza □ .... 23 0S 33 0 E
Gaza Strip ...... 31 29N 34 25 E

Gazaoua .... 13 32N 7 55 E
Gaziantep ...... 37 6N 37 23 E
Gboko .... 7 17N 9 4 E
Gbongan .... 7 28N 4 20 E
Gcuwa .... 32 20S 28 11 E
Gdańsk .... 54 22N 18 40 E
Gdańska, Zatoka . 54 30N 19 15 E
Gdynia .... 54 35N 18 33 E
Gebeit Mine ..... 21 3N 36 29 E
Gedaref .... 14 2N 35 28 E
Gedera .... 31 49N 34 46 E
Gedser .... 54 35N 11 55 E
Geelong .... 38 2S 144 20 E
Geelvink, Chan. .. 28 30S 114 10 E
Geeraadsbergen .. 50 45N 3 53 E
Geidam .... 12 57N 11 57 E
Geili .... 16 1N 32 37 E
Geita .... 2 48S 32 12 E
Gela .... 37 3N 14 15 E
Gelderland □ .... 52 5N 6 10 E
Geldrop .... 51 25N 5 32 E
Geleen .... 50 57N 5 49 E
Gelibolu .... 40 28N 26 43 E
Gelsenkirchen ... 51 30N 7 5 E
Gemas .... 2 37N 102 36 E
Gembloux ...... 50 34N 4 43 E
Gemena .... 3 20N 19 40 E
General Acha 37 20S 64 38W
General Alvear .. 36 0S 60 0W
General Belgrano . 36 0S 58 30W
General Guido ... 36 40S 57 40W
General Juan
 Madariaga 37 0S 57 0W
General Paz 27 45S 57 36W
General Pico 35 45S 63 50W
General Pinedo ... 27 15S 61 30W
General Roca 30 0S 67 40W
General Villegas . 35 0S 63 0W
Geneva, Switz.=
 Genève .... 46 12N 6 9 E
Geneva, U.S.A. ... 42 53N 77 0W
Geneva, L.=
 Léman, L. .... 46 26N 6 30 E
Genève .... 46 12N 6 9 E
Genil, R. 37 42N 5 19W
Genissiat .... 46 1N 5 48 E
Genk .... 50 58N 5 32 E
Genoa=Genova .. 44 24N 8 56 E
Genova .... 44 24N 8 56 E
Génova, G. di .... 44 0N 9 0 E

Gent .... 51 2N 3 37 E
Geographe, B. .... 33 30s 115 15 E
Geographe, Chan. . 24 30s 113 0 E
George .... 33 58s 22 29 E
George, L. 43 30N 73 30w
George R.=Port
Nouveau-Quebec 58 30N 65 50w
George Town
Australia .... 41 5s 148 55 E
George Town,
W. Malaysia .... 5 25N 100 19 E
Georgetown,
Australia .... 18 17s 143 33 E
Georgetown, Ont. . 43 40N 80 0w
Georgetown, P.E.I. 46 13N 62 24w
Georgetown,
Gambia 13 30N 14 47w
Georgetown,
Guyana 6 50N 58 12w
Georgetown,
U.S.A. 33 22N 79 15w
Georgia ■ 32 0N 82 0w
Georgia Str. 49 20N 124 0w
Georgian B. 45 15N 81 0w
Georgian S.S.R. □ . 41 0N 45 0 E
Georgiu-Dezh .... 51 3N 39 20 E
Georgiyevsk ..... 44 12N 43 28 E
Gera .... 50 53N 12 5 E
Geraldton,
Australia .... 28 48s 114 32 E
Geraldton,
Canada 49 44N 86 59w
Gerdine, Mt. 61 32N 152 50w
Gerede .... 40 45N 32 10 E
Gerlogubi ...... 6 53N 45 3 E
Germansen
Landing 55 43N 124 40w
Germiston ...... 26 15s 28 5 E
Gero .... 35 48N 137 14 E
Gerona .... 41 58N 2 46 E
Gers □ .... 43 35N 0 38 E
Gevaudan, Reg. ... 44 40N 3 40 E
Geyser 47 17N 110 30w
Geysir 64 19N 20 18w
Gezer .... 31 52N 34 55 E
Ghaghara, R. .... 25 45N 84 40 E
Ghana ■ 6 0N 1 0w
Ghardaïa .... 32 31N 3 37 E
Ghat .... 24 59N 10 19 E
Ghazal, Bahr

el, R. .... 9 31N 30 25 E
Ghazaouet 35 8N 1 50w
Ghaziabad .... 28 42N 77 35 E
Ghazipur ...... 25 38N 83 35 E
Ghazni .... 33 30N 68 17 E
Ghazni □ .... 33 0N 68 0 E
Ghent=Gent .... 51 2N 3 37 E
Ghor □ .... 34 0N 64 20 E
Ghost River 51 25N 83 20w
Ghudames ...... 30 11N 9 29 E
Ghugus .... 19 55N 79 15 E
Ghulam
Mohammed Barr. 25 30N 67 0 E
Ghurian .... 34 17N 61 25 E
Giant Mts.=
Krkonose ...... 50 50N 16 10 E
Giant's Causeway . 55 15N 6 30w
Giarre .... 37 44N 15 10 E
Gibara 21 0N 76 20w
Gibeon .... 25 7s 17 45 E
Gibraltar ■ 36 7N 5 22w
Gibraltar, Str. of . 35 55N 5 40w
Gibson, Des. .... 24 0s 126 0 E
Giessen .... 50 34N 8 40 E
Gifu .... 35 30N 136 45 E
Gifu □ .... 36 0N 137 0 E
Giganta, Sa. de la . 25 30N 111 30w
Gigha, I. 55 42N 5 45w
Gijón 43 32N 5 42w
Gila, R. 32 43N 114 33w
Gila Bend 32 57N 112 43w
Gilan □ .... 37 0N 49 0 E
Gilbedi .... 13 40N 5 45 E
Gilbert Is. .... ♪ 0N 176 0 E
Gilbert Plains ... 51 9N 100 28w
Gilbert River ... 18 9s 142 50 E
Gilgai .... 31 15s 119 56 E
Gilgandra ...... 31 42s 148 39 E
Gilgil .... 0 30s 36 20 E
Gilgit .... 35 50N 74 15 E
Gillam 56 20N 94 40w
Gilliat .... 20 40s 141 28 E
Gillingham ..... 51 23N 0 34 E
Gilmour 44 48N 77 37w
Gilroy 37 10N 121 37w
Gindie .... 23 45s 148 10 E
Gingin .... 31 22s 115 37 E
Ginnosar ...... 32 51N 35 32 E
Giong, Teluk, B. . 4 5N 118 20 E
Girardot 4 18N 74 48w

Girdle Ness 57 9N 2 2w
Giresun .... 40 45N 38 30 E
Girga .... 26 17N 31 55 E
Giridih .... 24 10N 86 21 E
Girishk .... 31 47N 64 24 E
Gironde, R. 45 30N 1 0w
Gironde □ 44 45N 0 30w
Girvan 55 15N 4 50w
Gisborne ...... 38 39s 178 5 E
Gisenyi .... 1 41s 29 30 E
Gitega .... 3 26s 29 56 E
Giurgiu .... 43 52N 25 57 E
Giv'at Olga .... 32 28N 34 53 E
Giv'atayim ..... 32 4N 34 49 E
Giza=El Giza ... 30 0N 31 10 E
Gizhiga .... 62 0N 150 27 E
Gizhiginskaya
Guba .... 61 0N 158 0 E
Giżycko .... 54 2N 21 48 E
Gjoa Haven 68 20N 96 0w
Gjøvik .... 60 47N 10 43 E
Glace Bay 46 11N 59 58w
Glacier B. Nat.
Monument 58 45N 136 30w
Glacier Nat. Park . 48 40N 114 0w
Gladewater 32 30N 94 58w
Gladstone, Queens. 23 52s 151 16 E
Gladstone,
S. Australia ... 33 17s 138 22 E
Gladstone, Canada 50 13N 98 57w
Glâma, R. ...... 59 12N 10 57 E
Glasgow, U.K. ... 55 52N 4 14w
Glasgow, U.S.A. . 37 2N 85 55w
Glastonbury 51 9N 2 42w
Glauchau ...... 50 50N 12 33 E
Glazov .... 58 0N 52 30 E
Gleichen 50 50N 113 0w
Glen Affric 57 15N 5 0w
Glen Canyon Dam 37 0N 111 25w
Glen Canyon
Nat. Recreation
Area 37 30N 111 0w
Glen Coe 56 40N 5 0w
Glen Garry 57 3N 5 7w
Glen More 57 12N 4 37w
Glen Thompson .. 37 38s 142 35 E
Glenalbyn ...... 36 30s 143 48 E
Glenbrook ...... 33 46s 150 37 E
Glencoe .... 28 11s 30 11 E
Glendale .... 17 22s 31 5 E

Glendale, Ariz. ... 33 40N 112 8w
Glendale, Calif. .. 34 7N 118 18w
Glendale, Oreg. ... 42 44N 123 29w
Glendive 47 7N 104 40w
Glenelg .... 34 58s 138 30 E
Glenelg, R. ..... 38 3s 141 9 E
Glengarriff 51 45N 9 33w
Glengyle .... 24 48s 139 37 E
Glenn Innes .... 29 44s 151 44 E
Glennies Creek .. 32 30s 151 8 E
Glenorchy ..... 36 55s 142 41 E
Glenore .... 17 50s 141 12 E
Glenormiston ... 22 55s 138 50 E
Glenrock 42 53N 105 55w
Glenrothes 56 12N 3 11w
Glens Falls 43 20N 73 40w
Glenties 54 48N 8 18w
Glenwood, Canada 49 21N 113 24w
Glenwood, U.S.A. 45 38N 95 21w
Glenwood Springs . 39 39N 107 15w
Gliwice .... 50 22N 18 41 E
Globe 33 25N 110 53w
Głogów .... 51 37N 16 5 E
Glorieuses, Is. ... 11 30s 47 20 E
Glossop 53 27N 1 56w
Gloucester,
Australia .... 32 0s 151 59 E
Gloucester, U.K. . 51 52N 2 15w
Gloucestershire □ . 51 44N 2 10w
Gloversville 43 5N 74 18w
Glückstadt ..... 53 46N 9 28 E
Gmünd .... 48 45N 15 0 E
Gmunden ...... 47 55N 13 48 E
Gniezno .... 52 30N 17 35 E
Gnowangerup ... 33 58s 117 59 E
Gô Công ...... 10 12N 107 0 E
Goa .... 15 33N 73 59 E
Goa □ .... 15 33N 73 59 E
Goaso 6 48N 2 30w
Goat Fell, Mt. ... 55 37N 5 11w
Goba .... 7 1N 39 59 E
Gobabis .... 22 16s 19 0 E
Gobi, Des. ..... 44 0N 111 0 E
Godavari, R. .... 16 37N 82 18 E
Godavari Pt. .... 17 0N 82 20 E
Godbout 49 20N 67 38w
Goderich 43 45N 81 41w
Golfito 8 41N 83 5w
Godhra .... 22 49N 73 40 E
Gods L. 54 40N 94 10w

Godthåb 64 10N 51 46w
Goei Hoop, K.die
=Good Hope,
C. of .... 34 24s 18 30 E
Goeree .... 51 50N 4 0 E
Goes .... 51 30N 3 55 E
Gogama 47 35N 81 35w
Gogango ...... 23 40s 150 2 E
Gogriàl .... 8 30N 28 0 E
Goiânia 16 35s 49 20w
Goias □ 12 10s 48 0w
Gojo .... 34 21N 135 42 E
Gojra .... 31 10N 72 40 E
Gokteik .... 22 26N 97 0 E
Gold Coast 4 0N 1 40w
Golden, Canada ... 51 20N 117 0w
Golden, U.S.A. .. 39 42N 105 30w
Golden B. ...... 40 40s 172 50 E
Goldfields ..... 37 45N 117 13 E
Goldsboro 35 24N 77 59w
Goldsworthy ... 20 21s 119 30 E
Goleniów ...... 53 35N 14 50 E
Golfito 8 41N 83 5w
Golfo Aranci ... 41 0N 9 38 E
Golspie 57 58N 3 58w
Goma .... 1 37s 29 10 E
Gombe .... 10 19N 11 2 E
Gomel .... 52 28N 31 0 E
Gomera, I. 28 10N 17 5w
Gómez Palacio .. 25 40N 104 40w
Gonābād ...... 34 15N 58 45 E
Gonaïves 19 20N 72 50w
Gonda .... 27 9N 81 58 E
Gonder .... 12 23N 37 30 E
Gondia .... 21 30N 80 10 E
Gonen .... 33 7N 35 39 E
Gongola, R. .... 9 30N 12 10 E
Goniri .... 11 30N 12 15 E
Gonja .... 4 15s 38 0 E
Gonzales 29 30N 97 30w
Good Hope, C. of . 34 24s 18 30 E
Goole 53 42N 0 52w
Goolgowi ...... 33 58s 154 39 E
Goomalling .... 31 19s 116 49 E
Goondiwindi ... 28 30s 150 21 E
Goor .... 52 13N 6 33 E
Goose Bay 53 15N 60 20w
Gop .... 22 5N 69 50 E
Gorakhpur ..... 26 47N 83 32 E
Gorda, Pta. 14 10N 83 10w

Gordon 42 49N 102 6W
Gordon River ..... 34 10s 117 15 E
Gordonia, Reg. ... 28 13s 21 10 E
Gordonvale .... 17 5s 145 50 E
Gore, Australia .. 28 17s 151 29 E
Gore, Ethiopia ... 8 12N 35 32 E
Gore, N.Z. .... 46 5s 168 58 E
Gorey 52 41N 6 18W
Gorgona, I. 3 0N 78 10W
Goris .... 39 31N 46 23 E
Gorízia .... 45 56N 13 37 E
Gorki=Gorkiy ..... 56 20N 44 0 E
Gorkiy .... 56 20N 44 0 E
Gorkovskoye
  Vdkhr .... 57 2N 43 4 E
Görlitz .... 51 10N 14 59 E
Gorlovka .... 48 25N 37 58 E
Gorna
  Oryakhovitsa ... 43 7N 25 40 E
Gorno Filinskoye . 60 5N 70 0 E
Gornyatski .... 67 49N 64 20 E
Gorontalo .... 0 35N 123 13 E
Goronyo .... 13 29N 5 39 E
Gort 53 4N 8 50W
Goryn, R. .... 52 8N 27 17 E
Gorzów
  Wielkopolski ... 52 43N 15 15 E
Gosford .... 33 23s 151 18 E
Goshen 41 36N 85 46W
Goslar .... 51 55N 10 23 E
Gospič .... 44 35N 15 23 E
Gosport 50 48N 1 8W
Göta kanal .... 58 45N 14 15 E
Göteborg .... 57 43N 11 59 E
Göteborgs och
  Bohus □ .... 58 30N 11 30 E
Gotha .... 50 56N 10 42 E
Gothenburg=
  Göteborg .... 57 43N 11 59 E
Gotland, I. ...... 57 30N 18 30 E
Götland, Reg. .... 58 0N 14 0 E
Götsu .... 35 0N 132 14 E
Göttingen .... 51 31N 9 55 E
Gottwaldov .... 49 14N 17 40 E
Gouda .... 52 1N 4 42 E
Gough, I. 40 10s 9 45W
Govin Res. 48 35N 74 40W
Goulburn .... 32 22s 149 31 E
Goundam 16 25N 3 45W
Gounou-Gaya ...... 9 38N 15 31 E

Governor's
  Harbour 25 10N 76 14W
Gower, Pen. 51 35N 5 10W
Goya 29 10s 59 10W
Gozo, I. .... 36 0N 14 13 E
Graaff-Reinet .... 32 13s 24 32 E
Gračac .... 44 18N 15 57 E
Gracias a
  Dios, C. 15 0N 83 20W
Grado .... 45 40N 13 20 E
Grafton, Australia . 29 35s 152 0 E
Grafton, U.S.A. .. 48 30N 97 25W
Graham, Canada ... 49 20N 90 30W
Graham, N.C. 36 5N 79 22W
Graham, Tex. 33 7N 98 38W
Graham I. 53 40N 132 30W
Graham Ld. 65 0s 64 0W
Grahamdale 51 30N 98 34W
Grahamstown ...... 33 19s 26 31 E
Grain Coast, Reg. . 4 20N 10 0W
Grajaú 5 50s 46 30W
Grampian □ 57 20N 2 45W
Grampian
  Highlands, Mts. . 56 50N 4 0W
Gran Canaria, I. . 27 55N 15 35W
Gran Chaco, Reg. . 25 0s 61 0W
Gran Paradiso, Mt. 49 33N 7 17 E
Gran Sasso
  d'Italia, Mt. ... 42 25N 13 30 E
Granada, Nic. 11 58N 86 0W
Granada, Sp. 37 10N 3 35W
Granard 53 47N 7 30W
Granby 45 25N 72 45W
Grand Bahama I. .. 26 40N 78 30W
Grand Bank 47 6N 55 48W
Grand Bassam 5 10N 3 49W
Grand Bourg 15 53N 61 19W
Grand Canyon 36 10N 112 45W
Grand Canyon
  Nat. Park 36 15N 112 20W
Grand Cayman, I. . 19 20N 81 20W
Grand Coulee Dam 48 0N 118 50W
Grand Falls 47 2N 67 46W
Grand Forks,
  Canada 49 0N 118 30W
Grand Forks,
  U.S.A. 48 0N 97 3W
Grand Haven 43 3N 86 13W
Grand Island 40 59N 98 25W
Grand Junction ... 39 0N 108 30W

Grand Lahou 5 10N 5 0W
Grand Marais 47 45N 90 25W
Grand' Mère 46 36N 72 40W
Grand Rapids,
  Canada 53 12N 99 19W
Grand Rapids,
  Mich. 42 57N 85 40W
Grand Rapids,
  Minn. 47 19N 93 29W
Grand St-Bernard,
  Col. du .... 45 53N 7 11 E
Grand Teton, Mt. . 43 45N 110 57W
Grande, B. 50 30s 68 20W
Grande, R. 25 57N 97 9W
Grand Baie 48 19N 70 52W
Grande-Entrée 47 30N 61 40W
Grande Prairie ... 55 15N 118 50W
Grande Rivière ... 48 26N 64 30W
Grangemouth 56 1N 3 43W
Grangeville 45 57N 116 4W
Granite City 38 45N 90 3W
Granity .... 41 39s 171 51 E
Granja 3 17s 40 50W
Granollers .... 41 39N 2 18 E
Grantham 52 55N 0 39W
Grantown-on-Spey 57 19N 3 36W
Grants 35 14N 107 57W
Grants Pass 42 30N 123 22W
Grantsville 40 35N 112 32W
Granville, France . 48 50N 1 35W
Granville, U.S.A. . 43 24N 73 16W
Graskop 24 56s 30 49W
Grass Valley 39 18N 121 0W
Grasse .... 43 38N 6 56 E
Gravelbourg 49 50N 105 35W
Gravenhurst 44 52N 79 20W
Gravesend,
  Australia ...... 29 35s 150 20 E
Gravesend, U.K. .. 51 25N 0 22 E
Grays .... 51 28N 0 23 E
Grayson 50 45N 102 40W
Graz .... 47 4N 15 27 E
Great Abaco I. ... 26 15N 77 10W
Great Australian
  Basin .... 24 30s 143 0 E
Great Australian
  Bight. .... 33 30s 130 0 E
Great Bahama
  Bank 23 15N 78 0W
Great Barrier I. ... 37 12s 175 25 E

Great Barrier
  Reef .... 19 0s 149 0 E
Great Basin 40 0N 116 30W
Great Bear L. 65 0N 120 0W
Great Bend 38 25N 98 55W
Great Bitter
  Lake .... 30 15N 32 40 E
Great Blasket, I. . 52 5N 10 30W
Great Bushman
  Land .... 29 20s 19 0 E
Great Divide, Mts. . 23 0s 146 0 E
Great Dividing
  Range .... 25 0s 147 0 E
Great Exuma I. ... 23 30N 75 50W
Great Falls 47 27N 111 12W
Great Fish, R. ... 33 30s 27 8 E
Great Inagua I. .. 21 0N 73 20W
Great Indian Des. . 28 0N 72 0 E
Great L.=
  Tonlé Sap ...... 13 0N 104 0 E
Great
  Namaqualand=
  Groot
  Namaqualand ... 26 0s 18 0 E
Great Orme's Hd. . 53 20N 3 52W
Great Ouse, R. ... 52 47N 0 22 E
Great Plains 42 0N 100 0w
Great Ruaha, R. .. 7 56s 37 52 E
Great Salt L. 41 0N 112 30W
Great Salt Lake
  Des. 40 20N 113 50W
Great Sandy Des. . 21 0s 124 0 E
Great Slave L. ... 61 30N 114 20W
Great Smoky Mt.
  Nat. Park 35 39N 83 30W
Great Victoria
  Des. .... 29 30s 126 30 E
Great Whale
  River=Poste
  de la Baleine ... 55 20N 77 40 E
Great Whernside,
  Mt. 54 9N 1 59W
Great Yarmouth ... 52 40N 1 45 E
Greater Antilles . 20 0N 74 0W
Greater
  Manchester □ ... 53 35N 2 15W
Greater Sunda Is. . 4 30s 113 0 E
Gredos, Sa. de ... 40 20N 5 0W
Greece ■ .... 40 0N 23 0 E

Greeley 40 30N 104 40W
Green Bay 44 30N 88 0W
Green B. 45 0N 87 30W
Green Island ..... 45 54s 170 27 E
Green River, Utah 39 0N 110 10W
Green River, Wyo. 41 32N 109 28W
Greencastle 39 40N 86 48W
Greeneville 31 50N 86 38W
Greenfield, Ind. . 39 47N 85 51W
Greenfield, Mass. . 42 38N 72 38W
Greenland ■ 66 0N 45 0W
Greenock 55 57N 4 45W
Greenore 54 2N 6 8W
Greenough, R. .... 28 51s 114 38 E
Greensboro 36 7N 79 46W
Greensburg, Ind. . 39 20N 85 30W
Greensburg, Pa. .. 40 18N 79 31W
Greenville, Liberia 5 7N 9 6W
Greenville, Mich. . 43 12N 85 14W
Greenville, Miss. . 33 25N 91 0W
Greenville, N.C. . 35 37N 77 26W
Greenville, Pa. .. 41 23N 80 22W
Greenville, S.C. . 34 54N 82 24W
Greenville, Tex. . 33 5N 96 5W
Greenwich, U.K. .. 51 28N 0 0 E
Greenwood, Miss. . 33 30N 90 4W
Greenwood, S.C. .. 34 13N 82 13W
Gregory Downs ... 18 35s 138 45 E
Gregory L. .... 20 10s 127 30 E
Greifswalder
  Bodden .... 54 12N 13 35 E
Gremikha .... 67 50N 39 40 E
Grenada ■ 33 45N 89 50W
Grenada, I. 12 10N 61 40W
Grenfell .... 33 52s 148 8 E
Grenen, C. .... 57 46N 10 34 E
Grenoble .... 45 12N 5 42 E
Gresik .... 9 13s 112 38 E
Gretna 30 0N 90 2W
Gretna Green 55 0N 3 3W
Grevenmacher .... 49 41N 6 26 E
Grey, R. .... 42 27s 171 12 E
Grey Res. 48 20N 56 30W
Greybull 44 30N 108 3W
Greymouth .... 42 29s 171 13 E
Greytown, N.Z. ... 41 5s 175 29 E
Greytown,
  S. Africa ...... 29 1s 30 36 E
Gridley 39 27N 121 47W
Griekwastad ...... 28 49s 23 15 E

Griffin 33 15N 84 16W
Griffith .... 34 14S 145 46 E
Griffith Mine 50 47N 93 25W
Grimsby 53 35N 0 5W
Grimsey, I. 66 33N 18 0W
Grimshaw 56 10N 117 40W
Grimstad .... 58 22N 8 35 E
Grinnell 41 45N 92 50W
Griqualand East,
   Reg. .... 30 30S 29 0 E
Griqualand West,
   Reg. .... 28 40S 23 30 E
Gris Nez, C. ..... 50 50N 1 35 E
Groblersdal ...... 25 15S 29 25 E
Grodno .... 53 42N 23 52 E
Grodzisk
   Mazowiecki .... 52 7N 20 37 E
Grong .... 64 25N 12 8 E
Groningen .... 53 15N 6 35 E
Groningen □ ...... 53 16N 6 40 E
Groot-Brakrivier . 34 2S 22 18 E
Groot Karasberge,
   Mts. .... 27 10S 18 45 E
Groot Karoo, Reg. 32 35S 23 0 E
Groot Kei, R. .... 32 41S 28 22 E
Groot
   Namakwaland=
   Namaland, Reg. . 26 0S 18 0 E
Groot Winterberg,
   Mt. .... 32 45S 26 50 E
Groote Eylandt, I. 14 0S 136 50 E
Grootfontein ...... 19 31S 18 6 E
Gross
   Glockner, Mt.... 47 5N 12 40 E
Grosseto .... 42 45N 11 7 E
Groveton 44 34N 71 30W
Groznyy .... 43 20N 45 45 E
Grudziądz .... 53 30N 18 47 E
Gryazi .... 52 30N 39 58 E
Gua .... 22 13N 85 20 E
Guachípas 25 40S 65 30W
Guacanayabo,
   G. de 20 40N 77 20W
Guadalajara,
   Mexico 20 40N 103 20W
Guadalajara, Sp. . 40 37N 3 12W
Guadalcanal ...... 9 0S 160 0 E
Guadalete, R. 36 35N 6 13W
Guadalquivir, R. . 36 47N 6 22W
Guadalupe 34 59N 120 33W

Guadalupe, Sa. de . 39 26N 5 25W
Guadalupe Pk. 31 50N 105 30W
Guadarrama,
   Sa. de 41 0N 4 0W
Guadeloupe, I. 16 20N 61 40W
Guadeloupe Pass. . 16 50N 68 15W
Guadiana, R. 37 14N 7 22W
Guadix 37 18N 3 11W
Guafo, B. del 43 35S 74 0W
Guaíra 24 5S 54 10W
Guaitecas, Is. 44 0S 74 30W
Guajira, Pen.
   de la 12 0N 72 0W
Gualeguay 33 10S 59 20W
Gualeguaychú 33 3S 58 31W
Guam, I. .... 13 27N 144 45 E
Guanabacoa 23 8N 82 18W
Guanabara □ 23 0S 43 25W
Guanacaste 10 40N 85 30W
Guanajay 22 56N 82 42W
Guanajuato 21 0N 101 20W
Guanajuato □ 20 40N 101 20W
Guanare 8 42N 69 12W
Guandacol 29 30S 68 40W
Guantánamo 20 10N 75 20W
Guaporé, R. 29 10S 51 54W
Guaqui 16 41S 68 54W
Guarapuava 25 20S 51 30W
Guarda 40 32N 7 20W
Guardafui, C.=
   Asir, Ras ..... 11 55N 51 0 E
Guasaualito 7 15N 70 44W
Guasipati 7 28N 61 54W
Guatemala 14 38N 90 31W
Guatemala ■ 15 40N 90 30W
Guaviare, R. 4 3N 67 44W
Guaxupé 21 10S 47 5W
Guayama 17 59N 66 7W
Guayaquil 2 15S 79 52W
Guayaquil, G. de . 3 10S 81 0W
Gubin .... 51 58N 14 45 E
Gubio .... 12 30N 12 42 E
Guchin-Us .... 45 28N 102 10 E
Gudbrandsdalen ... 62 0N 9 14 E
Gudivada .... 16 30N 81 15 E
Gudur .... 14 12N 79 55 E
Guecho 43 21N 2 59W
Guéckédou 8 40N 10 5W
Guelma .... 36 25N 7 29 E
Guelph 43 35N 80 20W

Güemes 24 50S 65 0W
Guéret .... 46 11N 1 51 E
Guérin Kouka .... 9 40N 0 40 E
Guernica 43 19N 2 40W
Guernsey, I. 49 30N 2 35W
Guerrero □ .... 17 30N 100 0 E
Guiana Highlands,
   Mts. 5 0N 60 0W
Guibes .... 26 41S 16 49 E
Guider .... 9 55N 13 59 E
Guildford 51 14N 0 34W
Guilvinec 47 48N 4 17W
Guimarães 2 9S 44 35W
Guimaras, I. ..... 10 35N 122 37 E
Guinea, Reg. ..... 9 0N 3 0 E
Guinea ■ 10 20N 10 0W
Guinea, G. of .... 3 0N 2 30 E
Guinea-Bissau ■ .. 12 0N 15 0W
Güines 22 50N 82 0W
Guingamp 48 34N 3 10W
Guiria 10 32N 62 1iW
Guiuan .... 11 2N 125 44 E
Gujarat □ .... 23 20N 71 0 E
Gujranwala .... 32 10N 74 12 E
Gujrat .... 32 40N 74 2 E
Gulbarga .... 17 20N 76 50 E
Gulfport 30 28N 89 3W
Gull Lake 50 10N 108 55W
Gulshad .... 46 45N 74 25 E
Gulu .... 2 48N 32 17 E
Gulwe .... 6 30S 36 25 E
Gum Lake .... 32 42S 143 9 E
Guma .... 37 37N 78 18 E
Gumbiro .... 10 1S 35 20 E
Gumla .... 23 2N 84 32 E
Gumma □ .... 36 30N 138 20 E
Gummi .... 12 4N 5 9 E
Guna .... 24 40N 77 19 E
Gundagai .... 35 3S 148 6 E
Gunnedah .... 30 59S 150 15 E
Gunning .... 34 47S 149 14 E
Gunnison, Colo. .. 38 32N 106 56W
Gunnison, Utah .. 39 11N 111 48W
Guntakal .... 15 11N 77 27 E
Guntersville 34 18N 86 16W
Guntur .... 16 23N 80 30 E
Gunungsitoli ..... 1 15N 97 30 E
Gunworth 51 20N 108 10W
Gürchän .... 34 55N 49 25 E
Gurdaspur .... 32 5N 75 25 E

Gurgaon .... 28 33N 77 10 E
Gurley .... 29 45S 149 48 E
Gurupá 1 20S 51 45W
Guryer .... 47 5N 52 0 E
Gusau .... 12 18N 6 31 E
Güstrow .... 53 47N 12 12 E
Gutha .... 28 58S 115 55 E
Guthrie 35 55N 97 30W
Guyana ■ 5 0N 59 0W
Guyenne, Reg. .... 44 30N 0 40 E
Guyra .... 30 15S 151 40 E
Gwa .... 17 30N 94 40 E
Gwadabawa .... 13 20N 5 15 E
Gwädar .... 25 10N 62 18 E
Gwagwada .... 10 15N 7 15 E
Gwalia .... 28 55S 121 20 E
Gwalior .... 26 12N 78 10 E
Gwanda .... 20 55S 29 0 E
Gwandy .... 12 30N 4 41 E
Gwaram .... 11 15N 9 51 E
Gwarzo .... 12 20N 8 55 E
Gwasero .... 9 30N 3 30 E
Gweedore 55 4N 8 15W
Gwelo .... 19 27S 29 49 E
Gwent □ 51 45N 3 0W
Gwio Kura .... 12 40N 11 2 E
Gwynedd □ 53 0N 4 0W
Gwoza .... 11 12N 13 40 E
Gydanskiy Pol. ... 70 0N 78 0 E
Gympie .... 26 11S 152 38 E
Gyöngyös .... 47 48N 20 15 E
Györ .... 47 41N 17 40 E
Gypsumville 51 45N 98 40W
Gyula .... 46 38N 21 17 E

H

Ha Dong .... 20 58N 105 46 E
Haarlem .... 52 23N 4 39 E
Haast, R. .... 43 50S 169 2 E
Hab Nadi Chauki . 25 0N 66 50 E
Habaswein .... 1 1N 39 29 E
Hachinohe .... 40 30N 141 29 E
Hachiōji .... 33 3N 139 50 E
Hackett .... 52 9N 112 28 E
Hadar Ramatayim . 52 8N 34 45 E
Hadd, Ras al ..... 22 35N 59 50 E

Haddington 55 57N 2 48W
Hadejia .... 12 30N 9 59 E
Hadera .... 32 27N 34 55 E
Hadhramawt, Reg. . 15 30N 49 30 E
Hadrian's Wall ... 55 0N 2 30 E
Haeju .... 38 3N 125 41 E
Haerhpin=Harbin . 45 46N 126 51 E
Hafar al Bâtin ... 28 25N 46 50 E
Hafizabad .... 32 5N 73 40 E
Haflong .... 25 10N 93 5 E
Hafnarfjörður 64 3N 21 55W
Hagalil, Reg. .... 32 53N 35 18 E
Hagen .... 51 21N 7 29 E
Hagerstown 39 39N 77 46W
Hagfors .... 60 3N 13 45 E
Hagi, Iceland 65 28N 23 25W
Hagi, Japan ...... 34 30N 131 30 E
Hague, C. de la .. 49 43N 1 57W
Hague, The=
   s'Gravenhage .. 52 7N 4 17 E
Haguenau .... 48 49N 7 47 E
Haifa .... 32 46N 35 0 E
Haig .... 30 55S 126 10 E
Haikow .... 20 0N 110 20 E
Hailar .... 49 12N 119 37 E
Hailar, R. .... 49 35N 117 55 E
Hailey 43 30N 114 15W
Haileybury 47 30N 79 38W
Hailun .... 47 24N 127 0 E
Hailung .... 42 46N 125 57 E
Haimen .... 31 48N 121 8 E
Hainan, I. .... 19 0N 110 0 E
Hainaut □ .... 50 30N 4 0 E
Haines Junction .. 60 45N 137 30W
Haining .... 30 16N 120 47 E
Haiphong .... 20 45N 105 42 E
Haitan Tao, I. ... 25 35N 119 45 E
Haiti ■ 19 0N 72 30W
Haiyen .... 36 45N 105 30 E
Hajdúböszörmény . 47 40N 21 30 E
Hajnówka .... 52 45N 23 36 E
Hajr, Reg. .... 24 0N 56 34 E
Hakodate .... 41 45N 140 44 E
Hakos, Mt. .... 23 25S 16 25 E
Haku-San, Mt. .... 36 9N 136 46 E
Hakui .... 36 53N 136 47 E
Hala .... 25 43N 68 25 E
Halab .... 36 10N 37 15 E
Halaib .... 22 5N 36 30 E
Halberstadt ...... 51 53N 11 2 E

Halcombe	40 8s 175 30 E	Hamlet	34 56N 79 40w
Halden	59 7N 11 30 E	Hamm	51 40N 7 58 E
Haldia	22 4N 88 4 E	Hammerfest	70 33N 23 50 E
Haldwani	29 25N 79 30 E	Hammond, Ind.	41 40N 87 30w
Haleakala, Mt.	20 42N 156 15w	Hammond, La.	30 30N 90 28w
Half Assini	5 1N 2 50w	Hampden	45 18s 170 50 E
Halhul	31 35N 35 7 E	Hampshire □	51 3N 1 20w
Hali	18 40N 41 15 E	Hampton	37 4N 76 8w
Haliburton	45 3N 78 30w	Hamra	24 2N 38 55 E
Halifax, Canada	44 38N 63 35w	Han Kiang, R.	30 32N 114 22 E
Halifax, U.K.	53 43N 1 51w	Han Pijesak	44 3N 18 59 E
Hall Lake	68 30N 81 0w	Hanau	50 8N 8 56 E
Hallands □	57 0N 12 37 E	Hanchung	33 10N 107 2 E
Halle, Belgium	50 44N 4 13w	Hancock	47 10N 88 35w
Halle, E. Germany	51 29N 12 0 E	Handa, Japan	34 53N 137 0 E
Hällefors	59 46N 14 30 E	Handa, Somalia	10 37N 51 2 E
Hallett	33 25s 138 55 E	Handeni	5 25s 38 2 E
Hallingdal	60 40N 8 45 E	Hanegev, Reg.	30 50N 35 0 E
Hällnäs	64 18N 19 40 E	Haney	49 12N 122 40w
Halls Creek	18 20s 128 0 E	Hanford	36 25N 119 45w
Halmahera, I.	0 40N 128 0 E	Hangchou=	
Halmstad	56 37N 12 56 E	Hangchow	30 12N 120 1 E
Halq el Oued	36 53N 10 10 E	Hangchow	30 12N 120 1 E
Hals	56 59N 10 20 E	Hangchow Wan, G.	30 30N 121 30 E
Halvad	23 3N 71 12 E	Hangö	59 59N 22 57 E
Hamã	35 5N 36 40 E	Hanh	51 32N 100 35 E
Hamada	34 50N 132 10 E	Hanita	33 5N 35 10 E
Hamadān	34 52N 48 32 E	Hankow	30 32N 114 20 E
Hamadān □	35 0N 48 40 E	Hanku	39 16N 117 50 E
Hamamatsu	34 45N 137 45 E	Hanmer	42 32s 172 50 E
Hamar	60 48N 11 7 E	Hanna	51 40N 112 0w
Hamburg	53 32N 9 59 E	Hannibal	39 42N 91 22w
Häme □	61 30N 24 30 E	Hannover	52 23N 9 43 E
Hämeenlinna	61 3N 24 26 E	Hanoi	21 5N 105 40 E
Hamelin Pool	26 22s 114 20 E	Hanover, Canada	44 9N 81 2w
Hameln	52 7N 9 24 E	Hanover, Germany=	
Hamersley Ra.	22 0s 117 45 E	Hannover	52 23N 9 43 E
Hamhung	40 0N 127 30 E	Hanover, S. Afr.	31 4s 24 29 E
Hami	42 54N 93 28 E	Hanover, N.H.	43 43N 72 17w
Hamilton,		Hanover, Pa.	39 46N 76 59w
Australia	37 37s 142 0 E	Hanover, I.	50 58s 74 40w
Hamilton, Bermuda	32 15N 64 45w	Hansi	29 10N 75 57 E
Hamilton, Canada	43 20N 79 50w	Hantan	36 42N 114 30 E
Hamilton, N.Z.	37 47s 175 19 E	Hanyang	30 30N 114 19 E
Hamilton, U.K.	55 47N 4 2w	Haparanda	65 52N 24 8 E
Hamilton, Mont.	46 20N 114 6w	Happy Valley	155 53N 60 10w
Hamilton, N.Y.	42 49N 75 31w	Hapur	28 45N 77 45 E
Hamilton, Ohio	39 20N 84 35w	Har-Ayrag	45 50N 109 30 E
Hamilton Hotel	22 45s 140 40 E	Har Us Nuur, L.	48 0N 92 0 E
Hamiota	50 11N 100 38w	Har Yehuda, Reg.	31 40N 35 0 E

Harad	24 15N 49 0 E	Harvey, Australia	33 4s 115 48 E
Haradera	4 33N 47 38 E	Harvey, U.S.A.	41 40N 87 40w
Harbin	45 46N 126 51 E	Harwich	51 56N 1 18 E
Harbour Breton	47 29N 55 50w	Haryana □	29 0N 76 10 E
Harbour Deep	50 25N 56 30w	Harz, Mts.	51 40N 10 40 E
Harbour Grace	47 40N 53 22w	Haslemere	51 5N 0 41w
Harburg	53 27N 9 58 E	Hassan	13 0N 76 5 E
Hardanger Fd.	60 15N 6 0 E	Hasselt	50 56N 5 21 E
Hardap Dam	24 28s 17 48 E	Hassi Messaoud	31 15N 6 35 E
Harderwijk	52 21N 5 36 E	Hassi R'Mel	32 35N 3 24 E
Harding	30 22s 29 55 E	Hastings, N.Z.	39 39s 176 52 E
Hardoi	27 26N 80 15 E	Hastings, U.K.	50 51N 0 36 E
Hardwar	29 58N 78 16 E	Hastings, Mich.	42 40N 85 20 E
Hardy, Pen.	55 30s 68 20w	Hastings, Neb.	40 34N 98 22w
Harer	9 20N 42 8 E	Hatch	32 45N 107 8w
Hargeisa	9 30N 44 2 E	Hatgal	50 40N 100 0 E
Hargshamn	60 12N 18 30 E	Hathras	27 36N 78 6 E
Harlech	52 52N 4 7w	Hatia	22 30N 91 15 E
Harlem	48 29N 108 39w	Hatteras, C.	35 10N 75 30w
Harlingen, Neth.	53 11N 5 25 E	Hattiesburg	31 20N 89 20w
Harlingen, U.S.A.	26 30N 97 50w	Hatvan	47 40N 19 45 E
Harlow	51 47N 0 9 E	Haugesund	59 23N 5 13 E
Harlowton	46 30N 109 54w	Haura	13 50N 47 35 E
Harney L.	43 0N 119 0w	Hauraki, G.	36 35s 175 5 E
Harney Basin	43 30N 119 0w	Haut-Rhin □	48 0N 7 15 E
Harney Pk.	43 52s 103 33w	Haute-Corse □	42 30N 9 0 E
Härnösand	62 38N 18 5 E	Haute-Garonne □	43 28N 1 30 E
Harriman	36 0N 84 35w	Haute-Loire □	45 5N 3 50 E
Harrington		Haute-Marne □	48 10N 5 20 E
Harbour	50 31N 59 30w	Hauterive	49 10N 68 25w
Harris, I.	57 50N 6 55w	Haute-Saône □	47 45N 6 10 E
Harrisburg, Ill.	37 42N 88 30w	Haute-Savoie □	46 0N 6 20 E
Harrisburg, Pa.	40 18N 76 52w	Haute-Vienne □	45 50N 1 10 E
Harrismith	28 15s 29 8 E	Hautes-Alpes □	44 40N 6 30 E
Harrison, Ohio	36 10N 93 4w	Hautes-Pyrénées □	43 0N 0 10 E
Harrison, R.	70 25N 151 0w	Hauts-de-Seine □	48 52N 2 15 E
Harrisonburg	38 28N 78 52w	Havana=	
Harrisonville	38 45N 93 45w	La Habana	23 0N 82 41w
Harriston	43 57N 80 53w	Havant	50 51N 0 59w
Harrogate	53 59N 1 32w	Havel, R.	52 53N 11 58 E
Harrow	51 35N 0 15w	Havelock	44 26N 77 53w
Hartford	41 47N 72 41w	Havelock North	39 42s 176 53 E
Hartland	46 20N 67 32w	Haverfordwest	51 48N 4 59w
Hartland Pt.	51 2N 4 32w	Haverhill	42 50N 71 2w
Hartlepool	54 42N 1 11w	Havering	51 33N 0 20 E
Hartley	18 10s 30 7 E	Havlíckuv Brod	49 36N 15 33 E
Hartley Bay	46 4N 80 45w	Havre	48 40N 109 34w
Hartmannberge	18 0s 12 30 E	Havre St. Pierre	50 18N 63 33w
Hartney	49 30N 100 35w	Havza	41 0N 35 35 E
Hartsville	34 23N 80 2w	Hawaii □	20 0N 155 0w

Hawaii, I.	20 0N 155 0w
Hawea, L.	44 28s 169 19 E
Hawera	39 35s 174 19 E
Hawick	55 25N 2 48w
Hawk Junction	48 5N 84 35w
Hawke, B.	39 25s 177 20 E
Hawker	31 59s 138 22 E
Hawke's Bay □	39 45s 176 35 E
Hawke's Harbour	53 2N 55 50w
Hawkesbury,	
Nova Scotia	45 40N 61 10w
Hawkesbury, Ont.	45 35N 74 40w
Hawthorne	38 37N 118 47w
Hay, Australia	34 30s 144 51 E
Hay, U.K.	52 4N 3 9w
Hay River	60 50N 115 50w
Hayden	40 30N 107 22w
Haydon	18 0s 141 30 E
Hayes, Mt.	63 37N 146 43w
Hayes, R.	57 3N 92 .9w
Hayling I.	50 40N 1 0w
Hays	38 55N 99 25w
Haywards Heath	51 0N 0 5w
Hazarān,	
Küh-e, Mt.	29 35N 57 20 E
Hazard	37 18N 83 10w
Hazaribagh	23 58N 85 26 E
Hazelton	55 20N 127 42w
Hazleton	40 58N 76 0w
Hazor	32 2N 35 2 E
Hazrat Imam	37 15N 68 50 E
Headlands	18 15s 32 2 E
Healdsburg	38 33N 122 51w
Heanor	53 1N 1 20w
Heard I.	53 0s 74 0 E
Hearst	49 40N 83 41w
Heart's Content	47 54s 53 27w
Heath Steele	48 30N 66 20w
Hebel	28 59s 147 48 E
Hebertville	47 0N 71 30w
Hebrides, Inner, Is.	57 20N 6 40w
Hebrides, Outer, Is.	57 50N 7 25w
Hebron, Canada	58 10N 62 50w
Hebron, Jordan	31 32N 35 6 E
Hecate Str.	53 10N 130 30w
Hedaru	4 30s 37 54 E
Hede	62 22N 13 43 E
Hedemora	60 18N 15 48 E
Hedmark □	61 45N 11 0 E
Heemstede	52 19N 4 37 E

Heerde .... 52 24N 6 2 E
Heerenveen ...... 52 57N 5 55 E
Heerlen .... 50 55N 6 0 E
Heidelberg,
  C. Prov. .... 34 6s 20 59 E
Heidelberg, Trans.. 26 30s 28 23 E
Heidelberg,
  W. Germ. ...... 49 23N 8 41 E
Heilbron .... 27 16s 27 59 E
Heilbronn .... 49 8N 9 13 E
Heilungkiang □ ... 47 30N 129 0 E
Heinola .... 61 13N 26 10 E
Heinsburg 53 50N 110 30w
Heinze Is. .... 14 25N 97 45 E
Hekla, Mt. 63 56N 19 35w
Helena, Ark. 34 30N 90 35w
Helena, Mont. ... 46 40N 112 0w
Helensburgh 56 0N 4 44w
Helensville .... 36 41s 174 29 E
Helez .... 31 36N 34 39 E
Heligoland, I. .... 54 10N 7 51 E
Hell-Ville .... 13 25s 48 16 E
Hellendoorn ..... 52 24N 6 27 E
Hellín 38 31N 1 40w
Helmand, Hamun . 31 0N 61 0 E
Helmand □ ...... 31 0N 64 0 E
Helmand, R. ..... 31 12N 61 34 E
Helmond .... 51 29N 5 41 E
Helmsdale 58 7N 3 40w
Helsingborg ..... 56 3N 12 42 E
Helsingfors=
  Helsinki ...... 60 15N 25 3 E
Helsingør .... 56 2N 12 35 E
Helsinki .... 60 15N 25 3 E
Helston 50 7N 5 17w
Helvellyn, Mt. .. 54 31N 3 1w
Helwân .... 29 50N 31 20 E
Hemel
  Hempstead 51 45N 0 28w
Hempstead 40 42N 73 37w
Hemse .... 57 15N 18 20 E
Henares, R. 40 24N 3 30w
Hendaye 43 23N 1 47w
Henderson, Ky. ... 37 50N 87 38w
Henderson, N.C. . 36 18N 78 23w
Henderson, Tex. . 32 5N 94 49w
Hendersonville .. 35 21N 82 28w
Hendon .... 28 5s 151 50 E
Hendrik Verwoerd
  Dam .... 30 38s 25 30 E

Hengelo .... 52 15N 6 48 E
Hengyang .... 26 57N 112 28 E
Henrietta Maria, C. 55 10N 82 30w
Henrique de
  Carvalho ...... 9 39s 20 24 E
Henryetta 35 2N 96 0w
Henty .... 35 30N 147 0 E
Henzada .... 17 38N 95 35 E
Heppner 45 27N 119 34w
Herat .... 34 20N 62 7 E
Herat □ .... 34 20N 62 7 E
Hérault □ .... 43 34N 3 15 E
Herbert 50 30N 107 10w
Herbert Downs ... 23 0s 139 11 E
Hercegnovi ...... 42 30N 18 33 E
Hercegovina □ .... 43 20N 18 0 E
Hereford, U.K. ... 52 4N 2 42w
Hereford, U.S.A. . 34 50N 102 28w
Hereford and
  Worcester □ 52 14N 1 42w
Herentals .... 51 12N 4 51 E
Herford .... 52 7N 8 40 E
Hermanus .... 34 27s 19 12 E
Hermidale .... 31 30s 146 42 E
Hermiston 45 50N 119 16w
Hermitage ...... 43 44s 170 5 E
Hermite, I. 55 50s 68 0w
Hermon, Mt.=
  Sheikh, Jabal ash 33 20N 26 0 E
Hermosillo 29 10N 111 0w
Hernad R. ...... 47 56N 21 8 E
Herne Bay ...... 51 22N 1 8 E
Herning .... 56 8N 9 0 E
Heron Bay 48 40N 85 25w
Herowabad ...... 37 37N 48 32 E
Herrera del
  Duque 39 10N 5 3w
Herrin 37 50N 89 0w
Herstal .... 50 40N 5 38 E
Hertford 51 47N 0 4w
Hertford □ 51 51N 0 5w
Herzliyya .... 32 10N 34 50 E
Hessen □ .... 50 57N 9 20 E
Hewett, C. 70 30N 68 0w
Hexham 54 58N 2 7w
Heysham 54 5N 2 53w
Heywood .... 38 8s 141 37 E
Hibbing 47 30N 93 0w
Hickory 35 46N 81 17w
Hida Sammyaku,

  Mts. .... 36 0N 137 10 E
Hidalgo □ 20 30N 99 10w
Hidalgo del Parral . 26 10N 104 50w
Hierro, I. 27 57N 17 56w
Hifung .... 22 59N 115 17 E
Higashiōsaka .... 34 39N 135 35 E
Higginsville .... 31 42s 121 38 E
High Lava Plat. . 3 40N 36 45 E
High Point 35 57N 79 58w
High Prairie 55 30N 116 30w
High River 50 30N 113 50w
High Veld ...... 26 30s 30 0 E
High Wycombe ... 51 37N 0 45w
Highland □ 57 30N 4 50w
Highland Park, Ill. . 42 10N 87 50w
Highland Park,
  Mich. 42 25N 83 6w
Hijāz, Reg. ..... 26 0N 37 30 E
Hikari .... 33 58N 131 56 E
Hikone .... 35 15N 136 10 E
Hikurangi ...... 37 54s 178 5 E
Hildesheim ..... 52 9N 9 55 E
Hillegom .... 52 18N 4 35 E
Hillingdon 51 33N 0 29w
Hillsboro, Kan. .. 38 28N 97 10w
Hillsboro, Oreg. . 45 31N 123 0w
Hillsboro, Tex. .. 32 0N 97 10w
Hillsport 49 27N 85 34w
Hillston .... 33 30s 145 31 E
Hilo 19 44N 155 5w
Hilversum ...... 52 14N 5 10 E
Himachal
  Pradesh □ .... 31 30N 77 0 E
Himalaya, Mts..... 29 0N 84 0 E
Himatnagar ..... 23 36N 72 58 E
Himeji .... 34 50N 134 40 E
Himi .... 36 50N 137 0 E
Hims=Homs .... 34 40N 36 45 E
Hinchinbrook, I. . 18 20s 146 15 E
Hinckley 52 33N 1 21w
Hindmarsh, L. .. 35 50s 141 55 E
Hindubagh ...... 30 56N 67 57 E
Hindukush, Mts. . 36 0N 71 0 E
Hindupur .... 13 49N 77 32 E
Hines Creek 56 20N 118 40w
Hingan .... 25 39N 110 43 E
Hingcheng ..... 40 21N 120 10 E
Hingham 44 30N 110 29w
Hingi .... 25 4N 105 2 E
Hingning ...... 24 2N 115 55 E

Hingoli .... 19 41N 77 15 E
Hingwa Wan, G. .. 25 0N 120 0 E
Hinnoy, I. ...... 68 40N 16 28 E
Hinton, Canada .. 53 26N 117 28w
Hinton, U.S.A. .. 37 40N 80 51w
Hirakud Dam .... 21 32N 83 45 E
Hiratsuka ...... 35 40N 139 36 E
Hirosaki .... 40 35N 140 25 E
Hiroshima ...... 34 30N 132 30 E
Hiroshima □ .... 34 30N 133 0 E
Hispaniola, I. 19 0N 71 0w
Hissar .... 29 12N 75 45 E
Hita .... 33 42N 130 52 E
Hitachi .... 36 40N 140 35 E
Hitchin 51 57N 0 16w
Hitoyoshi ...... 32 13N 130 45 E
Hitra, I. .... 63 30N 8 45 E
Hjälmaren, L. ... 59 18N 15 40 E
Hjørring .... 57 29N 9 59 E
Ho .... 6 37N 0 27 E
Hoadley 52 45N 114 30w
Hoai Nhon ..... 14 28N 109 1 E
Hobart, Australia . 42 50s 147 21 E
Hobart, U.S.A. .. 35 0N 99 5w
Hobbs 32 40N 103 3w
Hoboken .... 51 11N 4 21 E
Hobro .... 56 39N 9 46 E
Hichih .... 24 43N 107 43 E
Hochwan .... 30 0N 106 15 E
Hodaka-Dake, Mt. . 36 20N 137 30 E
Hodgson 51 20N 97 40w
Hódmezóvásárhely 46 28N 20 22 E
Hodna, Chott el .. 35 30N 5 0 E
Hodonin .... 48 50N 17 0 E
Hoek van Holland . 52 0N 4 7 E
Hoëveld .... 26 30s 30 0 E
Hofei .... 31 45N 116 36 E
Höfu .... 34 0N 130 30 E
Hoggar=
  Ahaggar, Mts. .. 23 0N 6 30 E
Hohpi .... 35 59N 114 13 E
Hoima .... 1 26N 31 21 E
Hokang .... 47 36N 130 28 E
Hokien .... 38 30N 116 2 E
Hokitika .... 42 42s 171 0 E
Hokkaidō □ .... 43 30N 143 0 E
Hokkaidō, I. .... 43 30N 143 0 E
Hokow .... 22 39N 103 57 E
Holan Shan .... 38 40N 105 50 E

Holbrook,
  Australia ...... 35 42s 147 18 E
Holbrook, U.S.A. . 35 0N 110 0w
Holdenville 35 5N 96 25w
Holderness, Pen. .. 53 45N 0 5w
Holguín 20 50N 76 20w
Hollams Bird I. .. 24 40s 14 30 E
Holland =
  Netherlands ■ .. 52 0N 5 30 E
Holland 42 47N 86 0w
Hollandia=
  Jayapura ...... 2 28N 140 38 E
Hollywood, Calif. . 34 0N 118 10w
Hollywood, Fla. ... 26 0N 80 9w
Holman Island .. 70 43N 117 43w
Holmsund ...... 63 41N 20 20 E
Holon .... 32 2N 34 47 E
Holstebro ...... 56 22N 8 33 E
Holy Cross 62 12N 159 47w
Holy, I., Eng. ... 55 42N 1 48w
Holy, I., Wales ... 53 17N 4 37w
Holyhead 53 18N 4 38w
Holyoke 42 14N 72 37w
Homalin .... 24 55N 95 0 E
Hombori .... 15 20N 1 38 E
Home Hill ..... 19 43s 147 25 E
Homedale 43 42N 116 59w
Homer 59 40N 151 35w
Homestead ..... 20 20s 145 40 E
Homs .... 34 40N 36 45 E
Honan □ .... 33 50N 113 15 E
Honda 12 5N 74 45w
Hondeklipbaai ... 30 19s 17 17 E
Hondo, R. 19 26N 99 13w
Honduras ■ 14 40N 86 30w
Honduras, G. de .. 16 50N 87 0w
Hønefoss .... 60 10N 10 12 E
Honfleur .... 49 25N 0 10 E
Hongha, R. ..... 22 0N 104 0 E
Hong Kong ■ ... 22 11N 114 14 E
Honiton 50 48N 3 11w
Honolulu 21 19N 157 52w
Honshū, I. ..... 36 0N 138 0 E
Hood, Pt. ...... 34 23s 119 34 E
Hoogeveen ..... 52 44N 6 30 E
Hoogezand ..... 53 11N 6 45 E
Hooghly, R. ..... 21 56N 88 4 E
Hook Hd. 52 8N 6 57w
Hoonah 58 15N 135 30w

Hoopeston 40 30N 87 40w
Hoorn .... 52 38N 5 4 E
Hoover Dam .. 36 0N 114 45w
Hope, Canada .... 49 25N 121 25 E
Hope, U.S.A. 33 40N 93 30w
Hope, Pt. 68 20N 166 40w
Hope Town 26 30N 76 30w
Hopefield .... 33 3s 18 22 E
Hopei □ .... 39 25N 116 45 E
Hopetown .... 29 34s 24 3 E
Hopetoun, Vic. .. 35 48s 142 25 E
Hopetoun,
   W. Australia .... 33 54s 120 6 E
Hopkinsville 36 52N 87 26w
Hoppo .... 21 32N 109 6 E
Hoquiam 47 0N 123 55w
Hordaland □ ..... 60 25N 6 45 E
Hormoz .... 27 35N 55 0 E
Hormoz, Jazireh-ye 27 4N 56 28 E
Hormoz, Küh-e ... 55 30N 55 30 E
Hormuz, Str. of .. 26 30N 56 30 E
Horn .... 48 39N 15 40 E
Horn, C.=
   Hornos, C. de ... 55 50s 67 30w
Horncastle 53 13N 0 8w
Hornell 42 23N 77 41w
Hornepayne 49 14N 84 48w
Hornos, C. de ... 55 50s 67 30w
Hornsby .... 33 42s 151 2 E
Hornsea 53 55N 0 10w
Horqueta 23 15s 56 55w
Horsens .... 55 52N 9 51 E
Horsham,
   Australia .... 36 44s 142 13 E
Horsham, U.K. 51 4N 0 20w
Horten .... 59 25N 10 32 E
Hoshangabad .... 22 45N 77 44 E
Hoshiarpur ...... 31 30N 75 58 E
Hospet .... 15 15N 76 20 E
Hospitalet de
   Llobregat ..... 41 21N 2 6 E
Hoste, I. 55 0s 69 0w
Hot Springs, Alas. . 64 55N 150 10w
Hot Springs, Ark. . 34 30N 93 0w
Hot Springs, S.D. . 43 25N 103 30w
Hotien .... 37 6N 79 59 E
Hoting .... 64 8N 16 15 E
Houghton-le-
   Spring 54 51N 1 28w
Houhora .... 34 49s 173 9 E

Houlton 46 5N 68 0w
Houma 29 35N 90 50w
Hourne, L. 57 7N 5 35w
Houston 29 50N 5 20w
Hove 50 50N 0 10w
Hövsgöl Nuur, L. . 51 0N 100 30 E
Howard .... 25 16s 152 32 E
Howatharra ..... 28 29s 114 33 E
Howe, C. .... 37 30s 150 0 E
Howick .... 29 28s 30 14 E
Howrah .... 22 37N 88 27 E
Howth Hd. 53 21N 6 0w
Hoy, I. 58 50N 3 15w
Høyanger .... 61 25N 6 50 E
Hradec Králové .. 50 15N 15 50 E
Hron, R. .... 47 49N 18 45 E
Hrvatska □ ...... 45 20N 16 0 E
Hsenwi .... 23 22N 97 55 E
Hsiamen .... 24 28N 118 7 E
Hsian=Sian ...... 34 2N 109 0 E
Hsiao Shan ...... 34 0N 111 30 E
Hsinchow .... 19 37N 109 17 E
Hsinchu .... 24 55N 121 0 E
Hsuchang .... 34 2N 114 0 E
Hsüchou=Suchow . 34 10N 117 20 E
Huacho 11 10s 77 35w
Hualien .... 24 0N 121 30 E
Huancane 15 10s 69 50w
Huancavelica 12 50s 75 5w
Huancayo 12 5s 75 0w
Huangliu .... 18 30N 108 46 E
Huánuco 9 55s 76 15w
Huaraz 9 30s 77 32w
Huascarán, Mt. ... 9 0s 77 30w
Huasco 28 24s 71 15w
Huatabampo 26 50N 109 50w
Hubli .... 15 22N 75 15 E
Huchow .... 30 57N 120 1 E
Huchuetenango ... 15 25N 91 30w
Huddersfield 53 38N 1 49w
Hudson 42 15N 73 46w
Hudson, R. 40 42N 74 2w
Hudson B. 60 0N 86 0w
Hudson Falls 43 18N 73 34w
Hudson Hope ... 56 0N 121 54w
Hudson Str. 62 0N 70 0w
Hué .... 16 30N 107 35 E
Huelva 37 18N 6 57w
Huesca 42 8N 0 25w

Hughenden .... 20 52s 144 10 E
Hughes, Australia . 30 40s 129 30 E
Hughes, U.S.A. .. 66 3N 154 16w
Huhehot .... 40 52N 111 36 E
Huila, Mt. 3 0N 76 0w
Huiling Shan, I. .. 21 35N 111 57 E
Huinca Renancó .. 34 51s 64 22w
Huixtla 15 9N 92 28w
Hukawng Valley .. 26 30N 96 30 E
Hukow .... 29 38N 116 25 E
Hulan .... 46 0N 126 44 E
Hülda .... 31 50N 34 51 E
Hulin .... 45 45N 133 0 E
Hull, Canada 45 20N 75 40w
Hull, U.K. 53 45N 0 20w
Hull, R. 53 44N 0 19w
Huma .... 51 44N 126 42 E
Huma, R. .... 51 40N 126 44 E
Humahuaca 23 10s 65 25w
Humaitá 7 35s 62 40w
Humansdorp ..... 34 2s 24 46 E
Humber, R. ...... 53 32N 0 8 E
Humberside □ 53 45N 0 20w
Humboldt, Canada 52 15N 105 9w
Humboldt, U.S.A. . 35 50N 88 55w
Humboldt, R. 40 2N 118 31w
Hün .... 29 2N 16 0 E
Hunaflói, B. 65 50N 21 0w
Hunan □ .... 27 30N 111 30 E
Hunchun .... 42 49N 130 31 E
Hunedoara ...... 45 40N 22 50 E
Hung Ho, R. .... 33 0N 117 0 E
Hungary ■ ...... 47 20N 19 20 E
Hunghai Wan, G. . 20 30N 115 0 E
Hungshui Ho, R. .. 23 70N 110 30 E
Hunghu .... 29 49N 113 30 E
Hungkiang ...... 27 0N 109 49 E
Hungnam .... 39 59N 127 40 E
Hungtze Hu, L. .. 33 20N 118 35 E
Hunsberge ...... 27 45s 17 12 E
Hunsruck, Mts. ... 50 0N 7 30 E
Hunstanton ...... 52 57N 0 30 E
Hunter, R. ...... 32 50s 151 40 E
Hunterville ...... 39 56s 175 35 E
Huntingdon,
   Canada 45 10N 74 10w
Huntingdon, U.K. . 52 20N 0 11w
Huntington, U.S.A. 40 28N 78 1w
Huntington, Ind. .. 40 52N 85 30w
Huntington, W. Va. 38 20N 82 30w

Huntington Beach . 34 40N 118 0w
Huntington Park .. 33 58N 118 15w
Huntly, N.Z. ..... 37 34s 175 11 E
Huntly, U.K. 57 27N 2 48w
Huntsville, Canada 45 20N 79 14w
Huntsville, Ala. ... 34 45N 86 35w
Huntsville, Tex. .. 30 50N 95 35w
Huonville .... 43 0s 147 5 E
Hupei □ .... 31 5N 113 5 E
Huron 44 30N 98 20w
Huron, L. 45 0N 83 0w
Hurricane ...... 37 10N 113 12 E
Hurunui, R. ..... 42 54s 173 18 E
Húsavik 66 3N 17 13w
Huskvarna ...... 57 47N 14 15 E
Hussein Bridge .. 31 53N 35 33 E
Hutag .... 49 25N 102 34 E
Hutchinson 38 3N 97 59w
Huwará .... 32 9N 35 15 E
Huy .... 50 31N 5 15 E
Hvar, I. .... 43 11N 16 28 E
Hvítá, R., Iceland . 63 50N 21 0w
Hvítá, R., Iceland . 64 40N 22 0w
Hwainan .... 32 44N 117 1 E
Hwang Ho, R. ... 37 32N 118 19 E
Hwangshih ...... 30 27N 115 0 E
Hweian .... 25 2N 118 56 E
Hweitseh .... 26 32N 103 6 E
Hwo Shan, Mts. .. 37 0N 112 30 E
Hwohsien .... 36 30N 111 42 E
Hyannis 42 3N 101 45w
Hyargas Nuur, L.. 49 0N 92 30 E
Hydaburg 55 15N 132 45w
Hyden .... 32 24s 118 46 E
Hyderabad, India . 17 10N 78 29 E
Hyderabad, Pak. .. 25 23N 68 36 E
Hyderabad □ ..... 25 3N 68 24 E
Hyères .... 43 8N 6 9 E
Hyères, Îs. d' .... 43 0N 6 28 E
Hyndman Pk. 44 4N 114 0w
Hyōgo □ .... 35 15N 135 0 E
Hyrum 41 35N 111 56w
Hythe .... 51 4N 1 5 E
Hyvinkää .... 60 38N 25 0 E

I

Iakora .... 23 6s 46 40 E
Ialomiţa, R. ...... 44 42N 27 51 E
Iaşi .... 47 10N 27 40 E
Iaurête 0 30N 69 5w
Ibadan .... 7 22N 3 58 E
Ibagué 4 27N 73 14w
Ibar, R. .... 43 43N 20 45 E
Ibarra 0 21N 78 7w
Ibb .... 14 1N 44 10 E
Iberian Pen. 40 0N 5 0w
Iberville 5 19N 73 17w
Ibicuy 33 55s 59 10w
Ibiza .... 38 54N 1 26 E
Ibiza, I. .... 39 0N 1 30 E
Ibonma .... 3 22s 133 31 E
Ibusuki .... 31 16N 130 39 E
Icá 14 0s 75 30w
Içana 0 21N 67 19w
Iceland ■ 65 0N 19 0w
Icha .... 55 30N 156 0 E
Ichang .... 30 48N 111 29 E
Ichchapuram .... 19 10N 84 40 E
Ichihara .... 35 35N 140 6 E
Ichinomiya ..... 35 20N 136 50 E
Ichun .... 47 42N 129 8 E
Idah .... 6 10N 6 40 E
Idaho □ 44 10N 114 0w
Idaho Falls 43 30N 112 10w
Idaho Springs ... 39 49N 105 30w
Idd el Ghanam ... 11 30N 24 25 E
Idehan Marzúq ... 24 50N 13 51 E
Idfû .... 25 0N 32 49 E
Idi .... 4 55N 97 45 E
Idi Amin Dada, L. . 0 25s 29 40 E
Idlip .... 35 55N 36 38 E
Idna .... 31 34N 34 58 E
Idutywa .... 32 8s 28 18 E
Ieper .... 50 51N 2 53 E
Ifakara .... 8 10s 36 35 E
Ifanadiana ...... 21 29s 47 39 E
Ife .... 7 30N 4 31 E
Ifon .... 6 58N 5 40 E
Igarapava 20 3s 47 47w
Igarapé Açu 1 4s 47 33w
Igarka .... 67 30N 87 20 E
Igawa .... 8 45s 34 23 E

Igbetti .... 8 44N 4 8 E
Igbo-Ora .... 7 10N 3 15 E
Igboho .... 8 40N 3 50 E
Igbor .... 7 30N 8 32 E
Iggesund .... 61 39N 17 10 E
Iglésias .... 39 19N 8 27 E
Igloolik Island 69 20N 81 30w
Ignace 49 30N 91 40w
Iguaçu, R. 25 30s 53 10w
Iguaçu Falls 25 40s 54 33w
Iguala 18 20N 99 40w
Igualada .... 41 37N 1 37 E
Iguape 24 43s 47 33w
Iguatu 6 20s 39 18w
Ihiala .... 5 40N 6 55 E
Ihosy .... 22 24s 46 8 E
Ihsien .... 41 45N 121 3 E
Iida .... 35 35N 138 0 E
Iisalmi .... 63 32N 27 10 E
Iizuka .... 33 38N 130 42 E
Ijebu-Igbo .... 6 56N 4 1 E
Ijebu-Ode .... 6 47N 3 52 E
Ijmuiden .... 52 28N 4 35 E
Ijsel, R. .... 52 30N 6 0 E
Ijsselmeer, L. .... 52 45N 5 20 E
Ikaría, I. .... 37 35N 26 10 E
Ikeda .... 34 1N 133 48 E
Ikeja .... 6 28N 3 45 E
Ikerre-Ekiti ...... 7 25N 5 19 E
Iki, I. .... 33 45N 129 42 E
Ikire .... 7 10N 4 15 E
Ikom .... 6 0N 8 42 E
Ikot Ekpene ...... 5 12N 7 40 E
Ikurun .... 7 55N 4 41 E
Ila .... 8 0N 4 51 E
Ilagan .... 17 9N 121 53 E
Ilan .... 46 14N 121 33 E
Ilanskiy .... 56 14N 96 3 E
Ilaro .... 6 53N 3 3 E
Ilbilbie .... 21 45s 149 20 E
Île de France,
  Reg. .... 49 0N 2 20 E
Ilebo .... 4 17s 20 47 E
Ilero .... 8 0N 3 20 E
Ilesha .... 8 57N 3 28 E
Ilfracombe,
  Australia ...... 23 30s 144 30 E
Ilfracombe, U.K. .. 51 13N 4 8w
Ilha Grande, B. da. 23 10s 44 30w
Ilhéus 15 0s 39 10w

Iliamna L. 59 30N 155 0w
Iliamna, Mt....... 60 5N 153 9w
Ilich .... 41 0N 68 10 E
Ilion 43 0N 75 3w
Iliysk=Kapchagai . 44 10N 77 20 E
Ilkeston 52 59N 1 19w
Ilkhuri Shan, Mts. . 51 30N 124 0 E
Illapel 32 0s 71 10w
Ille-et-
  Vilaine □ 48 10 1 30w
Illimani, Mt. 16 30s 67 50w
Illinois, R. 38 58N 90 27w
Illinois □ 40 15N 89 30w
Illizi .... 26 31N 8 32 E
Ilmen, Oz. .... 5 15N 31 10 E
Ilo 17 40s 71 20w
Ilobu .... 7 45N 4 25 E
Iloilo .... 10 45N 122 33 E
Ilongero .... 4 45s 34 55 E
Ilora .... 7 45N 3 50 E
Ilorin .... 8 30N 4 35 E
Ilwaki .... 7 55s 126 30 E
Imabari .... 34 4N 133 0 E
Iman .... 45 50N 133 40 E
Imandra, Oz. ...... 67 45N 33 0 E
Imari .... 33 15N 129 52 E
Immingham 53 37N 0 12w
Imo □ .... 4 15N 7 30 E
Imola .... 44 20N 11 42 E
Imperatriz 5 30s 47 29w
Impéria .... 43 52N 8 0 E
Imperial,
  Canada 51 21N 105 28w
Imperial, U.S.A. .. 32 52N 115 34w
Imperial Dam 32 50N 114 30w
Impfondo .... 1 40N 18 0 E
Imphal .... 24 15N 94 0 E
Imwas .... 31 51N 34 59 E
In Salah .... 27 10N 2 32 E
Inangahua
  Junction ...... 41 52s 171 59 E
Inari .... 68 54N 27 5 E
Inari, L. .... 69 0N 28 0 E
Inca .... 39 43N 2 54 E
Inchǒn .... 37 32N 126 45 E
Indaw .... 24 15N 96 5 E
Independence,
  Kans. 37 10N 95 50w
Independence, Mo. 39 3N 94 25w
Independence,

  Oreg. 44 53N 123 6w
India ■ .... 23 0N 77 30 E
Indian Cabin 59 50N 117 12w
Indian Head 50 30N 103 35w
Indian Ocean ...... 5 0s 75 0 E
Indiana 40 38N 79 9w
Indiana □ 40 0N 86 0w
Indianapolis 39 42N 86 10w
Indianola 41 20N 93 38w
Indiga .... 67 50N 48 50 E
Indonesia ■ ...... 5 0s 115 0 E
Indore .... 22 42N 75 53 E
Indramaju .... 6 21s 108 20 E
Indravati, R. ...... 18 43N 80 17 E
Indre □ .... 46 45N 1 30 E
Indre-et-Loire □ .. 47 12N 0 40 E
Indus, R. .... 24 20N 67 47 E
Inebolu .... 41 55N 33 40 E
Inegöl .... 40 5N 29 31 E
Ingersoll 43 4N 80 55w
Ingham .... 18 43s 146 10 E
Ingleborough, Mt. . 54 11N 2 23w
Inglewood, N.S.W. . 28 25s 151 8 E
Inglewood, Vic. ... 36 29s 143 53 E
Inglewood, N.Z. ... 39 9s 174 14 E
Inglewood 33 58N 118 27w
Ingolstadt 48 45N 11 26w
Ingulec .... 47 42N 33 4 E
Inhambane ...... 23 54s 35 30 E
Inhambane □ ...... 22 30s 34 20 E
Inharrime .... 24 30s 35 0 E
Ining, Kwangsi-
  Chuang ...... 25 8N 109 57 E
Ining
  Sinkiang-Uigur .. 43 57N 81 20 E
Inishmore, I. 53 8N 9 45w
Inishowen, Pen. ... 55 14N 7 15w
Inland Sea=
  Setonaikai .... 34 10N 133 10 E
Inn, R. .... 48 35N 13 28 E
Inner Mongolian
  Autonomous
  Rep. □ .... 44 50N 117 40 E
Innisfail,
  Australia ...... 17 33s 146 5 E
Innisfail, Canada .. 52 0N 114 0w
Innsbruck .... 47 16N 11 23 E
Inowrocław ...... 52 50N 18 20 E
Inscription, C. .... 25 29s 112 59 E
Insein .... 16 46N 96 18 E

Inta .... 66 2N 60 8 E
Interlaken .... 46 41N 7 50 E
International Falls . 48 30N 93 25w
Intiyaco 28 50s 60 0w
Inútil, B. 53 30s 70 15w
Inuvik 68 25N 133 30w
Inveraray 56 13N 5 5w
Inverbervie 56 50N 2 17w
Invercargill ...... 46 24s 168 24 E
Inverell .... 29 48s 151 36 E
Invergordon 57 41N 4 10w
Invermere 50 51N 116 9w
Inverness, Canada . 46 15N 61 19w
Inverness, U.K. ... 57 29N 4 12w
Inverurie 57 15N 2 21w
Inverway .... 17 50s 129 38 E
Investigator, Str. .. 35 30s 137 0 E
Inyangani, Mt. .... 18 20s 32 20 E
Inyokern 35 37N 117 54w
Inza .... 53 55N 46 25 E
Ioánnina .... 39 42N 20 55 E
Iola 38 0N 95 20w
Iona, I. 56 20N 6 25w
Ionia 42 59N 85 7w
Ionian Is.=
  Iónioi Nísoi ...... 38 40N 20 8 E
Ionian Sea .... 37 30N 17 30 E
Iónioi Nísoi, Is. ... 38 40N 20 8 E
Íos, I. .... 36 41N 25 20 E
Iowa □ 42 18N 93 30w
Iowa City 41 40N 91 35w
Iowa Falls 42 30N 93 15w
Ipameri 17 44s 48 9w
Ipiales 1 0N 77 45w
Ipin .... 28 58N 104 45 E
Ipiros □ .... 39 30N 20 30 E
Ipoh .... 4 36N 101 4 E
Ipswich,
  Australia ...... 27 38s 152 37 E
Ipswich, U.K. ..... 52 4N 1 9 E
Ipu 4 23s 40 44w
Iquique 20 19s 70 5w
Iquitos 3 45s 73 10w
Iracoubo .... 53 .N 53 10w
Iráklion .... 35 20s 25 12 E
Iran ■ .... 33 0N 53 0 E
Iran, Plat. of ...... 32 0N 57 0 E
Iranshahr .... 27 75N 60 40 E
Irapuato 20 40N 101 40w
Iraq ■ .... 33 0N 44 0 E

Irbid .... 32 35N 35 48 E
Ireland, I., Bermuda 32 19N 64 50w
Ireland, I., Europe 53 0N 8 0w
Irele .... 7 40N 5 40 E
Iret .... 60 10N 154 5 E
Iri .... 35 59N 127 0 E
Irian Jaya □ ...... 5 0s 140 0 E
Iriba .... 15 7N 22 15 E
Iringa .... 7 48s 33 43 E
Iriri, R. 3 52s 52 37w
Irish Republic ■ .. 53 0N 8 0 E
Irish Sea .... 54 0N 145 12 E
Irkineyeva .... 58 30N 96 49 E
Irkutsk .... 52 10N 104 20 E
Iron Mountain 45 49N 88 4w
Ironbridge 52 38N 2 29w
Ironton 38 35N 82 40w
Ironwood 46 30N 90 10w
Iroquois Falls 48 40N 80 40w
Irrawaddy, R. ...... 15 50N 95 6 E
Irshih .... 47 8N 119 57 E
Irtysh, R. .... 61 4N 68 52 E
Irumu .... 1 32N 29 53 E
Irún 43 20N 1 52w
Irvine 55 37N 4 40w
Irvinestown 54 28N 7 38w
Irwin, Pt. .... 35 4s 116 56 E
Irymple .... 34 14s 142 8 E
Isa .... 13 14N 6 24 E
Ísafjördur 66 5N 23 9w
Isahaya .... 32 50N 130 3 E
Isaka .... 3 56s 32 59 E
Isangi .... 0 52N 24 10 E
Isar, R. .... 48 49N 12 58 E
Íschia, I. .... 40 45N 13 51 E
Iscia Baidoa ...... 3 40N 43 0 E
Ise .... 34 29N 136 42 E
Ise-Wan, G. ...... 34 45N 136 45 E
Isère, R. .... 44 59N 4 51 E
Isère □ .... 45 10N 5 50 E
Iseyin .... 8 0N 3 36 E
Isfahan=Esfahan . 32 40N 51 38 E
Ishan .... 24 30N 108 41 E
Ishikari-Wan ...... 43 20N 141 20 E
Ishikawa □ .... 36 30N 136 30 E
Ishim, R. .... 57 45N 71 10 E
Ishinomaki .... 38 32N 141 20 E
Ishkuman .... 36 40N 73 50 E
Ishpeming 46 30N 87 40w
Isiolo .... 0 24N 37 33 E

Isipingo Beach .... 29 59s 30 57 E
Isiro .... 2 53N 27 58 E
Isisford .... 24 15s 144 21 E
Iskenderun .... 36 32N 36 10 E
Isla, R. 56 30N 3 25W
Islamabad .... 33 40N 73 0 E
Island, Pt. .... 30 20s 115 2 E
Island L. 53 40N 94 30W
Island Falls 49 35N 81 20W
Island Pond 44 50N 71 50W
Islands, B. of 49 11N 58 15W
Islas Malvinas=
Falkland Is. 51 30s 59 0W
Islay, I. 55 46N 6 10W
Isle of Man □ ... 54 15N 4 30W
Isle of Wight □ ... 36 54N 76 43W
Ismâ'ilîya .... 30 37N 32 18 E
Isna .... 25 17N 32 30 E
Isoka .... 10 4s 32 42 E
Isparta .... 37 47N 30 30 E
Ispica .... 36 47N 14 53 E
Israel ■ .... 32 0N 34 50 E
Isseka .... 28 22s 114 35 E
Issyk Kul, L. ..... 42 30N 77 30 E
Istanbul .... 41 0N 29 0 E
Istra, Pen. .... 45 10N 14 0 E
Itabira 19 29s 43 23W
Itabuna 14 48s 39 16W
Itacaré 14 18s 39 0W
Itaeté 13 0s 41 5W
Itaituba 4 10s 55 50W
Itajaí 27 0s 48 45W
Italy ■ .... 42 0N 13 0 E
Itapecuru-Mirim . 3 20s 44 15W
Itaperaba 12 32s 40 18W
Itaperuna 21 10s 42 0W
Itaquatiana 2 58s 58 30W
Itaqúi 29 0s 56 30W
Ithaca 42 25N 76 30W
Itháki, I. .... 38 25N 20 40 E
Itigi .... 5 42s 34 29 E
Ito .... 34 58N 139 5 E
Itu, Brazil 23 10s 47 15W
Itu, Nigeria ...... 5 10N 7 58 E
Ituiutaba 19 0s 49 50W
Ituliho .... 50 40N 121 30 E
Itumbiara 18 20s 49 10W
Ituna 51 10N 103 30W
Iturbe 23 0s 65 25W
Ivalo .... 68 38N 27 35 E

Ivanhoe .... 32 56s 144 20 E
Ivano-Frankovsk :. 49 0N 24 40 E
Ivanovo .... 57 0N 40 55 E
Iviza, I.=Ibiza, I. . 39 0N 1 30 E
Ivohibe .... 22 29s 46 52 E
Ivory Coast ■ ... 7 30N 5 0 E
Ivrea .... 45 30N 7 52 E
Ivugivik 62 18N 77 50W
Iwaki .... 37 3N 140 55 E
Iwakuni .... 34 15N 132 8 E
Iwata .... 34 49N 137 59 E
Iwate □ .... 39 30N 141 30 E
Iwo .... 7 39N 4 9 E
Ixtepec 16 40N 95 10W
Ixtlán 21 5N 104 28W
Izamal 20 56N 89 1W
Izegem .... 50 55N 3 12 E
Izhevsk .... 56 50N 53 0 E
Izmir .... 38 25N 27 8 E
Izmit .... 40 45N 29 50 E
Izra .... 32 51N 36 15 E
Izumi-sano ..... 34 40N 135 43 E
Izumo .... 35 20N 132 55 E

J

Jaba .... 32 20N 35 13 E
Jabalîya .... 31 32N 34 27 E
Jabalpur .... 23 9N 79 58 E
Jablah .... 35 20N 36 0 E
Jablonec .... 50 43N 15 10 E
Jaca 42 35N 0 33W
Jacareí 23 20s 46 0W
Jacarèzinho 23 5s 50 0W
Jackson,
Australia ...... 26 40s 149 30 E
Jackson, Ky. 37 35N 83 22W
Jackson, Mich. ... 42 18N 84 25W
Jackson, Minn. ... 43 35N 95 30W
Jackson, Tenn. ... 35 40N 88 50W
Jackson Bay 50 32N 125 57W
Jacksons .... 42 46N 171 32 E
Jacksonville, Fla. . 30 15N 81 38W
Jacksonville, Ill. .. 39 42N 90 15W
Jacksonville, Ill. .. 39 42N 90 15W
Jacksonville, N.C. . 34 50N 77 29W
Jacksonville, Tex. . 31 58N 95 12W

Jacksonville Beach 30 19N 81 26W
Jacmel 18 20N 72 40W
Jacobabad .... 28 20N 68 29 E
Jacobina 11 11s 40 30W
Jacob's Well ..... 32 13N 35 13 E
Jacques Cartier, Mt. 48 57N 66 0W
Jacques Cartier
Pass. 49 50N 62 30W
Jaén 37 44N 3 43W
Jaffa=Tel Aviv-
Yafo .... 32 4N 34 48 E
Jaffna .... 9 45N 80 2 E
Jagdalpur .... 19 3N 82 6 E
Jagersfontein .... 29 44s 25 27 E
Jaghbub .... 29 42N 24 38 E
Jagraon .... 30 50N 75 25 E
Jagtial .... 18 50N 79 0 E
Jaguarão 32 30s 53 30W
Jaguariaíva 24 10s 49 50W
Jaguey 22 35N 81 7W
Jagungal, Mt. ... 36 12s 148 28W
Jahrom .... 28 30N 53 31 E
Jaipur .... 26 54N 72 52 E
Jakarta .... 6 9s 106 49 E
Jakobstad .... 63 40N 22 43 E
Jalalabad .... 34 30N 70 29 E
Jalapa,
Guatemala 14 45N 89 59W
Jalapa, Mexico 19 30N 96 50W
Jalgaon .... 21 0N 75 42 E
Jalingo .... 8 55N 11 25 E
Jalisco □ 20 0N 104 0W
Jalna .... 19 48N 75 57 E
Jalor .... 25 20N 72 41 E
Jalpaiguri .... 26 32N 88 46 E
Jamaari .... 11 44N 9 53 E
Jamaica ■ 18 10N 77 30W
Jamalpur,
Bangladesh .... 24 52N 90 2 E
Jamalpur, India ... 25 18N 86 28 E
Jamari .... 11 2N 11 0 E
Jambi .... 1 38s 103 30 E
Jambi □ .... 1 30s 103 30 E
James B. 53 30N 80 30W
James, R. 44 50N 98 0W
Jamestown,
Australia ...... 33 10s 138 32 E
Jamestown, S.Afr. . 31 6s 26 45 E
Jamestown, N.D. .. 47 0N 98 30W
Jamestown, N.Y. .. 42 5N 79 18W

Jamkhandi .... 16 30N 75 15 E
Jammu .... 32 46N 75 57 E
Jammu and
Kashmir □ 34 25N 77 0w
Jamnagar .... 22 30N 70 0 E
Jamshedpur ..... 22 44N 86 20 E
Jämtlands □ ..... 62 40N 13 50 E
Jan Mayen, I. 71 0N 11 0w
Jand .... 33 30N 72 0 E
Jandowae .... 26 45s 151 7 E
Janesville 42 39N 89 1w
Jansenville ...... 32 57s 24 39 E
Januária 15 25s 44 25W
Jaora .... 23 40N 75 10 E
Japan ■ .... 36 0N 136 0 E
Japara .... 6 30s 110 40 E
Japurá, R. 3 8s 64 46W
Jarales 34 44N 106 51W
Jarama, R. 40 2N 3 39W
Jaramillo 47 10s 67 7W
Jardines de la
Reina, Is. 20 50N 78 50W
Jargalant .... 47 2N 115 1 E
Jarosław .... 50 2N 22 42 E
Jarvis I. 0 15s 159 55W
Jarwa .... 27 45N 82 30 E
Jāsk .... 25 38N 57 45 E
Jasło .... 49 45N 21 30 E
Jason Is, ... 51 0s 61 0w
Jasper, Canada ... 52 55N 118 0w
Jasper, U.S.A. 30 31N 82 58w
Jasper Nat.
Park 52 53N 118 3w
Jasper Place 53 33N 113 25w
Jászberény ...... 47 30N 19 55 E
Jataí 17 50s 51 45w
Jatibarang ...... 6 28s 108 18 E
Jatinegara ...... 6 13s 106 52 E
Játiva 39 0N 0 32w
Jatobal 4 35s 49 33w
Jatt .... 32 24N 35 2 E
Jaú 22 10s 48 30w
Jaunpur .... 25 46N 82 44 E
Java, I. .... 7 0s 110 0 E
Java Sea .... 4 35s 107 15 E
Java Trench ..... 10 0s 110 0 E
Jaya, Puncak, Mt. . 4 0s 137 20 E
Jayapura .... 2 28s 140 38 E
Jayawijaya,
Pengunungan .. 4 50s 139 0 E

Jaydot 49 15N 110 15w
Jean Marie River .. 62 0N 121 0w
Jebāl Barez,
Kūh-e .... 29 0N 58 0 E
Jebba, Morocco ... 35 11N 4 43w
Jebba, Nigeria ... 9 9N 4 48 E
Jebel, Bahr el, R. . 9 40N 30 30 E
Jedburgh 55 28N 2 33w
Jędrzejów .... 50 35N 20 15 E
Jefferson, Mt. 38 51N 117 0w
Jefferson City ... 36 8N 83 30w
Jeffersonville 38 20N 85 42w
Jega .... 12 15N 4 23 E
Jelenia Góra ..... 50 50N 15 45 E
Jelgava .... 56 41N 22 49 E
Jember .... 8 11s 113 41 E
Jemeppe .... 50 37N 5 30 E
Jena .... 50 56N 11 33 E
Jenín .... 32 28N 35 18 E
Jenkins 37 13N 82 41w
Jennings 30 10N 92 45w
Jequié 13 51s 40 5w
Jequitinhonha ... 16 30s 41 0w
Jerada 34 40N 2 10w
Jerantut .... 3 56N 102 22 E
Jérémie 18 40N 74 10w
Jerez de Gacia
Salinas 22 39N 103 0w
Jerez de la
Frontera 36 41N 6 7w
Jericho, Australia . 23 38s 146 6 E
Jericho, Jordan=
El Ariha .... 31 52N 35 27 E
Jerilderie .... 35 20s 145 41 E
Jerome 34 50N 112 0w
Jersey, I. 49 15N 2 10w
Jersey City 40 41N 74 8w
Jersey Shore 41 17N 77 18w
Jerseyville 39 5N 90 20w
Jerusalem .... 31 47N 35 10 E
Jervis Bay .... 35 8s 150 46 E
Jesselton=Kota
Kinabalu ...... 6 0N 116 12 E
Jessore .... 23 10N 89 10 E
Jeypore .... 18 50N 82 38 E
Jhal Jhao .... 26 20N 65 35 E
Jhang Maghiana .. 31 15N 72 15 E
Jhansi .... 25 30N 78 36 E
Jharsuguda ..... 21 51N 84 1 E
Jhelum .... 33 0N 73 45 E

Jhelum, R. .... 31 12N 72 8 E
Jhunjhunu .... 28 10N 75 20 E
Jiddah .... 21 29N 39 16 E
Jifna .... 31 58N 35 13 E
Jihchao .... 35 18N 119 28 E
Jihlava .... 49 28N 15 35 E
Jihlava, R. ...... 48 55N 16 37 E
Jijiga .... 9 20N 42 50 E
Jiloca, R. 41 21N   1 39W
Jima .... 7 40N 36 55 E
Jiménez 27 10N 105 0W
Jinja .... 0 25N 33 12 E
Jinnah Barrage ... 32 58N 71 33 E
Jinné .... 51 32N 121 25 E
Jinotega 13 6N 85 59W
Jinotepe 11 50N 86 10W
Jipijapa 1 0s 80 40W
Jisr ash
  Shughur ...... 35 49N 36 18 E
Jitarning .... 32 48s 117 57 E
Jiu, R. .... 43 47N 23 48 E
Joaçaba 27 5s 51 31W
João Belo ...... 25 7s 33 32 E
João Pessoa 7 10s 34 52W
Joaquin Villa
  González 25 10s 64 0W
Jodhpur .... 26 23N 73 2 E
Joggins 45 42N 64 27W
Johannesburg .. 26 10s 28 8 E
John O'Groats ... 58 39N   3 3W
Johnson City, N.Y. 42 9N 67 0W
Johnson City,
  Tenn. 36 18N 82 21W
Johnson's Crossing 60 33N 133 27W
Johnstown 43 1N 74 20W
Johor Baharu ... 1 45N 103 47 E
Joinvile .... 26 15s 48 55 E
Jokkmokk ..... 66 35N 19 50 E
Joliet 41 30N 88 0W
Joliette 46 3N 73 24W
Jolo, I. .... 6 0N 121 0 E
Jombang ...... 7 32s 112 12 E
Jones, C. 54 33N 79 35W
Jonesboro 35 50N 90 45W
Jönköping ..... 57 45N 14 10 E
Jönköpings □ ... 57 30N 14 30 E
Joplin 37 0N 94 25W
Jordan ■ ...... 31 0N 36 0 E
Jordan, R. ..... 31 46N 35 33 E
Jorhat .... 26 45N 94 20 E

Jörn .... 65 5N 20 12 E
Jos .... 9 53N   8 51 E
Jos Plat. ...... 9 45N   8 45 E
José Batlle y
  Ordóñez 33 20s 55 10W
José de San
  Martín 44 4s 70 26W
Joseph Bonaparte,
  G. .... 14 0s 29 0 E
Jotunheimen, Mts. . 61 30N   9 0 E
Jounieh .... 33 59N 35 30 E
Jouzjan □ 22 40N 81 10W
Juan de Fuca Str. .. 48 15N 124 0W
Juan Fernández,
  Arch. de 33 50s 80 0W
Juárez 37 40s 59 43W
Juàzeiro 9 30s 40 30W
Juazeiro do
  Norte 7 10s 39 18W
Jûbâ .... 4 57N 31 35 E
Jubaila .... 24 55N 46 25 E
Juby, C. 28 0N 12 59W
Júcar, R. 39 40N   2 18W
Juchitán 16 27N 95 5W
Judaea=Har
  Yehuda, Reg. .. 31 35N 34 57 E
Juiz de Fora ... 21 43s 43 19W
Juli 16 10s 69 25W
Julia Creek .... 20 40s 141 55 E
Juliaca 15 25s 70 10W
Julianatop, Mt. .. 3 40N 56 30W
Julianehåb 60 43N 46 0W
Jullundur ..... 31 20N 75 40 E
Jumento Cays ... 23 40N 75 40 E
Jumet .... 50 27N   4 25 E
Jumilla 38 28N   1 19W
Jumna, R.=
  Yamuna, R. ... 25 25N 81 50 E
Junagadh ..... 21 30N 70 30 E
Junction City, Kans. 39 4N 96 55W
Junction City, Oreg. 44 20N 123 12W
Jundah .... 24 46s 143 2 E
Jundiaí 23 10s 47 0W
Juneau 58 26N 134 30W
Junee 34 49s 147 32W
Junín 34 33s 60 57W
Junin de los
  Andes 39 45s 71 0W
Juquiá 24 19s 47 38W
Jura, I. 56 0N   5 50W

Jura, Mts. ...... 46 45N   6 30 E
Jura □ .... 46 47N   5 45 E
Jurado 7 7N 77 46W
Jurm .... 36 50N 70 45 E
Juruá, R. 2 37s 65 44W
Juruti 2 9s 56 4W
Justo Daract 33 52s 65 12W
Juticalpa 14 40N 85 50W
Jutland=
  Jylland, Reg.... 56 25N   9 30 E
Južna Morava, R. . 43 35N 21 20 E
Jyekundo ...... 33 0N 96 50 E
Jylland, Reg. ... 56 25N   9 30 E
Jyväskylä ...... 62 12N 25 47 E

K

K2, Mt. .... 36 0N 77 0 E
Kaap Plato ..... 28 30s 24 0 E
Kaapstad=
  Cape Town ... 33 55s 18 22 E
Kabaena, I. .... 5 15s 122 0 E
Kabale 9 38N 11 37W
Kabalo .... 6 0s 27 0 E
Kabambare ..... 4 41s 27 39 E
Kabarega Falls ... 2 15s 31 38 E
Kabarnet ...... 0 35N 35 50 E
Kabba .... 7 57N   6 3 E
Kabinda .... 6 23s 24 38 E
Kabongo ...... 7 22s 25 33 E
Kabra .... 23 25s 150 25 E
Kabul .... 34 28N 69 18 E
Kabul □ .... 34 0N 68 30 E
Kabwe .... 14 30s 28 29 E
Kachin □ ...... 26 0N 97 0 E
Kachiry .... 53 10N 75 50 E
Kachung ...... 1 48N 32 50 E
Kadan Kyun .... 12 30N 98 20 E
Kade 6 7N   0 56W
Kadina .... 34 0s 137 43 E
Kadiyerka ..... 48 35N 38 30 E
Kaduna .... 10 30N   7 21 E
Kaduna □ ..... 11 0N   7 30 E
Kaelé .... 10 15N 14 15 E
Kaerh .... 31 45N 80 22 E
Kaesŏng ...... 37 58N 126 35 E
Kafanchan .... 9 40N   8 20 E

Kafulwe .... 9 0s 29 1 E
Kafia Kingi .... 9 20N 24 25 E
Kafirévs, Åkra .. 38 9N 24 8 E
Kafr Kanna .... 32 45N 35 20 E
Kafr Ra'i ...... 32 23N 35 9 E
Kafue, R. ...... 15 56s 28 55 E
Kafulwe .... 9 0s 29 1 E
Kagan .... 39 43N 64 33 E
Kagawa □ ..... 34 15N 134 0 E
Kagoshima .... 31 36N 130 40 E
Kagoshima □ ... 30 0N 130 0 E
Kahama .... 4 8s 32 30 E
Kahe .... 3 30s 37 25 E
Kai, Kep ...... 5 55s 132 45 E
Kaiapoi .... 42 24s 172 40 E
Kaifeng .... 34 50N 114 27 E
Kaikohe ...... 35 25s 173 49 E
Kaikoura ...... 42 25s 173 43 E
Kailua 21 24N 157 44W
Kainji Res. .... 10 1N   4 40 E
Kaipara, Harbour . 36 25s 174 14 E
Kaiping .... 40 28N 122 10 E
Kairouan ...... 35 45N 10 5 E
Kaiserslautern ... 49 30N   7 43 E
Kaitaia .... 35 8s 173 17 E
Kaitangata .... 46 17s 169 51 E
Kaiyuan ...... 42 33N 124 4 E
Kajaani .... 64 17N 27 46 E
Kajiado .... 1 53s 36 48 E
Kakamega ..... 0 20N 34 46 E
Kake .... 34 6N 132 19 E
Kakegawa ..... 34 45N 138 1 E
Kakhovka ..... 46 46N 34 28 E
Kakinada=
  Cocanada .... 16 50N 82 11 E
Kakogawa ..... 34 46N 134 51 E
Kala .... 12 2N 14 40 E
Kalabagh ..... 33 0N 71 28 E
Kalabahi ...... 8 13s 124 31 E
Kalabáka ..... 39 42N 21 39 E
Kalach .... 50 22N 41 0 E
Kaladan, R. .... 20 9N 92 57 E
Kalahari, Des. ... 24 0s 22 0 E
Kalakan ...... 55 15N 116 45 E
Kalamata ..... 37 3N 22 10 E
Kalamazoo 42 20N 85 35W
Kalamunda .... 32 0s 116 0 E
Kalan .... 39 7N 39 32 E
Kalannie ...... 30 22s 117 5 E
Kalat .... 29 8N 66 31 E

Kalat-i-
  Ghilzai .... 32 15N 66 58 E
Kalemie ...... 5 55s 29 9 E
Kalewa .... 22 41N 95 32 E
Kalgoorlie .... 30 40s 121 22 E
Kaliakra, Nos. .. 43 21N 28 30 E
Kalibo .... 11 43N 122 22 E
Kalimantan □ ... 0 0 115 0 E
Kálimnos, I. .... 37 0N 27 0 E
Kalinin .... 56 55N 35 55 E
Kaliningrad .... 54 44N 20 32 E
Kalispell ...... 48 10N 114 22 E
Kalisz .... 53 17N 18 55 E
Kaliua .... 5 5s 31 48 E
Kallia .... 31 46N 35 30 E
Kalmalo ...... 13 40N   5 20 E
Kalmar .... 56 40N 16 20 E
Kalmar □ ..... 57 0N 16 15 E
Kalmyk A.S.S.R. □ 46 5N 46 1 E
Kalmykovo .... 49 0N 51 35 E
Kalocsa ...... 46 32N 19 0 E
Kalomo ...... 17 0s 26 30 E
Kaltag 64 20N 158 44W
Kaltungo ..... 9 48N 11 19 E
Kaluga .... 54 35N 36 10 E
Kalundborg .... 55 41N 11 5 E
Kama, R. ..... 55 45N 52 0 E
Kamachumu ... 1 37s 31 37 E
Kamaishi ..... 39 20N 142 0 E
Kamaran, I. .... 15 28N 42 35 E
Kamba .... 11 50N   3 45 E
Kambalda ..... 31 10s 121 37 E
Kambarka .... 56 17N 54 12 E
Kamchatka Pol. .. 57 0N 160 0 E
Kamembe ..... 2 29s 28 54 E
Kamen .... 53 50N 81 30 E
Kamenets
  Podolskiy ... 48 40N 26 30 E
Kamenka ..... 65 58N 44 0 E
Kamensk
  Shakhtinskiy .. 48 23N 40 20 E
Kamensk
  Uralskiy ..... 56 28N 61 54 E
Kamenskoye ... 62 45N 165 30 E
Kameoka ..... 35 0N 135 35 E
Kamina ...... 8 45s 25 0 E
Kamloops 50 40N 120 20W
Kampala ..... 0 20N 32 30 E
Kampen ...... 52 33N   5 53 E
Kampot ...... 10 36N 104 10 E

Kampuchea■ =
Cambodia ■ .... 12 15N 105 0 E
Kamsack 51 35N 101 50w
Kamskoye Vdkhr. . 58 0N 56 0 E
Kamyshin .... 50 10N 45 30 E
Kan Kiang, R. .... 29 45N 116 10 E
Kanab 27 3N 112 29w
Kananga .... 5 5s 22 18 E
Kanash .... 55 48N 47 32 E
Kanazawa .... 36 30N 136 38 E
Kanchanaburi .... 14 8N 99 31 E
Kanchenjunga,
Mt. .... 27 50N 88 10 E
Kanchipuram .... 12 52N 79 45 E
Kanchow .... 25 51N 114 59 E
Kanchwan ...... 36 29N 109 24 E
Kandagach ...... 49 20N 57 15 E
Kandahar .... 31 32N 65 30 E
Kandahar □ ..... 31 0N 65 0 E
Kandalaksha ..... 67 9N 32 30 E
Kandalakshskiy
Zaliv .... 66 0N 35 0 E
Kandangan ...... 2 50s 115 20 E
Kandavu, I. ..... 19 0s 178 15 E
Kandi, Benin .... 11 7N 2 55 E
Kandi, India .... 23 58N 88 5 E
Kandy .... 7 42N 80 37 E
Kane 41 39N 78 53w
Kane Basin 79 0N 70 0w
Kangar .... 6 27N 100 12 E
Kangaroo, I. .... 35 45s 137 0 E
Kangāvar .... 34 40N 48 0 E
Kangnŭng ...... 37 45N 128 54 E
Kangshan ...... 22 43N 120 14 E
Kangsu □ .... 38 0N 101 40 E
Kangto, Mt. ..... 27 50N 92 35 E
Kanin, Pol. ..... 68 0N 45 0 E
Kaniva .... 36 22s 141 18 E
Kankakee 41 6N 87 50w
Kankakee, R. 41 23N 88 16w
Kankan 10 30N 9 15w
Kannapolis 35 32N 80 37w
Kano .... 12 2N 8 30 E
Kano □ .... 12 0N 8 30 E
Kanoya .... 31 23N 130 51 E
Kanpetlet ...... 21 10N 93 59 E
Kanpur .... 26 35N 80 20 E
Kanrach .... 25 35N 65 20 E
Kansas, R. 39 7N 94 36w
Kansas □ 38 40N 98 0w

Kansas City,
Kans. 39 0N 94 40w
Kansas City, Mo. .. 39 3N 94 30w
Kansk .... 56 20N 96 37 E
Kantché .... 13 31N 8 30 E
Kantō □ .... 36 0N 120 0 E
Kantse .... 31 30N 100 29 E
Kanturk 52 10N 8 55w
Kanuma .... 36 44N 139 42 E
Kanye .... 25 0s 25 28 E
Kanyu .... 34 53N 119 9 E
Kaohsiung ..... 22 35N 120 16 E
Kaokoveld ..... 19 0s 13 0 E
Kaolack 14 5N 16 8w
Kaomi .... 36 25N 119 45 E
Kaoping .... 35 48N 112 55 E
Kaoyu Hu, L. .. 32 50N 119 25 E
Kapela, Ra. .... 45 0N 15 15 E
Kapfenberg .... 47 26N 15 18 E
Kapiri Mposha .. 13 59s 28 43 E
Kapisa □ ...... 34 45N 69 30 E
Kapps .... 22 32s 17 18 E
Kapsabet ..... 0 14N 35 5 E
Kapuas, R. .... 0 25s 109 24 E
Kapunda ...... 34 20s 138 56 E
Kapuskasing ... 49 25N 82 30w
Kaputar, Mt. ... 30 15s 130 10 E
Kaputir .... 2 5N 35 28 E
Kara .... 69 10N 65 25 E
Kara Bogaz Gol,
Zaliv .... 41 0N 53 30 E
Kara Kalpak
A.S.S.R. □ ... 43 0N 59 0 E
Kara Sea ..... 75 0N 70 0 E
Karabük ...... 41 12N 32 37 E
Karabutak .... 49 59N 60 14 E
Karachi □ .... 25 30N 67 0 E
Karad .... 17 54N 74 10 E
Karadeniz
Bogaži ...... 41 10N 29 5 E
Karadeniz
Dağlari, Mts. .. 41 30N 35 0 E
Karaganda .... 49 50N 73 0 E
Karagayly .... 49 26N 76 0 E
Karaikkudi .... 10 0N 78 45 E
Karaj .... 35 4N 51 0 E
Karakas ...... 48 20N 83 30 E
Karakorum, Mts. .. 35 20N 76 0 E
Karakoram P. ... 35 33N 77 46 E
Karaköse ..... 39 44N 43 3 E

Karalon .... 57 5N 115 50 E
Karambu .... 3 53s 116 6 E
Karasburg ...... 28 0s 18 44 E
Karasino .... 66 50N 86 50 E
Karasjok ...... 69 27N 25 30 E
Karasuk .... 53 44N 78 2 E
Karatau .... 43 10N 70 28 E
Karatau Ra. .... 44 0N 69 0 E
Karatsu .... 33 30N 130 0 E
Karawanken,
Mts. .... 46 30N 14 40 E
Karazhal ...... 48 2N 70 49 E
Karbalā .... 32 47N 44 3 E
Karcag .... 47 19N 21 1 E
Kareeberge .... 30 50s 22 0 E
Karelian
A.S.S.R. □ ... 65 30N 32 30 E
Kargasok ...... 59 3N 80 53 E
Kargat .... 55 10N 80 15 E
Kargil .... 34 32N 76 12 E
Kargopol ...... 61 30N 38 58 E
Kariba L. ...... 16 40s 28 25 E
Karikal .... 10 59N 79 50 E
Karima .... 18 30N 31 49 E
Karimata, Selat, Str. 2 0s 108 20 E
Karimnagar .... 18 26N 79 10 E
Kariya .... 34 58N 137 1 E
Karkaralinsk ... 49 30N 75 10 E
Karkinitskiy
Zaliv .... 45 36N 32 35 E
Karkur .... 32 29N 34 57 E
Karl-Marx-Stadt . 50 50N 12 55 E
Karlovac ...... 45 31N 15 36 E
Karlovy Vary .. 50 13N 12 51 E
Karlsborg ..... 58 33N 14 33 E
Karlshamn .... 56 10N 14 51 E
Karlskoga .... 59 22N 14 33 E
Karlskrona ... 56 10N 15 35 E
Karlsruhe .... 49 3N 8 23 E
Karlstad ..... 59 23N 13 30 E
Karluk 57 30N 155 0w
Karnal .... 29 42N 77 2 E
Karnaphuli Res. .. 22 40N 92 20 E
Karnataka □ ... 13 15N 77 0 E
Karnische Alpen,
Mts. .... 46 36N 13 0 E
Kärnten □ ..... 46 52N 13 30 E
Karonga ...... 9 57s 33 55 E
Karoonda ..... 35 1s 139 59 E
Kárpathos, I. ... 35 37N 27 10 E

Karpogory .... 63 59N 44 27 E
Kars .... 40 40N 43 5 E
Karsakpay .... 47 55N 66 40 E
Karshi .... 38 53N 65 48 E
Kartaly .... 53 3N 60 40 E
Karumo .... 2 25s 32 50 E
Karungu .... 0 50s 34 10 E
Karur .... 10 59N 78 2 E
Karwar .... 14 44N 74 5 E
Kasai, R. ...... 3 2s 16 57 E
Kasama .... 10 16s 31 9 E
Kasangulu ..... 4 15s 15 15 E
Kasaragod ..... 12 30N 74 58 E
Kasenyi .... 1 24N 30 26 E
Kasese .... 0 13N 30 3 E
Kāshān 34 5N 5130¼
Kashgar ...... 39 46N 75 52 E
Kashing ...... 30 45N 120 41 E
Kashmir □ .... 34 0N 78 0 E
Kasimov ...... 54 55N 41 20 E
Kaslo 49 55N 117 0w
Kasongo ...... 4 30s 26 33 E
Kásos, I. ..... 35 20N 26 55 E
Kassala .... 15 23N 36 26 E
Kassalâ □ ..... 15 20N 36 26 E
Kassel .... 51 19N 9 32 E
Kassue .... 6 58s 139 21 E
Kastamonu .... 41 25N 33 43 E
Kasulu .... 4 37s 30 5 E
Kasur .... 31 5N 74 25 E
Kata .... 58 46N 102 40 E
Katako Kombe ... 3 25s 24 20 E
Katanga, Reg.=
Shaba, Reg. ... 8 30s 25 0 E
Katanning .... 33 40s 117 33 E
Katha .... 24 10N 96 30 E
Katherine .... 14 27s 132 20 E
Kathiawar, Reg. .. 22 0N 71 0 E
Katiet .... 2 21s 99 14 E
Katihar ...... 25 34N 87 36 E
Katima Mulilo .. 17 28s 24 13 E
Katmai Mt. 58 20N 154 59w
Katmandu ..... 27 45N 85 12 E
Katombora .... 18 0s 25 30 E
Katompi ...... 6 2s 26 23 E
Katoomba ..... 33 41s 150 19 E
Katowice ..... 50 17N 19 5 E
Katrine, L. ... 56 15N 4 30 E
Katrineholm .. 59 9N 16 12 E
Katsina ...... 7 10N 9 20 E

Kattawaz
Urgan □ ...... 32 10N 62 20 E
Kattegat, Str. ... 57 0N 11 20 E
Katwijk-aan-Zee .. 52 12N 4 22 E
Kauai, I. 19 30N 155 30w
Kaukauveld ..... 20 0s 20 15 E
Kaukonen ...... 67 42N 24 58 E
Kaunas .... 54 54N 23 54 E
Kaura Namoda .. 12 37N 6 33 E
Kautokeino .... 69 0N 23 4 E
Kavacha .... 60 16N 169 51 E
Kaválla .... 40 57N 24 28 E
Kaw 4 30N 52 15w
Kawagoe ...... 35 55N 139 29 E
Kawaguchi .... 35 52N 138 45 E
Kawaihae 20 5N 155 50w
Kawambwa .... 9 48s 29 3 E
Kawanoe ..... 34 1N 133 34 E
Kawasaki .... 35 35N 138 42 E
Kawene 48 45N 91 15w
Kawerau ..... 38 7s 176 42 E
Kawhia
Harbour ..... 38 4s 174 49 E
Kawnro ...... 22 48N 99 8 E
Kawthaung ... 10 5N 98 36 E
Kawthoolei □ ... 18 0N 97 30 E
Kaya 13 25N 1 10w
Kayah □ ..... 19 15N 97 15 E
Kayambi .... 9 28s 31 59 E
Kayenta .... 36 46N 110 15 E
Kayes 25 11N 11 30w
Kayrunnera .. 30 40s 142 30 E
Kayseri .... 38 45N 35 30 E
Kayuagung .. 3 28s 104 46 E
Kazachye .... 70 52N 135 58 E
Kazakh S.S.R. □ .. 50 0N 58 0 E
Kazan ...... 55 48N 49 3 E
Kazanlŭk .... 42 38N 25 35 E
Kazanlük .... 42 30N 44 30 E
Kazbek, Mt. .. 42 30N 44 30 E
Kāzerūn .... 29 38N 51 40 E
Kazym, R. ... 63 54N 65 50 E
Kéa, I. ..... 37 30N 24 22 E
Kearney 40 45N 99 3w
Kebnekaise, Mt. .. 67 48N 18 30 E
Kebri Dehar .. 6 45N 44 17w
Kebumen .... 7 42s 109 40 E
Kecskemet .. 46 57N 19 35 E
Kedgwick .. 47 40N 67 20w
Kediri ..... 7 51s 112 -1 E

Name	Lat	Long
Cocos Is.	12 12s	96 54 E
Keelung=Chilung	25 3N	121 45 E
Keene	42 57N	72 17w
Keetmanshoop	26 35s	18 8 E
Keewatin	47 23N	93 0w
Keewatin, Reg.	63 20N	94 40w
Kefallinía, I.	38 28N	20 30 E
Kefamenanu	9 28s	124 38 E
Kefar Gil'adi	33 14N	35 35 E
Kefar Sava	32 11N	34 54 E
Kefar Szold	33 11N	35 34 E
Kefar Tavor	32 42N	35 24 E
Kefar Vitkin	32 22N	34 53 E
Kefar Yona	32 20N	34 54 E
Kefar Zetim	32 49N	35 27 E
Keffi	8 55N	7 43 E
Keflavik	64 2N	22 35w
Keighley	53 52N	1 54w
Keimoes	28 41s	21 0 E
Keita	14 46N	5 46 E
Keith, Australia	36 0s	140 20 E
Keith, U.K.	57 33N	2 58w
Keith Arm, B.	65 30N	122 0w
Kèl	69 30N	124 10 E
Kelang	3 2N	101 26 E
Kelibia	36 50N	11 3 E
Kellerberrin	31 36s	117 38 E
Kellogg	47 30N	116 5w
Kells=Ceanannas Mor	53 42N	6 53w
Kelowna	49 50N	119 25w
Kelsey Bay	50 25N	126 0w
Kelso, N.Z.	45 54s	169 15 E
Kelso, U.K.	55 36N	2 27w
Kelso, U.S.A.	46 10N	122 57w
Keluang	2 3N	103 18 E
Kelvington	52 20N	103 30w
Kem	65 0N	34 38 E
Kem, R.	64 57N	34 41 E
Kemerovo	55 20N	85 50 E
Kemi	65 47N	24 32 E
Kemijärvi	66 43N	27 22 E
Kemijoki, R.	65 47N	24 30 E
Kemmerer	41 52N	110 30w
Kempsey	31 1s	152 50 E
Kempten	47 42N	10 18 E
Kemptville	45 0N	75 38w
Ken, R.	54 50N	4 4w
Kendal, Indonesia	6 56s	110 14 E
Kendal, U.K.	54 19N	2 44w
Kendari	3 50s	122 30 E
Kende	11 30N	4 12 E
Kendenup	34 30s	117 38 E
Kendi	60 30N	151 0w
Kendrapara	20 35N	86 30 E
Kenema	7 50N	11 14w
Keng Tawng	20 45N	98 18 E
Keng Tung	21 0N	99 30 E
Kenho	50 43N	121 30 E
Kenitra	34 15N	6 40w
Kenmare	51 52N	9 35w
Kennedy, C.=Canaveral, C.	28 28N	80 31w
Kennet, R.	51 28N	0 57w
Kennett	36 7N	90 0w
Kennewick	46 11N	119 2w
Keno Hill	63 57N	135 25w
Kenora	49 50N	94 35w
Kenosha	42 33N	87 48w
Kensington	46 25N	63 34w
Kent	41 8N	81 20w
Kent □	51 12N	0 40 E
Kent Pen.	68 30N	107 0w
Kentau	43 32N	68 36 E
Kenton	40 40N	83 35w
Kentucky, R.	38 41N	85 11w
Kentucky □	37 20N	85 0w
Kentville	45 6N	64 29w
Kenya ■	2 20N	38 0 E
Kenya, Mt.	0 10s	37 18 E
Keokuk	40 25N	91 30w
Kephallinia, I.=Kefallinia, I.	38 28N	20 30 E
Kerala □	11 0N	76 15 E
Kerang	35 40s	143 55 E
Keray	26 15N	57 30 E
Kerch	45 20N	36 20 E
Kerem Maharal	32 39N	34 59 E
Kerguelen, I.	48 15s	69 10 E
Kericho	0 22s	35 15 E
Kerinci, Mt.	2 5s	101 0 E
Kerkenna, Is.	34 48N	11 1 E
Kerki	37 10N	65 0 E
Kérkira	39 38N	19 50 E
Kérkira, I.	39 35N	19 45 E
Kerkrade	50 53N	6 4 E
Kermadec Is.	31 8s	175 16w
Kermān	30 15N	57 1 E
Kermān □	30 0N	57 0 E
Kermānshāh	34 23N	47 0 E
Kermānshāh □	34 0N	46 30 E
Kermit	31 56N	103 3w
Kerripi	3 55N	31 52 E
Kerrobert	52 0N	109 11w
Kerrville	30 1N	99 8w
Kerry □	52 7N	9 35w
Kerry Hd.	52 26N	9 56w
Kerulen, R.	48 48N	117 0 E
Kerzaz	29 29N	1 25w
Keski-Suomen □	63 0N	25 0 E
Kestell	28 17s	28 42 E
Keswick	54 35N	3 9w
Keta	5 49N	1 0 E
Keta Lagoon	5 50N	1 0 E
Ketapang	1 55s	110 0 E
Ketchikan	55 25N	131 40w
Kete Krachi	7 55N	0 1w
Kettering	52 24N	0 44w
Kettle Falls	48 41N	118 2w
Kewanee	41 18N	90 0w
Keweenaw B.	47 0N	88 0w
Keweenaw Pt.	47 26N	87 40w
Key West	24 40N	82 15w
Keyser	39 26N	79 0w
Kezhma	59 15N	100 57 E
Khabarovo	69 30N	60 30 E
Khabarovsk	48 20N	135 0 E
Khairagarh	21 27N	81 2 E
Khairpur	27 32N	68 49 E
Khalij-e Fars	28 20N	51 45 E
Khalkís	38 27N	23 42 E
Khalmer Yu	67 58N	65 1 E
Khalturin	58 40N	48 50 E
Khamas Country	21 45s	26 30 E
Khamir	16 10N	43 45 E
Khan Tengri, Mt.	42 25N	80 10 E
Khān Yūnis	31 21N	34 18 E
Khanabad	36 45N	69 5 E
Khānaqin	34 23N	45 25 E
Khandwa	21 49N	76 22 E
Khandyga	62 30N	134 50 E
Khanewal	30 20N	71 54 E
Khaniá	35 30N	24 4 E
Khaníon, Kól.	35 33N	23 55 E
Khanka, Oz.	45 0N	132 30 E
Khanty-Mansiysk	61 0N	69 0 E
Khapcheranga	49 40N	112 0 E
Kharagpur	22 20N	87 25 E
Kharfa	22 0N	46 35 E
Kharkov	49 58N	36 20 E
Kharovsk	59 56N	40 13 E
Kharsaniya	27 10N	49 10 E
Khartoum=El Khartûm	15 31N	32 35 E
Khasab	26 14N	56 15 E
Khāsh	28 15N	61 5 E
Khashm el Girba	14 59N	35 58 E
Khashmor	28 30N	69 31 E
Khaskovo	41 56N	25 30 E
Khatanga	72 0N	102 20 E
Khatanga, R.	73 30N	109 0 E
Khavari □	37 20N	46 0 E
Khed Brahma	24 2N	73 8 E
Khemis Miliana	36 11N	2 14 E
Khenchela	35 28N	7 11 E
Khenifra	32 58N	5 46w
Kherson	46 35N	32 35 E
Khetinsiring	32 54N	92 50 E
Khilok	51 30N	110 45 E
Khíos	38 27N	26 9 E
Khíos, I.	38 20N	26 0 E
Khiva	41 30N	60 18 E
Khmelnitsky	49 23N	27 0 E
Khojak P.	30 55N	66 30 E
Kholm	57 10N	31 15 E
Kholmsk	35 5N	139 48 E
Khong, R.	14 7N	105 51 E
Khonh Hung	9 37N	105 50 E
Khonu	66 30N	143 25 E
Khoper, R.	52 0N	43 20 E
Khorasan □	34 0N	58 0 E
Khorat=Nakhon Ratchasima	14 59N	102 12 E
Khorog	37 30N	71 36 E
Khorramābād	33 30N	48 25 E
Khorromshahr	30 29N	48 15 E
Khouribga	32 58N	6 50w
Khugiani	31 28N	66 14 E
Khulna	22 45N	89 34 E
Khulna □	22 45N	89 35 E
Khushab	32 20N	72 20 E
Khuzestan □	31 0N	50 0 E
Khvor	33 45N	55 0 E
Khvormūj	28 40N	51 30 E
Khvoy	38 35N	45 0 E
Khyber P.	34 10N	71 8 E
Kialing		
Kiang, R.	30 2N	106 18 E
Kiama	34 40s	150 50 E
Kiamal	34 58s	142 18 E
Kiambu	1 8s	36 50 E
Kiamusze	46 45N	130 30 E
Kian	27 1N	114 58 E
Kiangling	30 28N	113 16 E
Kiangsi □	27 45N	115 0 E
Kiangsu □	33 0N	119 50 E
Kiangyin	31 51N	120 0 E
Kiaohsien	36 20N	120 0 E
Kibau	8 35s	35 18 E
Kiberege	7 55s	36 53 E
Kibiti	7 40s	38 54 E
Kibombo	3 57s	25 53 E
Kibwezi	2 27s	37 57 E
Kichiga	59 50N	163 5 E
Kicking Horse P.	51 27N	116 25w
Kidderminster	52 24N	2 13w
Kidete	6 25s	37 17 E
Kidugallo	6 49s	38 15 E
Kiel	54 16N	10 8 E
Kieler B.	54 30N	10 30 E
Kienko	31 50N	105 30 E
Kienow	27 0N	118 16 E
Kienshui	23 57N	102 45 E
Kiensi	26 58N	106 0 E
Kienteh	29 30N	119 28 E
Kienyang	27 30N	118 0 E
Kiev=Kiyev	50 30N	30 28 E
Kiffa	16 50N	11 15w
Kigali	1 5s	30 4 E
Kigoma-Ujiji	5 30s	30 0 E
Kihurio	4 32s	38 5 E
Kii-Suido, Chan.	33 0N	134 50 E
Kijabe	0 56s	36 33 E
Kikiang	28 58N	106 44 E
Kikinda	45 50N	20 30 E
Kikládhes, Is.	37 20N	24 30 E
Kikládhes □	37 20N	24 30 E
Kilcoy	26 59s	152 30 E
Kildare	53 10N	6 50w
Kildare □	53 10N	6 50w
Kilembe	0 15N	30 3 E
Kilgore	32 22N	94 40 E
Kilifi	3 40s	39 48 E
Kilimanjaro, Mt.	3 7s	37 20 E
Kilimatinde	5 55s	34 58 E
Kilindini	4 4s	39 40 E

Kilis .... 36 50N 37 10 E
Kilkee 52 41N 9 40w
Kilkenny 52 40N 7 17w
Kilkenny □ 52 35N 7 15w
Killala 54 13N 9 12w
Killaloe 52 48N 8 28w
Killarney, Canada . 49 10N 99 40w
Killarney, Eire ... 52 2N 9 30w
Killary Harbour .. 53 38N 9 52w
Killiecrankie,
P. of 56 44N 3 46w
Killin 56 27N 4 20w
Killybegs 54 38N 8 26w
Kilmany .... 38 8s 146 55 E
Kilmarnock 55 36N 4 30w
Kilmore .... 37 25s 144 53 E
Kilosa .... 6 48s 37 0 E
Kilrush 52 39N 9 30w
Kilwa Kisiwani ... 8 58s 39 32 E
Kilwa Kivinje .... 8 45s 39 25 E
Kimba .... 33 8s 136 23 E
Kimball 41 17N 103 20w
Kimberley, Canada 49 40N 116 10w
Kimberley,
S. Africa ...... 28 43s 24 46 E
Kimberley Downs . 17 24s 124 22 E
Kimberly 42 33N 114 25w
Kimchaek .... 40 41N 129 12 E
Kimchon .... 36 11N 128 4 E
Kimry .... 56 55N 37 15 E
Kinabalu, Mt. .... 6 0N 116 0 E
Kincaid 49 40N 107 0w
Kincardine 44 10N 81 40w
Kindersley 51 30N 109 10w
Kindia 10 0N 12 52w
Kindu .... 2 55s 25 50 E
Kineshma .... 57 30N 42 5 E
King, I. .... 39 50s 144 0 E
King, Mt. .... 10 35s 147 31 E
King Edward, R. .. 14 14s 126 35 E
King George B. ... 51 30s 60 30w
King George Is. .. 53 40N 80 30w
King Leopold,
Ras. .... 17 20s 124 20 E
King Sd. .... 16 50s 123 20 E
King William I. .. 69 0N 98 0w
King William's
Town .... 32 51s 27 22 E
Kingaroy .... 26 32s 151 51 E
Kingku .... 23 49N 100 30 E

Kingman 35 12N 114 2w
Kingoonya .... 30 54N 135 18 E
Kingpeng .... 43 30N 117 25 E
Kings Canyon
Nat. Park 37 0N 118 45w
Kings Lynn ...... 52 45N 0 25 E
Kingsbridge 50 14N 3 46w
Kingscourt 53 55N 6 48w
Kingston, Canada . 44 20N 76 30w
Kingston, Jamaica . 18 0N 76 50w
Kingston, N.Z. ... 45 20s 168 43 E
Kingston, N.Y. ... 41 55N 74 0w
Kingston, Pa. 41 19N 75 58w
Kingston South
East .... 36 52s 139 51 E
Kingstown 13 10N 61 10w
Kingsville,
Canada 42 3N 82 45w
Kingsville, U.S.A. . 27 30N 97 53w
Kingtai .... 37 4N 103 59 E
Kingtehchen ..... 29 8N 117 21 E
Kingtzekwan .... 33 25N 111 10 E
Kingussie 47 5N 4 2w
Kinhsien .... 36 6N 107 49 E
Kinhwa .... 29 5N 119 32 E
Kinistino 52 59N 105 0w
Kinkala .... 4 18s 14 49 E
Kinki □ .... 33 30N 136 0 E
Kinleith .... 38 20s 175 56 E
Kinloch .... 44 51s 168 20 E
Kinmen, I. ...... 24 25N 118 24 E
Kinneret .... 32 44N 35 34 E
Kinneret,
Yam, L. .... 32 49N 35 36 E
Kinross 56 13N 3 25w
Kinsale 51 32N 8 31w
Kinsale, Old Hd. .. 51 37N 8 32w
Kinsha, R. ...... 32 30N 98 0 E
Kinshasa .... 4 20s 15 15 E
Kinsiang .... 35 4N 116 25 E
Kinston 35 18N 77 35w
Kintiku .... 6 0s 35 20 E
Kintyre, Pen. 55 30N 5 35w
Kinyangiri ...... 4 35s 34 37 E
Kioga, L. .... 1 35N 33 0 E
Kioshan .... 32 50N 114 0 E
Kiparissía ...... 37 15N 21 40 E
Kiparissiakós
Kól. .... 37 25N 21 25 E
Kipawa Reserve

Prov. Park 47 0N 78 30w
Kipembawe ...... 7 38s 33 23 E
Kipengere Ra. .... 9 12s 34 15 E
Kipili .... 7 28s 30 32 E
Kipini .... 2 30s 40 32 E
Kirensk .... 57 50N 107 55 E
Kirgiz S.S.R. □ ... 42 0N 75 0 E
Kirikkale .... 39 51N 33 32 E
Kirillov .... 59 51N 38 14 E
Kirin .... 43 58N 126 31 E
Kirin □ .... 43 45N 125 20 E
Kirkcaldy 56 7N 3 10w
Kirkcudbright ... 54 50N 4 3w
Kirkee .... 18 34N 73 56 E
Kirkenes .... 69 40N 30 5 E
Kirkintilloch 55 57N 4 10w
Kirkland Lake 48 15N 80 0w
Kirksville 40 8N 92 35w
Kirkūk .... 35 30N 44 21 E
Kirkwall 58 59N 2 59w
Kirkwood .... 33 22s 25 15 E
Kirov .... 58 35N 49 40 E
Kirovabad .... 40 45N 46 10 E
Kirovakan .... 41 0N 44 0 E
Kirovograd ...... 48 35N 32 20 E
Kirovsk .... 67 48N 33 50 E
Kirovskiy .... 45 51N 48 11 E
Kirriemuir 56 41N 3 0w
Kirsanov .... 52 35N 42 40 E
Kirthar Ra. ..... 27 0N 67 0 E
Kiruna .... 67 50N 20 20 E
Kirup .... 33 40s 115 50 E
Kiryū .... 36 25s 139 20 E
Kisaki .... 7 27s 37 40 E
Kisangani .... 0 35N 25 15 E
Kisaran .... 2 47N 99 29 E
Kisaratzu .... 35 25N 139 59 E
Kiselevsk .... 54 5N 86 6 E
Kisengwa .... 6 0s 25 50 E
Kiserawe .... 6 53s 39 0 E
Kishanda .... 1 42s 31 34 E
Kishanganj ..... 26 3N 88 14 E
Kishangarh ..... 27 50N 70 30 E
Kishi .... 9 1N 3 45 E
Kishinev .... 47 0N 28 50 E
Kishiwada ...... 34 28N 135 22 E
Kishon .... 32 33N 35 12 E
Kishtwar .... 33 20N 75 48 E
Kisi .... 45 21N 131 0 E
Kisii .... 0 40s 34 45 E

Kisiju .... 7 23s 39 19 E
Kiska I. .... 52 0N 177 30 E
Kiskörös .... 46 37N 19 20 E
Kiskunfélegyháza . 46 42N 19 53 E
Kiskunhalas ..... 46 28N 19 37 E
Kislovodsk ...... 43 50N 42 45 E
Kiso-Gawa, R. ... 35 2N 136 45 E
Kisoro .... 1 17s 29 48 E
Kissidougou 9 5N 10 0w
Kistna, R.=
Krishna, R. ... 15 43N 80 55 E
Kisumu .... 0 3s 34 45 E
Kitai .... 44 0N 89 27 E
Kitaibaraki ..... 36 50N 140 45 E
Kitakyūshū ..... 33 50N 130 50 E
Kitale .... 1 0N 35 12 E
Kitangari ...... 10 40s 39 20 E
Kitchener,
Australia ..... 30 55s 124 8 E
Kitchener,
Canada 43 30N 80 30w
Kitega .... 3 30s 29 58 E
Kitgum .... 3 17N 32 52 E
Kíthira .... 36 9N 23 0 E
Kíthira, I. ...... 36 10N 23 0 E
Kíthnos, I. ...... 37 26N 24 27 E
Kitimat 53 55N 129 0w
Kitoma .... 1 5N 30 55 E
Kitsuki .... 33 35N 131 37 E
Kittanning 40 49N 79 30w
Kitui .... 1 17s 38 0 E
Kitwe .... 12 54s 28 7 E
Kityang .... 23 30N 116 29 E
Kiukiang .... 29 37N 116 2 E
Kiuling Shan,
Mts. .... 28 40N 115 0 E
Kiungchow ..... 19 57N 110 17 E
Kiungchow-
Haihsia, Str. ... 20 40N 110 0 E
Kivu, L. .... 1 48s 29 0 E
Kiyang .... 26 36N 111 42 E
Kiyev .... 50 30N 30 28 E
Kiyevskoye, Vdkhr. 51 0N 30 0 E
Kizel .... 59 3N 57 40 E
Kizlyar .... 43 51N 46 40 E
Kizyl-Arvat ..... 38 58N 56 15 E
Kizyl Kiva ...... 40 20N 72 35 E
Kladno .... 50 10N 14 7 E
Klagenfurt ...... 46 38N 14 20 E
Klaipeda .... 55 43N 21 10 E

Klamath Falls 42 20N 121 50w
Klarälven, R. .... 59 23N 13 32 E
Klaten .... 7 43s 110 36 E
Klatovy .... 49 23N 13 18 E
Klawak 55 35N 133 0w
Klawer .... 31 44s 18 36 E
Kleena Kleene ... 52 0N 124 50w
Klein Karoo ..... 33 45s 21 30 E
Klerksdorp ...... 26 51s 26 38 E
Klipplaat .... 33 0s 24 22 E
Kłodzko .... 50 28N 16 38 E
Klondike 64 0N 139 40w
Klouto .... 6 57N 0 44 E
Kluane, L. 61 25N 138 50w
Knaresborough ... 54 1N 1 29w
Knighton 52 21N 3 2w
Knokke .... 51 20N 3 17 E
Knoxville, Iowa .. 41 20N 93 5w
Knoxville, Tenn. .. 35 58N 83 57w
Knysna .... 34 2s 23 2 E
Koartac 61 5N 69 36w
Koba .... 6 37s 134 37 E
Kobarid .... 46 15N 13 30 E
Kobe .... 34 45N 135 10 E
København ...... 55 41N 12 34 E
Koblenz .... 50 21N 7 36 E
Kočani .... 41 55N 22 25 E
Kočevje .... 45 39N 14 50 E
Kōchi .... 33 30N 133 30 E
Kōchi □ .... 33 40N 133 30 E
Kodiak 57 48N 152 23w
Kodiak I. .... 57 30N 152 45 E
Kodok .... 9 53N 32 7 E
Koffiefontein .... 29 22s 24 58 E
Koforidua 6 3N 0 17w
Kōfu .... 35 40N 138 30 E
Kogin Baba ..... 7 55N 11 35 E
Kohat .... 33 40N 71 29 E
Kohima .... 25 35N 94 10 E
Kojonup 33 48s 117 10w
Kokand .... 40 30N 70 57 E
Kokanee Glacier
Prov. Park 49 47N 117 10w
Kokchetav ...... 53 20N 69 10 E
Kokhav Mikha'el . 31 37N 34 40 E
Kokiu .... 23 22N 103 6 E
Kokkola .... 63 50N 23 8 E
Koko .... 11 28N 4 29 E
Koko Nor, L. .... 37 0N 100 0 E
Kokomo 40 30N 86 6w

Koksoak, R. 58 30N 68 10W
Kokstad .... 30 32S 29 29 E
Kokuora ...... 61 30N 145 0 E
Kola .... 68 45N 33 8 E
Kolan .... 38 43N 111 32 E
Kolar .... 13 12N 78 15 E
Kolar Gold
　Fields ...... 12 58N 78 16 E
Kolarovgrad ...... 43 27N 26 42 E
Kolayat ...... 27 51N 72 59 E
Kolding ...... 55 30N 9 29 E
Kolepom, I. ...... 8 0S 138 30 E
Kolguyev .... 69 20N 48 30 E
Kolhapur ...... 16 43N 74 15 E
Kolín .... 50 2N 15 9 E
Köln .... 50 56N 9 58 E
Koło .... 52 14N 18 40 E
Kołobrzeg ...... 54 10N 15 35 E
Kolomna ...... 55 8N 38 45 E
Kolomyya ...... 48 31N 25 2 E
Kolosib .... 24 15N 92 45 E
Kolpashevo ...... 58 20N 83 5 E
Kolskiy Pol. ...... 67 30N 38 0 E
Kolskiy Zaliv ...... 69 23N 34 0 E
Kolwezi .... 10 40S 25 25 E
Kolyma, R. ...... 64 40N 153 0 E
Komandorskiye Is. 55 0N 167 0 E
Komárno ...... 47 49N 18 5 E
Komatipoort ...... 25 25S 31 57 E
Komatsu ...... 36 25N 136 30 E
Komenda 5 4N 1 28W
Komga .... 32 37S 27 56 E
Komi A.S.S.R. ...... 64 0N 55 0 E
Komoro ...... 36 19N 138 26 E
Komotiri ...... 41 9N 25 26 E
Kompong Bang ... 12 24N 104 40 E
Kompong Cham .. 11 54N 105 30 E
Kompong Som ... 10 38N 103 30 E
Komsberge ...... 32 40S 20 45 E
Komsomolets, Os. . 80 30N 95 0 E
Komsomolsk ...... 50 30N 137 0 E
Kondakovo ...... 69 20N 151 30 E
Kondinin ...... 32 34S 118 8 E
Kondoa ...... 4 0S 36 0 E
Konduga ...... 11 35N 13 26 E
Koudougou 12 10N 2 20W
Kondratyevo ...... 57 30N 98 30 E
Kong, Koh ...... 11 20N 103 0 E
Kongju .... 36 30N 127 0 E
Konglu ...... 27 13N 97 57 E

Kongmoon ...... 22 35N 113 1 E
Kongolo......... 5 22S 27 0 E
Kongsberg ...... 59 39N 9 39 E
Königsberg=
　Kaliningrad..... 54 42N 20 32 E
Kongsvinger ...... 60 12N 12 2 E
Kongwa .... 6 11S 36 26 E
Kønig Haakon
　VII Sea ...... 66 0S 35 0 E
Konin .... 52 12N 18 15 E
Konjic .... 43 42N 17 58 E
Konongo 6 40N 1 15W
Konosha ...... 61 0N 40 5 E
Konotop ...... 51 12N 33 7 E
Końskie ...... 51 15N 20 23 E
Konstanz.... 47 39N 9 10 E
Kontagora .... 10 23N 5 27 E
Konya ...... 37 52N 32 35 E
Konza ...... 1 45S 37 0 E
Kookynie ...... 29 17S 121 22 E
Kooline ...... 22 57S 116 20 E
Koolyanobbing ... 30 48S 119 46 E
Koonibba ...... 31 58S 133 27 E
Koorda ...... 30 48S 117 35 E
Kootenay Nat.
　Park 51 0N 116 0W
Koo-wee-rup ... 38 13S 145 28 E
Kopaonik
　Planina, Mts. ... 43 10N 21 0 E
Kopervik ...... 59 17N 5 17 E
Kopeysk ...... 55 7N 61 37 E
Köping ...... 59 31N 16 3 E
Kopparberg ...... 59 53N 14 59 E
Kopparbergs □ .. 61 20N 14 15 E
Korça .... 40 37N 20 50 E
Korčula, I. ...... 42 57N 17 0 E
Kordestân □ ...... 36 0N 47 0 E
Kordofân □ ...... 13 0N 29 0 E
Korea B. ...... 39 0N 124 0 E
Korhogo ...... 9 29N 5 28 E
Korinthiakós
　Kól. ...... 38 16N 22 30 E
Kórinthos ...... 37 26N 22 55 E
Kōriyama ...... 37 24N 140 23 E
Korla ...... 41 45N 86 4 E
Koro 14 1N 2 58W
Koro Sea 17 30S 179 45W
Korogwe ...... 5 5S 38 25 E
Koroit ...... 38 18S 142 24 E
Körös, R. ...... 46 30N 142 42 E

Korsakov .... 46 30N 142 42 E
Korsør .... 55 20N 11 9 E
Kortrijk ...... 50 50N 3 17 E
Korumburra ..... 38 26S 145 50 E
Koryakskiy
　Khrebet, Mts. ... 61 0N 171 0 E
Kos, I. .... 36 50N 27 15 E
Kościan ...... 52 5N 16 40 E
Kosciusko 33 3N 89 34W
Kosciusko I. 56 0N 133 40W
Kosciusko, Mt. .... 36 27S 148 16 E
Košice .... 48 42N 21 15 E
Koslan ...... 63 28N 48 52 E
Kosovska-
　Mitrovica .... 42 54N 20 52 E
Koster ...... 25 52S 26 54 E
Kôstî ...... 13 8N 32 43 E
Kostroma ...... 57 50N 41 58 E
Kostrzyn ...... 52 24N 17 14 E
Koszalin ...... 54 12N 16 8 E
Kota ...... 25 14N 75 49 E
Kota Baharu ...... 6 7N 102 14 E
Kota Kinabalu ... 6 0N 116 12 E
Kota Tinggi ...... 1 44N 103 53 E
Kotabaru ...... 3 20S 116 20 E
Kotabumi ...... 4 49S 104 46 E
Kotawaringin ...... 2 28S 111 27 E
Kotelnich ...... 58 20N 48 10 E
Kotka ...... 60 28N 26 55 E
Kotlas ...... 61 15N 47 0 E
Kotlik 63 2N 163 33W
Kotor ...... 42 25N 18 47 E
Kottagudem ...... 17 30N 80 40 E
Kottayam ...... 9 35N 76 33 E
Kotturu ...... 14 45N 76 13 E
Kotzebue 66 53N 162 39W
Koudougou 12 10N 2 20W
Kougaberge ...... 33 40S 23 55 E
Koula-Moutou ... 1 15S 12 25 E
Koumala ...... 21 38S 149 15 E
Kounradskiy ...... 47 20N 75 0 E
Kourou 5 9N 52 39W
Kouroussa 10 45N 9 45W
Kouvé ...... 6 30N 1 30 E
Kovdor ...... 67 34N 30 22 E
Kovel ...... 51 10N 25 0 E
Kovrov ...... 56 25N 41 25 E
Kowloon ...... 22 20N 114 15 E
Koyiu ...... 23 2N 112 28 E
Koyukuk, R. 64 56N 157 30W

Kozáni □ .... 40 20N 21 45 E
Kozhikode=
　Calicut .... 11 15N 75 43 E
Kozhva ...... 65 10N 57 0 E
Kpandu ...... 7 2N 0 18 E
Kpessi ...... 7 50N 1 25 E
Kra, Isthmus of=
　Kra, Kho Khot . 10 15N 99 30 E
Kra, Kho Khot ... 10 15N 99 30 E
Kraków ...... 50 4N 19 57 E
Kragerø ...... 58 56N 9 30 E
Kragujevac .... 44 2N 20 56 E
Krakatau, I.=
　Rakatau, P. ...... 6 10S 105 20 E
Kraksaan ...... 7 43S 113 23 E
Kraljevo ...... 43 44N 20 41 E
Kramatorsk ...... 48 50N 37 30 E
Kramfors ...... 62 55N 17 48 E
Kras, Reg ...... 45 30N 14 0 E
Krasavino ...... 60 58N 46 26 E
Kraskino ...... 42 45N 130 58 E
Krasnik ...... 50 55N 22 5 E
Krasnodar ...... 45 5N 38 50 E
Krasnokamsk ...... 58 0N 56 0 E
Krasnoselkupsk ... 65 20N 82 10 E
Krasnoturinsk ...... 59 39N 60 1 E
Krasnoufimsk ...... 56 30N 57 37 E
Krasnouralsk ...... 58 0N 60 0 E
Krasnovodsk ...... 40 0N 52 52 E
Krasnovishersk ... 60 23N 56 59 E
Krasnoyarsk ...... 56 8N 93 0 E
Krasnyy Yar ...... 46 43N 48 23 E
Kratie ...... 12 32N 106 10 E
Krefeld ...... 51 20N 6 22 E
Kremenchug ...... 49 5N 33 25 E
Kremenchugskoye,
　Vdkhr. ...... 49 20N 32 30 E
Kremnica ...... 48 45N 18 50 E
Krishna, R. ...... 15 43N 80 55 E
Krishnanagar ...... 23 24N 88 33 E
Kristiansand ...... 58 5N 7 50 E
Kristianstad ...... 56 5N 14 7 E
Kristianstads □ ... 56 0N 14 0 E
Kristiansund ...... 63 10N 7 45 E
Kristinehamn ...... 59 18N 14 13 E
Kristinestad ...... 62 18N 21 25 E
Kriti, I. ...... 35 15N 25 0 E
Kriti □ ...... 35 15N 25 0 E
Krivoy Rog ...... 47 51N 33 20 E
Krk, I. ...... 45 5N 14 56 E

Krkonose, Mts. .. 50 50N 16 10 E
Krokodil, R. ...... 25 26S 32 0 E
Kronobergs □ ...... 56 45N 14 30 E
Kronshtadt ...... 60 5N 29 35 E
Kroonstad ...... 27 43S 27 19 E
Kropotkin ...... 58 50N 115 10 E
Krosno .... 49 35N 21 56 E
Krotoszyn ...... 51 42N 17 23 E
Krugersdorp .... 26 5S 27 46 E
Kruisfontein .... 34 0S 24 43 E
Krung Thep ...... 13 45N 100 35 E
Kruševac .... 43 35N 21 28 E
Krymskaya .... 44 57N 37 50 E
Ksar El
　Boukhari .... 35 5N 2 52 E
Ksar-el-Kebir 35 0N 6 0W
Kuala ...... 2 46N 105 47 E
Kuala Dungun .... 4 46N 103 25 E
Kuala Kerai .... 5 32N 102 12 E
Kuala Kubu
　Baharu ...... 3 35N 101 38 E
Kuala Lipis ...... 4 22N 102 5 E
Kuala Lumpur .. 3 9N 101 41 E
Kuala Selangor .. 3 20N 101 15 E
Kuala Terengganu . 5 20N 103 8 E
Kualakapuas ...... 2 55S 114 20 E
Kualakurun ...... 1 10S 113 50 E
Kualapembuang .. 3 14S 112 38 E
Kualasimpang ... 4 16N 98 4 E
Kuantan ...... 3 49N 103 20 E
Kuba ...... 41 21N 48 22 E
Kubak ...... 27 10N 63 10 E
Kuban, R. ...... 45 20N 37 30 E
Kubokawa ...... 33 12N 133 8 E
Kucha ...... 41 50N 82 30 E
Kuching ...... 1 33N 110 25 E
Kuchinotsu ...... 32 36N 130 11 E
Kuda ...... 23 10N 71 18 E
Kudat ...... 7 0N 116 42 E
Kudus ...... 6 48N 110 51 E
Kueiyang=
　Kweiyang ...... 25 30N 106 35 E
Kufra, El
　Wâhât et ...... 24 17N 23 15 E
Kufstein ...... 47 35N 12 11 E
Kûhpâyeh ...... 32 44N 52 20 E
Kukawa ...... 12 58N 13 27 E
Kukerin ...... 33 13S 118 0 E
Kulgera ...... 25 50S 133 18 E
Kulin ...... 32 40S 118 2 E

Kulja .... 30 35 s 117 31 E
Kulsary .... 46 59 N 54 1 E
Kululu .... 9 28 N 33 1 E
Kulunda .... 52 45 N 79 15 E
Kulyab .... 37 55 N 69 50 E
Kum Darya, R. .. 41 0 N 89 0 E
Kum Tekei ...... 43 10 N 79 30 E
Kumaganum ..... 13 8 N 10 38 E
Kumai .... 2 52 s 111 45 E
Kumamoto ...... 32 45 N 130 45 E
Kumamoto □ .... 32 30 N 130 40 E
Kumara .... 42 37 s 171 12 E
Kumari .... 32 45 s 121 30 E
Kumasi .... 6 41 N 1 38 E
Kumba .... 4 36 N 9 24 E
Kumbarilla ..... 27 15 s 150 55 E
Kumbo .... 6 15 N 10 36 E
Kumagaya ...... 36 9 N 139 22 E
Kumertau ...... 52 46 N 55 47 E
Kumi .... 1 30 N 33 58 E
Kumla .... 59 8 N 15 10 E
Kumo .... 10 1 N 11 12 E
Kumon Bum, Mts. . 26 0 N 97 15 E
Kunar □ .... 35 15 N 71 0 E
Kundip .... 33 42 s 120 10 E
Kunduz .... 36 50 N 68 50 E
Kunduz □ .... 36 50 N 68 50 E
Kunene, R. ...... 17 20 s 11 50 E
Kungchuling .... 43 31 N 124 58 E
Kungho .... 36 28 N 100 45 E
Kungrad .... 43 6 N 58 54 E
Kungram .... 25 45 N 89 35 E
Kungsbacka ..... 57 30 N 12 7 E
Kunhsien .... 32 30 N 111 17 E
Kuningan .... 6 59 s 108 29 E
Kunlong .... 23 20 N 98 50 E
Kunlun Shan, Mts. 36 0 N 82 0 E
Kunming .... 25 11 N 102 37 E
Kunsan .... 35 59 N 126 35 E
Kununurra ...... 15 40 s 128 39 E
Kunwarara ...... 22 25 s 150 7 E
Kuopio .... 62 53 N 27 35 E
Kuopio □ .... 63 25 N 27 10 E
Kupa, R. .... 45 28 N 16 24 E
Kupang .... 10 19 s 123 39 E
Kupreanof I. ..... 56 50 N 133 30 w
Kura, R. .... 39 24 N 49 24 E
Kurashiki .... 34 40 N 133 50 E
Kurayoshi .... 35 26 N 133 50 E
Kure .... 34 14 N 132 32 E

Kurgaldzhino .... 50 35 N 70 20 E
Kurgan .... 55 30 N 65 0 E
Kurilskiye Os. ... 45 0 N 150 0 E
Kurino .... 31 57 N 130 43 E
Kurnool .... 15 45 N 78 0 E
Kurow .... 44 4 s 170 29 E
Kurri Kurri ..... 32 50 s 151 28 E
Kursk .... 51 42 N 36 11 E
Kurume .... 33 15 N 130 30 E
Kurunegala ..... 7 30 N 80 18 E
Kurya .... 61 15 N 108 10 E
Kushan .... 39 58 N 123 30 E
Kushikino ...... 31 44 N 130 16 E
Kushima .... 31 29 N 131 14 E
Kushimoto ...... 33 28 N 135 47 E
Kushiro .... 43 0 N 144 30 'E
Kushk .... 34 55 N 62 30 E
Kushka .... 35 20 N 62 18 E
Kushtia .... 23 55 N 89 5 E
Kuskokwim, R. .. 60 17 N 162 27 w
Kuskokwim B. ... 59 45 N 162 25 w
Kustanai .... 53 20 N 63 45 E
Kut, Ko .... 11 40 N 102 35 E
Kutahya .... 39 25 N 29 59 E
Kutaisi .... 42 19 N 42 40 E
Kutaraja=Banda
Aceh .... 5 35 N 95 20 E
Kutch, G. of. ... 22 50 N 69 15 E
Kutch, Rann of,
Reg. .... 24 0 N 70 0 N
Kutno .... 52 15 N 19 23 E
Kuttabul .... 21 5 s 148 48 E
Kutum .... 14 20 N 24 10 E
Kuwait ■ .... 29 30 N 47 30 E
Kuwana .... 35 0 N 136 43 E
Kuyang .... 41 8 N 110 1 E
Kuybyshev,
Kuyb. Obl. .... 53 12 N 50 9 E
Kuybyshev,
Tatar A.S.S.R. .. 54 57 N 49 5 E
Kuybyshev,
Novosibirsk
Obl. .... 55 27 N 78 19 E
Kuybyshevskoye
Vdkhr. .... 55 2 N 49 30 E
Kuyumba .... 61 10 N 97 10 E
Kuyto, Oz. ...... 64 40 N 31 0 E
Kuznetsk .... 53 12 N 46 40 E
Kuzomen .... 66 22 N 36 50 E
Kvarner, G. ..... 44 50 N 14 10 E

Kvarneric .... 44 43 N 14 37 E
Kwabhaca ...... 30 51 s 29 0 E
Kwakoegron .... 5 25 N 55 25 w
Kwale .... 4 15 s 39 31 E
Kwando, R. ..... 16 48 s 22 45 E
Kwangan .... 30 35 N 106 40 E
Kwangchou=
Kwangchow .... 23 10 N 113 10 E
Kwangchow .... 23 10 N 113 10 E
Kwangchow
Wan, G. .... 21 0 N 111 0 E
Kwangju .... 35 10 N 126 45 E
Kwangnan ...... 24 10 N 105 0 E
Kwangsi-Chuang
Aut.Dist. □ .... 23 30 N 108 55 E
Kwangtseh ..... 27 30 N 117 25 E
Kwangtung □ ... 23 35 N 114 0 E
Kwangyuan ..... 32 30 N 105 49 E
Kwanhsien ..... 30 59 N 103 40 E
Kwantung ...... 25 12 N 101 37 E
Kwara □ .... 8 30 N 5 0 E
Kwatisore ...... 3 7 s 139 59 E
Kwei Kiang, R. .. 23 30 N 110 30 E
Kweichih .... 30 40 N 117 30 E
Kweichow=
Fengkieh ...... 31 0 N 109 33 E
Kweichow □ .... 26 40 N 107 0 E
Kweihsien ...... 22 59 N 109 44 E
Kweiki .... 28 10 N 117 8 E
Kweilin .... 25 16 N 110 15 E
Kweiping .... 23 12 N 110 0 E
Kweiting .... 26 0 N 113 35 E
Kweiyang ...... 25 30 N 106 35 E
Kwidzyń .... 54 5 N 18 58 E
Kwiguk Island ... 62 45 N 164 28 w
Kwinana .... 32 15 s 115 47 E
Kwo Ho, R. ..... 33 20 N 116 50 E
Kwoka, Mt....... 0 31 s 132 27 E
Kwolla .... 8 55 N 9 18 E
Kyakhta .... 50 30 N 106 25 E
Kyancutta ...... 33 8 s 135 34 E
Kyaukpadaung .. 20 52 N 95 8 E
Kyaukpyu ...... 19 28 N 93 30 E
Kyaukse .... 21 36 N 96 10 E
Kyenjojo .... 0 40 N 30 37 E
Kyle Dam .... 20 14 s 31 0 E
Kynuna .... 21 35 s 141 55 E
Kyoga, L. .... 1 35 N 33 0 E
Kyogle .... 28 40 s 153 0 E
Kyongju .... 35 59 N 129 26 E

Kyonpyaw ...... 17 12 N 95 10 E
Kyōto .... 35 0 N 135 45 E
Kyōto □ .... 35 15 N 135 30 E
Kyrínia .... 35 20 N 33 19 E
Kystatyam ...... 67 15 N 123 0 E
Kytal Ktakh .... 65 30 N 123 40 E
Kyunhla .... 23 25 N 95 15 E
Kyūshū, I. ...... 32 30 N 131 0 E
Kyūshū □ .... 32 30 N 131 0 E
Kyustendil ...... 42 25 N 22 41 E
Kyusyur .... 70 20 N 127 0 E
Kyzyl .... 51 50 N 94 30 E
Kzyl Orda ...... 44 50 N 65 10 E

L

La Alcarria, Reg... 40 31 N 2 45 w
La Asunción ..... 11 2 N 63 53 w
La Banda .... 27 45 s 64 10 w
La Barca .... 20 20 N 102 40 w
La Blanquilla, I.. 11 51 N 64 37 w
La Boca .... 9 0 N 79 30 E
La Calera ...... 32 50 s 71 10 w
La Carlota ...... 33 30 s 63 20 w
La Carolina .... 38 17 N 3 38 w
La Ceiba,
Honduras ..... 15 40 N 86 50 w
La Ceiba, Ven... 9 30 N 71 0 w
La Chaux-de-Fonds 47 7 N 6 50 E
La Cocha .... 27 50 s 65 40 w
La Coruña ...... 43 20 N 8 25 w
La Crosse ...... 43 48 N 91 13 w
La Dorada ...... 5 30 N 74 40 w
La Estrada ...... 42 43 N 8 27 w
La Fayette ...... 40 22 N 86 52 w
La Folette ...... 36 23 N 84 9 w
La Grande ...... 45 15 N 118 0 w
La Grange ...... 33 4 N 85 0 w
La Guaira ...... 10 36 N 66 56 w
La Habana ...... 23 0 N 82 41 w
La Mabana ..... 23 8 N 82 22 w
La Junta .... 38 0 N 103 30 w
La Linea de la
Concepción ... 36 15 N 5 23 w
La Loche .... 56 29 N 109 27 w
La Louvière .... 50 27 N 4 10 E
La Malbaie ..... 47 40 N 70 10 w

La Mancha, Reg.. 39 10 N 2 54 w
La Martre, L. .... 63 0 N 118 0 w
La Mesa .... 32 48 N 117 5 w
La Orchila, I. ... 12 30 N 67 0 w
La Oroya .... 11 32 s 75 54 w
La Palma .... 37 21 N 6 38 w
La Palma .... 8 15 N 78 0 w
La Palma, I. .... 28 40 N 17 52 w
La Paragua ..... 6 50 N 63 20 w
La Paz, Arg. .... 30 50 s 59 45 w
La Paz, Bolivia .. 16 20 s 68 10 w
La Paz, Mexico .. 24 10 N 110 20 w
La Pedrera ..... 1 18 s 69 43 w
La Perouse, Str.. 45 40 N 142 0 E
La Piedad ...... 20 20 N 102 1 w
La Pine .... 40 53 N 80 45 w
La Plata .... 35 0 s 57 55 w
La Porte .... 41 40 N 86 40 w
La Reine .... 48 50 N 79 30 w
La Rioja .... 29 20 s 67 0 w
La Rioja, Reg. ... 42 20 N 2 20 w
La Robla .... 42 50 N 5 41 w
La Roche-sur-
Yon .... 46 40 N 1 25 w
La Rochelle ..... 46 10 N 1 9 w
La Roda .... 39 13 N 2 15 w
La Romana ..... 18 27 N 68 57 w
La Salle .... 41 20 N 89 5 w
La Sarre .... 48 45 N 79 15 w
La Serena ...... 29 55 s 71 10 w
La Spézia ...... 44 8 N 9 50 E
La Tagua .... 0 3 N 74 40 w
La Tortuga, I. ... 10 56 N 65 20 w
La Tuque .... 47 30 N 72 50 w
La Unión,
Chile .... 40 10 s 73 0 w
La Union,
Salvador ...... 13 20 N 87 50 w
La Urbana ...... 7 8 N 66 56 w
La Vega .... 19 20 N 70 30 w
La Vela .... 11 30 N 69 30 w
La Verendrye
Prov. Park .... 47 15 N 77 10 w
La Victoria ..... 10 14 N 67 20 w
Laaland=
Lolland, I. .... 54 45 N 11 30 E
Labbézenga .... 14 57 N 0 42 E
Labé .... 11 24 N 12 16 w
Labis .... 2 22 N 103 2 E
Laboulaye ...... 34 10 s 63 30 w

Labrador, Reg..... 53 20N 61 0w
Labrador City..... 52 42N 67 0w
Labuha .... 0 30s 127 30 E
Labuhan .... 6 26s 105 50 E
Lac la Biche 54 45N 111 50w
Lac Seul 50 28N 92 0w
Laccadive Is..... 10 0N 72 30 E
Lachine 45 30N 73 40w
Lachlan, R....... 34 21s 143 57 E
Lachute 45 39N 74 21w
Lackawanna 42 49N 78 50w
Lacombe 52 30N 113 50w
Laconia 43 32N 71 30w
Ladakh Ra....... 34 0N 78 0 E
Ladismith .... 33 28s 21 15 E
Lādiz .... 28 55N 61 15 E
Ladozhskoye, Oz. . 61 15N 30 30 E
Ladrone Is. ...... 17 0N 145 0 E
Lady Grey .... 30 43s 27 13 E
Ladybrand ...... 29 9s 27 29 E
Ladysmith,
     Canada 49 0N 124 0w
Ladysmith,
     S. Africa ..... 28 32s 29 46 E
Laesø, I. .... 57 15N 10 53 E
Lafayette 30 18N 92 0w
Lafia .... 8 30N 8 34 E
Lafiagi .... 8 52N 5 20 E
Laforest 47 4N 81 12w
Lågen, R. .... 61 8N 10 25 E
Laghman □ ...... 34 20N 70 0 E
Laghouat .... 33 50N 2 59 E
Lagonoy G....... 13 50N 123 50 E
Lagos, Nigeria ... 6 25N 3 27 E
Lagos, Port. 37 5N 8 41w
Lagos □ .... 6 25N 3 35 E
Lagos de
     Moreno 21 21N 101 55w
Lagrange .... 14 13s 125 46 E
Laguna .... 28 30s 48 50 E
Laguna Beach ... 33 31N 117 52w
Lagunas 21 0s 69 45w
Laha .... 48 9N 124 30 E
Lahad Datu ..... 5 0N 118 30 E
Lahaina 20 52N 156 41w
Lahat .... 3 45s 103 30 E
Lahijan .... 37 12N 50 1 E
Lahn, R......... 50 18N 7 37 E
Laholm .... 56 30N 13 2 E
Lahore .... 31 32N 74 22 E

Lahore □ .... 31 55N 74 5 E
Lai Chau .... 22 5N 103 3 E
Laichow Wan, G. . 37 30N 119 30 E
Laidley .... 27 39s 152 20 E
Laila .... 22 10N 46 40 E
Laingsburg ...... 33 9s 20 52 E
Laipin .... 23 42N 109 16 E
Lairg 58 1N 4 24w
Lais .... 3 35s 102 0 E
Laisamis .... 1 38N 37 50 E
Laiyang .... 36 58N 120 41 E
Lajes 27 48s 50 20w
Lake Charles 31 10N 93 10w
Lake City, Fla. ... 30 10N 82 40w
Lake City, S.C. ... 33 51N 79 44w
Lake Grace ...... 33 7s 118 28 E
Lake Harbour ... 62 30N 69 50w
Lake Havasu
     City 34 25N 114 20w
Lake King .... 33 5s 119 45 E
Lake Mead Nat.
     Rec. Area 36 20N 114 30w
Lake Nash ...... 20 57s 138 0 E
Lake Superior
     Prov. Park 47 45N 85 0w
Lake Traverse ... 45 56N 78 4w
Lake Worth 26 36N 80 3w
Lakefield 44 25N 78 16w
Lakeland 28 0N 82 0w
Lakeport 39 1N 122 56w
Lakes Entrance .. 37 50s 148 0 E
Lakeview........ 34 12N 109 59w
Lakewood 41 28N 81 50w
Lakhimpur ...... 27 14N 94 7 E
Lakonikós Kól. ... 36 40N 22 40 E
Lakselv .... 70 2N 24 56 E
Lala Ghat .... 24 30N 92 40 E
Lalín 42 40N 8 5w
Lalin .... 45 14N 126 52 E
Lalitpur .... 24 42N 78 28 E
Lama-Kara ...... 9 30N 1 15 E
Lamaing .... 15 25N 97 53 E
Lambaréné ...... 0 20s 10 12 E
Lame .... 10 27N 9 12 E
Lamego 41 5N 7 52w
Lameroo .... 35 19s 140 33 E
Lamesa 32 45N 101 57w
Lamía .... 38 55s 22 41 E
Lamitan .... 6 40N 122 10 E
Lammermuir Hills . 55 50N 24 0w

Lamon B. .... 14 30N 122 20 E
Lampedusa, I. .... 35 36N 12 40 E
Lampeter 52 6N 4 6w
Lampman 49 25N 102 50w
Lampung □ ...... 5 30s 105 0 E
Lamu .... 2 10s 40 55 E
Lanark 55 40N 3 48w
Lancashire □ 53 40N 2 30w
Lancaster, Canada . 45 17N 66 10w
Lancaster, U.K. ... 54 3N 2 48w
Lancaster, Calif... 34 47N 118 8w
Lancaster, Ky. 37 40N 84 40w
Lancaster, N.H. ... 44 29N 71 34w
Lancaster, S.C. ... 34 45N 80 47w
Lancaster Sd. 74 0N 84 0w
Lanchi .... 29 11N 119 30 E
Lanchou=
     Lanchow .... 36 4N 103 44 E
Lanchow .... 36 4N 103 44 E
Lanciano .... 42 15N 14 22 E
Landeck .... 47 9N 10 34 E
Lander 42 50N 108 49w
Landes □ 43 57N 0 48w
Landes, Reg. 44 0N 1 5w
Landi Kotal ...... 34 7N 71 6 E
Land's End 50 4N 5 42w
Landshut .... 48 31N 12 10 E
Landskrona ..... 56 53N 12 50 E
Lanett 33 0N 85 15w
Langchung ...... 31 31N 105 58 E
Langeberg ...... 33 55s 21 20 E
Langfeng .... 48 4N 121 10 E
Langholm 55 9N 2 59w
Langkawi, Pulau . 6 25N 99 45 E
Langlade, I. 46 50N 56 20w
Langreo 43 13N 5 42w
Langres .... 47 52N 5 20 E
Langres, Plat.
     de .... 47 45N 5 20 E
Langsa .... 4 30N 97 57 E
Langson .... 21 52N 106 42 E
Languedoc, Reg. .. 43 58N 3 22 E
Lansdowne House . 52 5N 88 0w
L'Anse au Loup .. 51 32N 56 50w
Lansing 42 47N 84 32w
Lanzarote, I. 29 0N 13 40w
Lao Cai .... 22 30N 103 57 E
Laoag .... 18 7N 120 34 E
Laoang .... 12 32N 125 8 E
Laois □ 53 0N 7 20w

Laon .... 49 33N 3 35 E
Laos ■ .... 17 45N 105 0 E
Lapeer 43 3N 83 20w
Lappi □ .... 64 33N 25 10 E
Lappland, Reg. ... 68 7N 24 0 E
Laptev Sea ...... 76 0N 125 0 E
L'Aquila .... 42 21N 13 24 E
Lār .... 27 40N 54 14 E
Larache 35 10N 6 5w
Laramie 41 15N 105 29w
Larder Lake 48 5N 79 40w
Laredo 27 34N 99 29w
Largeau .... 17 58N 19 6 E
Largs 55 48N 4 51w
Lárisa .... 39 38N 22 28 E
Larkana .... 27 32N 68 2 E
Lárnax .... 35 0N 33 35 E
Larne 54 52N 5 50w
Larne □ 54 55N 5 55w
Larrimah .... 15 35s 133 12 E
Larvik .... 59 4N 10 0 E
Laryak .... 61 15N 80 0 E
Las Anod .... 8 26N 47 19 E
Las Cruces 32 25N 106 50w
Las Flores 36 0s 59 0w
Las Heras 32 51s 68 49w
Las Khoreh ...... 11 4N 48 20 E
Las Lajas 38 30s 70 25w
Las Lomitas 24 35s 60 50w
Las Palmas ..... 28 10N 15 28 E
Las Plumas 43 40s 67 15w
Las Rosas 32 30s 61 40w
Las Varillas 32 0s 62 50w
Las Vegas, Nev. ... 36 10N 115 5w
Las Vegas, N. Mex. 35 35N 105 10w
Lashburn 53 10N 109 40w
Lashio .... 22 56N 97 45 E
Lassen Pk. 40 20N 121 0w
Latacunga 0 50s 78 35w
Latakia=
     Al Ladhiqiya ... 35 30N 35 45 E
Latchford 47 20N 79 50w
Latham .... 29 44s 116 20 E
Latina .... 41 26N 12 53 E
Latouche 60 0N 147 55w
Latrobe,
     Australia .... 41 14s 146 30 E
Latrun .... 31 50N 34 58 E
Latur .... 18 25N 76 40 E
Latvian S.S.R. □ .. 57 0N 25 0 E

Lau Is. 17 0s 178 30w
Lauchhammer ... 51 35N 13 40 E
Launceston,
     Australia .... 41 24s 147 8 E
Launceston, U.K. . 50 38N 4 21w
Laura .... 33 10s 138 18 E
Laurel, Miss..... 31 50N 89 0w
Laurel, Mont. ... 45 46N 108 49w
Laurencekirk 56 50N 2 30w
Laurens 34 32N 82 2w
Laurentian Plat. . 51 30N 65 0w
Laurentides
     Prov. Park 47 50N 71 50w
Lauringburg 34 50N 79 25w
Lausanne .... 46 32N 6 38 E
Lauzon 46 48N 71 4w
Laverton .... 28 44s 122 29 E
Lavi .... 32 47N 35 25 E
Lavrentiya 65 35N 171 0w
Lawra 10 39N 2 51w
Lawrence, N.Z. ... 45 55s 169 41 E
Lawrence, U.S.A. . 42 40N 71 9w
Lawrence 39 0N 95 10w
Lawrenceburg ... 35 12N 87 19w
Lawton 34 33N 98 25w
Lawu, Mt. ...... 7 40s 111 13 E
Layras 21 20s 45 0w
Laysan I. 25 30N 167 0w
Lazio □ .... 42 10N 12 30 E
Le Creusot ...... 46 50N 4 24 E
Le François 14 38N 60 57w
Le Havre .... 49 30N 0 5 E
Le Maire,
     Estrecho de 54 50s 65 0w
Le Mans .... 48 0N 0 10 E
Le Marinel ...... 10 25s 25 17 E
Le Mars 43 0N 96 0w
Le Moule 16 20N 61 22w
Le Puy .... 45 3N 3 52 E
Le Tréport ...... 50 3N 1 20 E
Le Verdon 45 32N 1 5w
Lea, R. .... 51 30N 0 1 E
Lead 44 20N 103 40w
Leader 50 50N 109 30w
Leadhills 55 25s 3 47w
Leadville 39 17N 106 23w
Lealui .... 15 10s 23 2 E
Leamington,
     Canada 42 10N 82 30w
Leamington, U.K. . 52 18N 1 32w

Learmonth ...... 22 40s 114 10 E
Leask 53 5N 106 45w
Leavenworth 39 25N 95 0w
Lebanon, Ind. ... 40 3N 86 55w
Lebanon, Mo. ... 37 40N 92 40w
Lebanon, N.H. ... 43 38N 72 15w
Lebanon, Ore. ... 44 31N 122 57w
Lebanon, Pa. ... 40 20N 76 28w
Lebanon, Tenn. ... 36 15N 86 20w
Lebanon ■ ..... 34 0N 36 0 E
Lebombo-berg .... 24 30s 32 0 E
Lebrija 36 53N 6 5w
Lebu 37 40s 73 47w
Lecce .... 40 20N 18 10 E
Lecco .... 45 50N 9 27 E
Łęczyca .... 52 5N 19 45 E
Ledbury 52 3N 2 25w
Ledesma 41 6N 5 59w
Leduc 53 20N 113 30w
Lee, R. 51 51N 9 2w
Leeds 53 48N 1 34w
Leek 53 7N 2 2w
Leesburg 28 47N 81 52w
Leeu-Gamka .... 32 43s 21 59 E
Leeuwarden .... 53 15N 5 48 E
Leeuwin, C. .... 34 20s 115 9 E
Leeward Is....... 16 30N 63 30w
Legazpi .... 13 10N 123 46 E
Leghorn =
  Livorno .... 43 32N 10 18 E
Legnica .... 51 12N 16 10 E
Leh .... 34 15N 77 35 E
Leicester 52 39N 1 9w
Leicester □ 52 40N 1 10w
Leichow Pantao,
  Pen. .... 20 40N 110 10 E
Leiden .... 52 9N 4 30 E
Leigh Creek .... 30 28s 138 24 E
Leine, R. .... 48 54N 10 1 E
Leinster □ 53 0N 7 10w
Lienyünchiangshih=
  Sinhailien .... 34 31N 119 0 E
Leipzig .... 51 20N 12 23 E
Leiria 39 46N 8 53w
Leith 55 59N 3 10w
Leith Hill 51 10N 0 23w
Leitrim 54 0N 8 5w
Leitrim □ 54 8N 8 0w
Leiyang .... 26 24N 112 51 E
Leland 33 25N 90 52w

Leleque 42 15s 71 0w
Léman, L. ...... 46 26N 6 30 E
Lembeni .... 3 48s 37 33 E
Lemery .... 13 58N 120 56 E
Lemesós .... 34 42N 33 1 E
Lemnos, I.=
  Límnos, I. ..... 39 50N 25 5 E
Lemvig .... 56 33N 8 20 E
Lena, R. .... 72 25N 126 40 E
Lena, R. .... 66 30N 126 3 E
Leninabad .... 40 17N 69 37 E
Leninakan .... 41 0N 42 50 E
Leningrad .... 59 55N 30 20 E
Leninogorsk .... 50 20N 83 30 E
Leninsk .... 48 40N 45 15 E
Leninsk
  Kuznetskiy .... 55 10N 86 10 E
Leninskoye .... 47 56N 132 38 E
Lenkoran .... 39 45N 48 50 E
Lenoir 35 55N 81 36w
Lenoir City 35 40N 84 20w
Lens .... 50 26N 2 50 E
Lensk .... 60 48N 114 55 E
Lentini .... 37 18N 15 0 E
Leo 11 3N 2 2w
Leoben .... 47 22N 15 5 E
Leominster, U.K. 52 15N 2 43w
Leominster, U.S.A. .. 42 30N 71 44w
León, Mexico 21 7N 101 30w
León, Nic. 12 20N 86 51w
León, Sp. 42 38N 5 34w
León, Reg. 41 30N 6 0w
León, Mt. de 42 30N 6 18w
Leongatha .... 38 30s 145 58 E
Leonora .... 28 49s 121 19 E
Léopold II, L.=
  Mai-Ndombe, L. .. 2 0s 18 0 E
Léopoldville=
  Kinshasa .... 4 20s 15 15 E
Leoville 53 39N 107 33w
Lepel .... 54 50N 28 40 E
Lepikha .... 64 45N 125 55 E
Lere .... 9 39N 14 13 E
Lérida .... 41 37N 0 39 E
Lerwick 60 10N 1 10w
Les Cayes 18 15N 73 46w
Les Sables-
  d'Olonne 46 30N 1 45w
Les Tres Marías,
  Is. 12 20N 106 30w

Lesbos, I.=
  Lésvos, I. .... 39 0N 26 20 E
Leskovac .... 43 0N 21 58 E
Leslie .... 26 16s 28 55 E
Lesotho ■ .... 29 40s 28 0 E
Lesozarodsk .... 45 30N 133 20 E
Lesser Antilles,
  Is. 12 30N 61 0w
Lesser Sunda
  Is. .... 7 30s 117 0 E
Lesuru .... 1 0N 35 15 E
Lésvos, I. .... 39 0N 26 20 E
Leszno .... 51 50N 16 30 E
Letchworth 51 58N 0 13w
Lethbridge 49 45N 112 45w
Lethem 3 20N 59 50w
Leti, Kep. .... 8 10s 128 0 E
Letiahau, R. .... 21 16s 24 0 E
Leticia 4 0s 70 0w
Letlhakane .... 24 0s 24 59 E
Letpadan .... 17 45N 96 0 E
Letpan .... 19 28N 93 52 E
Letsôk-au-Kyun ... 11 37N 98 15 E
Letterkenny 54 57N 7 42w
Leuser, Mt. .... 4 0N 96 51 E
Leuven .... 50 52 4 42 E
Levanger .... 63 45N 11 19 E
Levelland 33 38N 102 17w
Leven 56 12N 3 0w
Leven, L. 56 12N 3 22w
Leveque, C. .... 16 20s 123 0 E
Levin .... 40 37s 175 18 E
Levis 46 48N 71 9w
Lévka, Mt. .... 35 18N 24 3 E
Levkás, I. .... 38 40N 20 43 E
Levkôsia .... 35 10N 33 25 E
Lewes .... 50 53N 0 2 E
Lewis, I. 58 10N 6 40w
Lewis Ra. .... 20 3s 128 50 E
Lewisporte 49 15N 55 3w
Lewiston, Id. 45 58N 117 0w
Lewiston, Me. 44 6N 70 13w
Lewistown, Mont. . 47 0N 109 25w
Lewistown, Pa. ... 40 37N 77 33w
Lexington, Ky. .. 38 6N 84 30w
Lexington, Mo. .. 39 7N 93 55w
Lexington, Neb. .. 40 48N 99 45w
Lexington, N.C. .. 35 50N 80 13w
Leyte, I. .... 11 0N 125 0 E
Lhasa .... 29 39N 91 6 E

Lhatse Dzong ..... 29 10N 87 45 E
Lhokseumawe .... 5 20N 97 10 E
Li Kiang, R. .... 18 25N 98 45 E
Liangsiang .... 39 44N 116 8 E
Liaoning □ .... 41 15N 122 0 E
Liaotung, Pen. .. 40 0N 122 22 E
Liaotung Wan, G.. 40 30N 121 30 E
Liaoyang .... 41 17N 123 11 E
Liaoyuan .... 42 55N 125 10 E
Liard, R. 61 52N 121 18w
Liberal 37 4N 101 0w
Liberec .... 50 47N 15 7 E
Liberia ■ 6 30N 9 30w
Liberty 41 48N 74 45w
Lîbîya, Sahrâ', Des. 27 35N 25 0 E
Libourne 44 55N 0 14w
Libreville .... 0 25N 9 26 E
Libya ■ .... 28 30N 17 30 E
Licantén 34 55s 72 0w
Licata .... 37 6N 13 55 E
Lichfield 52 40N 1 50w
Lichinga .... 13 13s 35 11 E
Lichtenburg .... 26 8s 26 8 E
Lichtenstein ■ ... 47 8N 9 35 E
Liège .... 50 38N 5 35 E
Liège □ .... 50 32N 5 35 E
Lienz .... 46 50N 12 46 E
Liepaja .... 56 30N 21 0 E
Lier .... 51 7N 4 34 E
Liffey, R. 53 21N 6 16w
Lifford 54 50N 7 30w
Ligúria □ .... 44 30N 9 0 E
Ligurian Sea .... 43 15N 8 30 E
Lihou Reef and
  Cays .... 17 25s 151 40 E
Lihue 21 59N 152 24w
Likasi .... 10 55s 26 48 E
Likiang .... 26 50N 100 15 E
Likati .... 3 20N 24 0 E
Liling .... 27 47N 113 30 E
Lille .... 50 38N 3 3 E
Lille Bælt .... 55 30N 9 45 E
Lillehammer .... 61 8N 10 30 E
Lillesand .... 58 15N 8 23 E
Lillestrøm .... 59 58N 11 5 E
Lilliput .... 22 30s 29 55 E
Lillooet 50 42N 121 56w
Lilongwe .... 14 0s 33 48 E

Lima, Peru 12 0s 77 0w
Lima, Mont. 44 41N 112 38w
Lima, Ohio 40 42N 84 5w
Liman Katagum .. 10 5N 9 42 E
Limavady □ 55 0N 655½
Limavady 55 3N 6 58w
Limay, R. 39 0s 68 0w
Limay Mahuida .. 37 10s 66 45w
Limburg .... 50 22N 8 4 E
Limburg □ .... 51 20N 5 55 E
Limeira 22 35s 47 28w
Limerick 52 40N 8 38w
Limerick □ 52 30N 8 50w
Limfjorden .... 56 55N 9 0 E
Límnos, I. .... 39 50N 25 5 E
Limoeiro do
  Norte 5 5s 38 0w
Limoera 7 52s 35 27w
Limoges .... 45 50N 1 15 E
Limón 10 0N 83 2w
Limousin, Reg. .. 46 0N 1 0 E
Limpopo, R. .... 25 15s 33 30 E
Limuru .... 1 2s 36 35 E
Linares, Chile .. 35 50s 71 40w
Linares, Mexico .. 24 50N 99 40w
Linares, Sp. 38 10N 3 40w
Lincheng .... 37 26N 114 34 E
Lincoln □ 53 14N 0 32w
Lincoln, Arg. .. 34 55N 61 30w
Lincoln, N.Z. .. 43 38s 172 30 E
Lincoln, U.K. .. 53 14N 0 32w
Lincoln, Ill. 40 10N 89 20w
Lincoln, Neb. .. 40 50N 96 42w
Lincoln Wolds .. 53 20N 0 5w
Lindi .... 9 58s 39 38 E
Lindsay, Canada .. 44 22N 78 43w
Lindsay, U.S.A. .. 36 14N 119 6w
Lindley .... 27 52s 27 56 E
Linfen .... 36 5N 111 32 E
Lingayen .... 16 1N 120 14 E
Lingayen G. .... 16 10N 120 15 E
Lingen .... 52 32N 7 21 E
Lingga, Kep. .... 0 10 E 104 30 E
Lingling .... 26 13N 111 37 E
Linglo .... 24 20N 105 25 E
Lingshui .... 18 27N 110 0 E
Linguéré 15 25N 15 5w
Linhai .... 28 51N 121 7 E
Linho .... 40 50N 107 30 E
Lini .... 35 5N 118 20 E

Linkao	19 56N	109 42 E
Linkiang	46 2N	133 56 E
Linköping	58 28N	15 36 E
Linkow	45 16N	130 18 E
Linlithgow	55 58N	3 38w
Linnhe, L.	56 36N	5 25w
Linping	24 25N	114 32 E
Lins	21 40s	49 44w
Linsi	43 30N	118 5 E
Linsia	35 50N	103 0 E
Lintan	34 59N	103 49 E
Linton	39 0N	87 10w
Lintsing	36 50N	115 45 E
Linville	26 50s	152 11 E
Linz	48 18N	14 18 E
Lion, G. du	43 0N	4 0 E
Lípari, I.	38 26N	14 58 E
Lipari Is.	38 40N	15 0 E
Lipetsk	52 45N	39 35 E
Liping	26 16N	109 8 E
Lipno	52 49N	19 15 E
Lippe, R.	51 39N	6 38 E
Liptrap, C.	38 50s	145 55 E
Lira	2 17N	32 57 E
Liria	39 37N	0 35w
Lisala	2 12N	21 38 E
Lisboa	38 42N	9 10w
Lisboa □	39 0N	9 12w
Lisbon = Lisboa	39 0N	9 12w
Lisburn	54 30N	6 9w
Lisburn □	54 30N	6 5w
Lisburne, C.	68 50N	166 0w
Lishui	28 20N	119 48w
Lisieux	49 10N	0 12 E
Lismore, Australia	28 44s	153 21 E
Lismore, Eire	52 8N	7 58w
Listowel, Canada	44 4N	80 58w
Listowel, Eire	52 27N	9 30w
Litchfield	39 10N	89 40w
Lithgow	33 25s	150 8 E
Lithuanian S.S.R. □	55 30N	24 0 E
Litoměřice	50 33N	14 10 E
Little Abaco I.	26 50N	77 30w
Little Barrier, I.	36 12s	175 8 E
Little Bushman Land	29 10s	18 10 E
Little Current	45 55N	82 0w
Little Colorado, R.	36 11N	111 48w
Little Falls, Minn.	45 58N	94 19w
Little Falls, N.Y.	43 3N	74 50w
Little Inagua I.	21 40N	73 50w
Little Longlac	49 42N	86 58w
Little Namaqualand	29 0s	17 10 E
Little Ouse, R.	52 30N	0 22 E
Little Rann	23 25N	71 25 E
Little River	43 45s	172 49 E
Little Rock	34 41N	92 10w
Littlefield	33 57N	102 17w
Littlehampton	50 48N	0 32w
Liuan	31 45N	116 30 E
Liucheng	24 39N	109 14 E
Liuchow	24 10N	109 10 E
Liuwa Plain	14 20s	22 30 E
Livermore, Mt.	30 45N	104 8w
Liverpool, Australia	33 55s	150 52 E
Liverpool, Canada	44 5N	64 41w
Liverpool, U.K.	53 25N	3 0w
Livingston, Guatemala	15 50N	88 50w
Livingston, U.S.A.	45 40N	110 40w
Livingstone	17 46s	25 52 E
Livingstone Mts.	9 40s	34 20 E
Livingstonia	10 38s	34 5 E
Livny	52 30N	37 30 E
Livorno	43 32N	10 18 E
Liwale	9 48s	37 58 E
Lizard Pt.	49 57N	5 11w
Ljubljana	46 4N	14 33 E
Ljungan, R.	62 19N	17 23 E
Ljungby	56 49N	13 55 E
Ljusdal	61 46N	16 3 E
Ljusnan, R.	61 12N	17 8 E
Llandeilo	50 54N	4 0w
Llandovery	51 59N	3 49w
Llandrindod Wells	52 15N	3 23w
Llandudno	53 19N	3 51w
Llanelli	51 41N	4 11w
Llanes	43 25N	4 50w
Llangollen	52 58N	3 10w
Llanidloes	52 28N	3 31w
Llano Estacado, Reg.	34 0N	103 0w
Llanos, Reg.	3 25N	71 35w
Llanquihue, L.	41 10s	72 50w
Lloret de Mar	41 41N	2 53 E
Lloydminster	53 20N	110 0w
Llullaillaco, Mt.	24 30s	68 30w
Lobatse	25 12s	25 40 E
Lobería	38 10s	58 40w
Lobito	12 18s	13 35 E
Locarno	46 10N	8 47 E
Lochaber, Reg.	56 55N	5 0w
Lochalsh, Kyle of	57 17N	5 43w
Lochboisdale	57 10N	7 20w
Lochgilphead	56 2N	5 37w
Lochmaddy	57 36N	7 10w
Lochnagar, Mt.	56 57N	3 14w
Lochy, L.	56 58N	4 55w
Lock	33 34s	135 46 E
Lockeport	43 47N	65 4w
Lockerbie	55 7N	3 21w
Lockhart	29 55N	97 40w
Lod	31 57N	34 54 E
Loddon, R.	38 12N	121 16w
Lodja	3 30s	23 23 E
Lodwar	3 10N	35 40 E
Łódź	51 45N	19 27 E
Lofoten, Is.	68 10N	13 0 E
Logan, Ohio	39 35N	82 22w
Logan, Utah	41 45N	111 50w
Logan, W. Va.	37 51N	81 59w
Logan, Mt.	60 40N	140 0w
Logansport	31 58N	93 58w
Logar □	33 50N	69 0 E
Logrono	42 28N	2 32w
Loheia	15 45N	42 40 E
Loho	33 33N	114 5 E
Loimaa	60 50N	23 5 E
Loir, R.	47 33N	0 32w
Loir-et-Cher □	47 40N	1 20 E
Loire □	45 40N	4 5 E
Loire, R.	47 16N	2 11w
Loire-Atlantique □	47 25N	1 40w
Loiret □	47 58N	2 10 E
Loja, Ecuador	3 59s	79 16w
Loja, Sp.	37 10N	4 10w
Lokeren	51 6N	3 59 E
Lokitaung	4 12N	35 48 E
Lokka, L.	68 0N	27 50 E
Løkken	57 22N	9 41 E
Lokoja	7 47N	6 45 E
Lokolama	2 35s	19 50 E
Lokwei	19 12N	110 30 E
Lolland, L.	54 45N	11 30 E
Lom	43 48N	23 20 E
Lomami, R.	0 46N	24 16 E
Lombardia □	45 35N	9 45 E
Lomblen, I.	8 30s	116 20 E
Lombok, I.	8 35s	116 20 E
Lomé	6 9N	1 20 E
Lomela	2 5s	23 52 E
Lomela, R.	0 14s	20 42 E
Lomond	50 24N	112 36w
Lomond, L.	56 8N	4 38w
Lompoc	34 41N	120 32w
Łomza	53 10N	22 2 E
Loncoche	39 20s	72 50w
Londiani	0 10s	35 33 E
London, Canada	43 0N	81 15w
London, U.K.	51 30N	0 5w
London □	51 30N	0 5w
Londonderry	55 0N	7 20w
Londonderry □	55 0N	7 20w
Londonderry, C.	13 45s	126 55 E
Londonderry, I.	55 0N	71 0w
Londrina	23 0s	51 10w
Lone Pine	36 35N	118 2w
Long Beach	33 46N	118 12w
Long Eaton	52 54N	1 16w
Long I., Bahamas	23 20N	75 10w
Long I., Canada	44 23N	66 19w
Long I., U.S.A.	40 50N	73 20w
Long Range Mts.	48 0N	58 30w
Long Xuyen	10 19N	105 28 E
Longford	53 43N	7 50w
Longford □	53 42N	7 45w
Longiram	0 5s	115 45 E
Longmont	40 10N	105 4w
Longreach	23 28s	144 14 E
Longview, Tex.	32 30N	94 45w
Longview, Wash.	46 9N	122 58w
Lons-le-Saunier	46 40N	5 31 E
Lønsdal	66 46N	15 26 E
Looe	50 21N	4 26w
Loomis	49 15N	108 45w
Loon Lake	44 50N	77 15w
Loongana	30 52s	127 5 E
Loop Hd.	52 34N	9 55w
Lop Nor, L.	40 30N	90 30 E
Lopez, C.	0 47s	8 40 E
Lorain	41 20N	82 5w
Loralai	30 29N	68 30 E
Lorca	37 41N	1 42w
Lord Howe I.	31 33s	159 6 E
Lordsburg	32 15N	108 45w
Lorestan □	33 0N	48 30 E
Loreto, Brazil	7 5s	45 30w
Loreto, Italy	43 26N	13 36 E
Lorient	47 45N	3 23N
Lorn, Firth of	56 20s	5 40w
Lorne, Reg.	56 26N	5 10w
Lorraine, Reg.	49 0N	6 0 E
Lorrainville	47 21N	79 23w
Lorugumu	2 50N	35 15 E
Los Alamos	35 57N	106 17w
Los Andes	32 50s	70 40w
Los Angeles, Chile	37 28s	72 23w
Los Angeles, U.S.A.	34 0N	118 10w
Los Angeles Aqueduct	35 0N	118 20w
Los Banos	37 8N	120 56w
Los Blancos	23 45s	62 30w
Los Hermanos, Is.	11 45N	64 25w
Los Lagos	39 51s	72 50w
Los Mochis	25 45N	109 5w
Los Roques, Is.	11 50N	66 45w
Los Testigos, Is.	11 23s	63 6w
Los Vilos	32 0s	71 30w
Loshkalakh	62 45N	147 20 E
Losinj	44 35N	14 28 E
Lossiemouth	57 43N	3 17w
Lot □	44 39N	1 40 E
Lot, R.	44 18N	0 20 E
Lot-et-Garonne □	44 22N	0 30 E
Lota	37 5s	73 10w
Lotagipi Swamp	4 55s	35 0 E
Lothian □	55 55N	3 35w
Loto	28 50s	22 28 E
Loughborough	52 46N	1 11w
Loughrea	53 11N	8 33w
Louis Trichardt	23 0s	25 55 E
Louisbourg	45 55N	60 0w
Louiseville	46 20N	73 0w
Louisiade Arch.	11 10s	153 0 E
Louisiana □	30 50N	92 0w
Louisville, Ky.	38 15N	85 45w
Louisville, Miss.	33 7N	89 3w
Loulé	37 9N	8 0w
Loup City	41 19N	98 57w
Lourdes	43 6N	0 3w

Lourenço
  Marques=
  Maputo ...... 25 58s 32 32 E
Louth, Australia .. 30 30s 145 8 E
Louth, Eire 53 47N 6 33w
Louth, U.K. 53 23N 0 0
Louth □ 53 55N 6 30w
Love 53 29N 104 9w
Loveland 40 27N 105 4w
Lovelock 40 17N 118 25w
Lovisa .... 60 28N 26 12 E
Lowell 42 38N 71 19w
Lower Hutt ...... 41 10s 174 55 E
Lowestoft .... 52 29N 1 44 E
Łowicz ...... 52 6N 19 55 E
Lowville 43 48N 75 30w
Loxton .... 34 28s 140 31 E
Loyang ...... 34 41N 112 28 E
Loyung ...... 24 25N 109 25 E
Lozère □ .... 44 35N 3 30 E
Lu-ta .... 39 0N 121 31 E
Lualaba, R. ...... 0 26N 25 20 E
Luanda .... 8 58s 13 9 E
Luang Prabang .. 19 45N 102 10 E
Luangwa, R. ...... 15 40N 30 25 E
Luanshya ...... 13 3s 28 28 E
Luarca 43 32N 6 32w
Lubang Is. ...... 13 50N 120 12 E
Lubban .... 32 9N 35 14 E
Lubbock 33 40N 102 0w
Lübeck .... 53 52N 10 41 E
Lubefu .... 4 47s 24 27 E
Lublin .... 51 12N 22 38 E
Lubnân, Mts. ..... 34 0N 36 0 E
Lubuklinggau ..... 3 15s 102 55 E
Lubuksikaping ..... 0 10N 100 15 E
Lubumbashi ..... 11 32s 27 28 E
Lubushi .... 10 32s 30 30 E
Lubutu .... 0 45s 26 30 E
Lucania, Mt. 60 48N 141 25w
Lucca .... 43 50N 10 30 E
Luce B. 54 45N 4 48w
Lucena, Philippines 13 56N 121 37 E
Lucena, Sp. 37 27N 4 31w
Lučenec .... 48 18N 19 42 E
Lucerne=Luzern .. 43 3N 8 13 E
Luchow .... 29 2N 105 10 E
Luckenwalde ..... 52 5N 13 11 E
Lucknow .... 26 50N 81 0 E
Lüderitz .... 26 41s 15 8 E

Ludhiana .... 30 57N 75 56 E
Ludington 43 58N 86 27w
Ludlow 52 23N 2 42w
Ludvika .... 60 8N 15 14 E
Ludwigsburg ..... 48 53N 9 11 E
Ludwigshafen .... 49 27N 8 27 E
Lufkin 31 25N 94 40w
Luga .... 58 40N 29 55 E
Lugano .... 46 0N 8 57 E
Lugansk=
  Voroshilovgrad .. 48 35N 39 29 E
Lugazi .... 0 32N 30 42 E
Lugh Ganana ..... 3 48N 42 40 E
Lugo 43 2N 7 35w
Lugoj .... 45 42N 21 57 E
Lugovoy .... 43 0N 72 20 E
Luis Correia 3 0s 41 35w
Luján 34 45s 59 5w
Lukang .... 24 0N 120 19 E
Łuków .... 51 56N 22 23 E
Lukulu .... 14 35s 23 25 E
Luleå .... 65 35N 22 10 E
Lulonga, R. ...... 0 43N 18 23 E
Lulua, R. ...... 5 2s 21 7 E
Luluabourg=
  Kananga .... 5 55s 22 18 E
Lumberton 34 37N 78 59w
Lumbwa .... 0 12s 35 28 E
Lumsden .... 45 44s 168 27 E
Lun .... 47 55N 105 1 E
Lund .... 55 41N 13 12 E
Lundazi .... 12 20s 33 7 E
Lundy, I. 51 10N 4 41w
Lune, R. 54 2N 2 50w
Lüneburg .... 53 15N 10 23 E
Lüneburger
  Heide, Reg. ..... 53 0N 10 0 E
Lunenburg 44 22N 64 18w
Lunéville .... 48 36N 6 30 E
Lunghwa .... 41 15N 117 51 E
Lungkiang .... 47 22N 123 4 E
Lungkow .... 37 40N 120 25 E
Lungleh .... 22 55N 92 45 E
Lungsi .... 35 0N 104 35 E
Luni .... 26 0N 73 6 E
Luni, R. .... 24 40N 71 15 E
Luofu .... 0 1s 29 15 E
Luqa .... 35 35N 14 28 E
Lurgan 54 28N 6 20w
Lusaka .... 15 28s 28 16 E

Lushoto .... 4 47s 38 20 E
Lushun .... 38 48N 121 16 E
Luso .... 11 47s 19 52 E
Lü-ta .... 39 0N 122 0 E
Luton 51 53N 0 24w
Lutong .... 4 30N 114 0 E
Lutsk .... 50 50N 25 15 E
Luwingu .... 10 15s 30 4 E
Luxembourg ..... 49 37N 6 9 E
Luxembourg ■ .... 50 0N 6 0 E
Luxembourg □ .... 49 58N 5 30 E
Luxor=El Uqsur .. 25 41N 32 38 E
Luza .... 60 39N 47 10 E
Luzern .... 47 3N 8 18 E
Luziania 16 20s 48 0w
Luzon, I. .... 16 0N 121 0 E
Lvov .... 49 40N 24 0 E
Lwanhsien .... 39 45N 118 45 E
Lwasamaire ..... 0 53s 30 7 E
Lyakhovskiye Os. . 73 40N 141 0 E
Lyallpur .... 31 30N 73 5 E
Lybster 58 18N 3 16w
Lycksele .... 64 38N 18 40 E
Lydda=Lod ...... 31 57N 34 54 E
Lydenburg .... 25 10s 30 29 E
Lyell .... 41 48s 172 4 E
Lyell, Ra. .... 41 38s 172 20 E
Lyme Regis 50 44N 2 57w
Lymington 50 46N 1 32w
Lynchburg 37 23N 79 10w
Lyndhurst, N.S.W. . 33 41N 149 2 E
Lyndhurst, Queens. 18 56s 144 30 E
Lyndonville 44 32N 72 1w
Lynn 42 28N 70 57w
Lynn Lake 56 51N 101 3w
Lynton 51 14N 3 50w
Lyon .... 45 46N 4 50 E
Lyonnais, Reg. ... 45 45N 4 15 E
Lyons=Lyon ...... 45 46N 4 50 E
Lyons, G. of=
  Lion, G. du ..... 43 0N 4 0 E
Lyons, R. 25 2N 115 9w
Lysra .... 57 7N 57 47 E
Lytham
  St. Annes 53 45N 2 58w
Lyttelton .... 43 35s 172 44 E

M

Ma'ad .... 32 37N 35 36 E
Maanshan .... 31 40N 118 30 E
Maas, R. .... 51 49N 5 1 E
Maastricht .... 50 50N 5 40 E
Mablethorpe ..... 53 21N 0 14 E
Mabuki .... 2 57s 33 12 E
Macaé 20 20s 41 55w
McAllen 26 12N 98 15w
McAlester 34 57N 95 40w
Macapá 0 5N 51 10w
McArthur, R. ..... 15 54s 136 40 E
Macau 5 0s 36 40w
Macau ■ .... 22 16N 113 35 E
McBride 53 20N 120 10w
McCammon 42 41N 112 11w
Macclesfield 53 16N 2 9w
McClintock 57 45N 94 15w
M'Clintock Chan. . 71 0N 103 0w
McComb 31 20N 90 30w
McCook 40 15N 100 35w
McDonald I. ..... 54 0s 73 0 E
Macdonnell, Ras. .. 23 40s 133 0 E
Macdougall, L. ... 66 20N 98 30w
Macduff 57 40N 2 30w
Mace 48 55N 80 0w
Macedonia □,
  Greece=
  Makedhonia □ .. 40 39N 22 0 E
Macedonia □,
  Y.-slav.=
  Makedonija □ ... 41 53N 21 40 E
Maceió 9 40s 35 41w
Macenta 8 35N 9 20w
Macerata .... 43 19N 13 28 E
McGill 35 27N 114 50w
Macgillycuddy's
  Reeks, Mts. 52 2N 9 45w
Mach .... 29 50N 67 20 E
Machakos .... 1 30s 37 15 E
Machala 3 10s 79 50w
Macheřna .... 61 20N 172 20 E
Machilipatnam .. 16 11N 81 8 E
Machiques 10 4N 72 34w
Machynlleth 52 36N 3 51w
Macias Nguema
  Biyoga, I. ...... 3 30N 8 40 E

Macintyre, R. ..... 28 38s 150 47 E
Mackay, Australia . 21 36s 148 39 E
Mackay, U.S.A. .. 43 58N 113 37w
Mackay, L. .... 22 40s 128 35 E
McKeesport 40 29N 79 50w
Mackenzie, Reg. .. 61 30N 144 30w
Mackenzie 55 20N 123 5w
Mackenzie, R. .... 23 30s 150 0 E
Mackenzie, R. 69 15N 134 8w
Mackenzie City .. 6 0N 58 10w
Mackenzie Mts. .. 64 0N 130 0w
McKinlay .... 21 16s 141 17 E
McKinley, Mt. 63 10N 151 0w
McKinney 33 10N 96 40w
Mackinnon Road .. 3 40s 39 0 E
Macklin 52 20N 109 56w
Macksville .... 30 40s 152 56 E
Maclean .... 29 26s 153 16 E
Maclear .... 31 2s 28 23 E
Macleay, R. ...... 30 52s 153 1 E
McLennan 55 42N 116 50w
McLeod, L. .... 24 9s 113 47 E
McLure 50 55N 120 20w
M'Clure Str. 74 40N 117 30w
McMinnville,
  Oreg. 45 16N 123 11w
McMinnville,
  Tenn. 35 43N 85 45w
McMurray 56 45N 111 27w
McNary 34 4N 109 53w
Macomb 40 25N 90 40w
Mâcon .... 46 19N 4 50 E
Macon 32 50N 83 37w
McPherson 38 25N 97 40w
Macquarie Is. .... 54 36s 158 55 E
Macquarie, R. .... 30 7s 147 24 E
Macroom 51 54N 8 57w
Mada'in Sālih .... 26 51N 37 58 E
Madagali .... 10 56N 13 33 E
Madagascar ■ .... 20 0s 47 0 E
Madama .... 22 0N 14 0 E
Madang .... 5 0s 145 46 E
Madaoua .... 14 5N 6 27 E
Madara .... 11 45N 10 35 E
Madaripur .... 23 2N 90 15 E
Madauk .... 17 56N 96 52 E
Madaya .... 22 20N 96 10 E
Madden L. 9 20N 79 37w
Madeira, I. 32 50N 17 0w
Madeira, R. 3 22s 58 45w

Madera	37 0N 120 1W		
Madhya Pradesh □	21 50N 81 0 E		
Madinat al Shaab	12 50N 45 0 E		
Madingou	4 10s 13 33 E		
Madison, Ind.	38 42N 85 20W		
Madison, S.D.	44 0N 97 8W		
Madison, Wis.	43 5N 89 25W		
Madisonville	37 42N 86 30W		
Madiun	7 38s 111 32 E		
Mado Gashi	0 47N 39 12 E		
Madras, India	13 8N 80 19 E		
Madras, U.S.A.	44 40N 121 10W		
Madre, Laguna	25 0N 97 30W		
Madre de Dios, R.	10 59s 66 8W		
Madre de Dios, I.	50 20s 75 10W		
Madre del Sur, Sa.	17 30N 100 0W		
Madre Occidental, Sa.	27 0N 107 0W		
Madre Oriental, Sa.	25 0N 100 0W		
Madrid	40 25N 3 45W		
Madura, I.	7 0N 113 20 E		
Madura, Selat	7 30s 113 20 E		
Madura Motel	31 55s 127 0 E		
Madurai	9 55N 78 10 E		
Madurantakam	12 30N 79 50 E		
Mae Sot	16 43N 98 34 E		
Maebashi	36 23N 139 4 E		
Maesteg	51 36N 3 40W		
Maestra, Sa.	20 15N 77 0W		
Maestrazgo, Mts. de	40 30N 0 25W		
Maevatanana	16 56s 46 49 E		
Mafeking, Canada	52 40N 101 10W		
Mafeking, S.Africa	25 50s 25 38 E		
Mafia I.	7 45s 39 50 E		
Mafra, Brazil	26 7s 49 49w		
Mafra, Port.	38 56N 9 20W		
Mafupa	10 30s 29 7 E		
Magadan	59 30N 151 0 E		
Magadi	1 54s 36 19 E		
Magallanes, Estrecho de, Str.	52 30s 75 0w		
Magangue	9 14N 74 45w		
Magdalen Is.	47 30N 61 40w		
Magdalena, Arg.	35 4s 57 32w		
Magdalena, Mexico	30 50N 112 0w		
Magdalena, U.S.A.	34 10N 107 20w		
Magdalena, I., Chile	44 42s 73 10w		
Magdalena, I., Mexico	24 40N 112 15w		
Magdeburg	52 8N 11 36 E		
Magdi'el	32 10N 34 54 E		
Magee, I.	54 48N 5 44w		
Magelang	7 29s 110 13 E		
Magellan's Str.= Magallanes, Estrecho de	52 30s 75 0w		
Maggiore, L.	46 0N 8 35 E		
Maghar	32 54N 35 24 E		
Magherafelt	54 45N 6 36w		
Magherafelt □	54 45N 6 36w		
Magnitogorsk	53 20N 59 0 E		
Magnolia	33 18N 93 12w		
Magog	45 18N 72 9w		
Magrath	49 25N 112 50w		
Maguarinho, C.	0 15s 48 30w		
Magwe	20 10N 95 0 E		
Mahābād	36 50N 45 45 E		
Mahabo	20 23s 44 40 E		
Mahaddei Uen	3 0N 45 32 E		
Mahagi	2 20N 31 0 E		
Mahagi Port	2 3N 31 17 E		
Mahalapye	23 1s 26 51 E		
Mahallāt	33 55N 50 30 E		
Mahanadi, R.	20 0N 86 25 E		
Mahanoro	19 59s 48 48 E		
Maharashtra □	19 30N 75 30 E		
Mahbubnagar	16 45N 77 59 E		
Mahdia	35 28N 11 0 E		
Mahenge	8 45s 36 35 E		
Maheno	45 10s 170 50 E		
Mahia Pen.	39 9s 177 55 E		
Mahón	39 50N 4 18 E		
Mahone Bay	44 27N 64 23w		
Mahuta	11 32N 4 58 E		
Mai-Ndombe, L.	2 0s 18 0 E		
Maidenhead	51 31N' 0 42w		
Maidstone, Canada	53 5N 109 20w		
Maidstone, U.K.	51 16N 0 31 E		
Maiduguri	12 0N 13 20 E		
Maijdi	22 48N 91 10 E		
Maikala Ra.	22 0N 81 0 E		
Main, R.	54 43N 6 18w		
Main, R.	50 0N 8 18 E		
Maine □	45 20N 69 0w		
Maine, Reg.	48 0N 0 0 E		
Maine-et-Loire □	47 31N 0 30w		
Maingkwan	26 15N 96 45 E		
Mainland, I., Orkney	59 0N 3 10w		
Mainland, I., Shetland	60 15N 1 22w		
Mainpuri	27 18N 79 4 E		
Maintirano	18 3s 44 5 E		
Mainz	50 0N 8 17 E		
Maipú	37 0s 58 0w		
Maiquetía	10 36N 66 57w		
Mairabari	26 30N 92 30 E		
Maisí, C.	20 10N 74 10w		
Maitland	32 44s 151 36 E		
Maiyema	12 5N 4 25 E		
Maizuru	35 25N 135 22 E		
Majalengka	6 55s 108 14 E		
Majd el Kurum	32 56N 35 15 E		
Majene	3 27s 118 57 E		
Majorca, I.= Mallorca, I.	39 30N 3 0 E		
Majunga	17 0s 47 0 E		
Majunga □	16 30s 46 30 E		
Makania	4 21s 37 49 E		
Makarovo	57 40N 107 45 E		
Makasar, Selat, Str.	1 0s 118 20 E		
Makat	47 39N 53 19 E		
Makedhona □	40 39N 22 0 E		
Makedonija □	41 53N 21 40 E		
Makeni	8 55N 12 5w		
Makeyevka	48 0N 38 0 E		
Makgadikgadi Salt Pans	20 40s 25 45 E		
Makhachkala	43 0N 47 15 E		
Makindu	2 17s 37 49 E		
Makinsk	52 37N 70 26 E		
Makkah	21 30N 39 54 E		
Makkovik	55 0N 59 10w		
Maklakovo	58 16N 92 29 E		
Makó	46 14N 20 33 E		
Makokou	0 40N 12 50 E		
Makongolosi	8 23s 33 10 E		
Makran Coast Ra.	25 40N 4 0 E		
Maktau	3 25s 38 2 E		
Mâkū	39 15N 44 31 E		
Makurazaki	31 15N 130 20 E		
Makurdi	7 45N 8 32 E		
Mal Usen, R.	48 50N 49 39 E		
Malabar Coast, Reg.	11 0N 75 0 E		
Malacca=Melaka	2 15N 102 15 E		
Malacca, Str. of	3 0N 101 0 E		
Malad City	41 10N 112 20w		
Maladetta, Mt.	42 40N 0 30 E		
Málaga	36 43N 4 23w		
Malagarasi	5 5s 30 50 E		
Malagasy Rep.= Madagascar ■	19 0s 46 0 E		
Malaimbandy	20 20s 45 36 E		
Malakâl	9 33N 31 50 E		
Malakand	34 40N 71 55 E		
Malamyzh	50 0N 136 50 E		
Malang	7 59s 112 35 E		
Malangali	8 33s 34 57 E		
Malanje	9 30s 16 17 E		
Mälaren, L.	59 30N 17 10 E		
Malargüe	35 40s 69 30w		
Malartic	48 9N 78 9w		
Malatya	38 25s 38 20 E		
Malawi ■	13 0s 34 0 E		
Malawi, L.	12 30s 34 30 E		
Malaya, L.	4 0N 102 0 E		
Malayer	28 22N 56 38 E		
Malaysia ■	5 0N 110 0 E		
Malbon	21 5s 140 17 E		
Malbork	54 3N 19 10 E		
Malcolm	28 51s 121 25 E		
Malden I.	4 3s 154 59w		
Maldive Is.	6 0N 73 0w		
Maldonado	35 0s 55 0w		
Malea, Ákra	36 58s 23 7 E		
Malegaon	20 30N 74 30 E		
Malha	15 8N 26 12 E		
Malhão, Sa. do	37 20N 8 0w		
Mali ■	15 0N 10 0w		
Malimba Mts.	7 30s 29 30 E		
Malin Hd.	55 18N 7 16w		
Malindi	3 12s 40 5 E		
Malingping	6 45s 106 2 E		
Maliwun	10 14N 98 37 E		
Mallacoota, Inlet	34 40s 149 40 E		
Mallaig	57 0N 5 50w		
Mallawi	27 44N 30 44 E		
Mallorca, I.	39 30N 3 0 E		
Mallow	52 8N 8 39w		
Malmberget	67 11N 20 40 E		
Malmédy	50 26N 6 2 E		
Malmesbury	33 28s 18 41 E		
Malmö	55 36N 12 59 E		
Malmöhus □	55 45N 13 30 E		
Malolos	14 50N 21 2 E		
Malone	44 50N 74 19w		
Malta	48 20N 107 55w		
Malta ■	35 50N 14 30 E		
Malton	54 9N 0 48w		
Maluku, Js.	3 0s 128 0 E		
Malumfashi	11 48N 7 39 E		
Malvan	16 2N 73 30 E		
Malvern, U.K.	52 7N 2 19w		
Malvern, U.S.A.	34 22N 92 50w		
Malvern Hills	52 0N 2 19w		
Malvinas, Is.= Falkland Is. □	51 30s 59 0w		
Mamanguape	6 50s 35 4w		
Mamasa	2 55s 119 20 E		
Mambrui	3 5s 40 5 E		
Mamfe	5 50N 9 15 E		
Mammoth	32 46N 110 43w		
Mamoi	26 0N 119 25 E		
Mamoré, R.	10 23s 65 53w		
Mamou	10 15N 12 0w		
Mampawah	0 30N 109 5 E		
Man	7 30N 7 40w		
Man, I. of	54 15N 4 30w		
Man Na	23 27N 97 19 E		
Mana	5 45N 53 55w		
Manacapuru	3 10s 60 50w		
Manacor	39 32N 3 12 E		
Manado	1 40N 124 45 E		
Managua	12 0N 86 20w		
Managua, L. de	12 20N 86 30w		
Manakara	22 8s 48 1 E		
Mananjary	21 13s 48 20 E		
Manantenina	24 17s 47 19 E		
Manaos=Manaus	3 0s 60 0w		
Manapouri, L.	45 32s 167 32 E		
Manass	44 20N 86 21 E		
Manaung Kyun, I.	18 45N 93 40 E		
Manaus	3 0s 60 0w		
Manche □	49 10N 1 20w		
Manchester, U.K.	53 30N 2 15w		
Manchester, U.S.A.	42 58N 71 29w		
Manchouli	49 46N 117 24 E		
Manchuria, Reg.	40 0N 126 0 E		
Manda	10 30s 34 40 E		
Mandal	58 2N 7 25 E		

Mandala, Puncak,
  Mt. .... 4 30s 141 0 E
Mandalay .... 22 0N 96 10 E
Mandalgovi .... 45 40N 106 22 E
Mandali .... 33 52N 45 28 E
Mandan 46 50N 101 0w
Mandar, Teluk, G. 3 35s 119 4 E
Mandasaur ...... 24 4N 75 4 E
Mandimba .... 14 22s 35 33 E
Mandoto .... 19 34s 46 17 E
Mandritsara ..... 15 50s 48 49 E
Mandurah .... 32 32s 115 43 E
Mandya .... 12 30N 77 0 E
Manengouba, Mts.. 5 15N 9 15 E
Manfalût .... 27 20N 30 52 E
Manfredónia, G. di 41 30N 16 10 E
Mangalore ...... 12 55N 74 47 E
Mangaweka ..... 39 48s 175 47 E
Manggar .... 2 50s 108 10 E
Mangla Dam ..... 33 32N 73 50 E
Mangole, I. ..... 1 50s 125 55 E
Mangonui .... 35 1s 173 32 E
Mangueira, L. ... 33 0s 52 50w
Mangyai .... 38 6N 91 37 E
Mangyshlak Pol. .. 43 40N 52 30 E
Manhattan 39 10N 96 40w
Manhuaçu 20 15s 42 2w
Manica et
  Sofala □ ...... 19 10s 33 45 E
Manicaland □ .... 19 0s 32 30 E
Manicoré 6 0s 61 10w
Manicouagan,'L. .. 51 25N 68 15w
Manihiki, I. 11 0s 161 0w
Manikpur .... 25 5N 81 5 E
Manila .... 14 40N 121 3 E
Manila B. .... 14 0N 120 0 E
Manildra .... 33 11s 148 41 E
Manilla .... 30 45s 150 43 E
Manipur □ ...... 24 30N 94 0 E
Manisa .... 38 38N 27 30 E
Manistee 44 15N 86 20w
Manistique 45 59N 86 18w
Manitoba □ 55 30N 97 0w
Manitoba, L. 50 40N 98 30w
Manitou Springs .. 38 52N 104 55w
Manitoulin I. 45 40N 82 30w
Manitowoc 44 8N 87 40w
Manizales 5 5N 75 32w
Manja .... 21 26s 44 20 E
Manjakandriana ... 18 55s 47 47 E

Manjhand .... 25 50N 68 10 E
Manjil .... 36 46N 49 30 E
Manjimup .... 34 15s 116 6 E
Manjra, R. ...... 18 49N 77 52 E
Mankato, Kans. .. 39 49N 98 11w
Mankato, Minn. .. 44 8N 93 59w
Mankono 8 10N 6 10w
Mankulam ...... 9 7N 80 26 E
Manly .... 33 48s 151 14 E
Manmad .... 20 18N 74 28 E
Mannahill .... 32 26s 139 59 E
Mannar, G. of ... 8 30N 79 0 E
Mannar, I. ...... 9 4N 79 45 E
Mannheim ...... 49 28N 8 29 E
Manning 56 53N 117 39w
Mannum .... 34 57s 139 12 E
Manokwari ...... 0 54N 134 0 E
Manombo .... 22 57s 43 28 E
Manono .... 7 18s 27 25 E
Mansa, Zambia .. 11 13s 28 55 E
Mansel I. 62 0N 80 0w
Mansfield,
  Australia ...... 37 0s 146 0 E
Mansfield, U.K. .. 53 8N 1 12w
Mansfield, U.S.A. . 40 45N 82 30w
Mansura=
  El Mansura .... 31 0N 31 19 E
Manta 1 0s 80 40w
Manteca 37 50N 121 12w
Mantes-la-Jolie .. 49 0N 1 41 E
Manti 39 23N 111 32w
Mantiqueira, Sa.
  da 22 0s 44 0w
Mántova .... 45 10N 10 47 E
Mantua =Mantova 45 9N 10 48 E
Manukan .... 8 14N 123 3 E
Manukau .... 37 2s 174 54 E
Manych-Gudilo,
  Oz. .... 46 24N 42 38 E
Manyoni .... 5 45s 34 55 E
Manzai .... 32 20N 70 15 E
Manzanares 39 0N 3 22w
Manzanillo, Cuba . 20 20N 77 10w
Manzanillo, Mexico 19 0N 104 20w
Manzanillo, Pta... 9 30N 79 40w
Manzini .... 26 30s 31 25 E
Mao .... 14 4N 15 19 E
Maple Creek 49 55N 109 27w
Maplewood 38 33N 90 18w
Maputo .... 25 58s 32 32 E

Maputo, B. de ... 26 0s 32 50 E
Maputo □ .... 26 30s 32 40 E
Maqnā .... 28 25N 34 50 E
Maquinchao 41 15s 68 50w
Mar Sa. do 25 30s 49 0w
Mar Chiquita, L. .. 30 40s 62 50w
Mar del Plata ... 38 0s 57 30w
Mara .... 1 30s 34 32 E
Marabá 5 20s 49 5w
Maracaibo 10 40N 71 37w
Maracaibo, L. de . 9 40N 71 30w
Maracay 10 15N 67 36w
Maradah .... 29 4N 19 4 E
Maradi .... 13 35N 8 10 E
Maragheh ...... 37 30N 46 12 E
Marajó, I. de ... 1 0s 49 30w
Maralal .... 1 0N 36 58 E
Maramba =
  Livingstone .... 17 50N 25 50 E
Marand .... 38 30N 45 45 E
Marandellas .... 18 5s 31 42 E
Maranguape 3 55s 38 50w
Maranhão=São
  Luís 2 39s 44 15w
Maranhão □ 5 0s 46 0w
Marañón, R. 4 50s 75 35w
Maraş .... 37 37N 36 53 E
Marathón ...... 38 11N 23 58 E
Marathon ...... 20 51s 143 32 E
Marbat .... 17 0N 54 45 E
Marble Bar ..... 21 9s 119 44 E
March .... 57 33N 0 5 E
Marche □ .... 43 22N 13 10 E
Marche, Reg. ... 46 5N 2 10 E
Marche-en-
  Famenne ...... 50 14N 5 19 E
Marchena 37 18N 5 23w
Mardan .... 34 12N 72 2 E
Mardin .... 37 20N 40 36 E
Maree, L. 57 40N 5 30w
Mareeba .... 16 59s 145 28 E
Margaret Bay ... 51 20N 127 20w
Margaret River .. 18 0s 126 30 E
Margarita, Is. de . 11 0N 64 0w
Margate, S. Afr.. . 30 50s 30 20 E
Margate, U.K. ... 51 23N 1 24 E
Margherita, Mt. . 0 22N 29 51 E
Mari A.S.S.R. □ . 56 30N 48 0 E
Maria van
  Diemen, C. .... 34 29s 172 40 E

Mariakani .... 3 50s 39 27 E
Mariana Is. ...... 17 0N 145 0 E
Marianao 23 8N 82 24w
Marianna 30 45N 85 15w
Mariano Machado . 13 2s 14 40 E
Marib .... 15 25N 45 20 E
Maribor .... 46 36N 15 40 E
Maricourt 61 36N 71 57w
Marie-Galante, I.. 15 56N 61 16w
Mariehamn ..... 60 5N 19 57 E
Mariental ...... 24 36s 18 0 E
Mariestad ...... 58 43N 13 50 E
Marietta, Ga. ... 34 0N 84 30w
Marietta, Ohio .. 39 27N 81 27w
Marigot 15 32N 61 18w
Marniisk .... 56 10N 87 20 E
Marília 22 0s 50 0w
Marin 42 23N 8 42w
Marinduque, I. .. 13 25N 122 0 E
Marinette 45 4N 87 40w
Maringá 23 35s 51 50w
Marion, Ill. 37 45N 88 55w
Marion, Ind. 40 35N 85 40w
Marion, Iowa ... 42 2N 91 36w
Marion, Ohio ... 40 38N 83 8w
Marion, S.C. 34 11N 79 22w
Marion, Va. 36 51N 81 29w
Maritsa .... 41 1N 25 50 E
Marjan .... 32 5N 68 20 E
Market Drayton .. 52 55N 2 30w
Market Harborough 52 29N 0 55w
Market Rasen ... 53 24N 0 20w
Marks .... 51 45N 46 50 E
Marlborough .... 22 46s 149 52 E
Marlborough □ .. 41 45s 173 33 E
Marlborough
  Downs 51 25N 1 55w
Marlin 31 25N 96 50w
Marmagao ...... 15 25N 73 56 E
Marmara Denizi,
  Sea .... 40 45N 28 15 E
Marmora 44 28N 77 41w
Marne □ .... 49 0N 4 10 E
Marne, R. ...... 48 49N 2 24 E
Maroantsetra ... 15 26s 49 44 E
Maroochydore .. 26 35s 153 10w
Maroua .... 10 40N 14 20 E
Marovoay ...... 16 6s 46 39 E
Marquard ...... 28 40s 27 28 E
Marquesas Is. 9 0s 139 30w

Marquette 46 30N 87 21w
Marra, J. .... 7 20N 27 35 E
Marrakech 31 40N 8 0w
Marrakesh=
  Marrakech 31 40N 8 0w
Marrawah ...... 40 56s 144 41 E
Marree .... 29 39s 138 1 E
Marsa Brega .... 30 30N 19 20 E
Marsa Susa .... 32 52N 21 59 E
Marsabit .... 2 18N 38 0 E
Marsala .... 37 48N 12 25 E
Marsden .... 33 47N 147 32 E
Marseille .... 43 18N 5 23 E
Marseilles=
  Marseille .... 43 18N 5 23 E
Marshall, Minn. .. 44 25N 95 45w
Marshall, Mo. ... 39 8N 93 15w
Marshall, Tex. ... 32 29N 94 20w
Marshall Is. ..... 9 0N 171 0 E
Marshalltown ... 42 0N 93 0w
Marshfield 44 42N 90 10w
Martaban ...... 16 30N 97 35 E
Martaban, G. of .. 15 40N 96 30 E
Martapura,
  Kalimantan .... 3 22s 114 56 E
Martapura,
  Sumatera ...... 4 19s 104 22 E
Marte .... 12 23N 13 46 E
Marthaguy Creek . 30 16s 147 35 E
Martha's Vineyard. 41 25N 70 35w
Martigny .... 46 6N 7 3 E
Martinique, I. ... 14 40N 61 0w
Martinique Pass.. 15 15N 61 0w
Martins Ferry ... 40 5N 80 46w
Martinsburg 39 30N 77 57w
Martinsville, Ind. . 39 29N 86 23w
Martinsville, Va.. . 36 41N 79 52w
Marton .... 40 4s 175 23 E
Martos 37 44N 3 58w
Maru .... 12 22N 6 22 E
Marugame ..... 34 15N 133 55 E
Marulan .... 34 43s 150 3 E
Marungu Mts. ... 7 30s 30 0 E
Marwar .... 25 43N 73 45 E
Mary .... 37 40N 61 50 E
Mary Kathleen .. 20 35s 139 48 E
Mary River 70 30N 78 0w
Maryborough,
  Queens. .... 25 31s 152 37 E
Maryborough, Vic. 37 0s 143 44 E

Maryland □ 39 10N 76 40w
Maryport 54 43N 3 30w
Marystown 47 10N 55 10w
Marysvale 38 25N 112 17w
Marysville 39 14N 121 40w
Maryville 35 50N 84 0w
Marzūq .... 25 53N 14 10 E
Masai Steppe .... 4 30s 36 30 E
Masaka .... 0 21s 31 45 E
Masakali .... 13 2N 12 32 E
Masamba .... 2 30s 120 15 E
Masan .... 35 11N 128 32 E
Masandam, Ras. .. 26 30N 56 30 E
Masasi .... 10 45s 38 52 E
Masaya 12 0N 86 7w
Masba .... 10 35N 13 1 E
Masbate .... 12 20N 123 30 E
Masbate, I. ...... 12 20N 123 30 E
Mascara .... 35 26N 0 6 E
Maseru .... 29 18s 27 30 E
Mashhad .... 36 20N 59 35 E
Mashi .... 13 0N 7 54 E
Mashkode 47 2N 84 7w
Mashonaland
    North □ ...... 16 30s 30 0 E
Mashonaland
    South □ ...... 18 0s 31 30 E
Masindi .... 1 40N 41 43 E
Masindi Port ..... 1 43N 32 2 E
Masisi .... 1 23s 28 49 E
Masjed Soleyman . 31 55N 49 25 E
Mask, L. 53 36N 9 24w
Masoala, C. ...... 15 59s 50 13 E
Mason City 48 0N 119 0w
Masqat .... 23 37N 58 36 E
Massa .... 44 2N 10 7 E
Massachusetts □ .. 42 25N 72 0w
Massawa=Mitsiwa . 15 35N 39 25 E
Massena 44 52N 74 55w
Masset 54 0N 132 0w
Massif Central
    Reg. .... 45 30N 2 21 E
Massillon 40 47N 81 30w
Masterton ...... 40 56s 175 39 E
Mastung .... 29 50N 66 42 E
Masura .... 23 7N 38 52 E
Masuda .... 34 40N 131 51 E
Masurian Lakes=
    Mazurski,
    Pojezierze ..... 53 50N 21 0 E

Matabeleland □ ... 20 0s 27 30 E
Mataboor .... 1 41s 138 3 E
Matachewan 47 50N 80 55w
Matad .... 47 12N 115 29 E
Matadi .... 5 52s 13 31 E
Matagalpa 13 10N 85 40w
Matagami 49 45N 77 34w
Matale .... 7 30N 80 44 E
Matamoros 18 2N 98 17w
Matane 48 50N 67 33w
Matanuska 61 38N 149 0w
Matanzas 23 0N 81 40w
Mataram .... 8 41s 116 10 E
Mataranka ..... 14 55s 133 4 E
Mataró .... 41 32N 2 29 E
Matatiele ...... 30 20s 28 49 E
Mataura .... 46 11s 168 51 E
Matehuala 23 40N 100 50w
Mateke Hills .... 21 48s 31 0 E
Matera .... 40 40N 16 37 E
Mathura .... 27 30N 77 48 E
Matlock 53 8N 1 32w
Mato Grosso □ .. 14 0s 54 0w
Matombo ...... 7 3s 37 46 E
Matopo .... 20 36s 28 20 E
Matopo Hills ... 20 36s 28 20 E
Matozinhos 41 11N 8 42w
Matrah .... 23 37N 58 30 E
Matrûh .... 31 19N 27 9 E
Matsena .... 13 5N 10 5 E
Matsu, I. .... 26 9N 119 56 E
Matsue .... 35 25N 133 10 E
Matsumoto ..... 36 15N 138 0 E
Matsusaka ..... 34 34N 136 32 E
Matsuyama ..... 33 45N 132 45 E
Mattancheri .... 9 50N 76 15 E
Mattawa 46 20N 78 45w
Matterhorn, Mt. .. 45 58N 7 39 E
Matthew Town .. 20 57N 73 40w
Mattoon 39 30N 88 20w
Matua .... 2 58s 110 52 E
Maturín 9 45N 63 11w
Mau Ranipur ... 25 16N 79 8 E
Maués 3 20s 57 45w
Maui, I. .... 20 45s 156 20 E
Maulamyaing ... 16 30N 97 40 E
Maumere ...... 8 38s 122 13 E
Maun .... 20 0s 23 26 E
Mauna Loa, Mt. .. 19 50N 155 28 E

Maungmagan Is. .. 41 0s 97 48 E
Maungu .... 3 32s 38 42 E
Mauritania ■ 20 50N 10 0w
Mauritius ...... 20 0s 57 0 E
Maurienne, Reg. .. 45 15N 6 20 E
Mavqi'im ...... 31 38N 34 32 E
Mawkmai ...... 20 14N 97 50 E
Mawlaik .... 23 40N 94 26 E
Maxwelton ..... 39 51s 174 49 E
May Pen 17 58N 77 15w
Maya Mts. 16 30N 89 0w
Mayaguana I. ... 21 30N 72 44w
Mayagüez 18 12N 67 9w
Mayanup ...... 33 58s 116 25 E
Maydena ...... 42 45s 146 39 E
Mayenne 48 20N 0 38w
Mayenne □ 48 10N 0 40w
Mayerthorpe ... 53 57N 115 15w
Mayfield 36 45N 88 40w
Maykop .... 44 35N 40 25 E
Maynooth, Canada 45 14N 77 56w
Maynooth, Eire .. 53 22N 6 38w
Mayo 63 38N 135 57w
Mayo □ 53 47N 9 7w
Maysville 38 43N 84 16w
Mayumba ...... 3 25s 10 39 E
Mayya .... 61 44N 130 18 E
Mazabuka ..... 15 52s 27 44 E
Mazagão 0 20s 51 50w
Mazama 49 43N 120 8w
Mazan Deran □ .. 36 30N 53 30 E
Mazar-i-Sharif .. 36 41N 67 0 E
Mazarredo 47 10s 66 50w
Mazarrón 37 38N 1 19w
Mazatenango ... 14 35N 91 30w
Mazatlán 23 10N 106 30w
Mazurski,
    Pojezierze ..... 53 50N 21 0 E
Mbabane ...... 26 18s 31 6 E
M'Baiki .... 3 53N 18 1 E
Mbala .... 8 46s 31 17 E
Mbale .... 1 8N 34 12 E
Mbalmayo ..... 3 33N 11 33 E
Mbamba Bay ... 11 13s 34 49 E
Mbandaka ..... 0 1s 18 18 E
Mbanga .... 4 30N 9 33 E
Mbarara ...... 0 35s 30 25 E
Mbeya .... 8 54s 33 29 E
Mbuji-Mayi ..... 6 9s 23 40 E
Mbulamuti ..... 0 57N 33 0 E

Mbulu .... 3 45s 35 30 E
Mchinja .... 9 46s 39 45 E
Mchinji .... 13 47s 32 58 E
Mdina .... 35 51N 14 25 E
Mead, L. 36 1N 114 10w
Meadow .... 26 35s 114 30 E
Meadow Lake ... 54 10N 108 10w
Meadow Lake
    Prov. Park 52 25N 109 0w
Meadville 41 39N 80 9w
Meaford 44 40N 80 36w
Meath □ 53 32N 6 40w
Meaux .... 48 58N 2 50 E
Mecca=Makkah .. 21 30N 39 54 E
Mechelen ...... 51 2N 4 29 E
Mecklenburger, B. 54 20N 11 40 E
Meda P.O. ..... 17 20s 123 59 E
Medan .... 3 40N 98 38 E
Medanosa, Pta. .. 48 0s 66 0w
Médéa .... 36 12N 2 50 E
Medellín 6 15N 75 35w
Médenine ...... 33 21N 10 30 E
Mederdra 17 0N 15 38w
Medford 42 20N 122 52w
Medias .... 46 9N 24 22 E
Medicine Bow ... 41 56N 106 11w
Medicine Bow Ra. 41 10N 106 25w
Medicine Hat ... 50 0N 110 45w
Medina 43 15N 78 27w
Medina del Campo 41 18N 4 55w
Medina-Sidonia .. 36 28N 5 57w
Mediterranean
    Sea .... 35 0N 15 0 E
Médoc, Reg. 45 10N 0 56w
Medveditsa, R. .. 49 0N 43 58 E
Medvezhi Oshova . 71 0N 161 0 E
Medvezhyegorsk . 63 0N 34 25 E
Medway, R. .... 51 27N 0 44 E
Meeberrie ..... 26 57s 116 0 E
Meekatharra ... 26 32s 118 29 E
Meerut .... 29 1N 77 50 E
Mega .... 3 57N 38 30 E
Mégantic 45 36N 70 56w
Mégara .... 37 58N 23 22 E
Meghalaya □ ... 25 50N 91 0 E
Megiddo ...... 32 36N 15 11 E
Mehadia ...... 44 56N 22 23 E
Mehsana ...... 23 39N 72 26 E
Meihokow ..... 42 37N 125 46 E
Meihsien ...... 24 20N 116 0 E

Meiktila .... 21 0N 96 0 E
Meissen .... 51 10N 13 29 E
Mejillones 23 10s 70 30w
Mekele .... 13 33N 39 30 E
Mekhtar .... 30 33N 69 20 E
Meknès 33 57N 5 33w
Meko .... 7 30N 3 0 E
Mekong, R. ..... 10 33N 105 24 E
Melaka .... 2 15N 102 15 E
Melalap .... 5 10N 116 5 E
Melbourne ..... 37 45s 145 0 E
Melchor Múzquiz . 27 50N 101 40w
Melekess=
    Dimitrovgrad .. 54 25N 49 33 E
Melfort, Canada .. 52 50N 105 40w
Melfort, Rhod. .. 18 0s 31 25 E
Melilla 35 21N 2 57w
Melilot .... 31 22N 34 37 E
Melita 49 15N 101 5w
Melitopol ...... 46 50N 35 22 E
Melk .... 48 13N 15 20 E
Mellerud ...... 58 41N 12 28 E
Melo 32 20s 54 10w
Melrose 55 35s 2 44w
Melton Mowbray . 52 46N 0 52w
Melun .... 48 32N 2 39 E
Melville, I.,
    Australia ..... 11 30s 131 0 E
Melville, I.,
    Canada 75 30N 111 0w
Melville, I. 53 45N 59 40w
Melville Pen. 68 0N 84 0w
Memel .... 55 38N 29 36 E
Memel=Klaipeda . 55 43N 21 10 E
Memmingen .... 47 59N 10 12 E
Memphis 35 7N 90 0w
Menai Str. 53 7N 4 20w
Ménaka .... 15 59N 2 18 E
Menasha 44 13N 88 27w
Menate .... 0 12s 112 47 E
Mencheng ..... 33 27N 116 45 E
Mende .... 44 31N 3 30 E
Mendip Hills ... 51 17N 2 40w
Mendocino 39 26N 123 50w
Mendota 36 46N 120 24w
Mendoza 32 50s 68 52w
Mene de Mauroa . 10 45N 70 50w
Mene Grande ... 9 49N 70 56w
Menemen ...... 38 36N 27 4 E

Menen .... 50 47N 3 7 E
Menfi .... 37 36N 12 57 E
Menggala .... 4 20s 105 15 E
Mengtz .... 23 20N 103 20 E
Menindee .... 32 20N 142 25 E
Menominee 45 9N 87 39w
Menomonie 44 50N 91 54w
Menor, Mar 37 40N 0 45w
Menorca, I. .... 40 0N 4 0 E
Mentawai,
  Kep. .... 2 0s 99 0 E
Menton .... 43 50N 7 29 E
Menzel Temime .. 36 46N 11 0 E
Menzelinsk ..... 55 43N 53 8 E
Menzies .... 29 40s 120 58 E
Me'ona .... 33 1N 35 15 E
Meppel .... 52 42N 6 12 E
Merak .... 5 55s 106 1 E
Merano .... 46 40N 11 10 E
Merauke .... 8 29s 120 24 E
Merca .... 1 48N 44 50 E
Mercara .... 12 30N 75 45 E
Merced 37 25N 120 30w
Mercedes,
  Buenos Aires ... 34 40s 59 30w
Mercedes,
  Corrientes 29 10s 58 5w
Mercedes,
  San Luis 33 40s 65 30w
Mercedes,
  Uruguay 33 12s 58 0w
Merceditas 28 20s 70 35w
Mercer .... 37 16s 175 5 E
Mercy, C. 65 0N 62 30w
Mere 51 5N 2 16w
Meredith, C. ... 52 15s 60 40w
Mergui .... 12 30N 98 35 E
Mergui Arch.=
  Myeik Kyunzu .. 11 0N 98 0 E
Mérida, Mexico .. 20 50N 89 40w
Mérida, Sp. 38 55N 6 25w
Mérida, Ven. 8 36N 71 8w
Meriden 41 33N 72 47w
Meridian, Id. ... 43 41N 116 20w
Meridian, Miss. .. 32 20N 88 42w
Meriruma 1 15N 54 50w
Merksem .... 51 16N 4 25 E
Merowe .... 18 29N 31 46 E
Merredin .... 31 28s 118 18 E
Merrill 45 11N 89 41w

Merritt 50 10N 120 45w
Merroe .... 27 53s 117 50 E
Mersa Fatma .... 14 57N 40 17 E
Mersea I. .... 51 48N 0 55 E
Merseburg ...... 51 20N 12 0 E
Mersey, R. 53 25N 3 0w
Merseyside □ 53 25w 2 55w
Mersin .... 36 51N 34 36 E
Mersing .... 2 25N 103 50 E
Merthyr Tydfil .. 51 45N 3 23w
Mértola .... 37 40N 7 40 E
Mertzon 31 17N 100 48w
Meru .... 0 3N 37 40 E
Meru, Mt. ...... 3 15s 36 46 E
Mesa 33 20N 111 56w
Meshed=Mashhad . 36 20N 59 35 E
Mesilla 32 20N 107 0w
Mesolóngion ..... 38 27N 21 28 E
Mesopotamia,
  Reg.=Al
  Jazirah, Reg.... 33 30N 44 0 E
Messina, S.Africa .. 22 20s 30 12 E
Messina, Str. di ... 38 5N 15 35 E
Messíni .... 37 4N 22 1 E
Messiniakós Kól. .. 36 45N 22 5 E
Mesta, R. ...... 40 41N 24 44 E
Meta, R. 6 12N 67 28w
Metagama 47 0N 81 55w
Metán 25 30s 65 0w
Methven .... 43 38s 171 40 E
Metlakatia 55 8N 131 35w
Metropolis 37 10N 88 47w
Metulla .... 33 17N 35 34 E
Metz .... 49 8N 6 10 E
Meulaboh .... 4 11N 96 3 E
Meureudu .... 5 19N 96 10 E
Meurthe-et-
  Moselle □ ..... 48 52N 6 0 E
Meuse □ .... 49 8N 5 25 E
Meuse, R. ...... 51 49N 5 1 E
Mexia 31 38N 96 32w
Mexiana, I. 0 0 49 30w
Mexicali 32 40N 115 30w
Mexico, Mexico .. 19 20N 99 10w
Mexico, U.S.A. .. 39 10N 91 55w
Mexico ■ 20 0N 100 0w
México □ 19 20N 99 10w
Mezen, R. ...... 66 11N 43 59 E
Mezen .... 65 50N 44 20 E
Mézökövesd ..... 47 49N 20 35 E

Mezötur .... 47 0N 20 41 E
Mhlaba Hills ..... 18 30s 30 30 E
Mhow .... 22 33N 75 50 E
Miahuatlán 16 21N 96 36w
Miami 25 52N 80 15w
Miami Beach 25 49N 80 6w
Miandowāb .... 37 0N 46 5 E
Miandrivaso .... 19 31s 45 28 E
Miäneh .... 37 30N 47 40 E
Mianwali .... 32 38N 71 28 E
Miaoli .... 24 34N 120 48 E
Miass .... 54 59N 60 6 E
Michelson, Mt. .. 69 19N 144 17w
Michigan □ 44 40N 85 40w
Michigan, L. 44 0N 87 0w
Michigan City ... 41 42N 86 56w
Michikamau L. .. 54 0N 6 0w
Michipicoten I. ... 47 55N 85 45w
Michipicoten River 47 50N 84 58w
Michoacán □ 19 0N 102 0w
Michurinsk ..... 52 58N 40 27 E
Mid Glamorgan □ . 51 40N 3 25w
Middelburg, Neth. . 51 30N 3 36 E
Middelburg,
  C. Prov. ...... 31 30s 25 0 E
Middelburg, Trans. 25 49s 29 28 E
Middelveld, Reg. .. 26 30s 26 0 E
Middle Brook 48 40N 54 20w
Middlebury 44 0N 73 9w
Middlesboro 36 40N 83 40w
Middlesbrough ... 54 35N 1 14w
Middletown, Conn. 41 37N 72 40w
Middletown, N.Y. . 41 28N 74 28w
Middletown, Ohio . 39 29N 84 25w
Middleton 44 50N 65 5w
Middleton P.O. ... 22 22s 141 32 E
Midi, Canal du ... 43 45N 1 21 E
Midland,
  Australia ...... 31 54s 115 59 E
Midland, Canada .. 44 45N 79 50w
Midland, Mich. ... 43 37N 84 17w
Midland, Tex. ... 32 0N 102 3w
Midlands □ ..... 19 0s 29 30 E
Midnapore ...... 22 25N 87 21 E
Midongy du Sud .. 23 35s 47 1 E
Midway Is. 28 13N 177 22w
Midwest 43 27N 106 11w
Mie □ .... 34 20N 136 20 E
Międzychod ..... 52 35N 15 53 E
Międzyrzec

Podlaski .... 51 58N 22 45 E
Mienyang .... 31 18N 104 26 E
Miercurea Ciuc .. 46 21N 25 48 E
Mieres 43 18N 5 48w
Migdal .... 32 51N 35 30 E
Migdal Ha'Emeq .. 32 41N 35 14 E
Mihara .... 34 25N 133 5 E
Mikese .... 6 48s 37 55 E
Mikindani ...... 10 15s 40 2 E
Mikkeli □ ...... 61 56N 28 0 E
Mikun .... 62 20N 50 0 E
Milagro 2 0s 79 30w
Milan=Milano ... 45 28N 9 10 E
Milang .... 35 20s 138 55 E
Milano .... 45 28N 9 10 E
Milazzo .... 38 13N 15 13 E
Mildenhall ..... 52 20N 0 30 E
Mildura .... 34 13s 142 9 E
Miles .... 26 37s 150 10 E
Miles City 46 30N 105 50w
Milestone 50 0N 104 30w
Milford, Conn. .. 41 13N 73 4w
Milford, Del. ... 38 52N 75 26w
Milford, Utah ... 38 20N 113 0w
Milford Haven ... 51 43N 5 2w
Miling .... 30 30s 116 17 E
Millau .... 44 8N 3 4 E
Millertown Junction 48 49N 56 28w
Millicent .... 37 34s 140 21 E
Millinocket 45 45N 68 45w
Millom 54 13N 3 16w
Millville 39 22N 74 0w
Milne Inlet 72 30N 80 0w
Milo .... 24 28N 103 23 E
Mílos, I. .... 36 44N 24 25 E
Milton, N.Z. .... 46 7s 169 59 E
Milton, U.S.A. .. 41 0N 76 53w
Milton Keynes ... 52 3N 0 42w
Miltown Malbay .. 52 51N 9 25w
Milwaukee 43 9N 87 58w
Milwaukie 45 33N 122 39w
Minā al
  Ahmadī ...... 29 5N 48 10 E
Mina Saud ...... 28 45N 48 20 E
Mināb .... 27 10N 57 1 E
Minamata .... 32 10N 130 30 E
Minas 34 20s 55 15w
Minas de Rio
  Tinto □ 37 42N 6 22w
Minas Gerais □ .. 18 50s 46 0w

Minatitlán 17 58N 94 35w
Minbu .... 20 10N 95 0 E
Minch, Little,
  Chan. 57 40N 6 50w
Minch, North,
  Chan. 58 0N 6 0w
Mindanao, I. .... 8 0N 125 0 E
Mindanao Sea .... 9 0 124 0 E
Mindanao Trench . 8 0N 128 0 E
Minden .... 52 18N 8 54 E
Minden 32 40N 93 20w
Mindoro, I. ..... 13 0N 121 0 E
Mindoro Str. ..... 12 30N 120 30 E
Minehead 51 12N 3 29w
Mineral Wells ... 32 50N 98 5w
Mingan 50 20N 64 0w
Mingechaurskoye,
  Vdkhr. .... 40 56N 47 20 E
Mingela .... 19 52s 146 38 E
Mingenew .... 29 12s 115 21 E
Minho, R. 41 52N 8 51w
Minho Reg. 41 40N 8 30w
Minhow=Foochow 26 5N 119 18 E
Minilya .... 23 55s 114 0 E
Min Kiang, R. ... 26 0N 119 30 E
Minkiang .... 32 30N 114 10 E
Minna .... 9 37N 6 30 E
Minneapolis 44 58N 93 20w
Minnedosa 50 20N 99 50w
Minnesota □ 46 40N 94 0w
Minnipa .... 32 51s 135 9 E
Mino .... 35 32N 136 55 E
Minorca, I.=
  Menorca, I. ... 40 0N 4 0 E
Minot 48 10N 101 15w
Minsk .... 53 52N 27 30 E
Mińsk Mazowiecki. 52 10N 21 33 E
Minto .... 34 1s 150 51 E
Minto, L. 48 0N 84 45w
Minturn 39 45N 106 25w
Minusinsk ...... 53 50N 91 20 E
Minutang .... 28 15N 96 30 E
Minya Konka, Mt. . 29 34N 101 53 E
Miquelon, I. 47 8N 56 24w
Miraj .... 16 50N 74 45 E
Miranda 20 10s 50 15w
Miranda de Ebro . 42 41N 2 57w
Miranda do Douro 41 30N 6 16w
Miri .... 4 18N 114 0 E
Miriam Vale .... 24 20s 151 39 E

Mirim, L. 32 45s 52 50w
Mirpur Khas . . . . . . 25 30N 69 0 E
Mirzapur . . . . 25 10N 82 45 E
Mishan . . . . 45 31N 132 2 E
Mishawaka 41 40N 86 8w
Mishima . . . . 35 10N 138 52 E
Mishmar Alyalon . . 31 52N 34 57 E
Mishmar Ha
  'Emeq . . . . 32 37N 35 7 E
Mishmar Ha Negev 31 22N 34 48 E
Mishmar Ha
  Yarden . . . . 33 0N 35 56 E
Miskın . . . . 2344⅛ 56 52 E
Miskitos, Cayos . . . 14 26N 82 50w
Miskolc . . . . 48 7N 20 50 E
Misool, I. . . . . 2 0s 130 0 E
Misrātah . . . . 32 18N 15 3 E
Mission 26 15N 98 30w
Mission City 49 10N 122 15w
Mississippi □ 33 0N 90 0E
Mississippi, R. . . . 29 0N 89 15w
Mississippi,
  Delta of the . . . 29 10N 89 15w
Missoula 47 0N 114 0w
Missouri □ 38 25N 92 30w
Missouri, Plat. du
  Coteau du 46 0N 99 30w
Missouri, R. 38 50N 90 8w
Mistassini, L. 51 0N 73 40w
Mitchell,
  Australia . . . . . 26 29s 147 58 E
Mitchell, U.S.A. . . 43 40N 98 0w
Mitchell, Mt. 35 40N 82 20w
Mitchelstown 52 16N 8 18w
Mitylene, I.=
  Lésvos, I. . . . . . 39 0N 26 20 E
Mitilíni . . . . 39 6N 26 35 E
Mitla 16 55N 96 17w
Mito . . . . 36 20N 140 30 E
Mitsinjo . . . . 16 1s 45 52 E
Mitsiwa . . . . 15 35N 39 25 E
Mittagong . . . . . . 34 28s 150 29 E
Mittyack . . . . 35 8s 142 36 E
Mitumba,
  Chaîne des . . . . 10 0s 26 20 E
Mityana . . . . 0 24N 32 3 E
Miyagi □ . . . . 38 15N 140 45 E
Miyako . . . . 39 40N 141 75 E
Miyakonojo . . . . . 31 32N 131 5 E
Miyazaki . . . . 31 56N 131 30 E

Miyazaki . . . . 32 0N 131 30 E
Miyet, Bahr el . . . . 31 30N 35 30 E
Miyoshi . . . . 34 48N 132 32 E
Miyun . . . . 40 22N 116 49 E
Mizen Hd., Cork . . 51 27N 9 50w
Mizen Hd.,
  Wicklow 52 52N 6 4w
Mizoram □ . . . . . . 23 0N 92 40 E
Mizpe Ramon . . . . 20 36N 34 48 E
Mjanji . . . . 0 17N 33 59 E
Mjölby . . . . 58 20N 15 10 E
Mjøsa, L. . . . . 60 45N 11 0 E
Mkobela . . . . 10 57s 38 5 E
Mkushi . . . . 14 20s 29 20 E
Mkwaya . . . . 6 17s 35 40 E
Mladá Boleslav . . 50 27N 14 53 E
Mława . . . . 53 9N 20 25 E
Mlanje, Mt. . . . . . 16 2s 35 33 E
Mme . . . . 6 18N 10 14 E
Mo . . . . 66 15N 14 8 E
Moa, I. . . . . 8 0s 128 0 E
Moab 38 40N 109 35w
Moama . . . . 36 3s 144 45 E
Moba . . . . 7 3s 29 47 E
Mobaye . . . . 4 25N 21 5 E
Moberly 39 25N 92 25w
Mobert 48 41N 85 40w
Mobile 30 41N 88 3w
Mobutu Sese
  Seko, L. . . . . . . 1 30N 31 0 E
Moçambique . . . . 15 3s 40 42 E
Moçâmedes . . . . . 16 35s 12 30 E
Mochudi . . . . 24 27s 26 7 E
Moçimboa da Praia 11 25s 40 20 E
Mocoa 1 15N 76 45w
Moctezuma, R. . . . 21 59N 98 34w
Mocuba . . . . 16 54s 37 25 E
Modane . . . . 45 12N 6 40 E
Modderrivier . . . . 29 2s 24 38 E
Módena . . . . 44 39N 10 55 E
Modesto 37 43N 121 0w
Módica . . . . 36 52N 14 45 E
Moe . . . . 38 12s 146 19 E
Moengo 5 45N 54 20w
Moero, L. . . . . . . 9 0s 28 45 E
Moffat 55 20N 3 27w
Mogadiscio . . . . . 2 2N 45 25 E
Mogadishu=
  Mogadiscio . . . . 2 2N 45 25 E
Mogador=

Essaouira 31 32N 9 42w
Mogaung . . . . 25 20N 97 0 E
Mogi das Cruzes . . 23 45s 46 20w
Mogi Mirim 22 20s 47 0w
Mogilev . . . . 53 55N 30 18 E
Mogilvev
  Podolskiy . . . . . 48 20N 27 40 E
Mogocha . . . . 53 40N 119 50 E
Mogollon Mesa . . 43 40N 110 0w
Mogumber . . . . . . 31 2s 116 3 E
Mohács . . . . 45 58N 18 41 E
Moho . . . . 53 15N 122 27 E
Mohoro . . . . 8 6s 39 8 E
Mointy . . . . 47 40N 73 45 E
Mojave 35 8N 118 8w
Mojave Des. 35 0N 117 30w
Mojokerto . . . . . . 7 29s 112 25 E
Mokau, R. . . . . . . 38 42s 174 37 E
Mokpo . . . . 34 50N 126 30 E
Mokwa . . . . 9 18N 5 2 E
Mol . . . . 51 11N 5 5 E
Mold , ... 53 10N 3 10w
Moldanan S.S.R. □ 47 0N 28 0 E
Molde . . . . 62 46N 7 12 E
Molepolole . . . . . 24 28s 25 28 E
Molfetta . . . . 41 12N 16 35 E
Moline 41 30N 90 30w
Molise □ . . . . 41 45N 14 30 E
Mollendo 17 0s 72 0w
Mölndal . . . . 57 40N 12 3 E
Molokai, I. 21 8N 156 0w
Molong . . . . 33 5s 148 54 E
Molopo, R. . . . . . . 28 30s 20 13 E
Molteno . . . . 31 22s 26 22 E
Molucca Sea . . . . 4 0s 124 0 E
Moluccas, Is.=
  Maluku, Is. . . . . 1 0s 127 0 E
Moma . . . . 16 47s 39 4 E
Mombasa . . . . 4 2s 39 43 E
Mombo . . . . 4 57s 38 20 E
Mompos 9 14N 74 26w
Møn, I. . . . . 54 57N 12 15 E
Mona, Pta. 9 37N 82 36w
Mona, I. 18 5N 67 54w
Monach Is. 57 32N 7 40w
Monaco ■ . . . . . . 43 46N 7 23 E
Monadhliath Mts. . 57 10N 4 4w
Monaghan 54 15N 6 58w
Monaghan □ 54 10N 7 0w
Monahans 31 35N 102 50w

Monastir . . . . 35 50N 10 49 E
Monchegorsk . . . . 67 54N 32 58 E
Mönchengladbach . 51 12N 6 23 E
Monchique 37 19N 8 38w
Monclava 26 50N 101 30w
Moncton 46 7N 64 51w
Mondego, R. 40 9N 8 52w
Mondovì . . . . 44 23N 7 56 E
Monessen 40 9N 79 50w
Monet 48 10N 75 40w
Monforte de
  Lemos 42 31N 7 33w
Mong Kung . . . . . 21 35N 97 35 E
Mong Pan . . . . . . 20 19N 98 22 E
Mong Pawk . . . . . 22 4N 99 16 E
Mong Ton . . . . . . 20 25N 98 45 E
Mong Wa . . . . . . 21 26N 100 27 E
Mong Yai . . . . 22 28N 98 3 E
Monger, L. . . . . . . 29 25s 117 5 E
Monghyr . . . . 25 23N 86 30 E
Mongo . . . . 12 14N 18 43 E
Mongolia ■ . . . . . 47 0N 103 0 E
Mongonu . . . . 12 40N 13 32 E
Mongu . . . . 15 16s 23 12 E
Monk 47 7N 69 59w
Monkira . . . . 24 46s 140 30 E
Monmouth, U.K. . . 51 48N 2 43w
Monmouth, U.S.A. . 40 50N 90 40w
Mono, Pta. del . . . 12 0N 83 30w
Monópoli . . . . 40 57N 17 18 E
Monroe, La. 32 32N 92 4w
Monroe, Mich. . . . 41 55N 83 26w
Monroe, N.C. 35 2N 80 37w
Monroe, Wis. 42 38N 89 40w
Monrovia, Liberia . 6 18N 10 47w
Monrovia, U.S.A. . 34 7N 118 1w
Mons . . . . 50 27N 3 58 E
Mont Joli 48 37N 68 10w
Mont Laurier 46 35N 75 30w
Mont St.
  Michel 48 40N 1 30w
Mont Tremblant
  Prov. Park 46 30N 74 30w
Montagu . . . . 33 45s 20 8 E
Montague, I. 31 40N 144 46w
Montalbán 40 50N 0 45w
Montana □ 6 0s 73 0w
Montargis . . . . . . 48 0N 2 43 E
Montauban . . . . . . 44 0N 1 21 E

Montauk Pt. 41 4N 71 52w
Montbéliard . . . . . 47 31N 6 48 E
Mont-de-
  Marsan 43 54N 0 31w
Monte Alegre 2 0s 54 0w
Monte Azul 15 9s 42 53w
Monte Carlo . . . . 43 46N 7 23 E
Monte Caseros . . . 30 10s 57 50w
Monte Comán . . . 34 40s 68 0w
Monte Sant
  'Angelo . . . . . . 41 42N 15 59 E
Montebello 45 40N 74 55w
Montecristi 1 0s 80 40w
Montego Bay 18 30N 78 0w
Montejinnie . . . . . 16 40s 131 45 E
Montélimar . . . . . 44 33N 4 45 E
Montemorelos . . . 25 11N 99 42w
Montenegro=
  Crna Gora . . . . 42 40N 19 20 E
Monterey 36 35N 121 57w
Montería 8 46N 75 53w
Monterrey 25 40N 100 30w
Montes Claros . . . 16 30s 43 50w
Montesano 47 0N 123 39w
Montevideo 34 50s 56 11w
Montgomery, U.K. . 52 34N 3 9w
Montgomery,
  U.S.A. 32 20N 86 20w
Montgomery=
  Sahiwal . . . . . . 30 45N 73 8 E
Monticello, Utah . . 37 55N 109 27w
Montijo 38 52N 6 39w
Montilla 37 36N 4 40w
Montivideo 44 55N 95 40w
Montluçon . . . . . . 46 22N 2 36 E
Montmagny . . . . . 46 58N 70 43 E
Montmorency 46 53N 71 11w
Monto . . . . 24 52s 151 12 E
Montoro 38 1N 4 27w
Montpelier, Id. . . . 42 15N 11 29w
Montpelier, Vt. . . . 44 15N 72 38w
Montpellier . . . . . 43 37N 3 52 E
Montreal 45 31N 73 34w
Montreuil . . . . 50 27N 1 45 E
Montreux . . . . 46 26N 6 55 E
Montrose, U.K. . . . 37 55N 109 27w
Montrose, U.S.A. . 38 30N 107 52w
Montserrat, I. 16 40N 62 10w
Monywa . . . . 22 7N 95 11 E
Monze . . . . 16 17s 27 29 E

Monze, C. .... 24 47N 66 37 E
Monzón .... 41 52N 0 10 E
Mooliabeenee ..... 31 20s 116 2 E
Moonbeam 49 20N 82 10w
Moonie .... 27 46s 150 20 E
Moonta .... 34 6s 137 32 E
Moora .... 30 37s 115 58 E
Mooraberree ..... 25 13s 140 54 E
Moorarie .... 25 56s 117 35 E
Moore, L. .... 29 50s 117 35 E
Moore River ..... 31 6s 115 32 E
Moorreesburg ... 33 6s 18 38 E
Moorfoot Hills ... 55 44N 3 8w
Moorhead 47 0N 97 0w
Moose, R. 43 37N 75 22w
Moose Factory ... 52 20N 80 40w
Moose Jaw 50 30N 105 30w
Moose Lake 46 27N 92 48w
Moosomin 50 9N 101 40w
Moosonee 51 25N 80 51w
Mopeia Velha .... 17 30s 35 40 E
Mopti 14 30N 4 0w
Moquegua 17 15s 70 46w
Mora, Sweden .... 61 2N 14 38 E
Moradabad .... 28 50N 78 50 E
Moramanga .... 18 56s 48 12 E
Morant Pt. 17 55s 76 12w
Morar, L. 56 57N 5 40w
Moratuwa .... 6 45N 79 55 E
Morava, R. .... 48 10N 16 59 E
Morawa .... 29 13s 116 0 E
Morawhanna 8 30N 59 40w
Moray Firth 57 50N 3 30w
Morbihan □ 47 55N 2 50w
Morden 49 15N 98 10w
Mordialloc .... 38 1s 145 6 E
Mordovian
   A.S.S.R. □ ..... 54 20N 44 30 E
Møre og
   Romsdal □ ..... 63 0N 9 0 E
Morecambe 54 5N 2 52w
Morecambe B. 54 7N 3 0w
Moree .... 29 28s 149 54 E
Moorhead City ... 34 46N 76 44w
Moravian Hts.=
   Ceskomoravská V. 49 20N 15 30 E
Morea □=
   Pelopónnisos .... 37 40N 22 15 E
Morelia 19 40N 101 11w
Morella .... 23 0s 143 47 E

Morelos □ 18 40N 99 10w
Morena, Sa. 38 20N 4 0w
Morenci 33 7N 109 20w
Moreton, I. .... 27 10s 153 25 E
Morgan City 29 40N 91 15w
Morganton 35 46N 81 48w
Morgantown 39 39N 75 58w
Morgenzon .... 26 45s 29 36 E
Moriki .... 12 52N 6 30 E
Morinville 53 49N 113 41w
Morioka .... 39 45N 141 8 E
Morlaix 48 36N 3 52w
Mornington, I.,
   Australia ..... 16 30s 139 30 E
Mornington, I.,
   Chile 49 50s 75 30w
Moro G. .... 6 30N 123 0 E
Morocco ■ 32 0N 5 50w
Morogoro .... 6 50s 37 40 E
Moroleón 20 8N 101 32w
Morombé .... 21 45s 43 22 E
Morón 22 0N 78 30w
Mörön, R. .... 47 14N 110 37 E
Morón de la
   Frontera 37 6N 5 28w
Morondavo .... 20 17s 44 27 E
Morotai, I. .... 2 10N 128 30 E
Moroto .... 2 28N 34 42 E
Moroto, Mt. ..... 2 30N 34 43 E
Morpeth 55 11N 1 41w
Morrilton 35 10N 92 45w
Morrinhos 17 45s 49 10w
Morrinsville ..... 37 40s 175 32 E
Morris 49 25N 97 30w
Morris, Mt. ..... 26 9s 131 4 E
Morrisburg 44 55N 75 7w
Morristown, Tenn. . 36 18N 83 20w
Morro Bay 35 27N 120 54w
Morrosquillo, G. de 9 35N 75 40w
Morshansk .... 53 28N 41 50 E
Morteros 30 50s 62 0w
Mortes, R. 11 45s 50 44w
Mortlake .... 38 5s 142 50 E
Morundah .... 34 57s 146 19 E
Morven .... 26 22s 147 5 E
Morvern, Reg. 56 38N 5 44w
Morwell .... 38 10s 146 22 E
Moscos Is. .... 14 0N 97 45 E
Moscow 46 45N 116 59w
Moscow=Moskva . 55 45N 37 35 E

Mosel, R. .... 50 22N 7 36 E
Moselle, R. .... 50 22N 7 36 E
Moselle □ .... 48 59N 6 33 E
Mosgiel .... 45 53s 170 21 E
Moshi .... 3 22s 37 18 E
Mosjøen .... 65 51N 13 12 E
Moskva .... 55 45N 27 35 E
Moskva, R. .... 55 5N 38 50 E
Mosquera 2 35N 78 30w
Mosquitos,
   G. de los 9 15N 81 0w
Moss .... 59 27N 10 40 E
Moss Vale .... 34 32s 150 25 E
Mossbank 50 0N 106 0w
Mossburn .... 45 41s 168 15 E
Mosselbaai .... 34 11s 22 8 E
Mossendjo .... 2 55s 12 42 E
Mossgiel .... 33 15s 144 30 E
Mossman .... 16 28s 145 23 E
Mossoró 5 10s 37 15w
Mossuril .... 14 58s 40 42 E
Most .... 50 31N 13 38 E
Mosta .... 35 53N 14 26 E
Mostaganem .... 35 54N 0 5 E
Mostar .... 43 22N 17 50 E
Mostardas 31 2s 50 51w
Mosul=Al
   Mawsil .... 36 20N 43 5 E
Motala .... 58 32N 15 1 E
Motherwell 55 48N 4 0w
Motihari .... 26 37N 85 1 E
Motril 36 44N 3 37w
Motueka .... 41 7s 173 1 E
Mouila .... 1 50s 11 0 E
Moulins 46 35N 3 19¼
Moulmein=
   Maulamyaing ... 16 30N 97 40 E
Moultrie 31 11N 83 47w
Moundou .... 8 40N 16 10 E
Moundsville 39 53N 80 43w
Mount Airy 36 31N 80 37w
Mount Barker .... 34 38s 117 40 E
Mount Carmel, Ill. . 38 20N 87 48w
Mount Carmel, Pa. . 40 46N 76 25w
Mount Coolon .... 21 25s 147 25 E
Mount Darwin ... 16 47s 31 38 E
Mount Douglas ... 21 35s 146 50 E
Mount Eden ..... 36 53s 174 46 E
Mount Edgecumbe 57 3N 135 21w
Mount Elizabeth . 16 0s 125 50 E

Mount Forest 43 59N 80 43w
Mount Gambier ... 37 50s 140 46 E
Mount Garnet .... 17 41s 145 7 E
Mount Hope ..... 34 7s 135 23 E
Mount Isa .... 20 42s 139 26 E
Mount Keith ..... 27 15s 120 30 E
Mount Larcom ... 23 48s 150 59 E
Mount Lavinia ... 6 50N 79 50 E
Mount Magnet ... 28 2s 117 47 E
Mount
   Maunganui ... 37 40s 176 14 E
Mount Molloy .... 16 42s 145 20 E
Mount Morgan ... 23 40s 150 25 E
Mount Narryer ... 26 30s 115 55 E
Mount Newman ... 23 18s 119 45 E
Mount Pleasant,
   Iowa 41 0N 91 35w
Mount Pleasant,
   Mich. 43 38N 84 46w
Mount Pleasant,
   Texas 33 5N 95 0w
Mount Pleasant,
   Utah 39 40N 111 29w
Mount Rainier
   Nat. Park...... 46 50N 121 20w
Mt. Revelstoke
   Nat. Park...... 51 6N 118 0w
Mount Robson ... 52 56N 119 15w
Mount Sterling ... 38 0N 84 0w
Mount Surprise ... 18 10s 144 17 E
Mount Vernon, Ill. 38 19N 88 55w
Mount Vernon,
   N.Y. 40 57N 73 49w
Mount Vernon,
   Ohio 40 20N 82 30w
Mount
   Vernon, Wash.. 48 27N 122 18w
Mount
   Willoughby .... 27 58s 134 8 E
Mountain Home ... 43 3N 115 52w
Mountain Park ... 52 50N 117 15w
Mountain View ... 37 26N 122 5w
Mountainair 34 35N 106 15w
Mountmellick 53 7N 7 20w
Moura, Australia .. 24 35s 149 58 E
Moura, Brazil 1 25s 61 45w
Mourdi,
   Depression du .. 18 10N 23 0 E
Mouri 5 6N 1 14w
Mourne, Mts. 54 10N 6 0w

Mourne, R. 54 45N 7 25w
Mouscron .... 50 45N 3 12 E
Moutohora .... 38 27s 177 32 E
Mowming .... 21 50N 110 32 E
Mowping .... 37 25N 121 34 E
Moyale .... 3 30N 39 0 E
Moyle □ 55 10N 6 15w
Moza .... 31 48N 35 8 E
Mozambique ■ ... 19 0s 35 0 E
Mozambique Chan. 20 0s 39 0 E
Mozyr .... 52 0N 29 15 E
Mpanda .... 6 23s 31 40 E
Mpika .... 11 51s 31 25 E
Mporokoso .... 9 25s 30 5 E
Mpulungu .... 8 51s 31 5 E
Mpwapwa .... 6 30s 36 30 E
Msaken .... 35 49N 10 33 E
Msoro .... 13 35s 31 50 E
Mtito Andei ..... 2 41s 38 12 E
Mtwara .... 10 20s 40 20 E
Muaná 1 25s 49 15w
Muang Chiang
   Rai .... 19 52N 99 50 E
Muar=Bandar
   Maharani ...... 2 3N 102 34 E
Muarabungo ..... 1 40s 101 10 E
Muarakaman .... 0 2s 116 45 E
Muaratembesi ... 1 42s 103 2 E
Muaratewe .... 0 50s 115 0 E
Mubairik .... 23 22N 39 8 E
Mubende .... 0 33N 31 22 E
Mubi .... 10 18N 13 16 E
Muck, I. 56 50N 6 15w
Mucuri 18 0s 40 0w
Mueda .... 11 36s 39 28 E
Mufulira 12 32s 28 15w
Muhammad Qol ... 20 53N 37 9 E
Muheza .... 5 9s 38 48 E
Mühlhausen ..... 51 12N 10 29 E
Muine Bheag 52 42N 6 59w
Mukalla .... 14 33N 49 2 E
Mukden=Shenyang 41 48N 123 27 E
Mukeiras .... 13 59N 45 52 E
Mukinbudin ..... 30 55s 118 5 E
Mukomuko .... 2 20s 101 10 E
Mukono .... 0 28N 32 37 E
Muktsar .... 30 30N 74 30 E
Mulatas, Arch.
   de las 6 51N 78 31w
Mulchén 37 45s 72 20w

Mulde, R., ... 51 10N 12 48 E
Muleba .... 1 50s 31 37 E
Mulgrave 45 38N 61 31w
Mulhacén, Mt. ... 37 4N 3 20w
Mülheim 51 26N 6 53w
Mulhouse ..... 47 40N 7 20 E
Mull of Galloway,
  Pt. 54 40N 4 55w
Mull of Kintyre,
  Pt. 55 20N 5 45w
Mull, I. 56 27N 6 0w
Mullengudgery . 31 43s 147 29 E
Mullet, Pen. .. 54 10N 10 2w
Mullewa .... 28 29s 115 30 E
Mullingar 53 31N 7 20w
Mullumbimby .. 28 30s 153 30 E
Multan .... 30 15N 71 30 E
Mulwala .... 35 59s 146 0 E
Mumias .... 0 20N 34 29 E
Mun, R. .... 15 19N 105 31 E
Muna, I. .... 5 0s 122 30 E
Munabao .... 25 45N 70 17 E
München .... 48 8N 11 33 E
Muncie 40 10N 85 20w
Münden .... 51 25N 9 42 E
Mundiwindi .... 23 47s 120 9 E
Mundo Novo ... 11 50s 40 29w
Mundrabilla ... 31 52s 127 51 E
Mungallala .... 26 25s 147 34 E
Mungana .... 17 8s 144 27 E
Mungindi ...... 28 58s 149 1 E
Munhango ..... 12 9s 18 36 E
Munich=
  München ...... 48 8N 11 33 E
Muñoz Gamero,
  Pen. .... 52 30s 73 5 E
Munster □ 52 20N 8 40w
Münster .... 51 58N 7 37 E
Muntadgin .... 31 48s 118 30 E
Muntok .... 2 5s 105 10 E
Muonio, R. .... 67 48N 23 25 E
Mur, R. .... 46 18N 16 53 E
Murallón, Mt. .. 49 55s 73 30w
Murangá .... 0 45s 37 9 E
Muranisgar Mts. . 3 0N 35 0 E
Murashi .... 59 30N 49 0 E
Murchison,
  Australia ...... 36 39s 145 14 E
Murchison, N.Z. .. 41 49s 172 21 E
Murchison, R. .. 26 1s 117 6 E

Murcia 38 2N 1 10w
Murcia, Reg...... 38 35N 1 50w
Mureş, R......... 46 15N 20 13 E
Murfreesboro ... 35 50N 86 21w
Murgab .... 38 10N 73 59 E
Murgon .... 26 15s 151 54 E
Muritz See .... 53 25N 12 40 E
Murmansk ..... 68 57N 33 10 E
Murom .... 55 35N 42 3 E
Muroran .... 42 25N 141 0 E
Murphysboro ... 37 50N 89 20w
Murray, Ky. ... 36 40N 88 20w
Murray, Utah ... 40 41N 111 58w
Murray, R. .... 35 22s 139 22 E
Murray Bridge ... 35 6s 139 14 E
Murraysburg ... 31 58s 23 47 E
Murrayville .... 35 16s 141 11 E
Murree .... 33 56N 73 28 E
Murrin Murrin .. 28 50s 121 45 E
Murrumbidgee, R. . 34 43s 143 12 E
Murrurundi .... 31 42s 150 51 E
Murtoa .... 36 35s 142 28 E
Murupara ...... 38 30s 178 40 E
Murwara ...... 23 46N 80 28 E
Murwillumbah .. 28 18s 153 27 E
Mürzzuschlag .. 47 36N 15 41 E
Musala, Mt. ... 41 13N 23 27 E
Muscat=Masqat .. 23 37N 58 36 E
Muscatine 41 25N 91 5w
Mushao .... 2 2s 29 20 E
Mushie .... 2 56s 17 4 E
Mushin .... 6 32N 3 21 E
Muskegon 43 15N 86 17w
Muskegon
  Heights 43 12N 86 17w
Muskogee 35 50N 95 25w
Musmar .... 18 6N 35 40 E
Musoma .... 1 30s 33 48 E
Musselburgh ... 55 57N 3 3w
Musters, L. 45 20s 69 25w
Muswellbrook .. 32 16s 150 56 E
Mût .... 25 28N 28 58 E
Mutankiang ... 44 35N 129 30 E
Muttaburra ... 22 38s 144 29 E
Mutton Bay 50 50N 59 2w
Muya .... 56 27N 115 39 E
Muzaffarabad ... 34 25N 73 30 E
Muzaffarnagar . 29 26N 77 40 E
Muzaffarpur ... 26 7N 85 32 E
Muzhi .... 65 25N 64 40 E

Muztagh, Mt. ... 36 30N 87 22 E
Mvadhi Ousye ... 1 13N 13 12 E
Mvomero ...... 6 18s 37 28 E
Mwanza, Tanzania . 2 30s 32 58 E
Mwanza, Zaire ... 7 55s 26 43 E
Mwaya .... 9 32s 33 55 E
Mweka .... 4 50s 21 40 E
Mweru, L. ..... 9 0s 28 45 E
Mwirasandu .... 0 56s 30 22 E
My Tho .... 10 29N 106 23 E
Myanaung ..... 18 25N 95 10 E
Myaungmya .... 16 30N 95 0 E
Myeik Kyunzu .. 11 0N 98 0 E
Myingyan ..... 21 30N 95 30 E
Myitkyina ..... 25 30N 97 26 E
Mymensingh=
  Nasirabad ..... 24 42N 90 30 E
Myrtle Creek ... 43 0N 123 19w
Myrtle Point ... 43 0N 124 4w
Mysore .... 12 17N 76 41 E
Mývatn, L. 65 36N 17 0w
Mzimvubu, R. .. 31 30s 29 30 E

N

Na'an .... 31 53N 34 52 E
Naantali ...... 60 27N 21 57 E
Naas 53 12N 6 40w
Nababeep ...... 29 36s 17 46 E
Nabadwip ...... 23 34N 88 20 E
Nabenl .... 36 30N 10 51 E
Nabi Rubin .... 31 56N 34 44 E
Naboomspruit .. 24 32s 28 40 E
Nābulus .... 32 14N 35 15 E
Nachingwea ... 10 49s 38 49 E
Nackara .... 32 48s 139 12 E
Nacogdoches.... 31 33N 95 30w
Nacozari 30 30N 109 50w
Nadiad .... 22 41N 72 56 E
Nadūshan ..... 32 2N 53 35 E
Nadvoitsy ..... 63 52N 34 15 E
Nadym .... 63 35N 72 42 E
Nafada .... 11 8N 11 20 E
Naga .... 13 38N 123 15 E
Nagaland □ .... 26 0N 95 0 E
Nagano .... 36 40N 138 10 E
Nagano □ ...... 36 15N 138 0 E

Nagaoka .... 32 27N 138 51 E
Nagappattinam ... 10 46N 79 51 E
Nagasaki .... 32 47N 129 50 E
Nagasaki □ ..... 3250⅛N 129 40 E
Nagato .... 36 15N 138 16 E
Nagaur .... 27 15N 73 45 E
Nagercoil ...... 8 12N 77 33 E
Nagornyy ...... 55 58N 124 57 E
Nagoya .... 35 10N 136 50 E
Nagpur .... 21 8N 79 10 E
Nagykanizsa ... 46 28N 17 0 E
Nagykörös .... 47 2N 19 48 E
Naha .... 26 12N 127 40 E
Nahannai Butte . 61 5N 123 30w
Nahariyya ..... 33 1N 35 5 E
Nahavand ..... 34 10N 48 30 E
Nahf .... 32 56N 35 18 E
Nahuel Huapi, L.. 41 0s 71 32w
Naicam 52 30N 104 30w
Nain 56 34N 61 40w
Nainpur .... 22 26N 80 6 E
Nairn 57 35N 3 54w
Nairobi .... 1 17s 36 48 E
Naivasha ...... 0 40s 36 30 E
Najafābād ..... 32 40N 51 15 E
Najd, Reg. .... 26 30N 42 0 E
Najibabad ..... 29 40N 78 20 E
Nakamura ..... 33 0N 133 0 E
Nakasongola .. 1 19N 32 28 E
Nakhi Mubarak . 24 10N 38 10 E
Nakhichevan... 39 14N 45 30 E
Nakhodka ..... 43 10N 132 45 E
Nakhon Phanom . 17 23N 104 43 E
Nakhon Ratchasima 14 59N 102 12 E
Nakhon Sawan ... 15 35N 100 12 E
Nakhon Si
  Thammarat ... 8 29N 100 0 E
Nakina 50 10N 86 40w
Nakskov .... 54 50N 11 8 E
Nakuru .... 0 15s 35 5 E
Nakusp 50 20N 117 45w
Nal, R. .... 26 2N 65 19 E
Nalayh .... 47 43N 107 22 E
Nalchik .... 43 30N 43 33 E
Nalgonda ...... 17 6N 79 15 E
Nallamalai Hills .. 15 30N 78 50 E
Nālūt .... 31 54N 11 0 E
Nam Dinh ..... 20 25N 106 5 E
Nam-Phan, Reg. . 10 30N 106 0 E
Nam Tok ...... 14 21N 99 0 E

Nam Tso, L. .... 30 40N 90 30 E
Namaland, Reg. .. 29 43s 19 5 E
Namangan ..... 41 30N 71 30 E
Namapa .... 13 43s 39 50 E
Namasagali .... 1 2N 33 0 E
Namber .... 1 2s 134 57 E
Nambour ...... 26 38s 152 49 E
Nambucca Heads.. 30 40s 152 48 E
Namcha Barwa, Mt. 29 30N 95 10 E
Namib Des.=
  Namibwoestyn .. 22 30s 15 0w
Namibia■=
  S.W. Africa ■ .. 22 0s 18 0 E
Namibwoestyn .. 22 30s 15 0w
Namlea .... 3 10s 127 5 E
Nampa 43 40N 116 40w
Nampula ...... 15 6s 39 7 E
Namrole ...... 3 46s 126 46 E
Namsen, R. .... 64 27N 11 28 E
Namsos .... 64 29N 11 30 E
Namtu .... 23 5N 97 28 E
Namur .... 50 27N 4 52 E
Namur □ ...... 50 17N 5 0 E
Namutoni ..... 18 49s 16 55 E
Namwala ...... 15 44s 26 30 E
Namyung ..... 25 15N 114 5 E
Nan .... 18 48N 100 46 E
Nan Shan, Mts. . 38 0N 98 0 E
Nanaimo 49 10N 124 0w
Nanango ...... 26 40s 152 0 E
Nanao .... 37 0N 137 0 E
Nanchang ..... 28 34N 115 48 E
Nancheng ..... 27 30N 116 28 E
Nancheng=
  Hanchung .... 33 10N 107 2 E
Nanching=
  Nanking ...... 32 10N 118 50 E
Nanchung ..... 30 47N 105 59 E
Nancy .... 48 42N 6 12 E
Nanda Devi, Mt. . 30 30N 80 30 E
Nander .... 19 10N 77 20 E
Nandi .... 17 25s 176 50 E
Nandurbar .... 21 20N 74 15 E
Nandyal ...... 15 30N 78 30 E
Nanga-Eboko ... 4 40N 12 26 E
Nanga Parbat, Mt.. 35 10N 74 35 E
Nangal Dam ... 31 25N 76 38 E
Nangarhar □ ... 34 15N 70 30 E
Nankang ...... 25 42N 114 35 E
Nanking ...... 32 10N 118 50 E

Nankoku .... 33 39N 133 44 E
Nannine .... 26 51s 118 18 E
Nanning .... 22 51N 108 18 E
Nannup .... 33 59s 115 45 E
Nanping .... 26 45N 118 5 E
Nansei-Shotō, Is. .. 29 0N 129 0 E
Nanson .... 28 34s 114 46 E
Nantan .... 25 0N 107 35 E
Nantes 47 12N 1 33w
Nanticoke 41 12N 76 1w
Nanton 50 20N 113 50w
Nantou .... 23 57N 120 35 E
Nantucket I. 41 16N 70 3w
Nantung .... 32 0N 120 50 E
Nanuque 17 50s 40 21w
Nanyang .... 33 2N 112 35 E
Nanyuan .... 39 48N 116 23 E
Nanyuki .... 0 2N 37 4 E
Nao, C. de la .... 38 44N 0 14 E
Naoetsu .... 37 12N 138 10 E
Napa 38 18N 122 17w
Napanee 44 15N 77 0w
Napier .... 39 30s 176 56 E
Napier Broome, B. 14 0s 127 0 E
Napier Downs .... 16 20s 124 30 E
Naples=
    Nápoli ...... 40 50N 14 5 E
Napo, R. 3 20s 72 40w
Napoleon 46 32N 99 49w
Nápoli .... 40 50N 14 5 E
Nara .... 34 40N 135 49 E
Nara □ .... 34 30N 136 0 E
Naracoorte ...... 36 50s 140 44 E
Narasapur .... 16 26N 81 50 E
Narayanganj .... 23 31N 90 33 E
Narayanpet ..... 16 45N 77 30 E
Narbonne .... 43 11N 3 0 E
Narembeen ...... 32 4s 118 24 E
Naretha .... 31 0s 124 50 E
Narmada, R. .... 21 35N 72 35 E
Narok .... 1 20s 33 30 E
Narrabri .... 30 19s 149 46 E
Narran, R. ..... 29 45s 147 20 E
Narrandera ..... 34 42s 146 31 E
Narrogin .... 32 58s 117 14 E
Narromine ...... 32 12s 148 12 E
Narsinghpur .... 22 54N 79 14 E
Naruto .... 35 36N 140 25 E
Narvik .... 68 28N 17 26 E
Narym .... 59 0N 81 58 E

Narymskoye ...... 49 10N 84 15 E
Naryn .... 41 30N 76 10 E
Nasarawa .... 8 32N 7 41 E
Naser, Buheiret en 23 0N 32 30 E
Nashua, Mont. 48 10N 106 25w
Nashua, N.H. 42 50N 71 25w
Nashville 36 12N 86 46w
Nasik .... 20 2N 73 50 E
Nasirabad,
    Bangladesh .... 26 15N 74 45 E
Nasirabad, Pak. ... 28 25N 68 25 E
Nassau 25 0N 77 30w
Nassau, B. 55 20s 68 0w
Nasser, L.=Naser,
    Buheiret en .... 23 0N 32 30 E
Nássjö .... 57 38N 14 45 E
Nastapoka Is. 57 0N 77 0w
Nat Kyizio ...... 14 55N 98 0 E
Natagaima 3 37N 75 6w
Natal, Brazil 5 47s 35 13w
Natal, Indonesia .. 0 35N 99 0 E
Natal □ .... 28 30s 30 30 E
Natashquan 50 14N 61 46w
Natashquan, R. .. 50 6N 61 49w
Natchez 31 35N 91 25w
Natchitoches 31 47N 93 4w
Natimuk .... 36 35s 141 59 E
Natitingou ...... 10 20N 1 26 E
National City 32 45N 117 7w
Natividade 11 43s 47 47w
Natron, L. ...... 2 20s 36 0 E
Natuna Besar,
    Kep. .... 4 0N 108 0 E
Natuna Selatan,
    Kep. .... 3 0N 109 55 E
Naumburg ...... 51 10N 11 48 E
Naushahra ...... 33 9N 74 15 E
Nautanwa ...... 27 26N 83 25 E
Navajo Res. 36 55N 107 30w
Navalcarnero 40 17N 4 5w
Navan=An Uaimh 53 39N 6 40w
Navarino, I. 55 0s 67 30w
Navarra, Reg. ... 42 40N 1 40w
Navassa, I. 18 30N 75 0w
Navoi .... 40 9N 65 22 E
Navojoa 27 0N 109 30w
Navolok .... 62 33N 39 57 E
Návpaktos ...... 38 23N 21 42 E
Navplion .... 37 33N 22 50 E
Navsari .... 20 57N 72 59 E

Nawabshah .... 26 15N 68 25 E
Nawalgarh ...... 27 50N 75 15 E
Náxos, I. .... 37 5N 25·30 E
Nãy Band ...... 27 20N 52 40 E
Nayakhan ...... 62 10N 159 0 E
Nayarit □ 22 0N 105 0w
Nazaré, Brazil ... 13 0s 39 0w
Nazareth, Israel .. 32 42N 35 17 E
Nazir Hat ...... 22 35N 91 55 E
Ndala .... 4 46s 33 16 E
N'Délé .... 8 25N 20 36 E
Ndendé .... 2 29s 10 46 E
Ndjamena ...... 12 4N 15 8 E
Ndola .... 13 0s 28 34 E
Ndumbwe ...... 10 14s 39 58 E
Ndungu .... 4 28s 38 4 E
Neagh, L. 54 35N 6 25w
Near Is. 53 0N 172 0w
Neath 51 39N 3 49w
Nebo 39 27N 90 47w
Nebraska □ 41 30N 100 0w
Nebraska City ... 40 40N 95 52w
Nebrodi, Monti .. 37 55N 14 35 E
Neckar, R. ...... 49 31N 8 26 E
Necochea 38 30s 58 50w
Needles 34 50N 114 35w
Neemuch .... 24 30N 74 50 E
Neenah 44 10N 88 30w
Neepawa 50 20N 99 30w
Nefta .... 33 53N 7 58 E
Neftyannyye
    Kamni ...... 40 20N 50 55 E
Nefyn 52 57N 4 31w
Negaunee 46 30N 87 36w
Negoiu, Mt. ..... 45 48N 24 32 E
Negombo .... 7 12N 79 50 E
Negotin .... 44 16N 22 37 E
Negra Pt. ...... 18 40N 120 50 E
Negra, Pta. 6 6s 81 10w
Negro, R., Arg. .. 41 2s 62 47w
Negro, R., Brazil . 3 10s 59 58w
Negros, I. ...... 10 0N 123 0 E
Nehbandān ..... 31 35N 60 5 E
Neikiang .... 29 35N 105 10 E
Neisse, R. ...... 52 4N 14 47 E
Neiva 2 56N 75 18w
Nekemte .... 9 4N 36 30 E
Neksø .... 55 4N 15 8 E
Nelkan .... 57 50N 136 15 E
Nellore .... 14 27N 79 59 E

Nelma .... 47 30N 139 0 E
Nelson, Canada ... 49 30N 117 20w
Nelson, N.Z. .... 41 18s 173 16 E
Nelson, U.K. 53 50N 2 14w
Nelson □ ...... 42 11s 172 15 E
Nelson, Estrecho . 51 30s 75 0w
Nelson, R. 55 30N 96 50w
Nelson Forks 59 30N 124 0w
Nelspruit .... 25 29s 30 59 E
Néma 16 40N 7 15w
Nemuro .... 43 20N 145 35 E
Nemuro-Kaikyō,
    Str. .... 43 30N 145 30 E
Nemuy .... 55 40N 135 55 E
Nenagh 52 52N 8 11w
Nenana 63 34N 149 7w
Nene, R. .... 52 48N 0 13 E
Neosho 35 59N 95 10w
Nepal ■ .... 28 0N 84 30 E
Nepalganj ...... 28 0N 81 40 E
Nephi 39 43N 111 52w
Nerchinsk ...... 52 0N 116 39 E
Nerchinskiyzavod . 51 10N 119 30 E
Nerva 37 42N 6 30w
Nes Ziyyona 31 56N 34 48w
Nesher .... 32 45N 35 3 E
Ness, L. 57 15N 4 30w
Nesttun .... 60 19N 5 21 E
Netanya .... 32 20N 34 51 E
Netherlands ■ ... 52 0N 5 30 E
Nettilling L. 66 30N 71 0w
Neu Brandenburg . 53 33N 13 17 E
Neuchâtel ...... 47 0N 6 55 E
Neuchâtel, L. de . 46 53N 6 50 E
Neumünster .... 54 4N 9 58 E
Neunkirchen .... 49 23N 7 6 E
Neuquén .... 38 0s 68 0 E
Neustrelitz ..... 53 22N 13 4 E
Nevada 37 20N 94 40w
Nevada □ 39 20N 117 0w
Nevada, Sa. 37 3N 3 15w
Nevada de Sta.
    Marta, Sa. ... 10 55N 73 50w
Nevanka .... 56 45N 98 55 E
Nevers .... 47 0N 3 9 E
Nevertire ...... 31 50s 147 44 E
Nevis, I. 17 0N 62 30w
New Albany 38 20N 85 50w
New Amsterdam .. 6 15N 57 30w
New Bedford 41 40N 70 52w

New Bern 35 8N 77 3w
New Braunfels .. 29 43N 98 9w
New Brighton .. 43 29s 172 43 E
New Britain 41 41N 72 47w
New Britain, I. .... 6 0s 151 0 E
New Brunswick .. 40 30N 74 28w
New Brunswick □ . 46 50N 66 30w
New Bussa ...... 9 55N 4 33 E
New Caledonia, I. . 21 0s 165 0 E
New Castille=
    Castilla la
    Nueva 39 45N 3 20w
New Castle, Ind. .. 39 55N 85 23w
New Castle, Pa. .. 41 0N 80 20w
New Delhi ...... 28 37N 77 13 E
New Denver 50 0N 117 25w
New Forest, Reg. .. 50 53N 1 40w
New Glasgow ... 45 35N 62 36w
New Guinea, I. .. 5 0s 141 0 E
New Hampshire □ . 43 40N 71 40w
New Hanover ... 29 22s 30 31 E
New Haven 41 20N 72 54w
New Hebrides, I. . 15 0s 168 0 E
New Iberia 30 2N 91 54w
New Ireland, I. ... 3 0s 151 30 E
New Jersey □ ... 39 50N 74 10w
New Kensington . 40 36N 79 43w
New Liskeard ... 47 31N 79 41w
New London 41 23N 72 8w
New Mexico □ ... 34 30N 106 0w
New Norcia .... 30 58s 116 13 E
New Norfolk .... 42 46s 147 2 E
New Orleans 30 0N 90 5w
New Philadelphia . 40 29N 81 25w
New Plymouth .. 39 4s 174 5 E
New Providence I. . 25 0N 77 30w
New Radnor 52 15N 3 10w
New Romney .... 50 59N 0 57 E
New South Wales □ 33 0s 146 0 E
New Ulm 44 15w 94 30w
New Waterford .. 46 13N 60 4w
New Westminster . 49 10N 122 52w
New York 40 45N 74 0w
New York □ 42 40N 76 0w
New Zealand ■ .. 40 0s 173 0 E
Newala .... 10 58s 39 10 E
Newark, U.K. ... 53 6N 0 48w
Newark, N.J. ... 40 41N 74 12w
Newark, N.Y. ... 43 2N 77 10w
Newberry 46 20N 85 32w

Newburgh 41 30N 74 1w
Newbury 51 24N   1 19w
Newburyport 42 48N 70 50w
Newcastle,
  Australia .... 32 52s 151 49 E
Newcastle, Canada 47 1N 65 38w
Newcastle, Eire .. 52 27N   9 3w
Newcastle, S.Africa 27 45s 29 58 E
Newcastle, N.
  Ireland 54 13N   5 54w
Newcastle,
  Tyne and Tees .. 54 59N   1 37w
Newcastle Emlyn .. 52 2N   4 29w
Newcastle Waters . 17 30s 133 28 E
Newcastle-under-
  Lyme 53 2N   2 15w
Newdegate ...... 33 17N 118 58 E
Newe Etan ...... 32 30N 35 32 E
Newe Sha'anan ... 32 47N 34 59 E
Newe Zohar ..... 31 9N 35 21 E
Newenham, C. 58 37N 162 12w
Newfoundland □ .. 48 28N 56 0w
Newfoundland, I. .. 48 30N 56 0w
Newhaven .... 50 47N   0 4 E
Newman, Mt. .... 23 20s 119 34 E
Newmarket, Eire .. 52 13N   9 0w
Newmarket, U.K. .. 52 15N   0 23 E
Newnan 33 22N 84 48w
Newport, Gwent .. 51 35N   3 0w
Newport, I. of
  Wight 50 42N   1 18w
Newport, Ark. 35 38N 91 15w
Newport, Ky. 39 5N 84 23w
Newport, Oreg. ... 44 41N 124 2w
Newport, Rhode I. 41 30N 71 19w
Newport, Vt. 44 57N 72 17w
Newport Beach ... 33 40N 117 58w
Newport News ... 37 2N 76 54w
Newquay 50 24N   5 6w
Newry 54 10N   6 20w
Newry & Mourne □ 54 10N   6 20w
Newton, Iowa 41 40N 93 3w
Newton, Kans. 38 2N 97 30w
Newton, Mass. ... 42 21N 71 10w
Newton, N.J. 41 3N 74 46w
Newton Abbot ... 50 32N   3 37w
Newton Stewart .. 54 57N   4 30w
Newtonmore 57 4N   4 7w
Newtown, Australia 34 30s 151 10 E
Newtown, U.K. ... 52 31N   3 19w

Newtownabbey □ . 54 40N   5 55w
Newtownards 54 37N   5 40w
Neya .... 58 21N 43 49 E
Neyshābūr .... 36 10N 58 20 E
Nezhin .... 51 5N 31 55 E
Ngala .... 12 15N 14 15 E
Ngami Depression . 20 30s 22 46 E
Ngamo .... 19 3s 27 25 E
Nganjuk .... 7 32s 111 55 E
Ngaoundéré ...... 7 15N 13 35 E
Ngapara .... 44 57s 170 46 E
Ngawi .... 7 24s 111 26 E
Ngerengere ...... 6 47s 38 10 E
Ngomba .... 8 20s 32 53 E
Ngong .... 1 25s 36 39 E
Ngoring Nor, L. ... 34 50N 98 0 E
Ngorongoro Crater 3 11s 35 32 E
Ngudu .... 2 58s 33 25 E
Nguru .... 12 56N 10 29 E
Nguru Mts. ...... 6 0s 37 30 E
Nha Trang ...... 12 16N 109 10 E
Nhill .... 36 18s 141 40 E
Niagara Falls,
  Canada 43 7N 79 5w
Niagara Falls,
  U.S.A. 43 5N 79 0w
Niah .... 3 58s 113 46 E
Niamey .... 13 27N   2 6 E
Niangara .... 3 50N 27 50 E
Nias, I. .... 1 0N 97 40 E
Nicaragua ■ 11 40N 85 30w
Nicastro .... 39 0N 16 18 E
Nice .... 43 42N   7 14 E
Nichinan .... 31 28N 131 26 E
Nicholson Ra. .... 27 12s 116 40 E
Nicobar Is. ...... 9 0N 93 0 E
Nicola 50 8N 120 40w
Nicolet 46 17N 72 35w
Nicosia=Levkosia,
  Cyprus .... 35 10N 33 25 E
Nicoya, G. de ... 10 0N 85 0w
Nicoya, Pen. de .. 9 45N 85 40w
Nidd, R. 54 1N   1 12w
Nieder-
  Osterreich □ ... 48 25N 15 40 E
Niedersachsen □ . 52 45N   9 0 E
Nienburg .... 52 38N   9 15 E
Nieuw Amsterdam 5 53N   5 55w
Nieuw Nickerie ... 6 0N 57 10w
Nièvre □ .... 47 10N   5 40 E

Niğde .... 37 59N 34 42 E
Nigel .... 26 27s 28 25 E
Niger ■ .... 13 30N 10 0 E
Niger, R. .... 5 33N   6 33 E
Niger Delta ..... 4 0N   5 30 E
Niger □ .... 10 0N   5 30 E
Nigeria ■ .... 8 30N   8 0 E
Nightcaps ...... 45 57s 168 14 E
Niigata .... 37 58N 139 0 E
Niigata □ ...... 37 15N 138 45 E
Niihama .... 33 55N 133 10 E
Niihau, I. 21 55N 160 10w
Niimi .... 34 59N 133 28 E
Nijkerk .... 52 13N   5 30 E
Nijmegen .... 51 50N   5 52 E
Nike .... 6 26N   7 29 E
Nikiniki .... 9 40s 124 30 E
Nikki .... 9 58N   3 21 E
Nikolayev ...... 46 58N 32 7 E
Nikolayevsk ..... 50 10N 45 35 E
Nikolayevskna-Am 53 40N 140 50 E
Nikopol .... 47 35N 34 25 E
Nīl, Nahr en, R. .. 30 10N 31 6 E
Nīl el Abyad, R. .. 15 40N 32 30 E
Nīl el Azraq, R. .. 11 40N 32 30 E
Nīl el Azraq □ ... 12 30N 34 30 E
Niland 33 16N 115 30w
Nile, R.=
  Nīl, Nahren, R. . 30 10N 31 6 E
Niles 41 8N 80 40w
Nîmes .... 43 50N   4 23 E
Nimmitabel ..... 36 29s 149 15 E
Nimneryskiy .... 58 0N 125 10 E
Nimule .... 3 32N 32 3 E
Ninety Mile Beach,
  The .... 38 30s 147 10 E
Nineveh .... 36 25N 43 10 E
Ningming ...... 22 10N 107 59 E
Ningpo .... 29 50N 121 30 E
Ningsia Hui □ ... 37 45N 106 0 E
Ningteh .... 26 45N 120 0 E
Ningwu .... 39 2N 112 15 E
Ninh Binh ..... 20 15N 105 55 E
Ninove .... 50 51N   4 2 E
Niobrara, R. 42 45N 98 0w
Nioro 13 40N 15 50w
Niort 46 19N   0 29w
Nipawin 53 20N 104 0w
Nipawin Prov. Park 54 0N 104 40w
Nipigon 49 0N 88 17w

Nipigon, L. 49 40N 88 30w
Niquelandia 14 27s 48 27w
Nirasaki .... 35 42N 138 27 E
Niš .... 43 19N 21 58 E
Nisab .... 14 25N 46 29 E
Nishinomiya .... 34 45N 135 20 E
Niterói 22 52s 43 0w
Nith, R. 55 0N   3 35w
Nitra .... 48 19N 18 4 E
Nitra, R. ...... 47 46N 18 10 E
Nivelles .... 50 35N   4 20 E
Nivernais, Reg. .. 47 0N   3 40 E
Nizamabad ..... 18 45N 78 7 E
Nizamghat ...... 28 20N 95 45 E
Nizhne Kolymsk .. 68 40N 160 55 E
Nizhne-Vartovskoye 60 56N 76 38 E
Nizhneangarsk ... 56 0N 109 30 E
Nizhneudinsk .... 55 0N 99 20 E
Nizhniy Tagil .... 57 45N 60 0 E
Nizip .... 37 1N 37 46 E
Nizké Tatry, Mts. . 48 55N 20 0 E
Nizzanim .... 31 42N 34 37 E
Njombe .... 9 0s 34 35 E
Nkambe .... 6 35N 10 40 E
Nkawkaw 6 36N   0 49w
Nkhata Bay ..... 11 33s 34 16 E
Nkhota Kota .... 12 55s 34 15 E
Nkonge .... 0 15N 31 10 E
Nkongsamba .... 4 55N   9 55 E
Noakhali=Maijdi . 22 48N 91 10 E
Noatak 67 34N 162 59w
Nobeoka .... 32 36N 131 41 E
Nocera Inferiore . 40 45N 14 37 E
Noda .... 47 30N 142 5 E
Nogales, Mexico .. 31 36N 94 29w
Nogales, U.S.A. .. 31 33N 110 59w
Nōgata .... 33 48N 130 54 E
Noggerup ...... 33 32s 116 5 E
Noginsk .... 55 50N 38 25 E
Noire, Mts. 48 11N   3 40w
Noirmoutier, Î. de 46 58N   2 10w
Nok Kundi ..... 28 50N 62 45 E
Nokhuysk ...... 60 0N 117 45 E
Nome 64 30N 165 30w
Nonda .... 20 40s 142 28 E
Nong Khai ..... 17 50N 102 46 E
Noonamah ..... 12 38s 131 4 E
Noondoo ...... 28 35s 148 30 E
Noord Beveland, I. 51 45N   3 50 E
Noord Brabant □ . 51 40N   5 0 E

Noord Holland □ . 52 30N   4 45 E
Noordoost-Polder . 52 45N   5 45 E
Noordwijk ..... 52 14N   4 26 E
Nootka I. 49 40N 126 50w
Noranda .... 48 20N 79 0 E
Nord □ .... 50 15N   3 30 E
Nord-Ostsee Kanal 54 5N   9 15 E
Nordegg 52 29N 116 5w
Nordkapp ...... 71 11N 25 48 E
Nordland □ ..... 65 40N 13 0 E
Nordrhein
  Westfalen □ ... 51 45N   7 30 E
Nordvik .... 73 40N 110 57 E
Nore, R. 52 25N   6 58w
Norfolk, Nebr. ... 42 3N 97 25w
Norfolk, Va. 36 52N 76 15w
Norfolk □ ...... 52 39N   1 0 E
Norfolk I. ...... 28 58s 168 3 E
Norilsk .... 69 20N 88 0 E
Normal 40 30N 89 0w
Norman 35 12N 97 30w
Norman Wells ... 65 40N 126 45w
Normandie, Reg. . 48 45N   0 10 E
Normandin 48 49N 72 31w
Normandy, Reg.=
  Normandie, Reg. 48 45N   0 10 E
Normanton ..... 17 40s 141 10 E
Nornalup ...... 35 0s 116 49 E
Norquinco 41 51s 70 55w
Norrbotten □ ... 66 45s 23 0 E
Norristown 40 9N 75 15w
Norrköping ..... 58 37N 16 11 E
Norrland, Reg. .. 64 25N 18 0 E
Norrtälje ...... 59 46N 18 42 E
Norseman ...... 32 8s 121 43 E
Norsk .... 52 30N 130 0 E
Norte, C. do 1 40N 49 55w
North, C. ...... 34 23s 173 4 E
North I. .... 38 0s 176 0 E
North Adams ... 42 42N 73 6w
North America ... 45 0N 100 0w
North Battleford . 52 50N 108 10w
North Bay 46 20N 79 30w
North Belcher Is. . 56 30N 79 0w
North Bend,
  Canada 49 50N 121 35w
North Bend,Oreg. 43 28N 124 7w
North Berwick ... 56 4N   2 44w
North Borneo□=

Sabah □	6 0N	117 0 E
North Carolina □	35 30N	80 0w
North Channel	55 0N	5 30w
North Chicago	42 19N	87 50w
North Dakota □	47 30N	100 0w
North Dandalup	32 31s	115 58 E
North Down □	54 40N	5 45w
North Downs	51 17N	0 30w
North East Frontier Agency= Arunachal Pradesh	28 0N	95 0 E
North Esk, R.	56 54N	2 38w
North European Plain	55 0N	25 0 E
North Foreland, Pt.	51 22N	1 28 E
North Horr	3 20N	37 8 E
North Kamloops	50 40N	120 25w
North Korea ■	40 0N	127 0 E
North Lakhimpur	27 15N	94 10 E
North Magnetic Pole	76 5N	101 3w
North Minch	58 5N	5 55w
North Platte	41 10N	100 50w
North Ronaldsay, I.	59 20N	2 30w
North Saskatchewan, R.	53 15N	105 6w
North Sea	55 0N	5 0 E
North Sydney	46 12N	60 21w
North Tonawanda	43 5N	78 50w
N.-Trøndelag □	64 30N	12 30 E
North Truchas Pk.	36 0N	105 30w
North Tyne, R.	54 59N	2 8w
North Uist, I.	57 40N	7 15w
North Vancouver	49 25N	123 20w
North Village	32 15N	64 45w
North Walsham	52 49N	1 22 E
North West, C.	21 45s	114 9 E
North West Highlands, Mts.	57 35N	5 2w
North West Territories □	65 0N	100 0w
North York Moors	54 25N	0 50w
North Yorkshire □	54 20N	1 25w
Northallerton	54 20N	1 26w
Northam	31 35s	116 42 E
Northampton, Australia	28 21s	114 33 E
Northampton, U.K.	52 14N	0 54w
Northampton, Mass.	42 22N	72 39w
Northampton □	52 16N	0 55w
Northampton Downs	24 35s	145 48 E
Northcliffe	34 36s	116 7 E
Northern □	9 0N	1 30w
Northern Circars, Reg.	17 30N	82 30 E
Northern Ireland ■	54 45N	7 0w
Northern Mid-Atlantic Ridge	30 0N	40 0w
Northern Rhodesia■= Zambia ■	15 0s	28 0 E
Northern Territory □	16 0s	133 0 E
Northfield	44 37N	93 10w
Northumberland □	55 12N	2 0w
Northumberland, Is.	21 45s	150 20 E
Northumberland Str.	46 20N	64 0w
Northwich	53 16N	2 30w
Norton	17 52s	30 40 E
Norton Sd.	64 0N	165 0w
Norwalk, Conn.	41 7N	73 27w
Norwalk, Ohio	41 15N	82 37w
Norway ■	67 0N	11 0 E
Norway House	53 55N	98 50w
Norwegian Dependency	75 0s	15 0 E
Norwegian Sea	66 0N	1 0 E
Norwich, U.K.	52 38N	1 17 E
Norwich, N.Y.	42 32N	75 30w
Nosok	70 10N	82 20 E
Nosratabad	29 55N	60 0 E
Noss Hd.	58 29N	3 4w
Nossob, R.	26 55s	20 37 E
Nosy Bé, I.	13 20s	48 15 E
Nosy-Varika	20 35s	48 32 E
Noteč R.	52 44N	15 26 E
Notikewin	57 15N	117 5w
Noto	36 52N	15 4 E
Notre Dame B.	49 45N	55 30w
Notre Dame de Koartac=Koartac	60 55N	69 40w
Notre Dame d'Ivugivik= Ivugivik	62 20N	78 0w
Nottawasaga B.	44 40N	80 30w
Nottingham	52 57N	1 10w
Nottinghamshire □	53 10N	1 0w
Nouadhibou	21 0N	17 0w
Nouakchott	18 20N	15 50w
Nouméa	22 17s	166 30 E
Noupoort	31 10s	24 57 E
Nouveau Comptoir	53 2N	78 55w
Nova Cruz	6 28s	35 25w
Nova Friburgo	22 10s	42 30w
Nova Granada	20 29s	49 19w
Nova Lima	20 5s	44 0w
Nova Lisboa= Huambo	12 42s	15 54 E
Nova Scotia □	45 10N	63 0w
Nova Sofola	20 7s	34 48 E
Nova Venecia	18 45s	40 24 E
Novara	45 27N	8 36 E
Novaya Ladoga	60 7N	32 16 E
Novaya Lyalya	58 50N	60 35 E
Novaya Sibir, Os.	75 10N	150 0 E
Novaya Zemlya, I.	75 0N	56 0 E
Nové Zámky	47 59N	18 11 E
Novgorod	58 30N	31 25 E
Novi-Sad	45 18N	19 52 E
Novo Redondo	11 10s	13 48 E
Novocherkassk	47 27N	40 5 E
Novokazalinsk	45 40N	61 40 E
Novokiybyshevsk	53 7N	49 58 E
Novo-kuznetsk	54 0N	87 10 E
Novomoskovsk	54 5N	38 15 E
Novorossiyk	44 43N	37 52 E
Novoshakhtinsk	47 39N	39 58 E
Novosibirsk	55 0N	83 5 E
Novosibirskiye Os.	75 0N	140 0 E
Novotroitsk	51 10N	58 15 E
Novouzensk	50 32N	48 17 E
Novska	45 19N	17 0 E
Now Shahr	36 40N	51 40 E
Nowa Nowa	37 44s	148 3 E
Nowgong	26 20N	92 50 E
Nowra	34 53s	150 35 E
Nowy Sącz	49 40N	20 41 E
Nowy Tomyśl	52 19N	16 10 E
Noyon	49 34N	3 0 E
Nsanje	16 55s	35 12 E
Nsawam	5 50N	0 24w
Nsukka	7 0N	7 50 E
Nuanetsi	21 22s	30 45 E
Nuanetsi, R.	22 40s	31 50 E
Nuatja	7 0N	1 10 E
Nubian Des.	21 30N	33 30 E
Nûbîya, Es Sahrâ en	21 30N	33 30 E
Nueva Rosita	28 0N	101 20w
Nueve de Julio	35 30s	60 50w
Nuevitas	21 30N	77 20w
Nuevo, G.	43 0s	64 30w
Nuevo Laredo	27 30N	99 40w
Nuevo León □	25 0N	100 0w
Nuhaka	39 3s	177 45 E
Nukheila	19 1N	26 21 E
Nukus	42 20N	59 40 E
Nulato	64 43N	158 6w
Nullagine	21 53s	120 6 E
Nullarbor	31 26s	130 55 E
Nullarbor Plain	31 20s	128 0 E
Numan	9 29N	12 3 E
Numata	36 38N	139 3 E
Numazu	35 7N	138 51 E
Numurkah	36 0s	145 26 E
Nuneaton	52 32N	1 29w
Nunivak I.	60 0N	166 0w
Nunkiang	49 11N	125 12 E
Nunspeet	52 21N	5 45 E
Núoro	40 20N	9 20 E
Nuremburg= Nürnberg	49 26N	11 5 E
Nürnberg	49 26N	11 5 E
Nusa Tenggara Barat	8 50s	117 30 E
Nusa Tenggara Timur □	9 30s	122 0 E
Nushki	29 35N	65 59 E
Nutak	57 30N	61 59w
Nuweveldberge	32 10s	21 45 E
Nyabing	33 30s	118 7 E
Nyahanga	2 20s	33 37 E
Nyahua	5 25s	33 23 E
Nyahururu	0 2N	36 27 E
Nyakanazi	3 2s	31 10 E
Nyakanyazi	1 10s	31 13 E
Nyakrom	5 40N	0 50w
Nyâlâ	12 2N	24 58 E
Nyalikungu	2 35s	33 27 E
Nyanguge	2 30s	33 12 E
Nyanza □	2 20s	29 42 E
Nyasa, L.	12 0s	34 30 E
Nybro	56 44N	15 55 E
Nyda	66 40N	73 10 E
Nyenchen, Ra.	30 30N	95 0 E
Nyeri	0 23s	36 56 E
Nyika Plat.	10 30s	36 0 E
Nyíregyháza	48 0N	21 47 E
Nykarleby	63 32N	22 31 E
Nykøbing	54 56N	11 52 E
Nyköping	58 45N	17 0 E
Nylstroom	24 42s	28 22 E
Nynäshamn	58 54N	17 57 E
Nyngan	31 30s	147 8 E
Nyong, R.	3 17N	9 54 E
Nyora	38 20s	145 41 E
Nysa	50 40N	17 22 E
Nysa, R.	52 4N	14 46 E
Nyurba	63 17N	118 20 E
Nzega	4 10s	33 12 E
Nzérékoré	7 49N	8 48w

O

Oahe Dam	44 28N	100 25w
Oahe Res.	45 30N	100 15w
Oahu, I.	21 30N	158 0w
Oak Creek	40 15N	106 59w
Oak Park	41 55N	87 45w
Oak Ridge	36 1N	84 5w
Oakdale	30 50N	92 28w
Oakengates	52 42N	2 29w
Oakesdale	47 11N	117 9w
Oakey	27 25s	151 43 E
Oakham	52 40N	0 43w
Oakland	37 50N	122 18w
Oakleigh	37 54s	145 6 E
Oakover, R.	20 43s	120 33 E
Oakridge	43 47N	122 31w
Oakville, Man.	49 56N	97 58w
Oamaru	45 6s	170 58 E
Oaxaca □	17 0N	97 0w
Ob, R.	62 40N	66 0 E
Oba	49 4N	84 7w
Oban	56 25N	5 30w
Obed	53 30N	117 10w
Ober-Österreich □	48 10N	14 0 E
Oberhausen	51 28N	6 50 E
Obiaruku	5 51N	6 9 E
Obihiro	42 55N	143 10 E
Obluchye	49 10N	130 50 E
Obskaya Guba	70 0N	73 0 E
Obuasi	6 17N	1 40w
Obudu	6 40N	9 10 E

Ocala	29 11N	82 5w
Ocaña, Col.	8 15N	73 20w
Ocaña, Sp.	39 55N	3 30w
Occidental, Cord.	5 0N	76 0w
Ocean City	39 18N	74 34w
Ocean Falls	52 25N	127 40w
Oceanlake	45 0N	124 0w
Oceanside	33 13N	117 26w
Ochil Hills	56 14N	3 40w
Oconto	44 52N	87 53w
Ocatlán	20 21N	102 42w
Ocumare del Tuy	10 7N	66 46w
Ocussi	9 20s	124 30 E
Öda	5 50N	1 5w
Odáðahraun	65 5N	17 0w
Odawara	35 20N	139 6 E
Odda	60 3N	6 35 E
Oddur	4 0N	43 35 E
Ödemiş	38 15N	28 0 E
Odendaalsrus	27 48s	26 43 E
Odense	55 22N	10 23 E
Oder=Odra R.	53 33N	14 38 E
Oder Haff	53 46N	14 14 E
Odessa	46 30N	30 45 E
Odessa	31 51N	102 23w
Odienné	9 30N	7 34w
Odra, R.	53 33N	14 38 E
Odzi	18 58s	32 23 E
Oeiras	7 0s	42 8w
Oelwein	42 39N	91 55w
Oenpelli	12 20s	133 4 E
Offa	8 13N	4 42 E
Offaly □	53 20N	7 30w
Offenbach	50 6N	8 46 E
Ofir	41 30N	8 52w
Ogahalla	50 6N	85 51w
Ōgaki	35 25N	136 35 E
Ogallala	50 6N	85 51w
Ogbomosho	8 1N	3 29 E
Ogden	41 13N	112 1w
Ogdensburg	44 40N	75 27w
Oglio, R.	45 15N	10 15 E
Ogmore	22 37s	149 35 E
Ogoki	51 35N	86 0w
Ogooué, R.	1 0s	10 0 E
Ogun □	6 55N	3 38 E
Oguta	5 44N	6 44 E
Ogwashi-Uku	6 15N	6 30 E
O'Higgins, L.	49 0s	72 40w
Ohakune	39 24s	175 24 E
Ohio, R.	38 0N	86 0w
Ohio □	40 20N	83 0w
Ohre, R.	50 10N	12 30 E
Ohrid	41 8N	20 52 E
Ohrid, L.=		
Ohridsko, J.	41 8N	20 52 E
Ohridsko, J.	41 8N	20 52 E
Ohrigstad	24 41s	30 36 E
Oiapoque	3 50N	51 50w
Oil City	41 26N	79 40w
Oise □	49 28N	2 30 E
Ōita	33 15N	131 36 E
Ojos del Salado,		
Cerro, Mt.	27 0s	68 40w
Okahandja	22 0s	16 59 E
Okanagan	48 24N	119 24w
Okarito	43 15s	170 9 E
Okavango, R.	17 40s	19 30 E
Okavango Swamps	19 30s	23 0 E
Okaya	36 0N	138 10 E
Okayama	34 40N	133 54 E
Okayama □	35 0N	133 50 E
Okazaki	34 36N	137 0 E
Oke-Iho	8 1N	3 18 E
Okeechobee, L.	21 0N	80 50w
Okefenokee Swamp.	30 50N	82 15w
Okehampton	50 44N	4 1w
Okene	7 32N	6 11 E
Okha	53 40N	143 0 E
Okhotsk	59 20N	143 10 E
Okhotsk, Sea of	55 0N	145 0 E
Okhotskiy		
Perevoz	61 52N	135 35 E
Oknotsko		
kolymskoy	63 0N	157 0 E
Oki-Shotō	36 15N	133 15 E
Okiep	29 39s	17 53 E
Okigwi	5 52N	7 20 E
Okija	5 54N	6 55 E
Okinawa, I.	26 40N	128 0 E
Okinawa-guntō, Is.	26 0N	127 30 E
Okitipupa	6 31N	4 50 E
Oklahoma □	35 20N	97 30w
Oklahoma City	35 25N	97 30w
Okmulgee	35 38N	96 0w
Okrika	4 47N	7 4 E
Oktyabriskoy		
Revolyutsii Os.	79 30N	97 0 E
Oktyabrski	53 11N	48 40 E
Okura	43 55s	168 55 E
Okushiri-To, I.	42 15N	139 30 E
Okuta	9 14N	3 12 E
Öland, I.	56 45N	16 50 E
Olary	32 17s	140 19 E
Olathe	38 50N	94 50w
Olavarría	36 55s	60 20w
Ólbia	40 55N	9 30 E
Old Castille=		
Castilla la Vieja	39 45N	3 20w
Old Crow	67 35N	139 50w
Old Factory	52 36N	78 43w
Old Town	45 0N	68 50w
Oldcastle	53 46N	7 10w
Oldeani	3 25s	35 35 E
Oldenburg	53 10N	8 10 E
Oldenzaal	52 19N	6 53 E
Olds	51 50N	114 10w
Olean	42 8N	78 25w
Olekminsk	60 40N	120 30 E
Olenegorsk	68 9N	33 15 E
Olenek	68 20N	112 30 E
Oléron, Î. d'	45 55N	1 15w
Oleśnica	51 13N	17 22 E
Olga	43 50N	135 0 E
Olga, Mt.	25 20s	130 40 E
Olifants, R.	24 10s	32 40s
Olimbos, Oros	40 6N	22 23 E
Oliver	49 20N	119 30w
Ollague	21 15s	68 10w
Olney	38 40N	88 0w
Olomouc	49 38N	17 12 E
Olovyannaya	50 50N	115 10 E
Olsztyn	53 48N	20 29 E
Olt, R.	43 50N	24 40 E
Oltenita	44 7N	26 42 E
Olympia	47 0N	122 58w
Olympic Mts.	48 0N	124 0w
Olympic Nat. Park	47 35N	123 30w
Olympus Mt.	47 52s	123 40w
Omagh	54 36N	7 20w
Omagh □	54 35N	7 20w
Omaha	41 15N	96 0w
Omak	48 25N	119 24w
Oman ■	23 0N	58 0 E
Oman, G. of	24 30N	58 30 E
Omaruru	21 26s	16 0 E
Omate	16 45s	71 0w
Ombai, Selat, Str	8 30s	124 50 E
Omdurmân	15 40N	32 28 E
Omez	32 22N	35 0 E
Ōmiya	35 54N	139 38 E
Omo, R.	8 48N	37 14 E
Omsk	55 0N	73 38 E
Ōmura	33 8N	130 0 E
Ōmuta	33 0N	130 26 E
Onda	39 55N	0 17w
Ondangua	17 57s	16 4 E
Ondo	7 4N	4 47 E
Ondo □	7 0N	5 5 E
Ondörhaan	47 22N	110 31 E
Onega	64 0N	38 10 E
Onega, R.	63 0N	39 0 E
Onehunga	36 55N	174 30 E
Oneida	43 5N	75 40w
O'Neill	42 30N	98 38w
Oneonta	42 26N	75 5w
Onezhskaya Guba	64 30N	37 0 E
Onezhskoye, Oz.	62 0N	35 30 E
Ongarue	38 42s	175 19 E
Ongeville	33 58s	118 29 E
Ongole	15 33N	80 2 E
Onilahy, R.	23 34s	43 45 E
Onitsha	6 6N	6 42 E
Onoda	34 2N	131 10 E
Onslow	21 40s	115 0 E
Onstwedde	52 2N	7 4 E
Ontake-San, Mt.	35 50N	137 15 E
Ontario	34 2N	117 40w
Ontario, L.	43 40N	78 0w
Ontario □	52 0N	88 10w
Oodnadatta	27 33s	135 30 E
Ooldea	30 27s	131 50 E
Oorindi	20 40s	141 1 E
Oostende	51 15N	2 50 E
Oosterhout	51 38N	4 51 E
Oosterschelde, R.	51 30N	4 0 E
Ootacamund	11 30N	76 44 E
Opala, U.S.S.R.	52 15N	156 15 E
Opala, Zaïre	0 37s	24 21 E
Opari	3 56N	32 0 E
Opava	49 57N	17 58 E
Opelousas	30 35N	92 0w
Ophir	63 10N	156 31w
Opi	6 36N	7 28 E
Opobo	4 35N	7 34 E
Opole	50 42N	17 58 E
Oporto=Pôrto	41 8N	8 40w
Opotiki	38 1s	177 19 E
Opp	31 19N	86 13w
Oppland □	61 15N	9 30 E
Optic Lake	54 46N	101 13w
Opua	35 19s	174 9 E
Opunake	39 26s	173 52 E
Or Yehuda	32 2N	34 50 E
Oradea	47 2N	21 58 E
Öræfajökull, Mt.	64 2N	16 15w
Orai	25 58N	79 30 E
Orán	23 10s	64 20w
Oran	35 37N	0 39w
Orange, Australia	33 15s	149 7 E
Orange, Fr.	44 8N	4 47 E
Orange, U.S.A. □	30 0N	93 40w
Orange=Oranje, R.	28 30s	18 0 E
Orange, C.	4 20N	51 30w
Orange Free		
State □	28 30s	27 0 E
Orange Walk	17 15N	88 47w
Orangeburg	33 27N	80 53w
Orangeville	43 55N	80 5w
Oranienburg	52 45N	13 15 E
Oranje, R.	28 41s	16 28 E
Oranje-Vrystaat □	28 30s	27 0 E
Oranjemund	28 32s	16 29 E
Orapa	24 13s	25 25 E
Orbetello	42 26N	11 11 E
Orbost	37 40s	148 29 E
Orchy, Bridge of	56 30N	4 46w
Ord, Mt.	17 20s	125 34 E
Ord, R.	15 30s	128 21 E
Ord of Caithness	58 35N	3 37w
Ord River	17 23s	128 51 E
Ordu	40 55N	37 53 E
Ordzhonikidze	43 0N	44 35 E
Ore Mts.=		
Erzgebirge	50 25N	13 0 E
Örebro	59 20N	15 18 E
Örebro □	59 27N	15 0 E
Oregon □	44 0N	120 0w
Oregon City	45 28N	122 35w
Orekhovo-Zuyevo	55 50N	38 55 E
Orel	52 59N	36 5 E
Orem	40 27N	111 45w
Orenburg	51 45N	55 6 E
Orense	42 19N	7 55w
Orepuki	46 19s	167 46 E
Orford Ness, C.	52 6N	1 31 E
Orient Bay	49 20N	88 10w
Oriental, Cord.	5 0N	74 0w
Orihuela	38 7N	0 55w

Orillia 44 40N 79 24w
Orinoco, R. 8 37N 62 15w
Orion 49 28N 110 49w
Orissa □ . . . . 21 0N 85 0 E
Oristano . . . . 39 54N   8 35 E
Oristano, G. di . . . 39 50N   8 22 E
Orizaba 18 50N 97 10w
Orkanger . . . . 63 18N   9 52 E
Orkla, R. . . . . 63 18N   9 50 E
Orkney . . . . 26 42 s 26 40 E
Orkney □ 59 0N   3 0w
Orland 39 46N 120 10w
Orlando 28 30N 81 25w
Orléanais, Reg. . . 48 0N   2 0 E
Orléans, Fr. . . . . 47 54N   1 52 E
Orleans, I. d' . . . 46 54N 70 58w
Orléansville = El
   Asnam . . . . 36 10N   1 20 E
Orlik . . . . 52 30N 99 55 E
Ormara . . . . 25 16N 64 33 E
Ormoc . . . . 11 0N 124 37 E
Ormond . . . . 38 33 s 177 56 E
Ormskirk 53 35N   2 54w
Orne □ . . . . 48 40N   0 0 E
Örnsköldsvik . . . 63 17N 18 40 E
Orocué 4 48N 71 20w
Orodo . . . . 5 34N   7 4 E
Oromocto 45 54N 66 37w
Oron, Israel . . . . . 30 55N 35 1 E
Oron, Nigeria . . . 4 48N   8 14 E
Orós 6 15s 38 55w
Oroville 39 40N 121 30w
Orroroo . . . . 32 44 s 138 37 E
Orsha . . . . 54 30N 30 25 E
Orsk . . . . 51 20N 58 34 E
Orşova . . . . 44 41N 22 25 E
Ortegal, C. 43 43N   7 52w
Orthez 43 29N   0 48w
Ortigueira 43 40N   7 50w
Ortles, Mt. . . . . . . 46 31N 10 33 E
Ortona . . . . 42 21N 14 24 E
Oruro 18 0s 67 19w
Orvieto . . . . 42 43N 12 8 E
Orwell, R. . . . . . . 51 57N   1 17 E
Osa, Pen. de . 8 0N 84 0w
Osage, R. 38 35N 91 57w
Ōsaka . . . . 34 40N 135 30 E
Ōsaka □ . . . . 34 40N 135 30 E
Osborne 39 30N 98 45w
Osceola 35 40N 90 0w

Oshawa 43 50N 78 45w
Oshikango . . . . . . 17 9s 16 10 E
Oshkosh 44 3N 88 35w
Oshogbo . . . . . . 7 48N   4 37 E
Osijek . . . . 45 34N 18 41 E
Osipenko =
   Berdyansk . . . . . 46 45N 36 49 E
Oskaloosa 41 18N 92 40w
Oskarshamn . . . . . 57 15N 16 27 E
Oslo . . . . 59 55N 10 45 E
Oslofjorden . . . . . 58 30N 10 0 E
Osmaniye . . . . . . 37 5N 36 10 E
Osnabrück . . . . . . 52 16N   8 2 E
Osorio . . . . 29 53 s 50 17w
Osorno . . . . 40 25 s 73 0w
Oss . . . . 51 46N   5 32 E
Ossa, Mt., Austral. 41 54 s 146 0 E
Ossa, Mt., Greece . 39 47N 22 42 E
Ossining 41 9N 73 50w
Ostend = Oostende . 51 15N   2 50 E
Österdalälven, R. . . 60 33N 15 8 E
Östergötlands □ . . 58 24N 15 34 E
Östersund . . . . . . 63 10N 14 38 E
Østfold □ . . . . . . 59 25N 11 25 E
Ostfriesische Is. . . 53 45N   7 15 E
Ostia . . . . 41 43N 12 17 E
Ostrava . . . . 49 51N 18 18 E
Ostróda . . . . 53 42N 19 58 E
Ostrołeka . . . . . . 53 4N 21 38 E
Ostrów
   Wielkopolski . . . 51 39N 17 49 E
Ostrowiec-
   Swietokrzyski . . . 50 57N 21 23 E
Ōsumi-Kaikyō,
   Str. . . . . 30 55N 131 0 E
Ōsumi-Shotō, Is. . . 30 30N 130 45 E
Osuna 37 14N   5 8w
Oswego 43 29N 76 30w
Oswestry 52 52N   3 3w
Otago □ . . . . 44 45 s 169 10 E
Ōtake . . . . 34 27N 132 25 E
Otaki . . . . 40 45 s 175 10 E
Otaru . . . . 43 13N 141 0 E
Otavalo 0 20N 78 20w
Othello 46 53N 119 8w
Otira Gorge . . . . . 42 53 s 171 33 E
Otjiwarongo . . . . 20 30 s 16 33 E
Otorohanga . . . . . 38 11 s 175 12 E
Otranto . . . . 40 9N 18 28 E
Otranto, C. d' . . . 40 7N 18 30 E

Otranto, Str. of . . 40 15N 18 40 E
Ōtsu . . . . 42 35N 143 40 E
Ottawa, Canada . . 45 27N 75 42w
Ottawa, Ill. 41 20N 88 55w
Ottawa, Kans 38 40N 95 10w
Ottawa Is. 59 50N 80 0w
Ottawa, R. 45 20N 73 58w
Otter Rapids 55 42N 104 46w
Ottumwa 41 0N 92 25w
Otu . . . . 8 14N   3 22 E
Otukpa . . . . 7 9N   7 41 E
Oturkpo . . . . 7 10N   8 15 E
Otway, B. . . . . . . 53 30 s 74 0w
Otway, C. . . . . . . 38 52 s 143 31 E
Otway, Seno de . . 53 5 s 71 30w
Otwock . . . . 52 5N 21 20 E
Ouagadougou 12 25N   1 30w
Ouahigouya 13 40N   2 25w
Ouallene . . . . 24 41N   1 11 E
Ouargla . . . . 31 59N   5 25 E
Ouarzazate 30 55N   6 55w
Oubangi, R. . . . . . 0 30 s 17 42 E
Oudenaarde . . . . . 50 50N   3 37 E
Oudtshoorn . . . . . 33 35 s 22 14 E
Oueme, R. . . . . . . 6 29N   2 32 E
Ouessant, I. d' . . . 48 28N   5 6w
Ouesso . . . . 1 37N 16 5 E
Ouezzane 34 51N   5 42w
Ouidah . . . . 6 25N   2 0 E
Oujda 34 41N   1 45w
Ouled Djellal . . . . 34 28N   5 2 E
Oulu . . . . 65 1N 25 29 E
Oulu □ . . . . 64 36N 27 20 E
Oulujärvi, L. . . . . 64 25N 27 0 E
Our, R. . . . . 49 53N   6 18 E
Ouricuri . . . . 7 53 s 40 5w
Ouro Prêto . . . . . 20 20 s 43 30w
Ouse . . . . 42 25 s 146 42 E
Ouse, R.,
   E. Sussex . . . . 50 47N   0 3 E
Ouse, R.,
   N. Yorks 53 42N   0 41w
Outjo . . . . 20 5 s 16 7 E
Outlook 51 30N 107 0w
Ouyen . . . . 35 1 s 142 22 E
Ovalau, I. . . . . . . 17 40 s 178 48 E
Ovalle . . . . 30 33 s 71 18w
Ovamboland, Reg. . 17 20 s 16 30 E
Ovar . . . . 40 51N   8 40 E
Over Flakkee, I. . . 51 45N   4 5 E

Overijssel □ . . . . . 52 25N   6 35 E
Overpelt . . . . 51 12N   5 20 E
Oviedo 43 25N   5 50w
Owaka . . . . 46 27 s 169 40 E
Owase . . . . 34 7N 136 5 E
Owatonna 44 3N 93 17w
Owen Falls . . . . . 0 30N 33 5 E
Owen Sound 44 35N 80 55w
Owendo . . . . 0 17N   9 30 E
Owensboro 37 40N 87 5w
Owerri . . . . 5 29N   7 0 E
Owo . . . . 7 18N   5 30 E
Owosso 43 0N 84 10w
Oxelösund . . . . . . 58 43N 17 15 E
Oxford, U.K. 51 45N   1 15w
Oxford, N.C. 36 19N 78 36w
Oxford □ 51 45N   1 15w
Oxford House 54 46N 95 16w
Oxnard 34 10N 119 14w
Oyama . . . . 36 18N 139 48 E
Oyem . . . . 1 37N 11 35 E
Oymyakon . . . . . . 63 25N 143 10 E
Oyo . . . . 7 46N   3 56 E
Oyo □ . . . . 8 0N   3 30 E
Ozamiz . . . . 8 15N 123 50 E
Ozark 31 29N 85 39w
Ozark Plat. 37 20N 91 40w
Ozarks, L. of the . . 38 10N 93 0w

P

Pa Sak, R. . . . . . 15 30N 101 0 E
Paan . . . . 30 0N 99 3 E
Pa-an . . . . 16 45N 97 40 E
Paarl . . . . 33 45 s 18 46 E
Pabna . . . . 24 1N 89 18 E
Pacaraima, Sa. . . 5 0N 63 0w
Pacasmayo . . . . . 7 20 s 79 35w
Pachpadra . . . . . 25 57N 72 10 E
Pachuca 20 10N 98 40w
Pacific Groves . . . 37 36N 121 58w
Pacific Ocean 10 0N 140 0w
Padalarang . . . . . 7 50 s 107 30 E
Padang . . . . 1 0 s 100 20 E
Paddockwood 53 30N 105 30w
Paderborn . . . . . . 51 42N   8 44 E
Padlei 62 10N 97 5w

Padloping Island . . 67 0N 63 0w
Pádova . . . . 45 24N 11 52 E
Padstow 50 33N   4 57w
Padua = Pádova . . 45 24N 11 52 E
Paducah, Ky. 37 0N 88 40w
Paducah, Tes. 34 3N 100 16w
Paeroa . . . . 37 23 s 175 41 E
Pag, I. . . . . 44 50N 15 0 E
Pagadian . . . . . . 7 55N 123 30 E
Pagalu, I. . . . . . . 1 35 s   3 35 E
Page 47 11N 97 37w
Paghman . . . . . . 34 36N 68 57 E
Pago Pago . . . . . . 14 16 s 170 43w
Pagosa Springs . . . 37 16N 107 1w
Pagwa River . . . . 50 2 s 85 14 E
Pahala 20 25N 156 0w
Pahiatua . . . . 40 27 s 175 50 E
Paicheng . . . . 45 40N 122 52 E
Paignton 50 26N   3 33w
Painesville 41 42N 81 18w
Paint Hills =
   Nouveau
   Comptoir 53 2N 78 55w
Painted Des. 36 40N 112 0w
Paisley 55 51N   4 27w
Paita . . . . 5 5 s 81 0w
Paiyin . . . . 36 45N 104 4 E
Pak Phanang . . . . 8 21N 100 12 E
Pakanbaru . . . . . . 0 30N 101 15 E
Pakhoi . . . . 21 30N 109 10 E
Pakistan ■ . . . . . . 30 0N 70 0 E
Pakokku . . . . 21 30N 95 0 E
Pakongchow . . . . . 23 50N 113 0 E
Pakse . . . . 15 5N 105 52 E
Paktya □ . . . . . . 33 0N 69 15 E
Palamós . . . . 41 50N   3 10 E
Palana . . . . 59 10N 160 10 E
Palangkaraya . . . . 2 16 s 113 56 E
Palanpur . . . . . . 24 10N 72 25 E
Palapye . . . . 22 30 s 27 7 E
Palatka 29 40N 81 40w
Palau Is. . . . . 7 30N 134 30 E
Palauk . . . . 13 10N 98 40 E
Palawan, I. . . . . . 10 0N 119 0 E
Palawan Is. . . . . . 10 0N 115 0 E
Palayancottai . . . . 8 45N 77 45 E
Paleleh . . . . 1 10N 121 50 E
Palembang . . . . . . 3 0 s 104 50 E
Palencia 42 1N   4 34w
Palermo . . . . 38 8N 13 20 E

Palestine 31 42N 95 35w
Paletwa .... 21 30N 92 50 E
Palghat .... 10 46N 76 42 E
Pali .... 25 50N 73 20 E
Palimé .... 6 57N   0 37 E
Palisade 40 35N 101 10w
Palitana .... 21 32N 71 49 E
Palk B. .... 9 30N 79 30 E
Palk Str. .... 10 0N 80 0 E
Palm, Is. .... 18 40s 146 35 E
Palm Beach 26 46N 80 0w
Palm Springs 33 51N 116 35w
Palma, Moz. ...... 10 46s 40 29 E
Palma, Spain ..... 39 33N   2 39 E
Palma Soriano 20 15N 76 0w
Palmares 8 41s 35 36w
Palmas, C. 4 27N   7 46w
Palmas, G. di .... 39 0N   8 30 E
Palmeira dos
  Indios 9 25s 36 30w
Palmer 61 35N 149 10w
Palmer Ld. 73 0s 60 0w
Palmerston .... 45 29s 170 43 E
Palmerston North . 40 21s 175 39 E
Palmi .... 38 21N 15 51 E
Palmira, Col. 3 32N 76 16w
Palmyra Is. 5 52N 162 5w
Palo Alto 37 25N 122 8w
Palopo .... 3 0s 120 16 E
Palos, C. de 37 38N   0 40w
Palu .... 38 45N 40 0 E
Pama .... 11 19N   0 44 E
Pamekason .... 7 10s 113 29 E
Pamiencheng ...... 43 16N 124 4 E
Pamirs, Mts. ..... 38 0N 73 30 E
Pamlico Sd. 35 20N 76 0w
Pampa 35 35N 100 58w
Pampanua .... 4 22s 120 14 E
Pampas, Reg. 34 0s 64 0w
Pamplona, Col. ... 7 23N 72 39w
Pamplona, Spain .. 42 48N   1 38w
Panaji .... 15 25N 73 50 E
Panama 9 0N 79 25w
Panamá ■ 8 48N 79 55w
Panamá, B. de 8 50N 79 20w
Panamá, G. de 8 4N 79 20w
Panama Canal 9 10N 79 56w
Panarukan .... 7 40s 113 52 E
Panay, I. .... 11 10N 122 30 E

Panay G. .... 11 0N 122 30 E
Pančevo .... 44 52N 20 41 E
Pandharpur .... 17 41N 75 20 E
Panfilov .... 44 30N 80 0 E
Pang-Long .... 23 11N 98 45 E
Pangani .... 5 25s 38 58 E
Panjinad Barr. ... 29 22N 71 15 E
Pangfou=Pengpu .. 33 0N 117 25 E
Pangkalanberandan 4 1N 98 20 E
Pangkalansusu .... 4 2N 98 42 E
Pangnirtung 66 8N 65 44w
Panguitch 37 52N 112 30w
Pangyang .... 22 10N 98 45 E
Panitya .... 35 15s 141 0 E
Panjao .... 34 21N 67 0 E
Panjgur .... 27 0N 64 5 E
Panjim=Panaji ... 15 25N 73 50 E
Pankalpinang ..... 2 0s 106 0 E
Pankshin .... 9 25N 9 25 E
Panorama 21 21s 51 51w
Panshih .... 42 55N 126 3 E
Pantellaria, I. .. 36 52N 12 0 E
Pánuco 22 0N 98 25w
Panyam .... 9 27N   9 8 E
Paochang .... 41 46N 115 30 E
Paoki .... 34 25N 107 15 E
Paoshan .... 25 7N 99 9 E
Paoting .... 38 50N 115 30 E
Paotow .... 40 35N 110 3 E
Paoying .... 33 10N 119 20 E
Papá .... 47 22N 17 30 E
Papagayo, G. del . 10 4N 85 50w
Papakura .... 37 4s 174 59 E
Papantla 20 45N 97 41w
Papar .... 5 45N 116 0 E
Papua
  New Guinea ■ . 8 0s 145 0 E
Pará=Belém 1 20s 48 30w
Pará □ 3 20s 52 0w
Paracatú 17 10s 46 50w
Parachilna .... 31 10s 138 21 E
Paradise 47 27N 114 54w
Paragould 36 5N 90 30w
Paraguaipoa 11 21N 71 57w
Paraguaná, Penide 12 0N 70 0w
Paraguari 25 36s 57 0w
Paraguay ■ 23 0s 57 0w
Paraguay, R. 27 18s 58 38w
Paraiba=
  João Pessoa ... 7 10s 34 52w

Paraiba □ 7 0s 36 0w
Parainen .... 60 18N 22 18 E
Parakou .... 9 25N   2 40 E
Paramaribo 5 50N 55 10w
Paraná, Arg. 32 0s 60 30w
Paraná, Brazil ... 12 30s 47 40w
Paraná, R. 33 43s 59 15w
Paraná □ 24 30s 51 0w
Paranaguá 25 30s 48 30w
Paranapanema, R. . 22 40s 53 9w
Paranapiacaba,
  Sa. do 24 31s 48 35w
Paratinga 12 40s 43 10w
Paratoo .... 32 42s 139 22 E
Parbhani .... 19 8N 76 52 E
Pardes Hanna ..... 32 28N 34 57 E
Pardubice .... 50 3N 15 45 E
Pare .... 7 43s 112 12 E
Pare Mts. .... 4 0s 37 45 E
Paren .... 62 45N 163 0 E
Parent 47 55N 74 35w
Parepare .... 4 0s 119 40 E
Parfuri .... 22 28s 31 17 E
Parguba .... 62 58N 34 25 E
Paria, G. de 10 20N 62 0w
Pariaguan 8 51N 64 43w
Pariaman .... 0 47s 100 11 E
Parigi .... 0 50s 120 5 E
Parika 6 50N 58 20w
Paringul-Mare, Mt. 45 20N 23 37 E
Parintins 2 40s 56 50w
Paris, Canada 43 20N 80 25w
Paris, Fr. .... 48 50N   2 20 E
Paris, Tenn. 36 20N 88 20w
Paris, Tex. 33 40N 95 30w
Paris □ .... 48 0N   2 20 E
Park City 40 42N 111 35w
Park Ra. 40 0N 106 30w
Park Rynie .... 30 25s 30 35 E
Parkano .... 62 5N 23 0 E
Parker, Ariz 34 8N 114 16w
Parker, S.D. 43 25N 97 7w
Parkersburg 39 18N 81 31w
Parkerview 51 28N 103 18w
Parkes .... 33 9s 148 11 E
Parksville 49 20N 124 21w
Parma, Italy ..... 44 50N 10 20 E
Parma, U.S.A. 43 49N 116 59w
Parnaguá 10 10s 44 10w
Parnaíba, Piauí .. 3 0s 41 40w

Parnaiba, São
  Paulo 19 34s 51 14w
Parnaiba, R. 3 0s 41 50w
Parnassós, Mt. ... 38 17N 21 30 E
Pärnu .... 58 12N 24 33 E
Páros, I. .... 37 5N 25 12 E
Parowan 37 54N 112 56w
Parral 36 10s 72 0w
Parramatta .... 33 48s 151 1 E
Parras 25 30N 102 20w
Parrett, R. 51 13N   3 1w
Parrsboro 45 30N 64 10w
Parry Is. 77 0N 110 0w
Parry Sd. 42 20N 80 0w
Parsons 37 20N 95 10w
Parvatipuram ..... 18 50N 83 25 E
Parwan □ .... 35 0N 69 0 E
Parys .... 26 52s 27 29 E
Pasadena, Calif. . 34 5N 118 0w
Pasadena, Tex. ... 29 45N 95 14w
Pasaje 3 10s 79 40w
Pascagoula 30 30N 88 30w
Pasco 46 10N 119 0w
Pas-de-Calais □ .. 50 30N   2 30 E
Pasir Mas .... 6 2N 102 8 E
Pasirian .... 8 13s 113 8 E
Pasley, C. .... 33 52s 123 35 E
Paso de Indios ... 43 55s 69 0w
Paso Robles 35 40N 120 45w
Paspébiac 48 3N 65 17w
Passage West 51 52N   8 20w
Passau .... 48 34N 13 27 E
Passero, C. ...... 36 42N 15 8 E
Passo Fundo 28 10s 52 30w
Passos 20 45s 46 29w
Pasto 1 13N 77 17w
Pasuruan .... 7 40s 112 53 E
Patagonia, Reg. .. 45 0s 69 0w
Patchogue 40 46N 73 1w
Patea .... 39 45s 174 30 E
Pategi .... 8 50N   5 45 E
Patensie .... 33 46s 24 49 E
Paterno .... 37 34N 14 53 E
Paterson 40 55N 74 10w
Pathankot .... 32 18N 75 45 E
Pathfinder Res. .. 42 0N 107 0w
Patan .... 23 52s 72 4 E
Patani .... 0 20N 128 50 E
Pataokiang .... 41 58N 126 30 E
Patiala .... 30 23N 76 26 E

Patkai Bum, Mts... 27 0N 95 30 E
Patmos, I. .... 37 21N 26 36 E
Patna .... 25 35N 85 18 E
Patos, L. dos 31 20s 51 0w
Patos de Minas ... 18 35s 46 32w
Pátrai .... 38 14N 21 47 E
Pátraikos Kól. ... 38 17N 21 30 E
Patrocínio 18 57s 47 0w
Pattani .... 6 48N 101 15 E
Patti .... 31 17N 74 54 E
Patuca, R. 15 50N 84 18w
Pátzcuaro 19 30N 101 40w
Pau 43 19N   0 25w
Pauillac 45 11N   0 46w
Pauk .... 21 55N 94 30 E
Paulistana 8 9s 41 9w
Paulo Afonso 9 21s 38 15w
Paulpietersburg .. 27 23s 30 50 E
Paul's Valley 34 40N 97 17w
Pavia .... 45 10N   9 10 E
Pavlodar .... 52 33N 77 0 E
Pavlograd .... 48 30N 35 52 E
Pavlovo, Gorkiy .. 55 58N 43 5 E
Pavlovo, Yakut
  A.S.S.R. .... 63 5N 115 25 E
Pavlovsk .... 50 26N 40 5 E
Pawtucket 41 51N 71 22w
Payakumbah .... 0 20s 100 35 E
Payette 44 0N 117 0w
Payne Bay=Bellin . 60 0N 70 0w
Payne L. 59 30N 74 30w
Paynes Find ...... 29 15s 117 42 E
Paysandú 32 19s 58 8w
Payson 40 8N 111 41w
Pazardzhik .... 42 12N 24 20 E
Pe Ell 46 30N 122 59w
Peace, R. 59 30N 111 30w
Peace River 56 15N 117 18w
Peace River, Res. . 55 40N 123 40w
Peak, The., Mt. .. 53 24N   1 53w
Peak Downs Mine . 22 17s 148 11 E
Peak Hill .... 32 39s 148 11 E
Peake .... 35 25s 140 0 E
Pearl City 21 21N 158 0w
Pearl Harbor 21 20N 158 0w
Pearston .... 32 33s 25 7 E
Pebane .... 17 10s 38 8 E
Pebas 3 10s 71 55w
Peć .... 42 40N 20 17 E
Pechenga .... 69 30N 31 25 E

Pechora . . . . 65 15N 57 0 E
Pechora, R. . . . . 68 13N 54 10 E
Pechorskaya Guba . 68 40N 54 0 E
Pecos . . . . 31 25N 103 35 w
Pecos, R. . . . . 29 42N 101 22 w
Pécs . . . . 46 5N 18 15 E
Pedra Asul . . . . . . 16 1s 41 16 w
Pedregal . . . . 8 22N 82 27 w
Pedro Afonso . . . . 9 0s 48 10 w
Pedro Juan
  Caballero . . . . . . 22 30s 55 40 w
Peebles . . . . 55 40N 3 12 w
Peekskill . . . . 41 18N 73 57 w
Peel . . . . 54 14N 4 40 w
Peel, R. . . . . 67 0N 135 0 w
Pegasus, B. . . . . . . 43 20s 173 10 E
Pegu . . . . 17 20N 96 29 E
Pegu Yoma, Mts. . . 19 0N 96 0 E
Peh Kiang, R. . . . . 23 10N 113 10 E
Pehan . . . . 48 17N 120 31 E
Pehpei . . . . 29 44N 106 29 E
Pehuajó . . . . 36 0s 62 0 w
Peiping . . . . 39 45N 116 25 E
Peixe . . . . 12 0s 48 40 w
Pekalongan . . . . . . 6 53s 109 40 E
Pekin . . . . 40 35N 89 40 w
Peking=Peiping . . 39 45N 116 25 E
Pelabuhan Ratu,
  Teluk, G. . . . . . . 7 0s 106 32 E
Pelabuhanratu . . . . 7 5s 106 30 E
Peleaga, Mt. . . . . . 45 22N 22 55 E
Peleng, I. . . . . 1 20s 123 30 E
Pelican Narrows . . 55 12N 102 55 E
Pelican Portage . . . 55 51N 113 0 w
Pelican Rapids . . . 52 38N 100 42 E
Pelly, R. . . . . 62 47N 137 19 w
Pelly Bay . . . . 68 53N 89 51 w
Peloponnese□=
  Pelopónnisos □ . 37 40N 22 15 E
Pelopónnisos □ . . 37 40N 22 15 E
Peloro, C. . . . . 38 15N 15 40 E
Pelorus, Sd. . . . . . 40 59s 173 59 E
Pelotas . . . . 31 42s 52 23 w
Pelvoux, Massif du . 44 52N 6 20 E
Pemalang . . . . 6 53s 109 23 E
Pematang . . . . 0 12s 102 4 E
Pematangsiantar . . . 2 57N 99 5 E
Pemba . . . . 16 31s 27 22 E
Pemba I. . . . . 5 0s 39 45 E
Pemberton,

Australia . . . . . . 34 30s 116 0 E
Pemberton, Canada 50 25N 122 50 w
Pembroke, Canada 45 50N 77 15 w
Pembroke, N.Z.=
  Wanaka . . . . . . 44 33s 169 9 E
Pembroke, U.K. . . 51 41N 4 57 w
Penang□=
  Pinang □ . . . . . . 5 25N 100 15 E
Penápolis . . . . 21 24s 50 4 w
Peñas, C. de . . . . . 43 42N 5 52 w
Penas, G. de . . . . . 47 0s 75 0 w
Pendembu . . . . . . 8 6N 10 45 w
Pendleton . . . . . . 45 35N 118 50 w
Penedo . . . . 10 15s 36 36 w
Penetanguishene . . 44 50N 79 55 w
Penganga, R. . . . . . 19 53N 79 9 E
Penghu, I. . . . . 23 30N 119 30 E
Penglai . . . . 37 49N 120 47 E
Pengpu . . . . 33 0N 117 25 E
Penguin . . . . 41 8s 146 6 E
Penhalonga . . . . . . 18 54s 32 40 E
Peniche . . . . 39 19N 9 22 w
Penicuik . . . . 55 50N 3 14 w
Penki . . . . 41 20N 132 50 E
Penn Yan . . . . 42 40N 77 3 w
Pennine Ra. . . . . . 54 50N 2 20 w
Pennsylvania □ . . . 40 50N 78 0 w
Penny . . . . 53 58N 121 1 w
Penobscot, R. . . . . 44 30N 68 50 w
Penola . . . . 37 25s 140 47 E
Penonomé . . . . . . 8 37N 80 25 w
Penrhyn Is. . . . . . . 9 0s 150 0 w
Penrith, Australia . 33 43s 150 38 E
Penrith, U.K. . . . . 54 40N 2 45 w
Pensacola . . . . . . 30 30N 87 10 w
Penticton . . . . 49 30N 119 30 w
Pentland . . . . 20 32s 145 25 E
Pentland Firth . . . 58 43N 3 10 w
Pentland Hills . . . . 55 48N 3 25 w
Pen-y-Ghent, Mt. . . 54 10N 2 14 w
Penza . . . . 53 15N 45 5 E
Penzance . . . . 50 7N 5 32 w
Peoria . . . . 40 40N 89 40 w
Perabumilih . . . . . 3 27s 104 15 E
Perche, Reg. . . . . . 48 30N 1 0 E
Percival Lakes . . . 21 25s 125 0 E
Percy, Is. . . . . 21 39s 150 16 E
Perdu, Mt. . . . . . . 42 40N 0 1 E
Pereira . . . . 4 49N 75 43 w
Perekop . . . . 46 0N 33 0 E

Perenjori . . . . 29 26s 116 16 E
Pereyaslav
  khmelnitskiy . . . 50 3N 31 28 E
Pérez, I. . . . . 22 40N 89 30 w
Pergamino . . . . . . 33 52s 60 30 w
Peribonca, R. . . . . 48 45N 72 5 w
Perico . . . . 24 25s 65 10 w
Perigord, Reg. . . . . 45 0N 0 40 E
Périgueux . . . . . . 45 10N 0 42 E
Perim, I. . . . . 12 39N 43 25 E
Perm . . . . 58 0N 57 10 E
Pernambuco=
  Recife . . . . 8 0s 35 0 w
Pernambuco □ . . . . 8 0s 37 0 w
Pernik . . . . 42 36N 23 2 E
Peron, C. . . . . 25 30s 113 30 E
Perpignan . . . . . . 42 42N 2 53 E
Perry, Iowa . . . . . 41 48N 94 5 w
Perry, Okla. . . . . . 36 20N 97 20 w
Persia=Iran ■ . . . 35 0N 50 0 E
Persian G. . . . . . . 27 0N 50 0 E
Perth, Australia . . 31 57s 115 52 E
Perth, Canada . . . 44 55N 76 20 w
Perth, U.K. . . . . . 56 24N 3 27 w
Perth Amboy . . . . 40 31N 74 16 w
Peru ■ . . . . 8 0s 75 0 w
Peru, Ill. . . . . 41 18N 89 12 w
Peru, Ind. . . . . . . 40 42N 86 0 w
Perúgia . . . . 43 6N 12 24 E
Pervomaysk . . . . . 48 5N 30 55 E
Pervouralsk . . . . . 56 55N 60 0 E
Pésaro . . . . 43 55N 12 53 E
Pescara . . . . 42 28N 14 13 E
Peshawar . . . . . . 34 2N 71 37 E
Peshawar □ . . . . . 35 0N 72 50 E
Pesqueira . . . . . . 8 20s 36 42 w
Petah Tiqwa . . . . . 32 6N 34 53 E
Petaluma . . . . 38 13N 122 45 w
Petange . . . . 49 33N 5 55 E
Petauke . . . . 14 14s 31 12 E
Petawawa . . . . . . 45 54N 77 17 w
Petén Itzá, L. . . . . 16 58N 89 50 w
Peterbell . . . . 48 36N 83 21 w
Peterborough,
  Australia . . . . . . 32 58s 138 51 E
Peterborough, Can. 44 20N 78 20 w
Peterborough, U.K. 52 35N 1 14 w
Peterhead . . . . . . 57 30N 1 49 w
Peterlee . . . . 54 45N 1 18 w
Petersburg, Alas. . . 56 50N 133 0 w

Petersburg, Va. . . . 37 17N 77 26 w
Petit Cap . . . . 48 58N 63 58 w
Petit Goâve . . . . . 18 27N 72 51 w
Petit St. Bernard,
  Col du . . . . 45 41N 6 53 E
Petitcodiac . . . . . . 45 57N 65 11 w
Petite Saguenay . . . 47 59N 70 1 w
Petlad . . . . 22 30N 72 45 E
Petone . . . . 41 13s 174 53 E
Petoskey . . . . 45 21N 84 55 w
Petrich . . . . 41 24N 23 13 E
Petrolandia . . . . . . 9 5s 38 20 w
Petrolia . . . . 52 54N 82 9 w
Petrolina . . . . 9 24s 40 30 w
Petropavlovsk . . . . 55 0N 69 0 E
Petropavlovsk-
  kamchatskiy . . . . 53 16N 159 0 E
Petrópolis . . . . . . 22 33s 43 9 w
Petrovaradin . . . . 45 16N 19 55 E
Petrovsk . . . . 52 22N 45 19 E
Petrovsk-
  Zdbaykalskiy . . . 51 17N 108 50 E
Petrozavodsk . . . . 61 41N 34 20 E
Petrusburg . . . . . . 29 8s 25 27 E
Peureulak . . . . . . 4 48N 97 45 E
Pevek . . . . 69 15N 171 0 E
Pforzheim . . . . . . 48 53N 8 43 E
Phagwara . . . . 31 13N 75 47 E
Phala . . . . 23 45s 26 50 E
Phalodi . . . . 27 12N 72 24 E
Phan Rang . . . . . . 11 34N 108 59 E
Phan Thiet . . . . . . 11 1N 108 9 E
Phangan, Ko . . . . . 9 45N 100 4 E
Phangna . . . . 8 28N 98 30 E
Phanh Bho
  Ho Chi Minh . . . 10 58N 106 40 E
Pharo Dzong . . . . 27 45N 89 14 E
Phatthalung . . . . . 7 39N 100 6 E
Phenix City . . . . . 32 30N 85 0 w
Phetchabun . . . . . 16 24N 101 11 E
Phetchaburi . . . . . 16 25N 101 8 E
Philadelphia . . . . . 40 0N 75 10 w
Philippi . . . . 41 0N 24 19 E
Philippines ■ . . . . 12 0N 123 0 E
Philippolis . . . . . . 30 19s 25 13 E
Philipstown . . . . . 30 26s 24 29 E
Phillip, I. . . . . 38 30s 145 12 E
Phillott . . . . 27 53s 145 50 E
Philomath . . . . . . 44 28N 123 21 w
Phitsanulok . . . . . 16 50N 100 12 E

Phnom Dangrek
  Ra. . . . . 14 15N 105 0 E
Phnom Penh . . . . . 11 33N 104 55 E
Phoenix . . . . 33 30N 112 10 w
Phoenix Is. . . . . . . 3 30s 172 0 w
Phong Saly . . . . . . 21 41N 102 6 E
Phra Nakhon Si
  Ayutthaya . . . . . 14 25N 100 30 E
Phu Quoc, I. . . . . . 10 15N 104 0 E
Phuket . . . . 8 0N 98 28 E
Phuoc Le . . . . 10 30N 107 10 E
Piacenza . . . . 45 2N 9 42 E
Pialba . . . . 25 20s 152 45 E
Pian Creek . . . . . . 30 2s 148 12 E
Piatra Neamƫ . . . . 46 56N 26 22 E
Piani □ . . . . 7 0s 43 0 w
Picardie, Reg. . . . . 50 0N 2 15 E
Picardy, Reg.=
  Picardie, Reg. . . . 50 0N 2 15 E
Picayune . . . . 30 40N 89 40 w
Pichilemú . . . . . . 34 23s 72 2 E
Pickering . . . . 54 15N 0 46 w
Pickle Crow . . . . . 51 30N 90 0 w
Pico Truncado . . . 46 40s 68 10 w
Picton, Australia . . 34 12s 150 34 E
Picton, Canada . . . 44 1N 77 9 w
Picton, N.Z. . . . . . 41 18s 174 3 E
Pictou . . . . 45 41N 62 42 w
Picture Butte . . . . 49 55N 112 45 w
Picún Leufú . . . . . 39 30s 69 5 w
Pidurutalagala, Mt. . 7 10N 80 50 E
Piedras Blancas Pt. 35 45N 121 18 w
Piedras Negras . . . 28 35N 100 35 w
Piermonte □ . . . . 45 0N 7 30 E
Pierre . . . . 44 23N 100 20 w
Piet Retief . . . . . . 27 1s 30 50 E
Pietermaritzburg . . 29 35s 30 25 E
Pietersburg . . . . . 23 54s 29 25 E
Pietrosu, Mt. . . . . 47 8N 25 11 E
Pietrosul, Mt. . . . . 47 36N 24 38 E
Pigeon River . . . . 48 1N 89 42 w
Pigüé . . . . 37 36s 62 25 w
Piketberg . . . . . . 32 55s 18 40 E
Pikeville . . . . 37 30N 82 30 w
Piła . . . . 53 10N 16 48 E
Pilar . . . . 26 50s 58 10 w
Pilar . . . . 14 30s 49 45 w
Pilcomayo, R. . . . . 25 21s 57 42 w
Pilibhit . . . . 28 40N 78 50 E
Pilica, R. . . . . 51 52N 21 17 E

Pilos .... 36 55N 21 42 E
Pilsen=Plzeň ...... 49 45N 13 22 E
Pilzen=Plzeň ...... 49 45N 13 22 E
Pima 32 54N 109 50w
Pimba .... 31 18s 136 46 E
Pinang, I. .... 5 25N 100 15 E
Pinar del Rio 22 26N 83 40w
Pinawa 50 15N 95 50w
Pincher Creek 49 30N 113 35w
Pińczów .... 50 32N 20 35 E
Pindar .... 28 30s 115 47 E
Pindiga .... 9 58N 10 53 E
Pindos Óros ...... 40 0N 21 0 E
Pindus Mts.=
  Pindos Óros .... 40 0N 21 0 E
Pine, C. 46 37N 53 30w
Pine Bluff 34 10N 92 0w
Pine Creek .... 13 49s 131 49 E
Pine Falls 50 51N 96 11w
Pine Point 60 50N 114 40w
Pinega, R. .... 64 8N 41 54 E
Pinehill .... 23 38s 146 57 E
Pinerolo .... 44 47N 7 21 E
Pinetown .... 29 48s 30 54 E
Pineville 31 22N 92 30w
Ping, R. .... 15 42N 100 9 E
Pingaring .... 32 40s 118 32 E
Pingelly .... 32 29s 116 59 E
Pingkiang .... 28 45N 113 30 E
Pingliang .... 35 32N 106 50 E
Pingsiang .... 22 2N 106 55 E
Pingtingshan ..... 33 43N 113 28 E
Pingtung .... 22 38N 120 30 E
Pingyao .... 37 12N 112 10 E
Pinhel 40 18N 7 0w
Pinhsien .... 35 10N 108 10 E
Pinios, R. .... 39 54N 22 45 E
Pinjarra .... 32 37s 115 52 E
Pinkiang=
  Harbin .... 45 46N 126 51 E
Pinnaroo .... 35 13s 140 56 E
Pinos, I. de 21 40N 82 40w
Pinos, Pt. 36 50N 121 57w
Pinrang .... 3 46s 119 34 E
Pinsk .... 52 10N 26 8 E
Pinto Butte, Mt.... 49 22N 107 25w
Pintumba .... 31 50s 132 18 E
Pinyang .... 23 12N 108 35 E
Pinyug .... 60 5N 48 0 E
Pioche 38 0N 114 35N

Piombino .... 42 54N 10 30 E
Piotrków
  Trybunalski ... 51 23N 19 43 E
Pipestone 44 0N 96 20w
Pipinas .... 35 30N 57 19 E
Pipmuacan Res. ... 49 40N 70 25w
Pippingarra ...... 20 27s 118 42 E
Piqua 40 10N 84 10w
Piracicaba 22 45s 47 30w
Piracuruca 3 50s 41 50w
Piraeus=
  Piraiévs .... 37 57N 23 42 E
Piraiévs .... 37 57N 23 42 E
Pirané 25 44s 59 7w
Pirgos .... 37 40N 21 25 E
Piripiri 4 15s 41 46w
Piru .... 3 3s 128 12 E
Pisa .... 43 43N 10 23 E
Pisagua 19 40s 70 15w
Pisciotta .... 40 7N 15 12 E
Pisco 13 50s 76 5w
Pisek .... 49 19N 14 10 E
Pistóia .... 43 57N 10 53 E
Pitcairn I. 25 5s 130 5w
Pitea .... 65 20N 21 25 E
Piteşti .... 44 52N 24 54 E
Pithapuram .... 17 10N 82 15 E
Pithara .... 3020N 116 35 E
Pitlochry 56 43N 3 43w
Pittsburg, Calif. . 38 1N 121 50w
Pittsburg, Kans. .. 37 21N 94 43w
Pittsburgh, Pa. .. 40 25N 79 55w
Pittsburgh, Tex. .. 32 59N 94 58w
Pittsfield 42 28N 73 17w
Pittston 41 19N 75 50w
Pittsworth .... 27 41s 151 37 E
Piura 5 5s 80 45w
Pizzo .... 38 44N 16 10 E
Placentia 47 20N 54 0w
Placerville 38 47N 120 51w
Placetas 22 15N 79 44w
Plainfield 40 37N 74 28w
Plainview 34 10N 101 40w
Plaquemine 30 20N 91 15w
Plasencia 40 3N 6 8w
Plaster Rock 46 53N 67 22w
Plata, R. de la .. 34 45s 57 30w
Plate, R.=
  Plata, R. de la . 34 35s 57 30w
Plateau □ .... 8 30N 8 45 E

Plato 9 47N 74 47w
Platte, R. 41 4N 95 53w
Platteville 40 18N 104 47w
Plattsburgh 44 41N 73 30w
Plattsmouth 41 0N 96 0w
Plauen .... 50 29N 12 9 E
Pleasantville 39 25N 74 30w
Plenty, B. of .... 37 45s 177 0 E
Plesetsk .... 62 40N 40 10 E
Plessisville 46 14N 71 46w
Pleven .... 43 26N 24 37 E
Płock .... 52 32N 19 40 E
Ploieşti .... 44 57N 26 5 E
Plovdiv .... 42 8N 24 44 E
Plumtree .... 20 27s 27 55 E
Plymouth,
  Montserrat 16 42N 62 13w
Plymouth, U.K. ... 50 23N 4 9w
Plymouth, Ind. ... 41 20N 86 19w
Plzeň .... 49 45N 13 22 E
Pô, R. 11 10N 1 9w
Po, R. .... 44 57N 12 4 E
Po Hai, G. .... 38 40N 119 0 E
Pobé .... 6 58N 2 41 E
Pobedino .... 49 51N 142 49 E
Pocatello 42 50N 112 25w
Poços de
  Caldas 21 50s 46 45w
Podkamenndya
  Tunguska .... 61 50N 90 26 E
Podolsk .... 55 30N 37 30 E
Podporozny .... 60 55N 34 2 E
Pofadder .... 29 10s 19 22 E
Pohang .... 36 8N 129 23 E
Point Edward 43 10N 82 30w
Pointe-Noire ..... 4 48s 12 0 E
Pointe-à-Pitre ... 16 10N 61 30w
Poitiers .... 46 35N 0 20 E
Poitou, Reg. 46 25N 0 15w
Pokaran .... 26 55N 71 55 E
Pokataroo .... 29 30s 148 34 E
Poko .... 3 7N 26 52 E
Pokotu .... 48 46N 121 54 E
Pokrovsk .... 61 29N 129 6 E
Polacca 35 52N 110 25w
Poland ■ .... 52 0N 20 0 E
Polcura 37 17s 71 43w
Polden Hills 51 7N 2 50w
Poli .... 8 34N 12 54 E
Polillo Is. ...... 14 56N 122 0 E

Poljanovgrad ..... 42 35N 26 58 E
Pollachi .... 10 35N 77 0 E
Polnovat .... 63 50N 66 5 E
Polotsk .... 55 30N 28 50 E
Polson 47 45N 114 12w
Poltava .... 49 35N 34 35 E
Polyarny .... 69 8N 33 20 E
Pombal, Brazil ... 6 55s 37 50w
Pombal, Port. 39 55N 8 40w
Pomona 34 2N 117 49w
Pompano 26 12N 80 6w
Ponca City 36 40N 97 5w
Ponce 18 1N 66 37w
Pond Inlet 72 30N 75 0w
Pondicherry ...... 11 59N 79 50 E
Pondoland .... 31 10s 29 30 E
Ponferrada 42 32N 6 35w
Ponnyadaung, Mts. 22 0N 94 10 E
Ponoi .... 67 0N 41 0 E
Ponoka 52 35N 113 40w
Ponorogo .... 7 52s 111 29 E
Pont Lafrance 47 40N 64 58w
Ponta Grossa 25 0s 50 10w
Pontarlier .... 46 54N 6 20 E
Pontchartrain, L. . 30 12N 90 0w
Ponte Nova 20 25s 42 54w
Pontedera .... 43 40N 10 37 E
Pontefract 53 42N 1 19w
Ponteix 49 46N 107 29w
Pontevedra 42 26N 8 40w
Pontiac, Ill. 40 50N 88 40w
Pontiac, Mich. ... 42 40N 83 20w
Pontianak .... 0 3s 109 15 E
Pontine Mts.=
  Karadeniz
  Dağlari, Mts. ... 41 30N 35 0 E
Pontypool 51 42N 3 1w
Ponytpridd .... 51 36N 3 21 s
Ponziane, Ís. .... 40 55N 13 0 E
Poochera .... 32 43s 134 51 E
Poole 50 42N 2 2w
Poona=Pune .... 18 29N 73 57 E
Poopó, L. 18 30s 67 35w
Popanyinning ..... 32 40s 117 2 E
Popayán 2 27N 76 36w
Poperinge .... 50 51N 2 42 E
Popigay .... 71 55N 110 47 E
Poplar Bluff 36 45N 90 22w
Popocatepetl, Mt. . 19 10N 98 40w
Porbandar .... 21 44N 69 43 E

Porcupine, R. 66 35N 145 15w
Pori .... 61 29N 21 48 E
Porjus .... 66 57N 19 50 E
Porkkala .... 59 59N 24 26 E
Porlamar 10 57N 63 51w
Poronaysk .... 49 20N 143 0 E
Port Adelaide .... 34 46s 138 30 E
Port Alberni 49 15N 124 50w
Port Albert
  Victor .... 21 0N 71 30 E
Port Alfred, Canada 48 18N 70 53w
Port Alfred, S. Afr. 33 6s 26 55 E
Port Alice 50 25N 127 25w
Port Allegany 41 49N 78 17w
Port Angeles 48 0N 123 30w
Port Arthur,
  Canada=
  Thunder Bay ... 48 25N 89 10w
Port Arthur, China=
  Lushun .... 38 48N 121 16 E
Port Arthur,
  U.S.A. 30 0N 94 0w
Port Arthur=
  Thunder Bay ... 48 25N 89 10w
Port Augusta ..... 32 30s 137 50 E
Port aux Basques .. 47 32N 59 8w
Port-Bergé Vaovao 15 33s 47 40 E
Port Bou .... 42 25s 3 9 E
Port Broughton ... 33 37s 137 56 E
Port Canning ..... 22 18N 88 40 E
Port Cartier 50 10N 66 50w
Port Chalmers .... 45 49s 170 30 E
Port Chester 41 0N 73 41w
Port Colborne 42 50N 79 10w
Port Coquitlam ... 49 20N 122 45w
Port Darwin ...... 12 18s 130 55 E
Port de Paix 19 50N 72 50w
Port Dickson ..... 2 30N 101 49 E
Port Douglas ..... 16 30s 145 30 E
Port Edward 54 14N 130 18w
Port Elgin 44 25N 81 25w
Port Elizabeth ... 33 58s 25 40 E
Port Ellen 55 39N 6 12w
Port Erin 54 5N 4 45w
Port Étienne=
  Nouadhibou 21 0N 17 0w
Port Fairy .... 38 22s 142 12 E
Port-Gentil ...... 0 47s 8 40 E
Port Glasgow 55 57N 4 40w
Port Harcourt .... 4 43N 7 5 E

Port Hardy 50 41N 127 30w
Port Harrison=
  Inoucdouac 58 25N 78 15w
Port Hedland .... 20 25s 118 35 E
Port Henry 44 0N 73 30w
Port Hood 46 0N 61 32w
Port Hope 44 0N 78 20w
Port Jefferson ... 40 57N 73 4w
Port Kelang ..... 3 0N 101 24 E
Port Kembla .... 34 29s 150 56 E
Port Laoise 53 2N 7 20w
Port Lavaca 28 38N 96 38w
Port Lincoln .... 34 42s 135 52 E
Port-Lyautey=
  Kenitra 34 15N 6 40w
Port Macquarie . 31 25s 152 54 E
Port Maitland ... 44 0N 66 2w
Port Mellon 49 32N 123 31w
Port Menier 49 51N 64 15w
Port Moller 00 00N 00 00w
Port Moresby ... 9 24s 147 8 E
Port Nelson 57 5N 92 56w
Port Nolloth .... 29 17s 16 52 E
Port Nouveau-
  Quebec 58 30N 65 50w
Port of Spain ... 10 40N 61 20w
Port Orchard ... 47 31N 122 47w
Port Perry 44 6N 78 56w
Port Pirie ...... 33 10s 137 58 E
Port Radium 66 10N 117 40w
Port Said=
  Bûr Saîd .... 31 16N 32 18 E
Port St. Johns=
  Umzimvubu .. 31 38s 29 33 E
Port St. Servain . 51 21N 58 0w
Port Shepstone . 30 44s 30 28 E
Port Simpson ... 54 30N 130 20w
Port Stanley ... 42 40N 81 10w
Port Sudan=
  Bûr Sûdân ... 19 32N 37 9 E
Port Talbot 51 35N 3 48w
Port Townsend .. 48 0N 122 50w
Port-Vendres ... 42 32N 3 8 E
Port Vladimir .. 69 25N 33 6 E
Port Wakefield .. 34 12s 138 10 E
Port Weld ..... 4 50N 100 38 E
Portadown 54 27N 6 26w
Portage 43 31N 89 25w
Portage la Prairie . 49 58N 98 18w
Portalegre 39 19N 7 25w

Portales 34 12N 103 25w
Portarlington 53 10N 7 10w
Port-au-Prince ... 18 40N 72 20w
Porterville, S. Afr. . 33 0s 19 0 E
Porterville, U.S.A. . 36 5N 119 0w
Porthcawl 51 28N 3 42w
Portimão 37 8N 8 32w
Portland,
  Australia .... 33 13s 149 59 E
Portland, Me. ... 43 40N 70 15w
Portland, Oreg. .. 45 35N 122 30w
Portland Bill ... 50 31N 2 27w
Portland I. 50 32N 2 25w
Portland
  Promontory .. 59 0N 78 0w
Portmadoc 52 51N 4 8w
Portneuf 46 43N 71 55w
Porto, Port. ... 41 8N 8 40w
Pôrto Alegre ... 30 5s 51 3w
Porto Amélia=
  Pemba ...... 12 58s 40 30 E
Pôrto de Móz 1 41s 52 22w
Porto Empédocle . 37 18N 13 30 E
Porto Franco ... 9 45s 47 0w
Porto Grande ... 0 42N 51 24w
Pôrto Mendes ... 24 30s 54 15w
Pôrto Murtinho . 21 45s 57 55w
Porto Nacional .. 10 40s 48 30w
Porto-Novo ...... 6 23N 2 42 E
Porto Seguro ... 16 20s 39 0w
Porto Torres ... 40 50N 8 23 E
Porto União ... 26 10s 51 0w
Porto-Vecchio . 41 35N 9 16 E
Porto Velho ... 8 46s 63 54w
Portoferráio ... 42 50N 10 20 E
Portola 39 49N 120 28w
Portoscuso .... 39 12N 8 22 E
Portoviejo 1 0s 80 20w
Portpatrick 54 50N 5 7w
Portree 57 25N 6 11w
Portrush 55 13N 6 40w
Portsmouth, U.K. . 50 48N 1 6w
Portsmouth, N.H. . 43 5N 70 45w
Portsmouth, Ohio . 38 45N 83 0w
Portsmouth, Va. . 36 50N 76 50w
Portsoy 57 41N 2 41w
Porttipahta, I. ... 68 5N 26 40 E
Portugal ■ 40 0N 7 0w
Portuguese
  Guinea■=

Guinea Bissau ■ 12 0N 15 0w
Portumna 53 5N 8 12w
Porvenir 53 10s 70 30w
Provoo .... 60 27N 25 50 E
Posadas 27 30s 56 0w
Poseh .... 23 50N 106 0 E
Poshan=Tzepo .. 36 28N 117 58 E
Poso .... 1 20s 120 55 E
Posse 14 4s 46 18w
Poste de la Baleine 55 20N 77 40w
Poste Maurice
  Cortier .... 22 14N 1 2 E
Postmasburg .... 28 18s 23 5 E
Postojna ...... 45 46N 14 12 E
Potchefstroom ... 26 41s 27 7 E
Potenza ...... 40 40N 15 50 E
Potgietersrus ... 24 10s 29 3 E
Poti .... 42 10N 41 38 E
Potiskum ..... 11 39N 11 2 E
Potomac, R. 38 0N 76 20w
Potosí 19 38s 65 50w
Potatan ...... 10 56N 122 38 E
Potow .... 38 8N 116 31 E
Potrerillos 26 26s 69 29w
Potsdam,
  E. Germany .. 52 23N 13 4 E
Potsdam, U.S.A. . 44 40N 74 59w
Pottstown 40 15N 75 38w
Pottsville 40 39N 76 12w
Pouce Coupe ... 55 40N 120 10w
Poughkeepsie .. 41 40N 73 57w
Poverty B. .... 38 43s 178 0 E
Póvoa de Varzim . 41 25N 8 46w
Povenets ...... 62 48N 35 0 E
Powassan 46 5N 79 25w
Powder, R. 46 44N 105 26w
Powder River .. 43 5N 107 0w
Powell 44 45N 108 45w
Powell, L. 37 25N 110 45w
Powell River .. 49 48N 125 20w
Powys □ 52 20N 3 30w
Poyang ...... 28 59N 116 40 E
Poyang Hu, L. .. 29 10N 116 10 E
Poyarkovo ... 49 38N 128 45 E
Požarevac .... 44 35N 21 18 E
Poznań ...... 52 25N 17 0 E
Pozo Almonte .. 20 10s 69 50w
Pra, R. 5 1N 1 37w
Prachuap Khiri
  Khan .... 11 48N 99 47 E

Prado 17 20s 39 20w
Prague=Praha .. 50 5N 14 22 E
Praha .... 50 5N 14 22 E
Prainha 1 45s 53 30w
Prairie .... 20 50s 144 35 E
Prairie City ... 45 27N 118 44w
Prairie du Chien . 43 1N 91 9w
Prairies,Coteau des. 44 0N 97 0w
Praja .... 8 39s 116 37 E
Prata 19 25s 49 0w
Prato .... 43 5N 11 5 E
Pratt 37 40N 98 45w
Pravia 43 30N 6 12w
Preeceville 52 0N 102 50w
Premier 56 4N 130 1w
Prenzlau ...... 53 19N 13 51 E
Prepansko, J. .. 40 45N 21 0 E
Prerov .... 49 28N 17 27 E
Prescott, Canada . 44 45N 75 30w
Prescott, U.S.A. . 34 35N 112 30w
Presidencia Roque
  Saenz Peña ... 26 50s 60 30w
Presidente Epitácio 21 46s 52 6w
Presidente Prudente 15 45s 54 0w
Prešov .... 49 0N 21 15 E
Presque Isle 46 40N 68 0w
Pressburg=
  Bratislava ... 48 10N 17 7 E
Prestea 5 22N 2 7w
Presteign 52 17N 3 0w
Preston 53 46N 2 42w
Prestonpans ... 55 58N 3 0w
Prestwick 55 30N 4 38w
Pretoria ...... 25 44s 28 12 E
Préveza .... 38 57N 20 47 E
Pribilof Is. 56 0N 170 0w
Pribram ...... 49 41N 14 2 E
Price 39 40N 110 48w
Prieska .... 29 40s 22 42 E
Prikaspiyskaya
  Nizmennost ... 47 30N 50 0 E
Prikumsk .... 44 30N 44 10 E
Prilep .... 41 21N 21 37 E
Priluki .... 50 30N 32 15 E
Prince Albert .. 53 15N 105 50w
Prince Albert
  Nat. Park ... 54 0N 106 25w
Prince Albert Pen. 72 0N 116 0w
Prince Albert Sd. . 70 25N 115 0w
Prince Charles I. . 68 0N 76 0w

Prince Edward Is. . 45 15s 39 0 E
Prince Edward I. □ 44 2N 77 20w
Prince George .. 53 50N 122 50w
Prince of Wales, C. 53 50N 131 30w
Prince of Wales, I.,
  Australia .... 10 35s 142 0 E
Prince of Wales I.,
  Canada 73 0N 99 0w
Prince of Wales I.,
  U.S.A. 53 30N 131 30w
Prince Rupert 54 20N 130 20w
Princess Charlotte,
  B. .... 14 15s 144 0 E
Princeton, Canada . 49 27N 120 30w
Princeton, Ind. .. 38 20N 87 35w
Princeton, Ky. .. 37 6N 87 55w
Princeton, W.Va. . 37 21N 81 8w
Principé, I. .... 1 37N 7 25 E
Prins Albert ..... 33 12s 22 2 E
Priozersk ...... 61 2N 30 4 E
Pripet, R.=
  Pripyat, R. ... 51 20N 30 20 E
Pripyat, R. .... 51 20N 30 20 E
Priština ...... 42 40N 21 13 E
Pritchard 30 47N 88 5w
Probolinggo ... 7 46s 113 13 E
Proddatur .... 14 45N 78 30 E
Progreso 21 20N 89 40w
Prokopyevsk ... 54 0N 87 3 E
Prome .... 18 45N 95 30 E
Propriá 10 13s 36 51w
Proserpine ... 20 21s 148 36 E
Prosser 46 11N 119 52w
Prostějov ..... 49 30N 17 9 E
Provence, Reg. .. 43 40N 5 45 E
Providence ... 41 41N 71 15w
Providence Bay . 45 41N 82 15w
Providencia, I. de . 13 25N 81 26w
Provideniya ... 64 23N 173 18w
Provincial Cannery 51 33N 127 36w
Provins ...... 48 33N 3 15 E
Provo 40 16N 111 37w
Provost 52 25N 110 20w
Prudhoe, I. ... 21 23s 149 45 E
Prudhoe Bay .. 70 10N 148 0w
Prudhomme ... 52 22N 105 47w
Pruszków ..... 52 9N 20 49 E
Prut, R. ...... 45 28N 28 12 E
Przemyśl ..... 49 50N 22 45 E
Przeworsk .... 50 6N 22 32 E

Przhevalsk .... 42 30N 78 20 E
Pskov .... 57 50N 28 25 E
Puán 37 30s 63 0w
Pucallpa 8 25s 74 30w
Puchi .... 29 42N 113 54 E
Pudukkottai ...... 10 28N 78 47 E
Puebla 19 0N 98 10w
Puebla □ 18 30N 98 0w
Pueblo 38 20N 104 40w
Pueblo Hundido ... 26 20s 69 30w
Pueblonuevo 38 20N   5 15w
Puelches 38 5s 66 0w
Puente Alto 33 32s 70 35w
Puente Genil 37 22N   4 47w
Puerh .... 23 11N 100 56 E
Puerto Armuelles . 8 20N 83 10w
Puerto Asís 0 30N 76 30w
Puerto Ayacucho .. 5 40N 67 35w
Puerto Barrios ... 15 40N 88 40w
Puerto Berrío 6 30N 74 30w
Puerto Bolívar ... 3 10s 79 55w
Puerto Cabello ... 10 28N 68 1w
Puerto Cabezas ... 14 0N 83 30w
Puerto Carreño ... 6 12N 67 22w
Puerto Casado ... 22 19s 57 56w
Puerto Cortes ... 15 51N 88 0w
Puerto Cortés 8 20N 82 20w
Puerto Coyle 50 54s 69 15w
Puerto Cumarebo . 11 29N 69 21w
Puerto de Santa
  María 36 35N   6 15w
Puerto del Rosario 28 30N 13 52w
Puerto Deseado .. 47 45s 66 0w
Puerto Páez 6 13N 67 28w
Puerto Leguizamo . 0 12s 74 46w
Puerto Lobos 42 0s 65 3w
Puerto Madryn ... 42 48s 65 4w
Puerto Montt 41 28s 72 57w
Puerto Natales ... 51 45s 72 25w
Puerto Padre 21 13N 76 35w
Puerto Pirámides . 42 35s 64 20w
Puerto Piritu ... 10 5N 65 0w
Puerto Plata 19 40N 70 45w
Puerto Princesa . 9 55N 118 50 E
Puerto Quellón .. 43 7s 73 37w
Puerto Rico, I. .. 18 15N 66 45w
Puerto Saavedra . 38 47s 73 24w
Puerto Suárez ... 18 58s 57 52w
Puerto Varas 41 19s 72 59w
Puertollano 38 43N   4 7w

Pueyrredón, L. 47 20s 72 0w
Pugachev .... 52 0N 48 55 E
Puget Sd. 47 15N 123 30w
Puglia □ .... 41 0N 16 30 E
Pukaki, L. .... 44 5s 170 1 E
Pukatawagan 55 45N 101 20w
Pukekohe .... 37 12s 174 55 E
Pula .... 39 0N   9 0 E
Pulacayo 20 25s 66 41w
Pulantien .... 39 25N 122 0 E
Pulaski, N.Y. 43 32N 76 9w
Pulaski, Tenn. ... 35 10N 87 0w
Pulaski, Va. 37 4N 80 49w
Puławy .... 51 23N 21 59 E
Pulicat L. .... 13 40N 80 15 E
Pullman 46 49N 117 10w
Puloraja .... 4 55N 95 24 E
Pultusk .... 52 43N 21 6 E
Puluntohai ...... 47 2N 87 29 E
Punch .... 33 48N 74 4 E
Pune .... 18 29N 73 57 E
Punjab □ .... 31 0N 76 0 E
Puno 15 55s 70 3w
Punta Alta 38 53s 62 4w
Punta Arenas 53 0s 71 0w
Punta de Díaz ... 28 0s 70 45w
Punta Delgada ... 42 43s 63 38w
Punta Gorda 16 10N 88 45w
Punta Rieles 22 20s 59 40w
Puntabie .... 32 12s 134 5 E
Puntarenas 10 0N 84 50w
Punto Fijo 11 42N 70 13w
Purace, Mt. 2 21N 76 23w
Purbeck, I. of ... 50 40N   2 5w
Puri .... 19 50N 85 58 E
Purnea .... 25 45N 87 31 E
Pursat .... 12 34N 103 50 E
Purulia .... 23 17N 86 33 E
Purus, R. 3 42s 61 28w
Purwakarta ..... 6 35s 107 29 E
Purwodadi, Jawa . 7 7s 110 55 E
Purwodadi, Jawa . 7 51s 110 0 E
Purwokerto ..... 7 25s 109 14 E
Purworedjo ..... 7 43s 110 2 E
Pusan .... 35 5N 129 0 E
Pushchino ...... 54 20N 158 10 E
Pushkino .... 51 16N 47 9 E
Putao .... 27 28N 97 30 E
Putaruru .... 38 3s 175 47 E
Putehachi ...... 48 4N 122 45 E

Putien .... 22 28N 119 0 E
Puttalam .... 8 4N 79 50 E
Puttgarden ...... 54 28N 11 15 E
Putumayo, R. .... 3 7s 67 58 E
Puy de Dôme, Mt. . 45 46N   2 57 E
Puyallup 47 10N 122 22w
Puy-de-Dôme □ .. 45 47N   3 0 E
Pweto .... 8 25s 28 51 E
Pyatigorsk ...... 44 2N 43 0 E
Pyinmana .... 19 45N 96 20 E
Pyŏngyang ...... 39 0N 125 30 E
Pyrenees, Mts. .. 42 45N   0 20 E
Pyrénées-
  Atlantiques □ .. 43 15N   0 45w
Pyrénées-
  Orientales □ ... 42 35N   2 25 E
Pyu .... 18 30N 96 35 E

Q

Qabatiya .... 32 25N 35 16 E
Qadam .... 32 55N 66 45 E
Qadhima .... 22 20N 39 13 E
Qal'at al Mu'azzam 27 43N 37 27 E
Qal'at Sâlih .... 31 31N 47 16 E
Qal'at Sura .... 26 10N 38 40 E
Qala-i-Kirta .... 32 15N 63 0 E
Qala Nau ...... 35 0N 63 5 E
Qalqîlya .... 32 12N 34 58 E
Qâra .... 29 38N 26 30 E
Qasr-e Qand .... 26 15N 60 45 E
Qasr Farâfra .... 27 0N 28 1 E
Qasr Hamam ... 21 5N 46 5 E
Qatar ■ .... 25 30N 51 15 E
Qattara
  Depression=
  Qattara,
  Munkhafed el ... 29 30N 27 30 E
Qattara,
  Munkhafed el ... 29 30N 27 30 E
Qazvin .... 36 15N 50 0 E
Qena .... 26 10N 32 43 E
Qesari .... 32 30N 34 53 E
Qeshm .... 26 55N 56 10 E
Qeshm, I. ...... 26 50N 56 0 E
Qeys, Jazireh-ye . 26 32N 53 56 E
Qezi'ot .... 30 52N 34 28 E

Qila Safed ...... 29 0N 61 30 E
Qila Saifullah .... 30 45N 68 17 E
Qiryat Bialik .... 32 50N 35 5 E
Qiryat 'Eqron ... 31 52N 34 49 E
Qiryat Gat ..... 31 36N 34 47 E
Qiryat Hayyim ... 32 49N 35 4 E
Qiryat Mal'akhi .. 31 44N 34 45 E
Qiryat Shemona .. 33 13N 35 35 E
Qiryat Tiv'om ... 32 43N 35 8 E
Qiryat Yam .... 32 51N 35 4 E
Qîzân .... 16 57N 42 3 E
Qom .... 34 40N 51 4 E
Quairading ..... 32 0s 117 21 E
Qualeup .... 33 48s 116 48 E
Quan Long ..... 9 7N 105 8 E
Quang Ngai .... 15 13N 108 58 E
Quang Tri ..... 16 45N 107 13 E
Quantock Hills .. 51 8N 3 10 E
Quaraí 30 15s 56 20w
Qûchân .... 37 10N 58 27 E
Que Que ...... 18 58s 29 48 E
Queanbeyan .... 35 17s 149 14 E
Québec 46 52N 71 13w
Québec □ 50 0N 70 0w
Queen Charlotte
  Is. 53 10N 132 0w
Queen Charlotte
  Str. 51 0N 128 0w
Queen Elizabeth Is. 75 0N 95 0w
Queen Maud G. .. 68 15N 102 0w
Queensland □ ... 15 0s 142 0 E
Queenstown,
  Australia .... 42 4s 145 35 E
Queenstown, N.Z. 45 1s 168 40 E
Queenstown,
  S.Africa ..... 31 52s 26 52 E
Queimadas 11 0s 39 38w
Quela .... 9 10s 16 56 E
Quelimane ..... 17 53s 36 58 E
Quemoy, I. =
  Kinmen, I. .... 24 25N 118 25 E
Quequén 38 30s 58 30w
Querêtaro 20 40N 100 23w
Querêtaro □ 20 30N 100 30w
Quesnel 53 5N 122 30w
Quetico 48 45N 90 55w
Quetico Prov. Park 48 15N 91 45w
Quetta .... 30 15N 66 55 E
Quetta □ ...... 30 15N 68 30 E

Quezaltenango 14 40N 91 30w
Quezon City ..... 14 38N 121 0 E
Qui Nhon .... 13 40N 109 13 E
Quibdo 5 42N 76 40w
Quiberon 47 29N   3 9w
Quilân, C. 43 15s 74 30w
Quilengues ..... 14 12s 15 12 E
Quillota 32 54s 71 16w
Quilon .... 8 50N 76 38 E
Quilpie .... 26 35s 144 11 E
Quimili 27 40s 62 30w
Quimper 48 0N   4 9w
Quimperlé 47 53N   3 33w
Quincy, Mass..... 42 14N 71 0w
Quincy.Fla...... 30 34N 84 34w
Quincy, Ill. 39 55N 91 20w
Quines 32 14s 65 48w
Quintana Roo □ .. 19 0 E 88 0w
Quintanar de la
  Orden 39 36N   3 5w
Quintero 32 45s 71 30w
Quito 0 15s 78 35w
Quixadã 4 55s 39 0w
Qumran 31 43N 35 27N
Quoin, I. ...... 26 15N 128 0 E
Quorn .... 32 25s 138 0 E
Qurug-Tagh, Mts. 41 30N 90 0 E
Qûs .... 25 55N 32 50 E
Quseir .... 26 7N 34 16 E

R

Ra'anana .... 32 12N 34 52 E
Raane .... 64 40N 24 28 E
Raasay, I. 57 25N   6 4w
Raba .... 8 36s 118 55 E
Rabai .... 3 50s 39 31 E
Rabat 34 2N   6 48w
Rabaul .... 4 24s 152 18 E
Rabigh .... 22 50N 39 5 E
Race, C. 46 40N 53 18w
Racibórz ...... 50 7N 18 18 E
Racine 42 41N 87 51w
Radford 37 8N 80 32w
Radom .... 51 23N 21 12 E
Radomir .... 42 37N 23 4 E
Radomsko ..... 51 5N 19 28 E

Radstock 51 17N 2 25w
Radville 49 30N 104 15w
Rae 62 45N 115 50w
Rae Bareli .... 26 18N 81 20 E
Rae Isthmus 66 40N 87 30w
Raetihi .... 39 25s 175 17 E
Rafaela 31 10s 61 30w
Rafhā .... 29 35N 43 35 E
Rafsanjān .... 30 30N 56 5 E
Rāgā .... 8 28N 25 41 E
Ragama .... 7 0N 79 54 E
Raglan, Australia . 23 42s 150 49 E
Raglan, N.Z. .... 37 55s 174 55 E
Ragusa .... 36 56N 14 42 E
Rahad el Bardi ... 11 20N 23 40 E
Raichur .... 16 10N 77 20 E
Raigarh .... 21 56N 83 25 E
Railton .... 41 25s 146 28 E
Rainier, Mt. 46 50N 121 50w
Rainy River 48 50N 94 30w
Raipur .... 21 17N 81 45 E
Raith 48 50N 90 0w
Raj Nandgaon ... 21 5N 81 5 E
Rajahmundry ... 17 1N 81 48 E
Rajapalaiyam .... 9 25N 77 35 E
Rajasthan □ ..... 26 45N 73 30 E
Rajgarh .... 24 2N 76 45 E
Rajkot .... 22 15N 70 56 E
Rajshahi .... 24 22N 88 39 E
Rajshahi □ ...... 25 0N 89 0 E
Rakaia .... 43 45s 172 1 E
Rakaia, R. ...... 43 54s 172 12 E
Rakatau, P. ..... 6 10s 105 20 E
Raleigh, Australia . 30 27s 153 2 E
Raleigh, Canada . 49 30N 92 5w
Rám Allāh ...... 31 55N 35 10 E
Ram Head ...... 37 47s 149 30 E
Rama .... 36 5N 35 21 E
Ramanathapuram . 9 25N 78 55 E
Ramat Gan ..... 32 4N 34 48 E
Ramat Ha Sharon . 32 7N 34 50 E
Ramat Ha Shofet . 32 36N 35 5 E
Rambre Kyun, I. . 19 0N 94 0 E
Ramelau, Mt. ... 8 55s 126 22 E
Ramgarh .... 23 39N 85 31 E
Rāmhormoz .... 31 15N 49 35 E
Ramisi .... 4 35s 39 15 E
Ramla .... 31 55N 34 52 E
Ramnad .... 9 25N 78 55 E
Ramona 33 1N 116 56w

Ramoutsa .... 24 50s 25 52 E
Rampart 65 30N 150 10w
Rampur .... 23 25N 73 53 E
Rampur Hat .... 24 10N 87 50 E
Ramsey, Canada . 47 25N 82 20w
Ramsey, U.K. 54 20N 4 21w
Ramsgate ...... 51 20N 1 25 E
Ranaghat .... 23 15N 88 35 E
Rancagua 34 10s 70 50w
Ranchester 44 57N 107 12w
Ranchi .... 23 19N 85 27 E
Ranco, L. 40 15s 72 25w
Randers .... 56 29N 10 1 E
Randfontein .... 26 8s 27 45 E
Randolph 43 55N 72 39w
Rāneå .... 65 53N 22 18 E
Rangaunu, B. ... 34 51s 173 15 E
Rangia .... 26 15N 91 20 E
Rangitaiki, R. ... 37 54s 176 53 E
Rangitata, R. .... 44 11s 171 30 E
Rangkasbitung ... 6 22s 106 16 E
Rangon=
  Rangoon ...... 16 45N 96 20 E
Rangoon .... 16 45N 96 20 E
Rangpur .... 25 42N 89 22 E
Raniganj .... 23 40N 87 15 E
Raniwara .... 24 47N 72 10 E
Rankin Inlet 62 30N 93 0w
Rankins Springs . 33 49s 146 14 E
Rannoch 56 41N 4 20w
Rannoch, L. 56 41N 4 20w
Ranohira .... 22 29s 45 24 E
Ranong .... 9 56N 98 40 E
Rantauprapat ... 2 15N 99 50 E
Rantemario, Mt. . 3 15s 119 57 E
Rantis .... 32 4N 35 3 E
Rantoul 40 18N 88 10w
Rapa Iti, Is. 27 35s 144 20w
Rapang .... 3 45s 119 55 E
Rapid City 44 0N 103 0w
Rarotonga, I. ... 21 30s 160 0w
Rasa, Pte. 40 55s 63 20N
Ra's Al-Unuf .... 25 50N 56 5 E
Ra's al Tannurah . 26 40N 50 10 E
Rashad .... 11 55N 31 0 E
Rashīd .... 31 21N 30 22 E
Rasht .... 37 20N 49 40 E
Rat Is. .... 51 50N 178 15 E
Ratangarh ...... 28 5N 74 35 E

Rath Luirc 52 21N 8 40w
Rathdrum, Eire . 52 57N 6 13w
Rathdrum, U.S.A. . 47 50N 116 58w
Rathenow ...... 52 38N 12 23 E
Rathkeale 52 32N 8 57w
Rathlin, I. 55 18N 6 14w
Ratisbon=
  Regensburg .... 49 1N 12 7 E
Ratlam .... 23 20N 75 0 E
Ratnagiri ...... 16 57N 73 18 E
Raton 37 0N 104 30w
Rattray Hd. 57 38N 1 50w
Raukumara, Ra. . 38 5s 177 55 E
Rauma .... 61 10N 21 30 E
Ravar .... 31 20N 56 51 E
Ravenna .... 44 28N 12 15 E
Ravensburg ..... 47 48N 9 38 E
Ravenshoe ..... 17 37s 145 29 E
Ravensthorpe ... 33 35s 120 2 E
Ravi, R. .... 30 35N 71 38 E
Ravine .... 0 15N 36 15 E
Rawalpindi ..... 33 38N 73 8 E
Rawalpindi □ ... 33 38N 73 8 E
Rawdon 46 3N 73 40w
Rawene .... 35 25s 173 32 E
Rawlinna ...... 30 58s 125 28 E
Rawlins 41 50N 107 20w
Rawson 43 15s 65 0w
Ray, C. 47 33N 59 15w
Rayagada ...... 19 15N 83 20 E
Raychikhinsk ... 49 46N 129 25 E
Raymond, Canada . 49 30N 112 35w
Raymond, U.S.A. . 46 45N 123 48w
Raymondville ... 26 30N 97 50w
Raymore 50 25N 104 31w
Rayne 30 16N 92 16w
Raz, Pte. du 48 2N 4 47w
Ré, I. de 46 12N 1 30w
Reading, U.K. ... 51 27N 0 57w
Reading, U.S.A. . 40 20N 75 53w
Realicó 35 0s 64 15w
Rebi .... 5 30s 134 7 E
Recife 8 0s 35 0w
Reconquista 29 10s 59 45w
Recreo 29 25s 65 10w
Red, R. 48 10N 97 0w
Red Bluff 40 11N 122 11w
Red Deer 52 20N 113 50w
Red Lake 51 1N 94 1w
Red Oak 41 0N 95 10w

Red Sea .... 20 0N 39 0 E
Red Wing 44 32N 92 35w
Redbridge ...... 51 35N 0 7 E
Redcar 54 37N 1 4w
Redcliff 50 10N 110 50w
Redcliffe ...... 27 12s 153 0 E
Redding 40 30N 122 25w
Redditch 52 18N 1 57w
Redlands 34 0N 117 0w
Redmond,
  Australia ...... 34 55s 117 40 E
Redmond, U.S.A. . 44 19N 121 11w
Redonda, I. 16 58N 62 19w
Redondela 42 15N 8 38w
Redondo 38 39N 7 37w
Redondo Beach . 33 52N 118 26w
Redruth 50 14N 5 14w
Redstone 52 8N 123 42w
Redvers 49 35N 101 40w
Redwater 53 55N 113 0w
Redwood City .. 37 30N 122 15w
Ree, L. 53 35N 8 0w
Reedley 34 40N 119 27w
Reedsport 43 45N 124 4w
Reefton .... 42 6s 171 51 E
Regavim ...... 32 32N 35 2 E
Regensburg .... 49 1N 12 7 E
Reggio nell'Emilia . 44 42N 10 38 E
Réggio di Calábria . 38 7N 15 38 E
Regina 50 30N 104 35w
Registan, Reg. .. 30 15N 65 0 E
Rehoboth ...... 17 55s 15 5 E
Rehovot .... 31 54N 34 48 E
Reichenbach ... 50 36N 12 19 E
Reid .... 35 17s 149 8 E
Reid River ..... 19 45s 146 48 E
Reidsville 36 21N 79 40w
Reigate 51 14N 0 11w
Reims .... 49 15N 4 0 E
Reina .... 32 43N 35 18 E
Reina
  Adelaida, Arch. . 52 20s 74 0w
Reindeer L. 57 20N 102 20w
Reinga, C. ..... 34 25s 172 43 E
Reinosa 43 2N 4 15w
Reisengebirge .. 50 40N 15 45 E
Reitz .... 27 48s 28 29 E
Rekinniki ..... 60 38N 163 50 E
Remanso 9 41s 42 4w

Rembang .... 6 42s 111 21 E
Remeshk ...... 26 55N 58 50 E
Remscheid ..... 51 11N 7 12 E
Rendsburg ..... 54 18N 9 41 E
Rene 66 2N 179 25w
Renfrew, Canada . 45 30N 76 40w
Renfrew, U.K. .. 55 52N 4 24w
Rengat .... 0 30s 102 45 E
Renk .... 11 47N 32 49 E
Renkum .... 51 58N 5 43 E
Renmark ...... 34 11s 140 43 E
Rennes 48 7N 1 41w
Reno 39 30N 119 0w
Renton 47 30N 122 9w
Republican, R. .. 39 3N 96 48w
Repulse Bay 66 30N 86 30w
Reserve 33 50N 108 54w
Resistencia 27 30s 59 0w
Reşiţa .... 45 18N 21 53 E
Resolution I.,
  Canada 61 30N 65 0w
Resolution, I., N.Z. 45 40s 166 40 E
Ressano Garcia . 25 25s 32 0 E
Retalhulen 14 33N 91 46w
Réthímnon ..... 35 15N 24 40 E
Réunion, Í. .... 22 0s 56 0 E
Reus .... 41 10N 1 5 E
Reutlingen ..... 48 28N 9 13 E
Revelstoke 51 0N 118 0w
Revilla Gigedo Is. . 18 40N 112 0w
Rewa .... 24 33N 81 25 E
Rewari .... 28 15N 76 40 E
Rexburg 43 45N 111 50w
Rey Malabo .... 3 45N 8 50 E
Reykanes, Pen. . 63 48N 22 40w
Reykjavik ...... 64 10N 21 57 E
Reynosa 26 5N 98 18w
Reza'iyeh ...... 37 40N 45 0 E
Rhayader 52 19N 3 30w
Rheden .... 52 0N 6 3 E
Rhein, R. ...... 51 42N 6 20 E
Rhein-Donau-Kanal 49 45N 11 0 E
Rheine .... 52 17N 7 25 E
Rheinland-Pfalz □ . 50 50N 7 0 E
Rhine, R. =
  Rhein, R. ..... 51 42N 6 20 E
Rhinelander 45 38N 89 29w
Rhir, C. 30 38N 9 54w
Rhode Island □ . 41 38N 71 37w
Rhodes, I.=

Ródhos, I. . . . . . . 36 15N 28 10 E
Rhodesia ■ . . . . 20 0s 28 30 E
Rhodope, Mts. =
   Rhodopi Planina 41 40N 24 20 E
Rhodopi Planina . . 41 40N 24 20 E
Rhön, Mts. . . . . . . 50 25N 10 0 E
Rhondda 51 39N 3 30w
Rhône □ . . . . 45 54N 4 35 E
Rhône, R. . . . . . . 43 28N 4 42 E
Rhum, I. 57 0N 6 20w
Rhyl 53 19N 3 29w
Riachão 7 20s 46 37w
Riau □ . . . . 1 0N 102 35 E
Riau, Kep. . . . . . . 0 30N 104 20 E
Ribadeo 43 35N 7 5w
Ribas do Rio Pardo 20 27s 53 46w
Ribatejo, Reg. 39 15N 8 30w
Ribble, R. 54 13N 2 20w
Ribe . . . . 55 19N 8 44 E
Ribeirão Prêto . . . 21 10s 47 50w
Riccarton . . . . . . 43 32s 172 37 E
Rice Lake 44 10N 78 10w
Richards B. . . . . . 28 48s 32 6 E
Richibucto 46 42N 64 54w
Richland 44 49N 117 9w
Richmond,
   Australia . . . . . . 20 43s 143 8 E
Richmond, N.Z. . . 41 4s 173 12 E
Richmond, C. Prov 31 23s 23 56 E
Richmond, Natal
   S. Africa . . . . . 29 54s 30 8 E
Richmond, Surrey . 51 28N 0 18w
Richmond, Yorks. . 54 24N 1 43w
Richmond, Calif. . . 38 0N 122 30w
Richmond, Ind. . . 39 50N 84 50w
Richmond, Ky. . . 37 40N 84 20w
Richmond, Utah . . 41 55N 111 48w
Richmond, Va. . . . 37 33N 77 27w
Richmond Gulf, L. 56 20N 75 50w
Richwood 38 17N 80 32w
Ridgedale 53 0N 104 10w
Ridgetown 42 26N 81 52w
Ridgway 41 25N 78 43w
Riding Mountain
   Nat. Park 50 55N 100 25w
Ried . . . . 48 14N 13 30 E
Riet, R. . . . . 29 0s 23 54 E
Rieti . . . . 42 23N 12 50 E
Rifle 39 40N 107 50w
Riga . . . . 56 53N 24 8 E

Rigolet 54 10N 58 23w
Rijau . . . . 11 7N 5 14 E
Rijeka . . . . 45 20N 14 21 E
Rijssen . . . . 52 19N 6 30 E
Rijswijk . . . . 52 4N 4 22 E
Riley 39 18N 96 50w
Rima, R. . . . . 13 10N 5 15 E
Rimi . . . . 12 58N 7 43 E
Rimini . . . . 44 3N 12 33 E
Rîmnicu Sărat . . . 45 26N 27 3 E
Rîmnicu Vîlcea . . . 45 9N 24 21 E
Rimouski 48 27N 68 30w
Rineanna 52 42N 85 7w
Ringim . . . . 12 8N 9 10 E
Ringkøbing . . . . . 56 5N 8 15 E
Rio Amazonas,
   Estuario do 1 0N 49 0w
Rio Branco, Brazil 9 58s 67 49w
Rio Branco,
   Uruguay 32 34s 53 25w
Rio Claro 10 20N 61 25w
Rio Cuarto 33 10s 64 25w
Rio de Janeiro . . . 23 0s 43 12w
Rio de Janeiro □ . . 22 50s 43 0w
Rio do Sul 27 95s 49 37w
Rio Gallegos 51 35s 69 15w
Rio Grande, Brazil 32 0s 52 20w
Rio Grande, R. . . 37 47N 106 15w
Rio Grande do
   Norte □ 5 45s 36 0w
Rio Grande do
   Sul □ 30 0s 54 0w
Rio Largo 9 28s 35 50w
Rio Mulatos 19 40s 66 50w
Rio Muni □ . . . . 1 30N 10 0 E
Rio Negro 26 0s 50 0w
Rio Verde, Brazil 17 43s 50 56w
Rio Verde,
   Mexico 21 56N 99 59w
Rio Vista 38 11N 121 44w
Riobamba 1 50s 78 45w
Ríohacha 11 33N 72 55w
Ríosucio 5 30N 75 40w
Rioscio 7 27N 77 7w
Ripon, U.K. 54 8N 1 31w
Ripon, U.S.A. . . 43 51N 88 50w
Rishon Le Zion . . 31 58N 34 48 E
Rishpon . . . . . 32 12N 34 49 E
Risør . . . . 58 43N 9 13 E
Riti . . . . 7 57N 9 41 E

Ritzville 47 10N 118 21w
Riva . . . . 45 53N 10 50 E
Rivadavia, Arg. . . 24 5s 63 0w
Rivadavia, Chile . 29 50s 70 35w
Rivas 11 30N 85 50w
Rivera 31 0s 55 50w
Riverhead 40 53N 72 40w
Riverhurst 50 55N 106 50w
Rivers □ . . . . 5 0N 6 30 E
Riversdale . . . . . 34 7s 21 15 E
Riverside, Calif. . . 34 0N 117 15w
Riverside, Wyo. . . 41 12N 106 57w
Riverton, Australia 34 10s 138 46 E
Riverton, Canada . 51 5N 97 0w
Riverton, N.Z. . . 46 21s 168 0 E
Riverton, U.S.A. . 43 1N 108 27w
Riviera di Levante 44 23N 9 15 E
Riviera di Ponente 43 50N 7 58 E
Rivière Bleue . . . 47 56N 69 2w
Rivière du Loup . . 47 50N 69 30w
Rivière Pentecôte . 49 57N 67 1w
Riyadh = Ar Riyád 24 41N 46 42 E
Rize . . . . 41 0N 40 30 E
Rjukan . . . . 59 54N 8 33 E
Roanne . . . . 46 3N 4 4 E
Roanoke, Ala. . . 33 9N 85 23w
Roanoke, Va. . . . 37 19N 79 55w
Roanoke Rapids . 36 36N 77 42w
Roatán, I. de . . . 16 23N 86 26w
Robertson . . . . . 33 46s 19 50 E
Roberval 48 32N 72 15w
Roblin 51 21N 101 25w
Robson, Mt. . . . 53 10N 119 10w
Robstown 27 47N 97 40w
Roca, C. da . . . 38 40N 9 31w
Rocadas . . . . . 16 45s 15 0 E
Rocas, Is. 4 0s 34 1w
Rocha 34 30s 54 25w
Rochdale 53 36N 2 10w
Rochefort 45 56N 0 57w
Rochelle 41 55N 89 5w
Rocher River . . 61 12N 114 0w
Rochester,
   Australia . . . 36 22s 144 41 E
Rochester, U.K. . 51 22N 0 30 E
Rochester, Minn. 44 1N 92 28w
Rochester, N.H. . 43 19N 70 57w
Rochester, N.Y. . 43 10N 77 40w
Rock Hill 34 55N 81 2w
Rock Island . . . 41 30N 90 35w

Rock Sound 24 54N 76 12w
Rock Springs 46 55N 106 11w
Rockall, I. 57 37N 13 42w
Rockford, Ill. 42 20N 89 0w
Rockford, Mich. . . 43 7N 85 33w
Rockhampton . . . 23 22s 150 32 E
Rockingham . . . . 32 15s 115 38 E
Rockland, Mass. . 44 6N 69 8w
Rockville, Md. . . . 39 7N 77 10w
Rocky Gully . . . . 34 30s 117 0 E
Rocky Mount . . . 35 55N 77 48w
Rocky Mountain
   House 52 22N 114 55w
Rocky Mts. 48 0N 110 0w
Rockyford 51 13N 113 8w
Rødbyhavn . . . . 54 39N 11 22 E
Roddickton 50 51N 56 8w
Rodez . . . . 44 21N 2 33 E
Ródhos . . . . . . 36 15N 28 10 E
Ródhos, I. . . . . 36 15N 28 10 E
Rodney, C. . . . 36 17s 174 50 E
Rodriguez, I. . . 20 0s 65 0 E
Roebourne . . . 20 44s 117 9 E
Roebuck, B. . . 18 5s 122 20 E
Roebuck Plains
   P.O. . . . . . . 17 56s 122 28 E
Roermond . . . . 51 12N 6 0 E
Roes Welcome Sd. 65 0N 87 0w
Roeselare . . . . 50 57N 3 7 E
Rogaland □ . . . 59 12N 6 20 E
Rogers 36 20N 94 0w
Roggan River . . 54 24N 78 5w
Roggeveldberge . 32 10s 20 10 E
Rohri . . . . 27 45N 68 51 E
Rohtak . . . . . . 28 55N 76 43 E
Rolândia 23 5s 52 0w
Rolla 38 0N 91 42w
Rollingstone . . 19 2s 146 24 E
Rolleston . . . . 43 35s 172 24 E
Rolleville 23 41N 76 0w
Roma, Australia 26 32s 148 49 E
Roma, Italy . . . 41 54N 12 30 E
Roma, Sweden . 57 32N 18 28 E
Roman . . . . . . 43 8N 23 54 E
Romania ■ =
   Rumania ■ . . . 46 0N 25 0 E
Romanzof, C. . . 61 49N 165 56w
Rome, Italy =
   Roma . . . . . 41 54N 12 30 E
Rome, Ga. 34 20N 85 0w

Rome, N.Y. 43 14N 75 29w
Romney Marsh . . 51 0N 1 0 E
Romorantin-
   Lanthenay . . . 47 21N 1 45 E
Romsdalen, R. . . 62 25N 7 50 E
Ronaldsay,
   North I. 59 23N 2 26w
Ronaldsay,
   South I. 58 47N 2 56w
Roncador, S. do . 12 30s 52 30w
Roncevoux 43 0N 1 23w
Ronda 36 46N 5 12w
Rondônia □ . . . 11 0s 63 0w
Rondonópolis . . 16 28s 54 38w
Rongai . . . . . . 0 10s 35 51 E
Rønne . . . . . . 55 6N 14 44 E
Ronsard, C. . . . 24 46s 113 10 E
Ronse . . . . . . 50 45N 3 35 E
Roodepoort-
   Maraisburg . . 26 11s 27 54 E
Roorkee . . . . . 29 52N 77 59 E
Roosendaal . . . 51 32N 4 29 E
Roosevelt Res. . 33 46N 111 0w
Roper, R. . . . . 14 43s 135 27 E
Roraima □ . . . 2 0N 61 30w
Roraima, Mt. . . 5 10N 60 40w
Rosa, Mte. . . . 45 57N 7 53 E
Rosario, Arg. . . 33 0s 60 50w
Rosário, Brazil . 3 0s 44 15w
Rosario, Mexico . 23 0s 105 52w
Rosario de la
   Frontera . . . 25 50s 65 0w
Rosário do Sul . 30 15s 54 55w
Rosas . . . . . . 42 19N 3 10 E
Rosas, G. de . . 42 10N 3 15 E
Roscommon . . 53 38N 8 11w
Roscommon □ . 53 40N 8 15w
Roscrea 52 57N 7 47w
Rose Blanche . . 47 38N 58 45w
Rose Harbour . . 52 15N 131 10w
Rose Valley . . . 52 19N 103 49w
Roseau 48 56N 96 0w
Rosenberg 29 30N 95 48w
Rosebud 31 5N 97 0w
Roseburg 43 10N 123 10w
Rosedale . . . . 38 11s 146 48 E
Rosetown 51 35N 108 0w
Rosetta = Rashîd 31 21N 30 22 E
Roseville 38 46N 121 41w
Rosewood . . . . 35 38s 147 52 E

Rosh Ha'Ayin .... 32 5N 34 47 E
Rosh Pinna ...... 32 58N 35 32 E
Rosignol 6 15N 57 30W
Roskilde .... 55 38N 12 3 E
Roslavl .... 53 57N 32 55 E
Ross, N.Z. .... 42 53 S 170 49 E
Ross, U.K. 51 55N 2 34W
Ross □ .... 70 0 S 170 5W
Ross
  Dependency □ .. 70 0 S 170 0W
Ross Sea .... 74 0 S 178 0 E
Rossland 49 6N 117 50W
Rosslare 52 17N 6 23W
Rosso 16 30N 15 49W
Rossosh .... 50 15N 39 20 E
Rosthern 52 40N 106 20W
Rostock .... 54 4N 12 9 E
Rostov .... 47 15N 39 45 E
Roswell 33 26N 104 32W
Rosyth 56 2N 3 26W
Rother, R. 50 59N 0 40W
Rotherham 53 26N 1 21W
Rothes 57 31N 3 12W
Rothesay 55 50N 5 3W
Roti, I. .... 10 50 S 123 0 E
Roto .... 33 0 S 145 30 E
Rotorua .... 38 9 S 176 16 E
Rotorua, L. ...... 38 5 S 176 18 E
Rotterdam ...... 51 55N 4 30 E
Rottnest, I. ..... 32 0 S 115 27 E
Rottweil .... 48 9N 8 38 E
Rotuma, I. ...... 12 25 S 177 5 E
Roubaix .... 50 40N 3 10 E
Rouen .... 49 27N 1 4 E
Rouergue, Reg. .. 44 20N 2 20 E
Roumania ■ =
  Rumania ■ ... 46 0N 25 0 E
Round, Mt. ..... 30 26 S 152 16 E
Roundup 46 25N 108 35W
Rousay, I. 59 10N 3, 2W
Roussillon, Reg. .. 45 24N 4 49 E
Rouxville .... 30 11 S 26 50 E
Rouyn 48 20N 79 0W
Rovaniemi ...... 66 29N 25 41 E
Rovereto .... 45 53N 11 3 E
Rovigo .... 45 4N 11 48 E
Rovinj .... 45 18N 13 40 E
Rovno .... 50 40N 26 10 E
Roxas .... 11 36N 122 49 E
Roxburgh ...... 45 33 S 169 19 E

Roy Hill .... 22 37 S 119 58 E
Royal Oak 42 30N 83 5W
Royale, I. 48 0N 89 0W
Royan 45 37N 1 2W
Rtishchevo ...... 52 35N 43 50 E
Ruapehu, Mt. .... 39 18 S 175 35 E
Rubeho Mts. .... 6 50 S 36 25 E
Rubio 7 43N 72 22W
Rubtsovsk ...... 51 30N 80 50 E
Ruby .... 38 27 S 145 55 E
Rudall .... 33 43 S 136 17 E
Rudnichny ...... 59 38N 52 26 E
Rudnogorsk ..... 57 15N 103 42 E
Rudnyy .... 52 57N 63 7 E
Rudolf, L. =
  Turkana, L. .... 4 10N 36 10 F
Rufa'a .... 14 44N 33 32 E
Rufiji, R. .... 8 0 S 39 20 E
Rufino .... 34 20 S 62 50W
Rufisque 14 43N 17 17W
Rugby, U.K. 52 23N 1 16W
Rugby, U.S.A. 48 21N 100 0W
Rügen, I. .... 54 22N 13 25 E
Ruhâma .... 31 31N 34 43 E
Ruhengeri ...... 1 30 S 29 36 E
Ruhr, R. .... 51 27N 6 44 E
Ruki, R. .... 0 5N 18 17 E
Rukungiri ...... 0 53 S 29 58 E
Rukwa, L. ...... 7 50 S 32 10 E
Rum Jungle ..... 13 0 S 130 59 E
Rumania ■ ..... 46 0N 25 0 E
Rumbalara ...... 25 20 S 134 29 E
Rumford 44 30N 70 30W
Rumoi 43 56N 141 39W
Rumuruti ...... 0 17N 36 32 E
Runanga .... 42 25 S 171 15 E
Runcorn 53 20N 2 44W
Rungwa .... 6 55 S 33 32 E
Rungwe, Mt. .... 9 11 S 33 32 E
Runka .... 12 28N 7 20 E
Rupat, I. .... 1 45N 101 40 E
Rupert House =
  Fort Rupert 51 30N 78 40W
Rusape .... 18 35 S 32 8 E
Ruse .... 43 48N 25 59 E
Rushden 52 17N 0 37W
Rushville 39 38N 85 22W
Rushworth ..... 36 32 S 145 1 E
Russas .... 4 56 S 37 58W
Russell, Canada .. 50 50N 101 20W

Russell, U.S.A. ... 38 56N 98 55W
Russellville, Ala. .. 34 30N 87 44W
Russellville, Ark. .. 35 15N 93 0W
Russian Soviet
  Federal Socialist
  Rep. .... 60 0N 80 0 E
Russkaya Polyana . 53 47N 73 53 E
Rustenburg ..... 25 41 S 27 14 E
Ruston 32 30N 92 40W
Ruteng .... 8 26 S 120 30 E
Ruth 39 15N 115 1W
Rutherglen,
  Australia ...... 36 5 S 146 29 E
Rutherglen, U.K. .. 55 50N 4 11W
Rutland 43 38N 73 0W
Rutshuru ...... 1 13 S 29 25 E
Ruvu .... 6 49 S 38 43 E
Ruvuma, R. ..... 10 29 S 40 28 E
Ruwenzori, Mts. .. 0 30N 29 55 E
Ruzomberok .... 49 3N 19 17 E
Rwanda ■ ...... 2 0 S 30 0 E
Ryan, L. 55 0N 5 2W
Ryazan .... 54 38N 39 44 E
Ryazhsk .... 53 40N 40 7 E
Rybache .... 46 40N 81 20 E
Rybachiy Pol. .... 69 43N 32 0 E
Rybinsk .... 58 3N 38 52 E
Rybinskoye, Vdkhr. 58 30N 38 25 E
Ryde 50 44N 1 9W
Rye .... 50 57N 0 46 E
Rye, R. 54 12N 0 53W
Rypin .... 53 3N 19 32 E
Ryūkyū, Is. ..... 26 0N 128 0 E
Rzeszów .... 50 5N 21 58 E
Rzhev .... 56 15N 34 18 E

S

Sa'ad .... 31 28N 34 33 E
Sa'ādatābād .... 30 10N 53 5 E
Saale, R. .... 51 57N 11 55 E
Saar, R. .... 49 20N 6 45 E
Saarbrücken .... 49 15N 6 58 E
Saaremaa, I. .... 58 30N 22 30 E
Saarland □ ..... 49 20N 0 75 E
Saba, I. 17 30N 63 10W
Sabadell .... 41 28N 2 7 E

Sabah □ .... 6 0N 117 0 E
Sabalan, Kuhha-ye 38 15N 47 49 E
Sabanalargo 10 38N 74 55W
Sabang .... 5 50N 95 15 E
Sabará .... 19 55 S 43 55W
Sabastiya ...... 32 17N 35 12 E
Sabáudia ...... 41 17N 13 2 E
Sabhah .... 27 9N 14 29 E
Sabie .... 25 4 S 30 48 E
Sabinas 27 50N 101 10W
Sabinas Hidalgo .. 26 40N 100 10W
Sabine, R. 30 0N 93 45W
Sable, C., Canada . 43 29N 65 38W
Sable, C., U.S.A. .. 25 5N 81 0W
Sable I. 44 0N 60 0W
Sabou 12 1N 2 28W
Sabzevār ...... 36 15N 57 40 E
Sabzvāran ..... 28 45N 57 50 E
Saco 43 29N 70 28W
Sacramento .... 38 39N 121 30 E
Sacramento, R. .. 38 3N 121 56W
Sacramento Mts. . 32 30N 105 30W
Sádaba 2 19N 1 12W
Sadd el Aali .... 24 5N 32 54 E
Sade .... 11 22N 10 45 E
Sado, I. .... 38 15N 138 30 E
Safaniya ...... 28 5N 48 42 E
Safed Koh ..... 34 15N 64 0 E
Safford 32 54N 109 52W
Saffron Walden .. 52 5N 0 15 E
Safi 32 20N 9 17W
Saga, Indonesia .. 2 40 S 132 55 E
Saga, Japan .... 33 15N 130 18 E
Saga □ .... 33 15N 130 20 E
Sagaing .... 22 0N 96 0 E
Sagar .... 23 50N 78 50 E
Sagil .... 50 15N 91 15 E
Saginaw 43 26N 83 55W
Saginaw B. 43 50N 83 40W
Saglouc 62 30N 74 15W
Sagres 37 0N 8 58W
Sagua la Grande .. 22 50N 80 10W
Saguache 38 10N 106 4W
Saguenay, R. 48 10N 69 45W
Sagunto 39 42N 0 18W
Sahagun 42 18N 5 2W
Sahara 23 0N 5 0W
Saharanpur ..... 29 58N 77 33 E
Sahiwal .... 30 45N 73 8 E
Sa'idābād ...... 29 30N 55 45 E

Saidapet .... 13 0N 80 15 E
Saidu .... 34 50N 72 15 E
Saighan .... 35 10N 67 55 E
Saigon=Phanh
  Bho Ho Chi Minh 10 58N 106 40 E
Saihut .... 15 12N 51 10 E
Saijo .... 33 0N 133 5 E
Saiki .... 32 35 S 131 50 E
St. Abbs Hd. 55 55N 2 10W
St. Albans, U.K. .. 51 46N 0 21W
St. Albans, U.S.A. . 44 49N 73 5W
St. Albans Hd. .. 50 34N 2 3W
St. André, C. .... 16 10 S 44 27 E
St. Andrews 56 20N 2 48W
St. Arnaud ..... 36 32 S 143 16 E
St. Asaph 53 15N 3 27W
St. Augustin 51 19N 58 48W
St. Augustine ... 29 52N 81 20W
St. Austell 50 20N 4 48W
St. Barthélemy, I. 17 50N 62 50W
St. Bees Hd. .... 54 30N 3 38 E
St. Boniface 49 50N 97 10W
St. Bride's B. 51 48N 5 15W
St. Brieuc 48 30N 2 46W
St. Catherine's Pt. 50 34N 1 18W
St. Charles 38 46N 90 30W
St. Christopher, I. 17 20N 62 40W
St. Clair, L. 42 30N 82 45W
St. Claude 49 40N 98 22W
St. Cloud 45 30N 94 11W
St. Cœur de Marie 48 39N 71 43W
St. Cricq, C. .... 25 17 S 113 6 E
St. Croix, I. 17 30N 64 40W
St. Davids 51 54N 5 16W
St. David's Hd. .. 51 54N 5 16W
St. David's I. 32 22N 64 39W
St. Denis ...... 48 56N 2 22 E
St. Elias, Mt. ... 60 20N 141 59W
St. Étienne ..... 45 27N 4 22 E
St. Félicien 48 40N 72 25W
St. Fintan's 48 10N 58 50W
St. Flour ...... 45 2N 3 6 E
St. Francis, C. .. 34 14 S 24 49 E
St. Gabriel
  de Brandon ... 46 17N 73 24W
St. Gallen ..... 47 25N 9 23 E
St. George,
  Australia ...... 28 1 S 148 41 E
St. George,
  Bermuda 32 24N 64 42W

St. George, Canada 45 11N 66 57w
St. George, U.S.A. 37 10N 113 35w
St. George, C. 29 36N 85 2w
St. George Hd. ... 35 11s 150 45 E
St. George West . 50 33N 96 7w
St. Georges,
  Belgium .... 50 37N 4 20 E
St. Georges,
  Canada 46 42N 72 35w
St. George's, Fr.
  Guiana 4 0N 52 0w
St. Georges,
  Grenada 12 5N 61 43w
St. George's B. .. 48 20N 59 0w
St. George's Chan. 52 0N 6 0w
St. George's I. 32 22N 64 40w
St. Helena, I. .... 15 55 s 5 44w
St. Helenabaai ... 32 40 s 18 10 E
St. Helens,
  Australia .... 41 20 s 148 15 E
St. Helens, U.K. .. 53 28N 2 44w
St. Helens, U.S.A. 45 55N 122 50w
St. Hyacinthe 45 40N 72 58w
St. Ives, Cambridge 52 20N 0 5w
St. Ives, Cornwall . 50 13N 5 29w
St. Jean 45 20N 73 50w
St. Jean Baptiste . 49 15N 97 20w
St. Jérôme 45 55N 74 0w
St. John 45 20N 66 8w
St. John, L. 48 40N 72 0w
St. John's, Antigua 17 6N 61 51w
St. John's, Canada . 47 45N 52 40w
St. Johnsbury 44 25N 72 1w
St. Joseph, Mich. .. 42 6N 86 29w
St. Joseph, Mo. ... 39 46N 94 51w
St. Jovite 46 8N 74 38w
St. Kilda .... 45 53 s 170 31 E
St. Kilda, I. 57 50N 8 40w
St. Kitts, I.=
  St. Christopher, I. 17 20N 62 40w
St. Laurent 50 25N 97 58w
St. Lawrence 46 54N 55 23w
St. Lawrence, G. of 48 25N 62 0w
St. Lawrence, I. ... 63 0N 170 0w
St. Lawrence, R. .. 49 15N 67 0w
St. Leonard 47 12N 67 58w
St. Lin 45 44N 73 46w
St. Lô 49 7N 1 5w
St. Louis, France .. 47 35N 7 34 E
St. Louis, Senegal . 16 8N 16 27w

St. Louis, U.S.A. .. 38 40N 90 20w
St. Lucia, C. ..... 28 32 s 32 29 E
St. Lucia, I. 14 0N 60 50w
St. Lucia, L. ..... 28 5 s 32 30 E
St. Lucia Chan. .. 14 15N 61 0w
St. Maarten, I. 18 0N 63 5w
St. Malo 48 39N 2 1w
St. Marc 19 10N 72 5w
St. Maries 47 17N 116 34w
St. Martin, I. 18 0N 63 0w
St. Martins 45 22N 65 38w
St. Marys, Australia 41 32 s 148 11 E
St. Marys, U.S.A. . 41 30N 78 33w
St. Marys, I. 49 55N 6 17w
St. Matthew I. ... 60 30N 172 45w
St. Michael's Mt. .. 50 7N 5 30w
St. Moritz .... 46 30N 9 50 E
St. Nazaire 47 17N 2 12w
St. Neots 52 14N 0 16w
St. Niklaas ...... 51 10N 4 8 E
St. Omer .... 50 45N 2 15 E
St. Pacôme 47 24N 69 58w
St. Pamphile 46 58N 69 48w
St. Pascal 47 32N 69 48w
St. Paul, Canada .. 51 34N 57 47w
St. Paul, U.S.A. .. 44 54N 93 5w
St. Paul, I.,
  Atlantic Oc. 0 50N 31 40w
St. Paul, I.,
  Indian Oc. ... 30 40 s 77 34 E
St. Peter 44 15N 93 57w
St. Peter Port 49 27N 2 31w
St. Petersburg ... 27 45N 82 40w
St. Pierre 46 40N 56 0w
St. Pierre, L. 46 10N 72 50w
St. Pierre et
  Miquelon □ 46 49N 56 15w
St. Quentin ..... 49 50N 3 16 E
St. Siméon 47 51N 69 54w
St. Stephen 45 16N 67 17w
St. Thomas, Canada 42 47N 81 12w
St. Thomas,
  Virgin Is. 18 21N 64 56w
St. Tite 46 45N 72 40w
St. Tropez .... 43 17N 6 38 E
St. Troud .... 50 48N 5 10 E
St. Valéry .... 50 10N 1 38 E
St. Vincent, I. 13 10N 61 10w
St. Vincent Pass. . 13 30N 61 0w
St. Walburg 53 39N 109 12w

Ste. Anne de
  Beaupré 47 2N 70 58w
Ste. Cecile 47 56N 64 34w
Ste. Marie 14 48N 61 1w
Ste. Marie, C. .... 25 36 s 45 8 E
Ste. Marie de la
  Madeleine 46 26N 71 0w
Ste. Rose 16 20N 61 45w
Ste. Rose du lac .. 51 10N 99 30w
Saintes 45 45N 0 37w
Saintonge, Reg. ... 45 40N 0 50w
Sairang .... 23 50N 92 45 E
Saitama □ .... 36 25N 137 0 E
Sajama, Mt. ..... 18 6 s 68 54w
Saka .... 0 11 s 39 30 E
Sakai .... 34 30N 135 30 E
Sakaide .... 34 32N 133 50 E
Sakaiminato ..... 35 33N 133 15 E
Sakania .... 38 55N 139 56 E
Sakété .... 6 40N 2 32 E
Sakhalin .... 51 0N 143 0 E
Sakhnin .... 32 52N 35 12 E
Sakishima-
  gunto, Is. ...... 24 30N 124 0 E
Sakrivier .... 30 54 s 20 28 E
Sala .... 59 58N 16 35 E
Sala-y-Gomez, I. .. 26 28 s 105 28w
Saladillo .... 35 40 s 59 55w
Salado, R.,
  Buenos Aires .. 36 0 s 57 30w
Salado, R., Sta. Fe. 31 40 s 60 41w
Salaga 8 31N 0 31w
Salamanca, Chile . 32 0 s 71 25w
Salamanca, Sp. ... 40 58N 5 39w
Salamanca, U.S.A. . 42 10N 78 42w
Salamis .... 37 56N 23 30 E
Salatiga .... 7 19 s 110 30 E
Salavat .... 53 21N 55 55 E
Salaverry .... 8 15 s 79 0w
Salawati, I. ...... 1 7 s 130 54 E
Salazar .... 9 18 s 14 54 E
Saldanha .... 33 0 s 17 58 E
Sale, Australia ... 38 7 s 147 0 E
Sale, U.K. 53 26N 2 19w
Salé 34 3N 6 48w
Salekhard .... 66 30N 66 25 E
Salem, India ..... 11 40N 78 11 E
Salem, Mass. 42 29N 70 53w
Salem, Ohio 40 52N 80 50w
Salem, Oreg. 45 0N 123 0w

Salem, Va. 37 19N 80 8w
Sälen .... 61 41N 11 27 E
Salerno .... 40 40N 14 44 E
Salford 53 30N 2 17w
Salihli .... 38 29N 28 9 E
Salima .... 13 47 s 34 26 E
Salina 38 50N 97 40w
Salina I. .... 38 35N 14 50 E
Salina Cruz 16 10N 95 10w
Salinas, Brazil ... 16 20 s 42 10w
Salinas, U.S.A. ... 36 40N 121 38w
Salinas, B. de 11 4N 85 45w
Salinas Grandes .. 29 30 s 65 0w
Salinópolis ...... 0 40 s 47 20w
Salisbury,
  Australia ...... 34 46 s 138 38 E
Salisbury,
  Rhodesia ...... 17 50 s 31 2 E
Salisbury, U.K. ... 51 4N 1 48w
Salisbury, Md. ... 38 20N 75 38w
Salisbury, N.C. ... 35 42N 80 29w
Salisbury Plain ... 51 13N 2 0w
Salmon 45 12N 113 56w
Salmon, R. 45 51N 116 46w
Salmon Arm 50 40N 119 15w
Salmon Gums .... 32 59 s 121 38 E
Salmon River Mts. 45 0N 114 30w
Salo .... 60 22N 23 3 E
Salonica=
  Thessaloniki .... 40 38N 23 0 E
Salonta .... 46 49N 21 42 E
Salop □ 52 36N 2 45w
Salsk .... 46 28N 41 30 E
Salt Lake City 40 45N 111 58w
Salta .... 24 47 s 65 25w
Saltcoats 55 38N 4 47w
Saltillo 25 30N 100 57w
Salto .... 31 20 s 58 10w
Salton Sea 33 20N 116 0w
Saltpond 5 15N 1 3w
Saltspring 48 54N 123 37w
Salûm .... 31 31N 25 7 E
Salur .... 18 27N 83 18 E
Saluzzo .... 44 39N 7 29 E
Salvador, Brazil .. 13 0 s 38 30w
Salvador, Canada .. 52 20N 109 25w
Salvador ■ 13 50N 89 0w
Salween, R. ..... 16 31N 97 37 E
Salzburg .... 47 48N 13 2 E
Salzburg □ ...... 47 25N 13 15 E

Salzgitter .... 52 2N 10 22 E
Sam Rayburn Res. 31 15N 94 20w
Sama .... 60 10N 60 15 E
Samagaltai ...... 50 36N 95 3 E
Samangan □ ..... 36 15N 67 40 E
Samar, I. .... 12 0N 125 0 E
Samaria, Reg.=
  Shomron, Reg. .. 32 15N 35 13 E
Samarinda .... 0 30 s 117 9 E
Samarkand ...... 39 40N 67 0 E
Sambalpur ...... 21 28N 83 58 E
Sambhal .... 28 35N 78 37 E
Sambhar .... 26 52N 75 5 E
Sambiase .... 38 57N 16 17 E
Sambre, R. ...... 50 28N 4 52 E
Samchŏk .... 37 27N 129 10 E
Same .... 4 2 s 37 38 E
Samoa Is. .... 14 0 s 171 0w
Sámos, I. .... 37 45N 26 50 E
Samothráki, I. .... 40 28N 25 38 E
Sampacho .... 33 20 s 64 50w
Sampang .... 7 11 s 113 13 E
Sampit .... 2 20 s 113 0 E
Samshui .... 23 7N 112 58 E
Samsun .... 41 15N 36 15 E
Samui, Ko ...... 9 30N 100 0 E
Samut Prakan ... 13 32N 100 40 E
Samut Songkhram 13 24N 100 1 E
San 13 15N 4 43w
San, R., Cambodia 13 32N 105 57 E
San, R., Poland ... 50 45N 21 51 E
San Ambrosio, I. .. 26 21 s 79 52w
San Andrés, I. de . 12 42N 81 46w
San Andrés Tuxtla 18 30N 95 20w
San Angelo 31 30N 100 30w
San Antonio, Chile 33 40 s 71 40w
San Antonio, Sp. .. 38 58N 1 27 E
San Antonio,U.S.A. 29 30N 98 30w
San Antonio,
  C., Arg. .... 36 15 s 56 40w
San Antonio,
  C., Chile 21 50N 84 57w
San Antonio de
  los Banos 22 54N 82 31w
San Antonio
  Oeste .... 40 40 s 65 0w
San Benedetto ... 45 2N 10 57 E
San Benito 26 5N 97 32w
San Bernardino ... 34 7N 117 18w
San Bernardino Str. 12 37N 124 12 E

San Bernardo 33 40s 70 50w
San Bernardo, I. de 9 45N 75 50w
San Blas, Cord. de   9 15N 78 30w
San Carlos, Arg. .. 33 50s 69 0w
San Carlos,
  Philippines ..... 10 29N 123 25 E
San Carlos,
  Uruguay 34 46s 54 58w
San Carlos, Ven.. 1 55N 67 4w
San Carlos, Ven.. 9 40N 68 36w
San Carlos de
  Bariloche 41 10s 71 25w
San Carlos del
  Zulía 9 1N 71 55w
San Carlos L. .. 33 13N 110 24w
San Clemente,
  U.S.A. 33 29N 117 45w
San Clemente I. ... 33 0N 118 30w
San Cristóbal,
  Dom. Rep. 18 25N 70 6w
San Cristóbal, Arg. 30 20s 61 10w
San Cristóbal, Ven. 7 46N 72 14w
San Cristóbal de
  las Casas 16 50N 92 33w
San Diego 32 50N 117 10w
San Diego, C. .. 54 40s 65 10w
San Felipe, Chile . 32 43s 70 50w
San Felipe, Ven. . 10 20N 68 44w
San Felíu de
  Guíxals ..... 41 45N 3 1 E
San Felix, I. .. 26 30s 80 0w
San Fernando,
  Philippines .... 15 5N 120 37 E
San Fernando,
  Philippines .. 16 40N 120 23 E
San Fernando, Sp. 36 22N 6 17w
San Fernando,
  Trinidad 10 20N 61 30w
San Fernando,
  U.S.A. 34 15N 118 29w
San Fernando de
  Apure 7 54N 67 28w
San Fernando de
  Atabapo 4 3N 67 42w
San Francisco, Arg. 31 30s 62 5w
San Francisco,
  U.S.A. 37 35N 122 30w
San Francisco, R... 32 59N 109 22w
San Francisco de
  Macoris 19 19N 70 15w

San Francisco de
  Monte del Oro . . 32 36s 66 8w
San Francisco del
  Oro 26 52N 105 50w
San Gil 6 33N 73 8w
San Gottardo,
  P. del .... 46 33N 8 33 E
San Ignacio 26 52s 57 3w
San Joaquin, R. .. 36 43N 121 50w
San Jorge, G. de,
  Arg. 46 0s 66 0w
San José,
  Costa Rica 10 0N 83 57w
San José,
  Guatemala 14 0N 90 50w
San Jose,
  Philippines .... 15 45N 120 55 E
San Jose,
  Philippines .... 10 50N 122 5 E
San Jose, U.S.A. . 37 20N 122 0w
San José, G. .. 42 20s 64 20w
San José de Jáchal . 30 5s 69 0w
San José de Mayo . 34 27s 56 27w
San José de Ocune   4 15N 70 20w
San José del
  Boquerón 26 5s 63 38w
San José del Cabo . 23 0N 109 50w
San José del
  Guaviare 2 35N 72 38w
San José do
  Río Prêto 21 0s 49 30w
San Juan, Arg. .. 31 30s 68 30w
San Juan, Dom.
  Rep. 18 49N 71 12w
San Juan, Mexico . 21 20N 102 50w
San Juan,
  Puerto Rico 18 40N 66 11w
San Juan, R. 37 18N 110 28w
San Juan
  Capistrano .. 33 29N 117 46w
San Juan de
  los Morros 9 55N 67 21w
San Juan del
  Norte, B. de .. 11 30N 83 40w
San Juan Mts. .. 38 30N 108 30w
San Julián 49 15s 68 0w
San Justo 30 55s 60 30w
San Leandro ... 37 40N 122 6w
San Lorenzo,
  Ecuador 1 15N 78 50w

San Lorenzo, Mt.. 47 40s 72 20w
San Lucas, C. de .. 22 50N 110 0w
San Luis 33 20s 66 20w
San Luis de la Paz . 21 18N 100 31w
San Luis Obispo .. 35 17N 120 40w
San Luis Potosí .. 22 9N 100 59w
San Luis Potosí □ . 22 30N 100 30w
San Marcos,
  Guatemala 14 59N 91 52w
San Marcos, U.S.A. 29 53N 98 0w
San Marino .... 43 56N 12 25 E
San Marino ■ .. 43 56N 12 25 E
San Mateo 37 32N 122 25w
San Matías, G.... 41 30s 64 0w
San Miguel,
  Salvador 13 30N 88 12w
San Miguel de
  Tucumán 26 50s 65 20w
San Nicolás de
  los Arroyas .. 33 17s 60 10w
San Pedro, Arg... 24 10s 57 15w
San Pedro,
  Dom. Rep. 18 30N 69 18w
San Pedro de las
  Colonias 25 50N 102 59w
San Pedro del
  Paraná 26 43s 56 13w
San Pedro Sula .. 15 30N 88 0w
San Quintin ..... 16 1N 120 56 E
San Rafael 34 40s 68 30w
San Remo ...... 43 48N 7 47 E
San Roque 28 15s 58 45w
San Rosendo 37 10s 72 50w
San Salvador 13 40N 89 20w
San Salvador, I. .. 24 0N 74 40w
San Salvador de
  Jujuy 23 30s 65 40w
San Sebastián, Arg. 53 10s 68 30w
San Sebastián,
  Spain 43 17N 1 58w
San Severo ...... 41 41N 15 23 E
San Simon 32 14N 109 16w
San Valentín, Mt. . 46 30s 73 30w
San Vicente de la
  Barquera 43 30N 4 29w
Sana .... 15 27N 44 12 E
Sana, R. .... 45 3N 16 23 E
Sanaga, R....... 3 35N 9 38 E
Sanana .... 2 5s 125 50 E
Sanandaj .... 35 25N 47 7 E

Sancti Spíritus ... 21 52N 79 33w
Sand Lake 47 46N 84 31w
Sand Springs 36 12N 96 5w
Sandakan .... 5 53N 118 10 E
Sanday, I. 59 14N 2 30w
Sanders 35 12N 109 25w
Sandgate .... 27 20s 153 5 E
Sandnes .... 58 50N 5 45 E
Sandomierz .... 50 40N 21 43 E
Sandoway ...... 18 20N 94 30 E
Sandpoint 48 20N 116 40w
Sandringham .... 52 50N 0 30 E
Sandstone ..... 28 0s 119 15 E
Sandusky 41 25N 82 40w
Sandveld ...... 32 0s 18 15 E
Sandviken .... 60 38N 16 46 E
Sandwip Chan. .. 22 35N 91 35 E
Sandy, C. ...... 24 41s 153 8 E
Sanford, Fla. ... 28 45N 81 20w
Sanford, N.C. ... 35 30N 79 10w
Sanford, Mt. .. 62 30N 143 0w
Sanger 36 47N 119 35w
Sanggau .... 0 5N 110 30 E
Sangihe, Pulau .. 3 45N 125 30 E
Sangli .... 16 55N 74 33 E
Sangmelina .... 2 57N 12 1 E
Sangonera, R. .. 37 59N 1 4w
Sangre de
  Cristo Mts. ... 37 0N 105 0w
Sangsang ...... 29 30N 86 0 E
Sangwa .... 5 30s 26 0 E
Sanlucar de
  Barrameda ... 36 47N 6 21w
Sanlúcar-la-
  Mayor 37 26N 6 18w
Sanmenhsia .... 34 46N 111 30 E
Sanok .... 49 35N 22 10 E
Sanquhar 55 21N 3 56w
Sansanné-Mango .. 10 20N 0 30 E
Santa Ana,
  Ecuador 1 10s 80 20w
Santa Ana,
  Mexico 30 31N 111 8w
Santa Ana,
  Salvador 14 0N 89 40w
Santa Ana,
  U.S.A. 33 48N 117 55w
Santa Barbara,
  Mexico 26 48N 105 50w

Santa Bárbara,
  U.S.A. 34 25N 119 40w
Santa Catalina,
  G. of 33 0N 118 0w
Santa Catalina I. . 33 20N 118 30w
Santa Catarina □ . 27 25s 48 30w
Santa Clara,
  Cuba 22 20N 80 0w
Santa Clara,
  U.S.A. 37 21N 122 0w
Santa Cruz,
  Arg. 50 0s 68 50w
Santa Cruz,
  Canary Is. ... 28 29s 16 26w
Santa Cruz,
  Costa Rica ... 10 15N 85 41w
Santa Cruz,
  Philippines ... 14 20N 121 30 E
Santa Cruz,
  Calif. 36 55N 122 10w
Santa Cruz,
  N. Mex. 35 59N 106 1w
Santa Cruz, I. .. 0 38s 90 23w
Santa Cruz, R. .. 50 10s 68 20w
Santa Cruz
  do Sul 29 42s 52 25w
Santa Fe, Arg. .. 31 35s 60 41w
Sante Fe, U.S.A. .. 35 40N 106 0w
Santa Filomena .. 9 0s 45 50w
Santa Inés, I. .. 54 0s 73 0w
Santa Isabel 36 10s 67 0w
Santa Lucia Ra. .. 36 0N 121 30w
Santa Margarita, I. 24 30N 112 0w
Santa Mariá,
  Brazil 29 40s 53 40w
Santa Maria,
  U.S.A. 34 58N 120 29w
Santa Maria de
  Vitória 13 24s 44 12w
Santa Maria di
  Leuca, C....... 39 48N 18 20 E
Santa Marta 11 15N 74 13w
Santa Monica 34 0N 118 30w
Santa Paula 34 20N 119 2w
Santa Rosa, Arg. . 36 40s 64 30w
Santa Rosa,
  Brazil 27 52s 54 29w
Santa Rosa,
  Honduras 14 40N 89 0w
Santa Rosa,

Calif. 38 20N 122 50W
Santa Rosa,
  N. Mex. 34 58N 104 40W
Santa Rosa I. . . 34 0N 120 15W
Santa Rosalía . . . 27 20N 112 30W
Santa Vitória do
  Palmar 33 32s 53 25W
Santai . . . . 31 10N 105 2 E
Santana do
  Livramento 30 55s 55 30W
Santander 43 27N 3 51W
Santaquin 40 0N 111 51W
Santarem, Brazil . . 2 25s 54 42W
Santarém, Port. . . 39 12N 8 42W
Santiago, Brazil . . 29 11s 54 52W
Santiago, Chile . . . 33 24s 70 50W
Santiago, Dom.
  Rep. 19 30N 70 40W
Santiago, Panama . 8 0N 81 0W
Santiago de
  Compostela 42 52N 8 37W
Santiago de
  Cuba 20 0N 75 49W
Santiago del
  Estero 27 50s 64 15W
Santiago
  Ixcuintla 21 50N 105 11W
Santo Amaro 12 30s 38 50W
Santo Ângelo 28 15s 54 15W
Santo Domingo . . 18 30N 70 0W
Santo Tomé 28 40s 56 5W
Santoña 43 29N 3 20W
Santos 24 0s 46 20W
Santu . . . . 25 59N 113 3 E
Santuaho . . . . . . 26 36N 119 42 E
Sanur . . . . 32 22N 35 15 E
Sanyuan . . . . . . 34 35N 108 54 E
São Borja 28 45s 56 0W
São Carlos 22 0s 47 50W
São Cristóvão . . . 11 15s 37 15W
São Domingos . . . 13 25s 46 10W
São Francisco . . . 16 0s 44 50W
São Francisco, R. . . 10 30s 36 24W
São Francisco
  do Sul 26 15s 48 36W
São Gabriel 30 10s 54 30W
São João del Rei . 21 8s 44 15W
São João do
  Araguaia 5 23s 48 46W
São João do

Piauí 8 10s 42 15W
São Leopoldo 29 50s 51 10W
São Lourenço 16 30s 55 5W
São Luís 2 39s 44 15W
São Marcos, B. de . 2 0s 44 0W
São Mateus 18 44s 39 50W
São Paulo 23 40s 56 50W
São Paulo □ 22 0s 49 0W
São Roque, C. de . 5 30s 35 10W
São Salvador
  do Congo . . . . . 6 18s 14 16 E
São Sebastião,
  I. de 23 50s 45 18W
São Tomé, I. . . . . 0 10N 7 0 E
São Vicente,
  C. de 37 0N 9 0W
Saône, R. . . . . . . 45 44N 4 50 E
Saône-et-
  Loire □ . . . . 46 25N 4 50 E
Sapele . . . . 5 50N 5 40 E
Saposoa 6 55s 76 30W
Sapporo . . . . 43 0N 141 15 E
Sapulpa 36 0N 96 40W
Saqqez . . . . 36 15N 46 20 E
Saragossa=
  Zaragoza 41 39N 0 53W
Sarajevo . . . . . . 43 52N 18 26 E
Saranac Lake . . . 44 20N 74 10W
Saranda . . . . 5 45s 34 59 E
Sarandí del Yi . . . 33 21s 55 58W
Sarangani B. . . . . 6 0N 125 13 E
Saransk . . . . 54 10N 45 10 E
Sarapul . . . . 56 28N 53 48 E
Sarasota 27 10N 82 30W
Saratoga Springs . 43 5N 73 47W
Saratov . . . . 51 30N 46 2 E
Saravane . . . . . . 15 42N 106 3 E
Sarawak □ . . . . . . 2 0s 113 0 E
Sarbaz . . . . 26 38N 61 19 E
Sarbisheh . . . . . . 32 30N 59 40 E
Sarda, R. . . . . . . 27 22N 81 23 E
Sardarshahr . . . . 28 30N 74 29 E
Sardegna, I. . . . . 39 57N 9 0 E
Sardinia, I.=
  Sardegna, I. . . . 39 57N 9 0 E
Sargodha . . . . . . 32 10N 72 40 E
Sargodha □ . . . . . 31 45N 72 0 E
Sarh . . . . 9 5N 18 23 E
Sarī . . . . 36 30N 53 11 E
Sarikamiş . . . . . . 40 22N 42 35 E

Sarikei . . . . 2 8N 111 30 E
Sarina . . . . 21 22s 149 13 E
Sariwon . . . . . . 38 31N 125 44 E
Sark, I. 49 25N 2 20W
Sarlat-la-
  Canéda . . . . . . 44 54N 1 13 E
Sarmiento 45 35s 69 5W
Sarnia 42 58N 82 29W
Sarny . . . . 51 17N 26 40 E
Saronikós Kól. . . . 37 45N 23 45 E
Sarpsborg . . . . . . 59 16N 11 12 E
Sarthe □ . . . . . . 47 58N 0 10 E
Sarthe, R. 47 30N 0 32W
Sartynya . . . . . . 63 30N 62 50 E
Sarur . . . . 23 17N 58 4 E
Sary Tash . . . . . 39 45N 73 40 E
Sary Shagan . . . . 46 12N 73 48 E
Sasabeneh . . . . . . 7 59N 44 43 E
Sasaram . . . . . . 24 57N 84 5 E
Sasebo . . . . 33 15N 129 50 E
Saskatchewan □ . . 54 0N 103 30W
Saskatchewan, R. . 53 12N 99 16W
Saskatoon 52 10N 106 45W
Saskylakh . . . . . 71 55N 114 1 E
Sasolburg . . . . . . 26 46s 27 49 E
Sasovo . . . . 54 25N 41 55 E
Sassandra 5 0N 6 8W
Sassandra, R. . . . 4 58N 6 5W
Sássari . . . . 40 44N 8 33 E
Sassnitz . . . . . . 54 29N 13 39 E
Satara . . . . 17 44N 73 58 E
Satka . . . . 55 3N 59 1 E
Satmala Hills . . . 20 15N 74 40 E
Satna . . . . 24 35N 80 50 E
Sátoraljaújhely . . 48 25N 21 41 E
Satpura Ra. . . . . 21 40N 75 0 E
Satu Mare . . . . . 47 48N 22 53 E
Satun . . . . 6 43N 100 2 E
Sauda . . . . 59 38N 6 21 E
Sauðarkrókur . . . 65 45N 19 40W
Saudi Arabia ■ . . 26 0N 44 0 E
Sault Ste. Marie,
  Canada 46 30N 84 20W
Saulte Ste. Marie,
  U.S.A. 46 27N 84 22W
Saumur 47 15N 0 5W
Saurbaer 64 24N 21 35W
Sauri . . . . 11 30N 6 35 E
Sava, R. . . . . . . 44 50N 20 26 E
Savaii, I. 13 35s 172 25W

Savalou . . . . 7 57N 2 4 E
Savanna 42 5N 90 10W
Savannah 32 4N 81 4W
Savannah, R. . . . 32 2N 80 53W
Savannakhet . . . . 16 30N 104 49 E
Savant Lake 50 20N 90 40W
Savé . . . . 8 2N 2 17 E
Save, R. . . . . . . 43 47N 1 17 E
Sáveh . . . . 35 2N 50 20 E
Savelugu 9 38N 0 54W
Savoie □ . . . . . . 45 26N 6 35 E
Savoie, Reg. . . . . 45 30N 5 20 E
Savona . . . . 44 19N 8 29 E
Sawai . . . . 3 0s 129 5 E
Sawankhalok . . . 17 19N 99 54 E
Sawatch Mts. . . . 38 30N 106 30W
Sawknah . . . . . . 29 4N 15 47 E
Sawmills . . . . . . 19 30s 28 2 E
Sawu Sea . . . . . 9 30s 121 50 E
Saya . . . . 9 30N 3 18 E
Sayabec 38 35N 67 41W
Sayda . . . . 33 35N 35 25 E
Saynshand . . . . . 44 55N 110 11 E
Sayre 42 0N 76 30W
Sazin . . . . 35 35N 73 30 E
Sca Fell, Mt . . . 54 27N 3 14W
Scandinavia, Reg. . 65 0N 15 0 E
Scapa Flow 58 52N 3 0W
Scarborough 54 17N 0 24W
Schaffhausen . . . 47 42N 8 36 E
Schefferville . . . 54 50N 66 40W
Schelde, R. . . . . 51 22N 4 15 E
Schenectady 42 50N 73 58W
Scheveningen . . . 52 6N 4 18 E
Schiedam . . . . . . 51 55N 4 25 E
Schio . . . . 45 42N 11 21 E
Schleswig-
  Holstein □ . . . . 54 10N 9 40 E
Schouten, Kep. . . 1 0s 136 0 E
Schreiber 48 45N 87 20W
Schumacher 48 30N 81 16W
Schurz 38 59N 118 57W
Schwäbische Alb,
  Mts. . . . . 48 30N 9 30 E
Schwangcheng . . 45 27N 126 27 E
Schwangyashan . . 46 35N 131 15 E
Schwarzrand, Mts. . 26 0s 17 0 E
Schwarzwald . . . . 48 0N 8 0 E
Schweinfurt . . . . 50 3N 10 12 E
Schweizer-Reneke . 27 11s 25 18 E

Schwerin . . . . . . 53 37N 11 22 E
Schwyz . . . . 47 2N 8 39 E
Sciacca . . . . . . 37 30N 13 3 E
Scilla . . . . 38 15N 15 44 E
Scilly Is. 49 55N 6 15W
Scobey 48 47N 105 30W
Scone, Australia . 32 0s 150 52 E
Scone, U.K. 56 25N 3 26W
Scotia Sea 56 5s 56 0W
Scotland ■ 57 0N 4 0W
Scott City 38 30N 100 52W
Scottsbluff 41 55N 103 35W
Scottsburg . . . . 30 15s 30 47 E
Scottsdale . . . . . 41 9s 147 31 E
Scranton 41 22N 75 41W
Scunthorpe 53 35N 0 38W
Sea Lake . . . . . . 35 28s 142 55 E
Seaforth 43 35N 81 25W
Seal, R. 59 4N 94 48W
Searchlight 35 31N 111 57W
Searcy 35 15N 91 45W
Seattle 47 41N 122 15W
Sebastián
  Vizcaíno, B. . . . 28 0N 114 0W
Sebastopol 38 16N 122 56W
Sebring 27 36N 81 47W
Secretary, I. . . . 45 15s 166 56 E
Secunderabad . . 17 28N 78 30 E
Sedalia 38 40N 93 18W
Sedan . . . . 49 43N 4 57 E
Seddon . . . . . . 41 40s 174 7 E
Seddonville . . . . 4133 E 172 1 E
Sede Ya'aqov . . 32 43N 35 7 E
Sedgewick 52 48N 111 41W
Sedom . . . . 31 5N 35 20 E
Sedro Woolley . . 48 30N 122 15W
Seeheim . . . . . . 26 32s 17 52 E
Segamat . . . . . . 2 30N 102 50 E
Ségou 13 30N 6 10W
Segovia 40 57N 4 10W
Segre, R. . . . . . 41 40N 0 43 E
Séguéla 7 57N 6 40W
Seguin 29 34N 97 58W
Segura, R. 38 6N 0 54W
Sehkonj, Kuh-e . . 30 0N 57 30 E
Sehore . . . . . . 23 10N 77 5 E
Seille, R. . . . . . 49 7N 6 11 E
Seinäjoki . . . . . 62 47N 22 50 E
Seine, R. . . . . . 49 30N 0 20 E

Seine-et-Marne □ . 48 45N   3 0 E
Seine-Maritime □ . 49 40N   1 0 E
Seine-St.-Denis . 48 55N   2 28 E
Seke .... 3 20s 33 31 E
Sekenke .... 4 18s 34 11 E
Sekondi-Takoradi . 5 2N   1 48w
Selatan □,
  Kalimantan ..... 3 0s 115 0 E
Selatan □,
  Sulawesi .... 3 0s 120 0 E
Selatan □,
  Sumatera ...... 3 0s 105 0 E
Selby 53 47N   1 5w
Seldovia 59 27N 151 43w
Selebi-Pikwe ..... 22 0s 27 45 E
Selenge .... 49 25N 103 59 E
Sélibaby 15 20N 12 15w
Selkirk, Canada .. 50 10N 97 20w
Selkirk, U.K. 55 33N   2 50w
Selkirk Mts. 51 0N 117 10w
Selma, Ala. 32 30N 87 0w
Selma, Calif. 36 39N 119 30w
Selsey Bill 50 43N   0 48w
Selukwe .... 19 40s 30 0 E
Selva 29 50s 62 0w
Semarang .... 7 0s 110 26 E
Semeru, Mt. ...... 8 4s 113 3 E
Seminoe Res. 42 0N 107 0w
Seminole, Okla. .. 35 15N 96 45w
Seminole, Tex. ... 32 41N 102 38w
Semiozernoye ..... 52 35N 64 0 E
Semipalatinsk .... 50 30N 80 10 E
Semnān .... 35 55N 53 25 E
Semnān □ .... 36 0N 54 0 E
Semporna .... 4 30N 118 33 E
Sena Madureira ... 9 5s 68 45w
Senador Pompeu ... 5 40s 39 20w
Senanga .... 16 2s 23 14 E
Sendai, Kagoshima 31 50N 130 20 E
Sendai, Miyagi ... 38 15N 141 0 E
Seneca 44 10N 119 2w
Seneca Falls 42 55N 76 50w
Senegal ■ 14 30N 14 30w
Senegal, R. 16 30N 15 30w
Senegambia, Reg. . 14 0N 14 0w
Senekal .... 28 18s 27 36 E
Senhor-do Bonfim . 10 30s 40 10w
Senj .... 45 0N 14 58 E
Senlis .... 49 13N   2 35 E
Sennâr .... 13 30N 33 35 E

Senneterre 48 25N 77 15w
Sens .... 48 11N   3 15 E
Sentolo .... 7 55s 110 13 E
Senya Beraku 5 28N   0 31w
Seo de Urgel ..... 42 22N   1 23 E
Seoul=Soul .... 37 20N 126 15 E
Separation Pt. ... 53 40N 57 16w
Sept Iles 50 13N 66 22w
Sequim 48 3N 123 9w
Sequoia Nat. Park 36 20N 118 30w
Seraing .... 50 35N   5 32 E
Seram, I. .... 3 10s 129 0 E
Seram Sea .... 3 0s 130 0 E
Serampore .... 22 44N 88 30 E
Serang .... 6 8s 106 10 E
Serbia □ .... 43 30N 21 0 E
Šerdobsk .... 52 28N 44 10 E
Seremban .... 2 43N 101 53 E
Serengeti Nat. Park 2 40s 35 0 E
Serenje .... 13 11s 30 52 E
Sergipe □ 10 30s 37 30w
Seria .... 4 37N 114 30 E
Serian .... 1 10N 110 40 E
Sérifos .... 37 8N 24 34 E
Serov .... 59 40N 60 20 E
Serowe .... 22 25s 26 43 E
Serpa Pinto ...... 14 48s 17 52 E
Serpentine .... 32 23 s 115 59 E
Serpukhov .... 54 55N 37 28 E
Sérrai .... 41 5N 23 32 E
Serrezuela .... 30 40 s 65 20w
Serrinha .... 11 39 E 39 0w
Sertania 8 5s 37 20w
Serule .... 21 57 s 27 11 E
Sese Is. .... 0 30s 32 30 E
Sesheke .... 17 29s 24 13 E
Sestao 43 18N   3 0w
Sète .... 43 25N   3 42 E
Sete Lagôas 19 27s 44 16w
Sétif .... 36 9N   5 26 E
Seto .... 35 14N 137 6 E
Setonaikai .... 34 10N 133 10 E
Settat 33 0N   7 40w
Setté Cama .... 2 32s   9 57 E
Settle 54 5N   2 18w
Setúbal 38 30N   8 58w
Setúbal, B. de ... 38 40N   8 56w
'Seulimeum .... 5 27N 95 15 E
Sevan L. ....
Sevastopol .... 44 35N 33 30 E

Severn, R., Canada 56 2N 87 36w
Severn, R., U.K. .. 51 25N   3 0w
Severnaya
  Zemlya, I. ..... 79 0N 100 0 E
Severnyye
  Uvaly, Reg. .... 58 0N 48 0 E
Severodvinsk ..... 64 27N 39 58 E
Sevilla 37 23N   6 0w
Seville=Sevilla .. 37 23N   6 0w
Seward 60 0N 149 40w
Seward Pen. 65 0N 164 0w
Seychelles, Is. .. 5 0s 56 0 E
Seydisfjördur 65 16N 14 0w
Seymour, Australia 36 58s 145 10 E
Seymour, U.S.A. .. 39 0N 85 50w
Sfax .... 34 49N 10 48 E
Sfintu-Gheorghe .. 45 52N 25 48 E
's-Gravenhage .... 52 7N   4 17 E
Shaba, Reg. ...... 8 30s 25 0 E
Shabani .... 20 17s 30 2 E
Shabunda .... 2 40s 27 16 E
Shadrinsk .... 56 5N 63 38 E
Shaffa .... 10 30N 12 6 E
Shaftesbury 51 0N   2 12w
Shagamu .... 6 51N   3 39 E
Shāhābād .... 37 40N 56 50 E
Shāhbād .... 34 10N 46 30 E
Shahcheng .... 40 18N 115 27 E
Shahdād .... 30 30N 57 40 E
Shahdadkot .... 27 50N 67 55 E
Shahhat .... 32 40N 21 35 E
Shāhī .... 36 30N 52 55 E
Shāhpūr .... 38 12N 44 45 E
Shahreza .... 32 0N 51 55 E
Shahrig .... 30 15N 67 40 E
Shāhrūd .... 36 30N 55 0 E
Shahsavar .... 36 45N 51 12 E
Shaikhabad .... 34 0N 68 45 E
Shajapur .... 23 20N 76 15 E
Shakhty .... 47 40N 40 10 E
Shakhunya .... 57 40N 47 0 E
Shaki .... 8 41N   3 21 E
Shalu .... 24 24N 120 26 E
Sham, Jabal ash .. 23 10N 57 5 E
Shama 5 1N   1 42w
Shamil .... 29 32N 77 18 E
Shamo, L. .... 5 45N 37 30 E
Shamokin 40 47N 76 33w
Shamva .... 17 18s 31 34 E
Shan □ .... 21 30N 98 30 E

Schanchengtze .... 42 2N 123 47 E
Shanga .... 9 1N   5 2 E
Shangani, R. ..... 18 41s 27 10 E
Shanghai .... 31 10N 121 25 E
Shangjao .... 28 25N 117 25 E
Shangkiu .... 34 28N 115 42 E
Shangshui .... 33 42N 115 4 E
Shanh .... 10 14N 12 2 E
Shannon .... 40 33s 17 25 E
Shannon, R. 52 30N   9 53w
Shansi □ .... 37 0N 113 0 E
Shantou=
  Shantow .... 23 25N 116 40 E
Shantow .... 23 25N 116 40 E
Shantung □ .... 37 0N 118 0 E
Shanyang .... 33 39N 110 2 E
Shaohing .... 30 0N 120 32 E
Shaowu .... 27 25N 117 30 E
Shaoyang .... 27 10N 111 30 E
Shapinsay, I. 59 2N   2 50w
Shaqra .... 25 15N 45 16 E
Sharin Gol .... 49 12N 106 27 E
Sharjah .... 25 23N 55 26 E
Shark, B. .... 25 15s 133 20 E
Sharon 41 14N 80 31w
Sharya .... 58 12N 45 40 E
Shashi .... 21 40s 28 40 E
Shashi, R. .... 22 14s 29 20 E
Shasi .... 30 16N 112 20 E
Shasta, Mt. 41 45N 122 0w
Shasta Res. 40 50N 122 15w
Shaunavon 49 35N 108 40w
Shawano 44 45N 88 38w
Shawinigan 46 35N 72 50w
Shawnee 35 15N 97 0w
Shebele, Wabi .... 2 0N 44 0 E
Sheboygan 43 46N 87 45w
Shebshi Mts. ..... 8 30N 12 0 E
Shediac 46 14N 64 32w
Sheerness .... 51 26N   0 47 E
Shefar'am .... 32 48N 35 10 E
Sheffield 53 23N   1 28w
Shekhupura .... 31 42N 73 58 E
Shekki .... 22 30N 113 15 E
Sheklung .... 23 5N 113 55 E
Shelburne,

Nova Scotia 43 47N 65 20w
Shelburne, Ont. .. 44 4N 80 15w
Shelby, Mont. 48 30N 111 59w
Shelby, N.C. 35 18N 81 34w
Shelbyville, Ind. . 39 30N 85 42w
Shelbyville, Tenn. . 35 30N 86 25w
Sheldrake 50 20N 64 51w
Shelikhova Zaliv . 59 30N 157 0 E
Shell Lake 53 19N 107 6w
Shellbrook 53 13N 106 24w
Shelter Bay 50 30N 67 20w
Shelton, Alaska .. 55 20N 105 0w
Shelton, Wash. ... 47 15N 123 6w
Shemakha .... 40 50N 48 28 E
Shenandoah, Iowa . 40 50N 95 25w
Shenandoah, Pa. .. 40 49N 76 13w
Shenandoah, R. ... 39 19N 77 44w
Shendam .... 9 10N   9 30 E
Shendî .... 16 46N 33 33 E
Shensi □ .... 35 0f 109 0 E
Shenyang .... 41 35N 123 30 E
Shepparton .... 36 18s 145 25 E
Sherborne 50 56N   2 31w
Sherbro I. 7 30N 12 40w
Sherbrooke 45 24N 71 57w
Sheridan 44 50N 107 0w
Sherman 33 40N 96 35w
Sherridon 55 10N 101 5w
s'Hertogenbosch .. 51 41N   5 19 E
Sherwood Forest .. 53 5N   1 5w
Shesheke .... 17 50s 24 0 E
Shetland □ 60 30N   1 30w
Shevchenko .... 44 25N 51 20 E
Shevut'Am .... 32 19N 34 55 E
Shibam .... 16 0N 48 36 E
Shibarghan .... 36 40N 65 48 E
Shibushi .... 31 25N 131 8 E
Shickshock Mts. .. 48 40N 66 30w
Shiel, L. 56 48N   5 32w
Shiga □ .... 35 20N 136 0 E
Shigatse .... 29 10N 89 0 E
Shihchiachuangi=
  Shihkiachwang . 38 0N 114 32 E
Shihkiachwang .... 38 0N 114 32 E
Shihpu .... 29 12N 121 58 E
Shihwei .... 51 28N 119 59 E
Shikarpur .... 27 57N 68 39 E
Shikoku, I. ...... 33 45N 133 30 E
Shikoku □ .... 33 30N 133 30 E
Shillelagh 52 46N   6 32w

Shilka . . . . 52 0N 115 55 E
Shillong . . . . 25 30N 92 0 E
Shimada . . . . 34 49N 138 19 E
Shimane □ . . . . 35 0N 132 30 E
Shimanovsk . . . . . . 52 15N 127 30 E
Shimizu . . . . 35 0N 138 30 E
Shimodate . . . . 36 20N 139 55 E
Shimoga . . . . 13 57N 75 32 E
Shimonoseki . . . . . 33 58N 131 0 E
Shimpek . . . . 44 50N 74 10 E
Shin, L. 58 7N 4 30w
Shin Dand . . . . 33 12N 62 8 E
Shingū . . . . 33 40N 135 33 E
Shinyanga . . . . 3 45s 33 27 E
Shippegan 47 45N 64 45w
Shirane-San, Mt. . . 35 40N 138 15 E
Shiráz . . . . 29 42N 52 30 E
Shire, R. . . . . 17 42s 35 19 E
Shiukwan . . . . 24 58N 113 3 E
Shivpuri . . . . 25 18N 77 42 E
Shizuoka . . . . 35 0N 138 30 E
Shizuoka □ . . . . . . 35 15N 138 40 E
Shkodra . . . . 42 6N 19 20 E
Shoal Lake 50 30N 100 35w
Shoeburyness . . . . 51 13N 0 49 E
Shohsien . . . . 39 30N 112 25 E
Sholapur . . . . 17 43N 75 56 E
Shologontsy . . . . . 66 13N 114 14 E
Shomera . . . . 33 4N 35 17 E
Shómrón, Reg. . . . 32 15N 35 13 E
Shoshone 43 0N 114 27w
Shoshong . . . . 22 0s 26 30 E
Show Low 34 16N 110 0w
Shreveport 32 30N 93 50w
Shrewsbury 52 42N 2 45w
Shucheng . . . . 31 25N 117 2 E
Shuikiahu . . . . 32 14N 117 4 E
Shumagin Is. 55 0N 159 0w
Shumikha . . . . 55 15N 63 30 E
Shunat Nimran . . . 31 54N 35 37 E
Shunchang . . . . . . 26 52N 117 48 E
Shungnak 66 53N 157 2w
Shuqra . . . . 13 22N 45 34 E
Shúsf . . . . 31 50N 60 5 E
Shushtar . . . . 32 0N 48 50 E
Shuweika . . . . 32 20N 35 1 E
Shwangliano . . . . . 43 39N 123 40 E
Shwebo . . . . 22 30N 95 45 E
Shwegu . . . . 24 15N 96 50 E
Shyok . . . . 34 15N 78 5 E

Shyok, R. . . . . 35 13N 75 53 E
Si Racha . . . . 13 20N 101 10 E
Siahan Ra. . . . . . . 27 30N 64 40 E
Siakwan . . . . 25 45N 100 10 E
Sialkot . . . . 32 32N 74 30 E
Siam = Thailand ■ . 15 0N 100 0 E
Siam, G. of . . . . . . 11 30N 101 0 E
Sian . . . . 34 2N 109 0 E
Sian Kiang, R. . . . . 22 30N 110 10 E
Siangfan . . . . 32 15N 112 2 E
Siangtan . . . . 28 0N 112 55 E
Siangyang . . . . 32 18N 111 0 E
Siao Hingan
  Ling, Mts. . . . . . 49 0N 127 0 E
Siargao, I. . . . . 9 52N 126 3 E
Siauhai . . . . 55 56N 23 15 E
Sibbald 51 24N 110 10w
Sibenik . . . . 43 48N 15 54 E
Siberia, Reg. . . . . . 66 0N 120 0 E
Siberut, I. . . . . 1 30s 99 0 E
Sibi . . . . 29 30N 67 48 E
Sibiti . . . . 3 38s 13 19 E
Sibiu . . . . 45 45N 24 9 E
Sibolga . . . . 1 50N 98 45 E
Sibsagar . . . . 27 0N 94 36 E
Sibu . . . . 2 19N 111 51 E
Sibutu Pass. . . . . . 4 50N 120 0 E
Sibuyan, I. . . . . . . 12 25N 122 40 E
Sibuyan Sea . . . . . 12 50N 122 20 E
Sichang . . . . : 28 0N 102 10 E
Sicilia □ . . . . 37 30N 14 30 E
Sicilia, I. . . . . 37 30N 14 30 E
Sicuani 14 10s 71 10w
Sidi Barráni . . . . . 31 32N 25 58 E
Sidi bel Abbès . . . 35 13N 0 10w
Sidi Ifni 29 29N 10 3w
Sidlaw Hills 56 32N 3 10w
Sidmouth 50 40N 3 13w
Sidney, Canada . . . 48 39N 123 24w
Sidney, U.S.A. . . . 40 18N 84 6w
Sidoardjo . . . . 7 30s 112 46 E
Siedlce . . . . 52 10N 22 20 E
Siegen . . . . 50 52N 8 2 E
Siem Reap . . . . . . 13 20N 103 52 E
Siena . . . . 43 20N 11 20 E
Sieyang . . . . 34 20N 108 48 E
Sierra Gorda 23 0s 69 15w
Sierra Leone ■ . . . 9 0N 12 0w
Sierra Nevada, Mts. 40 0N 121 0w
Sifnos, I. . . . . 37 0N 24 45 E

Sighet . . . . 47 57N 23 32 E
Sighisoara . . . . . . 46 12N 24 50 E
Sigli . . . . 5 25N 96 0 E
Siglufjörður 66 12N 18 55w
Sigsig 3 0s 78 50w
Sigtuna . . . . 59 36N 17 44 E
Sigüenza 41 3N 2 40w
Siguiri 11 31N 9 10w
Sigurd 38 57N 112 0w
Sihanoukville =
  Kompong Som . . 10 40N 103 30 E
Sihsien . . . . 29 55N 118 23 E
Siirt . . . . 37 57N 41 55 E
Si Kiang, R. . . . . . 22 0N 114 0 E
Sikandarabad . . . . 28 30N 77 39 E
Sikar . . . . 27 39N 75 10 E
Sikasso 11 7N 5 35w
Sikeston 36 52N 89 35w
Sikhote
  Alin Khrebet . . . 46 0N 136 0 E
Sikkim □ . . . . 27 50N 88 50 E
Sil, R. 42 27N 7 43w
Silamulun, R. . . . . 42 30N 121 0 E
Silat adh Dhahr . . . 32 19N 35 11 E
Silesia, Reg. =
  Slask, Reg. . . . . 51 0N 16 45 E
Silghat . . . . 26 35N 93 0 E
Siliguri . . . . 26 45N 88 25 E
Silistra . . . . 44 6N 27 19 E
Siljan, L. . . . . 60 55N 14 45 E
Silkeborg . . . . 56 10N 9 32 E
Silva Porto = Bié . . 12 22s 16 55 E
Silver City,
  Panama Canal
  Zone 9 21N 79 53w
Silver City, U.S.A. . 32 50N 108 18w
Silver Creek 42 33N 79 9w
Silwan . . . . 31 59N 35 15 E
Simanggang . . . . . 1 15N 111 25 E
Simba . . . . 2 11s 37 35 E
Simcoe, Canada . . 42 50N 80 20w
Simcoe, L. 44 20N 79 20w
Simenga . . . . 62 50N 107 55 E
Simeria . . . . 45 51s 23 1 E
Simeulue, I. . . . . . 2 45N 95 45 E
Simferopol . . . . . . 44 55N 34 3 E
Simla 31 2N 77 15
Simmie 49 56N 108 6w
Simplonpass . . . . . 46 15N 8 0 E
Simpson, Des. . . . 25 0s 137 0 E

Siná', Gebel el
  Tih Es . . . . 29 'ON 33 30 E
Sinai = Es Siná' . . . 29 0N 34 0 E
Sinaloa □ 25 50N 108 20w
Sincelejo 9 18N 75 24w
Sincheng 34 25N 113 56w
Sincorá, Sa. do . . . 13 30s 41 0w
Sind Sagar Doab . . 32 0N 71 30 E
Sindangbarang . . . . 7 27s 107 9 E
Sines . . . . 37 56N 8 51 E
Sinfeng . . . . 26 59N 106 55 E
Singa . . . . 13 10N 33 57 E
Singaparna . . . . . . 7 23s 108 4 E
Singapore ■ . . . . . 1 17N 103 51 E
Singida . . . . 4 49s 34 48 E
Singitikós Kól. . . . . 40 6N 24 0 E
Singkling Hkamti . . 26 0N 95 45 E
Singkawang . . . . . 1 0N 109 5 E
Singkep . . . . 0 30s 104 20 E
Singora = Songkhla . 7 13N 100 37 E
Singtai . . . . 37 2N 114 30 E
Singtze . . . . 29 30N 116 4 E
Sinhailien . . . . 34 31N 119 0 E
Sinhsien . . . . 38 25N 112 45 E
Sinhwa . . . . 27 30N 111 0 E
Sining . . . . 36 35N 101 50 E
Sinjār . . . . 36 19N 41 52 E
Sinjil . . . . 32 3N 35 15 E
Sinkat . . . . 18 55N 36 49 E
Sinkiang . . . . 35 35N 111 25 E
Sinkiang-Uigur □ . . 42 0N 85 0 E
Sinkin . . . . 39 30N 122 29 E
Sinnamary 5 23N 52 57W
Sinnûris . . . . 29 26N 30 31 E
Sinoia . . . . 17 20s 30 8 E
Sinop . . . . 42 1N 35 11 E
Sinsiang . . . . 35 15N 113 55 E
Sintang . . . . 0 5N 111 35 E
Sintra 38 47N 9 25w
Sinuiju . . . . 40 5N 124 24 E
Sinyang . . . . 32 6N 114 2 E
Sion . . . . 46 14N 7 20 E
Sioux City 42 32N 96 25w
Sioux Falls 43 35N 96 40w
Sioux Lookout . . . 50 10N 91 50w
Siparia 10 15N 61 30w
Siping . . . . 33 25N 114 10 E
Siquia, R. 12 30N 84 30w
Sir Bani Yas, I. . . . 24 20N 54 0 E
Sir Edward Pellew

Group, Is. . . . . . . 15 40s 137 10 E
Sir James
  McBrien, Mt. . . . 62 7N 127 41w
Siracusa . . . . 37 4N 15 17 E
Sirajganj . . . . 24 25N 89 47 E
Siret, R. . . . . 47 55N 26 5 E
Síros . . . . 37 28N 24 56 E
Sirsa . . . . 29 33N 75 4 E
Sisak . . . . 45 30N 16 21 E
Sisaket . . . . 15 8N 104 23 E
Sisophon . . . . 13 31N 102 59 E
Sistan
  Baluchistan □ . . 27 0N 62 0 E
Sitapur . . . . 27 38N 80 45 E
Sitges . . . . 41 17N 1 47 E
Sitka 57 9N 134 58w
Sittang Myit, R. . . . 18 20N 96 45 E
Sittard . . . . 51 0N 5 52 E
Situbondo . . . . 7 45s 114 0 E
Sivand . . . . 30 5N 52 55 E
Sivas . . . . 39 43N 36 58 E
Siverek . . . . 37 50N 39 25 E
Siwa . . . . 29 11N 25 31 E
Siwalik Ra. . . . . . . 28 0N 83 0 E
Sizewell . . . . 52 13N 1 38 E
Sjaelland, I. . . . . . 55 30N 11 30 E
Skadarsko,
  Jezero, L. . . . . . 42 10N 19 15 E
Skagen . . . . 57 43N 10 35 E
Skagerrak, Str. . . . 57 30N 9 0 E
Skagway 59 30N 135 20w
Skara . . . . 58 25N 13 30 E
Skaraborg □ . . . . . 58 20N 13 30 E
Skardu . . . . 35 20N 73 35 E
Skeena, R. 54 15N 130 5w
Skenna Mts. 56 40N 128 0w
Skegnwss . . . . . . 53 9N 0 20 E
Skeldon 6 0N 57 20w
Skellefteå . . . . . . 64 45N 20 59 E
Skelleftehamn . . . . 64 41N 21 14 E
Skibbereen 51 33N 9 16w
Skiddaw, Mt. 54 39N 3 9w
Skien . . . . 59 12N 9 35 E
Skierniewice . . . . . 51 58N 20 19 E
Skikda . . . . 36 50N 6 58 E
Skipton 53 57N 2 1w
Skíros, I. . . . . 38 55N 24 34 E
Skive . . . . 56 33N 9 2 E
Skoghall . . . . 59 20N 13 30 E
Skopje . . . . 42 1N 21 32 E

Skoplje＝Skopje ... 42 1N 21 32 E
Skövde .... 58 24N 13 50 E
Skovorodino ..... 53 59N 123 55 E
Skowhegan 44 49N 69 40W
Skudeneshavn ... 59 10N 5 10 E
Skull 51 32N 9 40W
Skwierzyna ...... 52 46N 15 30 E
Skye, I. 57 15N 6 10W
Slaney, R. 52 52N 6 45W
Slask, Reg. ..... 51 0N 16 45 E
Slatina .... 44 28N 24 22 E
Slaton 33 27N 101 38W
Slave Coast ..... 6 0N 2 30 E
Slave Lake 55 25N 114 50W
Slavgorod .... 53 10N 78 50 E
Slavyansk .... 45 15N 38 11 E
Sleaford 53 0N 0 22W
Sleat, Sd. of 57 5N 5 47W
Sliedrecht ...... 51 50N 4 45 E
Sliema .... 35 55N 14 29 E
Sligo 54 17N 8 28W
Sligo □ 54 10N 8 40W
Slite .... 57 42N 18 45 E
Slobodskoy ...... 58 40N 50 6 E
Slough 51 30N 0 35W
Slovenia□＝
  Slovenija ..... 45 58N 14 30 E
Slovenija □ ..... 45 58N 14 30 E
Slovenské
  Rudohorie, Mts.. 50 25N 13 0 E
Słupsk .... 54 28N 17 1 E
Slyudyanka ...... 51 40N 103 30 E
Smeaton 53 30N 105 49W
Smederevo .... 44 40N 20 57 E
Smith 55 10N 114 0W
Smith Arm, B. ... 66 30N 123 0W
Smithers 54 45N 127 10W
Smithfield, S. Afr . 30 13s 26 32 E
Smithfield, U.S.A. . 35 31N 78 16W
Smiths Falls 44 55N 76 0W
Smithton .... 40 53s 145 6 E
Smoky Falls 50 10N 82 10W
Smoky Hill, R. ... 39 3N 96 48W
Smolensk .... 54 45N 32 0 E
Smolikas, Mt. .... 40 9N 20 58 E
Smooth Rock Falls 49 17N 81 37W
Snaefell, Mt. 54 18N 4 26W
Snaefellsjökull.Mt.. 64 50N 23 49W
Snake, R. 46 12N 119 2W
Snake River Plain . 43 13N 113 0W

Sneek .... 53 2N 5 40 E
Sneeuberg .... 31 46s 24 20 E
Sněžka, Mt. ..... 50 41N 14 55 E
Snøhetta, Mt. ... 62 19N 9 16 E
Snow Lake 54 53N 101 2W
Snowdon, Mt. ... 53 4N 4 8W
Snowflake 34 30N 110 4w
Snowshoe Pk. ... 48 13N 115 41W
Snowy, Mts. .... 36 15s 148 20 E
Snyder 32 45N 100 57W
Soalala .... 16 6s 45 20 E
Soap Lake 47 29N 119 31W
Sobral 3 50s 40 30W
Soche .... 38 24N 77 20 E
Sochi .... 43 35N 39 40 E
Society Is. 17 0s 151 0w
Socorro, Col. 6 29N 73 16W
Socorro, U.S.A. .. 34 3N 106 58W
Socotra, I. ...... 12 30N 54 0 E
Soda Creek 52 25N 122 10W
Soda Springs 42 4N 111 40w
Söderhamn ...... 61 18N 17 10 E
Söderköping ..... 58 31N 16 35 E
Södermanlands □ . 59 10N 16 30 E
Södertälje .... 59 12N 17 50 E
Sodo .... 7 0N 37 57 E
Soekmekaar ..... 23 30s 29 55 E
Soest, Neth. ..... 52 9N 5 19 E
Sofala ＝ Beira ... 19 50s 34 52 E
Sofia ＝ Sofiya ... 42 45N 23 20 E
Sofiya .... 42 45N 23 20 E
Sogamoso 5 43N 72 56w
Sogn og Fjordane □ 61 40N 6 0 E
Sohâg .... 26 27N 31 43 E
Soignes .... 50 35N 4 5 E
Soissons .... 49 25N 3 19 E
Soke .... 37 48N 27 28 E
Sokodé .... 9 0N 1 11 E
Sokol .... 59 30N 40 5 E
Sokólka .... 53 25N 23 30 E
Sokoto .... 13 2N 5 16 E
Sokoto, R. ...... 11 20N 4 10 E
Sokoto □ .... 11 40N 5 15 E
Solai .... 0 2N 36 12 E
Solano .... 16 25N 121 15 E
Soledad, Col. 10 55N 74 46w
Soledad, U.S.A. .. 36 27N 121 16W
Soledad, Ven. 8 10N 63 34w
Solent 50 45N 1 25W
Soligalich .... 59 5N 42 10 E

Solikamsk .... 59 38N 56 50 E
Sollefteå .... 63 10N 17 20 E
Sóller .... 39 43N 2 45 E
Sologne, Reg. .... 47 40N 2 0 E
Solok .... 0 55s 100 40 E
Sololá .... 14 49N 91 10 E
Solomon Is. ..... 8 0s 159 0 E
Solothurn .... 47 13N 7 32 E
Soltānābād ...... 36 29N 58 5 E
Soltāniyeh ...... 36 20N 48 55 E
Sölvesborg ...... 56 5N 14 35 E
Solvychegodsk ... 61 21N 46 52 E
Solwezi .... 12 20s 26 26 E
Solway Firth 54 45N 3 38W
Somabula .... 19 40s 29 38 E
Somali Rep. ■ ... 7 0N 47 0 E
Somerset, Bermuda 32 20N 64 55w
Somerset, Ky. 37 5N 84 40w
Somerset □ 51 9N 3 0w
Somerset East .... 32 42s 25 35 E
Somerset West ... 34 8s 18 50 E
Somerset I.,
  Bermuda 32 20N 64 55w
Somerset I., Canada 73 30N 93 0w
Someş, R. .... 47 9N 23 55 E
Somme □ .... 40 0N 2 15 E
Somme, R. ...... 50 11N 1 39 E
Somovit .... 43 45N 24 48 E
Somport, Pto. de . 42 48N 0 31W
Sondags, R. ...... 33 44s 25 51 E
Sønderborg ...... 54 55N 9 49 E
Søndre Strømfjord . 66 30N 50 52W
Sonepat .... 29 0N 77 5 E
Sonepur .... 20 55N 83 50 E
Songea .... 10 40s 35 40 E
Songefjorden .... 61 10N 5 30 E
Songkhla .... 7 13N 100 37 E
Sonmiani .... 25 25N 66 40 E
Sonora 30 33N 100 37W
Sonora □ 37 59N 120 27W
Sonsonate 13 45N 89 45w
Soochow .... 31 18N 120 41 E
Sopot .... 54 27N 18 31 E
Sopron .... 47 41N 16 37 E
Sop's Arm 49 46N 56 56w
Sør Trøndelag □ .. 63 0N 11 0 E
Sorata 15 50s 68 50w
Sorel 46 0N 73 10w
Sorgono .... 40 1N 9 7 E
Soria 41 43N 2 32w

Sorkh, Kuh-e ..... 35 40N 58 30 E
Sorocaba 23 31s 47 35W
Sorong .... 0 55s 131 15 E
Soroti .... 1 43N 33 35 E
Sørøya, I. .... 70 35N 22 45 E
Sorrento .... 40 38N 14 23 E
Sorsele .... 65 31N 17 30 E
Sortavala .... 61 42N 30 41 E
Sosnogorsk ...... 63 37N 53 51 E
Sosnovka .... 54 9N 109 35 E
Sosnowiec ...... 50 20N 19 10 E
Souanke .... 2 10N 14 10 E
Soúdas, Kol. ..... 35 28N 24 10 E
Soul .... 37 33N 126 58 E
Sources, Mt. aux . 28 45s 28 50 E
Soure 0 35s 48 30W
Souris 49 40N 100 20W
Souris, R. 49 39N 99 34w
Sousa 7 0s 38 10w
Sousel 2 38s 52 29w
Sousse .... 35 50N 10 33 E
South Africa ■ ... 30 0s 25 0 E
South America ... 10 0s 60 0w
South Australia □ . 32 0s 139 0 E
South Bend, Ind.
  U.S.A. 41 38N 86 20w
South Bend,
  Wash. 46 44N 123 52w
South Boston 36 42N 78 58w
South Carolina □ .. 33 45N 81 0w
South Charleston . 38 20N 81 40w
South China Sea .. 10 0N 111 0 E
South Dakota □ ... 45 0N 100 0w
South Esk, R. 56 40N 2 40w
South Georgia, I. .. 54 30s 37 0w
South Glamorgan □ 51 28N 3 26w
South Grafton ... 42 11s 71 42w
South Haven 42 22N 86 20w
South Horr ...... 2 12N 36 56 E
South Invercargill . 46 26s 168 23 E
South Island .... 43 50s 171 0 E
South Korea ■ ... 36 0N 128 0 E
South Magnetic
  Pole .... 66 30s 139 30 E
South Milwaukee . 42 50N 87 52w
South Orkney Is. .. 63 0s 45 0w
South Platte, R. .. 41 7N 100 42w
South Porcupine .. 48 30N 81 12w
South River 45 52N 79 21w
South Sandwich Is. 57 0s 27 0w

South
  Saskatchewan, R. 53 15N 105 5w
South Shetland Is. . 62 0s 59 0w
South Shields 54 59N 1 26w
South Sioux City .. 42 30N 96 30w
South Tyne, R. ... 54 59N 2 8W
South Uist, I. 57 10N 7 10w
South West Africa ■22 0s 18 0 E
South Yemen ■ ... 15 0N 48 0 E
South Yorkshire □ . 52 45N 1 25w
Southampton,
  Canada 44 30N 81 25w
Southampton,
  U.K. 50 54N 1 23w
Southampton,
  U.S.A. 40 54N 72 22w
Southampton I. ... 64 30N 84 0w
Southend .... 51 32N 0 43 E
Southern Alps, Mts. 43 41s 170 11 E
Southern Cross ... 31 12s 119 15 E
Southern Mid-
  Atlantic Ridge . 30 0s 15 0w
Southern Ocean .. 62.0s 160 0w
Southern
  Uplands, Mts. .. 55 30N 4 0w
Southport,
  Australia ...... 28 0s 153 25 E
Southport, U.K. ... 53 38N 3 1w
Southwold ...... 52 19N 1 41 E
Soutpansberge ... 22 55s 29 30 E
Sovetsk .... 57 38N 48 53 E
Sovetskaya Gavan . 48 50N 140 0 E
Spain ■ 40 0N 5 0w
Spalding 52 47N 0 9w
Spandau .... 52 32N 13 13 E
Spaniard's Bay ... 47 38N 53 20w
Spanish Fork 40 10N 111 37w
Spanish Pt. 32 12N 64 45w
Spanish Town 18 0N 77 20w
Sparks 39 30N 119 45w
Sparta 43 55N 91 10w
Spartanburg 35 0N 82 0w
Spárti .... 37 5N 22 25 E
Spartivento,
  C., Italy ...... 37 56N 16 4 E
Spartivento,
  C., Sardinia ... 38 52N 8 50 E
Spassk-Dal'niy ... 44 40N 132 40 E
Spátha, Ákra .... 35 42N 23 43 E
Spearfish 44 32N 103 52w

Speed .... 35 21s 142 27 E
Speightstown 13 18N 59 30w
Speke G. .... 2 20s 32 50 E
Spenard 61 0N 149 50w
Spence Bay 69 32N 93 31w
Spencer 43 5N 95 3w
Spencer, G. ...... 34 30s 137 0 E
Spenser, Mts. .... 42 15s 172 45 E
Sperrin Mts. 54 50N 7 0w
Spey, R. 57 40N 3 6w
Speyer .... 49 19N 8 26 E
Spezia=La Spezia . 44 8N 9 50 E
Spinazzola .... 40 58N 16 5 E
Spirit River 55 45N 119 0w
Spithead 50 46N 1 12w
Split .... 43 31N 16 26 E
Spokane 47 45N 117 25w
Spoleto .... 42 44N 12 44 E
Sporades, Is.=
  Sporádhes,
  Voríai .... 39 15N 23 30 E
Sporádhes, Voríai . 39 15N 23 30 E
Spree, R. .... 52 32N 13 13 E
Springbok .... 29 42s 17 54 E
Springburn .... 43 40s 171 32 E
Springdale, Canada 49 30N 56 6w
Springdale, U.S.A. 36 10N 94 5w
Springerville 34 10N 109 16w
Springfield, N.Z. 43 19s 171 56 E
Springfield, Ill. 39 58N 89 40w
Springfield, Mass. 42 8N 72 37w
Springfield, Mo. . 37 15N 93 20w
Springfield, Ohio 39 50N 83 48w
Springfield, Ore. 44 2N 123 0w
Springfield, Tenn. 36 35N 86 55w
Springfontein .... 30 15s 25 40 E
Springhill 45 40N 64 4w
Springs .... 26 13s 28 25 E
Springsure .... 24 8s148 6 E
Springvale,
  Queens. .... 23 33s 140 42 E
Springvale,
  W.Australia .... 17 48s 127 41 E
Springville, N.Z. 42 31N 78 41w
Springville, Utah 40 14N 111 35w
Spurn Hd. 53 34N 0 8w
Squamish 49 45N 123 10w
Squillace .... 38 45N 16 28 E
Sragen .... 7 28s110 59 E
Sredinnyy Khrebet 57 0N 160 0 E

Sredne
  Tamborskoye ... 50 55N 137 45 E
Srednekolymsk .... 67 20N 154 40 E
Srednevilyuysk ... 63 50N 123 5 E
Sremska Mitrovica. 44 58N 19 37 E
Srépok, R. .... 13 33N 106 16 E
Sretensk .... 52 10N 117 40 E
Sri Lanka ■ ...... 7 30N 80 50 E
Srikakulam .... 18 14N 84 4 E
Srinagar .... 34 12N 74 50 E
Srnetica .... 44 25N 16 33 E
Staffa, I. 56 26N 6 21w
Stafford 52 49N 2 9w
Stafford □ 52 53N 2 10w
Staines 51 26N 0 30w
Stalingrad =
  Volgograd ..... 48 40N 44 25 E
Stalybridge 53 29N 2 2w
Stamford, Australia 21 15s 143 46 E
Stamford, U.K. ... 52 39N 0 29w
Stamford, Conn. .. 41 5N 73 30w
Stamford, Tex. ... 32 58N 99 50w
Standerton .... 26 55s 29 13 E
Stanger .... 29 18s 31 21 E
Stanke Dimitrov .. 42 27N 23 9 E
Stanley, Australia 40 46s 145 19 E
Stanley, Falkland Is. 51 40s 58 0w
Stanley, U.S.A. .. 44 10N 114 59w
Stanley Falls =
  Chutes Boyoma . 0 12N 25 25 E
Stanleyville =
  Kisangani ..... 0 41N 52 11 E
Stann Creek 17 0N 88 20w
Stanovoy Khrebet . 55 0N 130 0 E
Stanthorpe .... 28 36s 151 59 E
Stanton 69 45N 128 52w
Stara Planina .... 43 15N 23 0 E
Stara Zagora ..... 42 26N 25 39 E
Staraya Russa .... 57 58N 31 10 E
Starbuck I. 5 37s 155 55w
Stargard Szczecinski 53 20N 15 0 E
Starkville 37 10N 104 31w
Start Pt. 50 13N 3 38w
Staryy Keydzhan .. 60 0N 144 50 E
State College 40 47N 77 49w
Statesboro 32 26N 81 46w
Statesville 35 48N 80 51w
Staunton 38 7N 79 4w
Stavanger .... 58 57N 5 40 E
Stavrapol .... 45 2N 41 59 E

Stawell .... 36 58s 142 47 E
Steamboat Springs . 40 30N 106 58w
Steelton 40 17N 76 50w
Steen River 59 40N 117 12w
Steep, Pt. .... 26 8s113 8 E
Stefanie, L. =
  Chew Bahir .... 4 40N 30 50 E
Steiermark □ ..... 47 26N 15 0 E
Steilrandberg .... 17 30s 13 0 E
Steinbach 49 32N 96 40w
Steinkjer .... 63 59N 11 31 E
Stellaland .... 26 45s 24 50 E
Stellarton 45 34N 62 40w
Stellenbosch ..... 33 58s 18 50 E
Stelvio, P. de ... 46 32N 10 27 E
Stendal .... 52 36N 11 50 E
Stepanakert ...... 40 0N 46 25 E
Stephen 48 30N 96 53w
Stephens Creek ... 31 50s 141 30 E
Stephenville,
  Canada 48 31N 58 30w
Stephenville,
  U.S.A. 32 12N 98 12w
Stepnoi =
  Elista .... 46 25N 44 17 E
Stereá Ellas □ ... 38 55N 22 0 E
Sterkstroom ...... 31 32s 26 32 E
Sterling, Colo. .. 40 40N 103 15w
Sterling, Ill. ... 41 45N 89 45w
Sterlitamak ...... 53 40N 56 0 E
Stettin=Szczecin . 53 27N 14 27 E
Stettler 52 25N 112 40w
Steubenville 40 21N 80 39w
Stevens Point 44 32N 89 34w
Stewart, I., Chile 54 50s 71 30w
Stewart, I., N.Z. 46 58s 167 54 E
Stewart River 63 25N 139 30w
Steynsburg .... 31 15s 25 49 E
Steytlerville .... 33 17s 24 19 E
Stikine, R. 56 40N 132 30w
Stilfontein ...... 26 50s 26 50 E
Stillwater, Minn. 45 3N 92 47w
Stillwater, Okla. 36 5N 97 3w
Stillwater Mts. .. 39 45N 118 6w
Štip .... 41 42N 22 10 E
Stockerau .... 48 24N 16 12 E
Stockholm .... 59 17N 18 3 E
Stockholms □ ..... 59 40N 18 45 E

Stockport 53 25N 2 11w
Stockton, Australia 32 56s 151 47 E
Stockton, U.K. ... 54 34N 1 20w
Stockton, U.S.A. . 38 0N 121 20w
Stoke-on-Trent ... 53 1N 2 11w
Stokes Bay 45 0N 81 22w
Stolbovaya .... 64 50N 153 50 E
Stonehenge,
  Australia ..... 24 22s 143 17 E
Stonehenge, U.K. . 51 9N 1 45w
Stonehaven 56 58N 2 11w
Stonewall 50 10N 96 50w
Storavan, L. ..... 65 45N 18 10 E
Store Baelt ...... 55 28N 11 0 E
Støren .... 63 3N 10 18 E
Storm Lake 42 35N 95 5w
Stormberg .... 31 16s 26 17 E
Stornoway 58 12N 6 23w
Storsjön, L. ..... 60 35N 16 45 E
Stoughton 49 40N 103 0w
Stour, R., Dorset 50 43N 1 46w
Stour, R., Hereford
  and Worcester . 52 20N 2 15w
Stour, R., Kent .. 51 18N 1 22 E
Stour, R., Suffolk 51 52N 1 16 E
Stourbridge 52 28N 2 8w
Stowmarket .... 52 11N 1 0 E
Strabane 54 50N 7 28w
Strabane □ 54 50N 7 28w
Strahan .... 42 8s145 24 E
Stralsund .... 54 17N 13 5 E
Strand .... 34 9s 18 48 E
Strangford, L. ... 54 30N 5 37w
Stranraer 54 54N 5 0w
Strasbourg, Canada 51 10N 104 55w
Strasbourg, Fr. .. 48 35N 7 42 E
Stratford, Australia 37 59s147 5 E
Stratford, Canada . 43 23N 81 0w
Stratford, N.Z. .. 39 20s 174 19 E
Stratford-on-Avon 52 12N 1 42w
Strath Spey 57 15N 3 40w
Strathalbyn ...... 35 13s 138 53 E
Strathclyde □ 55 30N 5 0w
Strathmore 51 5N 113 25w
Strathmore, Reg. . 58 23N 4 40w
Strathroy 42 58N 81 38w
Strathy, Pt. 58 35N 4 0w
Streaky Bay ...... 32 51s 134 18 E
Streator 41 9N 88 52w
Strelka .... 58 5N 93 10 E

Strezhevoy .... 60 42N 77 34 E
Strómboli, I. .... 38 48N 15 12 E
Stromeferry 57 20N 5 33w
Strömstad .... 58 55N 11 15 E
Stronsay, I. 59 8N 2 38w
Stroud 51 44N 2 12w
Struer .... 56 30N 8 35 E
Struma, R. .... 40 47N 23 51 E
Struthers 41 6N 80 38w
Stung Treng ...... 13 26N 106 0 E
Sturgeon Bay 44 52N 87 20w
Sturgeon Falls ... 46 25N 79 57w
Sturt Cr. .... 20 8s127 24 E
Stutterheim ...... 32 33s 27 28 E
Stuttgart, U.S.A. 34 30N 91 33w
Stuttgart,
  W.Germany ..... 48 46N 9 10 E
Styr, R. .... 52 7N 26 35 E
Suakin .... 19 0N 37 20 E
Suancheng .... 30 58N 118 57 E
Suanhwa .... 40 35N 115 0 E
Suao .... 24 32N 121 42 E
Subang .... 7 30s 107 45 E
Subotica .... 46 6N 19 29 E
Suchitato 13 56N 89 0w
Suchou=Soochow .. 31 18N 120 41 E
Suchow .... 34 10N 117 20 E
Suck, R. 53 16N 8 3w
Sucre 19 0s 65 15w
Sudan ■ .... 15 0N 30 0 E
Sudbury 46 30N 81 0w
Sûdd .... 8 20N 29 30 E
Sudetes, Mts.=
  Sudety, Mts. .. 50 20N 16 45 E
Sudety, Mts. ..... 50 20N 16 45 E
Sudirman,
  Pengunungan,
  Ra. .... 4 30s137 0 E
Sueca 39 12N 0 21w
Suez = El Suweis . 28 40N 33 0 E
Suffolk 36 47N 76 33w
Suffolk □ .... 52 16N 1 0 E
Sufu .... 39 44N 75 53 E
Suguluk = Saglouc 62 10N 75 40w
Suhar .... 24 20N 56 40 E
Suhbaatar .... 50 17N 106 10 E
Suhsien .... 33 28N 117 54 E
Suichung .... 40 45N 120 46 E
Suichwan .... 26 26N 114 32 E
Suihwa .... 46 40N 126 57 E

Suikhai.......... 21 17N 110 19 E
Suiping.......... 33 15N 114 6 E
Suir, R. 52 15N 7 0W
Sukabumi ..... 6 56s 106 57 E
Sukadana....... 1 10s 110 0 E
Sukhumi .... 43 0N 41 0 E
Sukkur......... 27 50N 68 46 E
Sulaiman Ra. .... 30 30N 69 50 E
Sulam Tsor ..... 33 4N 35 6 E
Sulawesi, I. ...... 2 0s 120 0 E
Sulina .... 45 10N 29 40 E
Sulitàlma .... 67 17N 17 28 E
Sulitjelma .... 61 7N 16 8 E
Sullana 5 0s 80 45w
Sullivan 39 5N 87 26w
Sulphur 30 20N 93 22w
Sulphur Springs .. 33 5N 95 30w
Sultanpur....... 26 18N 82 10 E
Sulu Arch........ 6 0N 121 0 E
Sulu Sea .... 8 0N 120 0 E
Suluq .... 31 44N 20 14 E
Sumalata .... 1 0N 122 37 E
Sumatera □...... 0 40N 100 20 E
Sumatera, I. ..... 0 40N 100 20 E
Sumatra 46 45N 107 37w
Sumatra, I. =
  Sumatera, I. .... 0 40N 100 20 E
Sumba, Selat, Str. . 9 0s 118 40 E
Sumbawa, I. ...... 9 45s 119 35 E
Sumbawa Besar .. 8 30s 117 26 E
Sumbawanga ..... 7 57s 31 35 E
Sümber .... 46 40N 108 50 E
Sumbing, Mt. .... 7 19s 110 3 E
Sumedang .... 6 49s 107 56 E
Sumenep .... 7 3s 113 51 E
Summerside 46 29N 63 41w
Summit 47 50N 72 20w
Summit Lake 54 20N 122 40w
Summit Pk. 37 20N 106 48w
Sumoto .... 34 21N 134 54 E
Sumperk .... 49 59N 17 0 E
Sumter 33 55N 80 10w
Sumy .... 50 57N 34 50 E
Sunart, L. 56 42N 5 35w
Sunbury 40 50N 76 46w
Sunchon .... 34 52N 127 31 E
Sunda, Selat .... 6 0s 105 45 E
Sundarbans, Reg... 22 0N 89 0 E
Sunderland 54 54N 1 22w

Sundridge 45 45N 79 25w
Sundsvall .... 62 23N 17 17 E
Sungaigerung ..... 4 58s 105 7 E
Sungaipakning .... 1 19N 102 0 E
Sungaipenuh ..... 2 1s 101 20 E
Sungaitiram ...... 0 45s 117 8 E
Sungari, R. ...... 47 30N 132 30 E
Sungguminasa .... 5 17s 119 30 E
Sungkiang .... 31 0N 121 20 E
Sungpan .... 32 50N 103 20 E
Sungtzu Hu, L.... 30 10N 111 45 E
Sunnyside 46 24N 120 2w
Sunshine .... 37 48s 144 52 E
Sunyani 7 21N 2 22w
Supaul .... 26 10N 86 40 E
Superior, Ariz. ... 33 19N 111 9w
Superior, Wis. ... 46 45N 92 0w
Superior, L. 47 40N 87 0w
Supu .... 27 57N 110 15 E
Sûr, Lebanon .... 33 19N 35 16 E
Sûr, Oman ...... 22 34N 59 32 E
Sura, R. .... 56 6N 46 0 E
Surabaya .... 7 17s 112 45 E
Surakarta .... 7 35s 110 48 E
Surat .... 21 12N 72 55 E
Surat Thani ..... 9 3N 99 28 E
Suratgarh .... 29 18N 73 55 E
Surgut .... 61 20N 73 28 E
Suri .... 23 50N 87 34 E
Surif .... 31 40N 35 4 E
Surinam ■ 4 0N 56 15w
Surrey □ 51 16N 0 30w
Surt .... 31 11N 16 46 E
Surt, Khalij ...
Surtsey, I. 63 27N 20 15w
Suruga-Wan, G. .. 34 45s 138 30 E
Susa .... 45 8N 7 3 E
Susaki .... 33 22N 133 17 E
Susanino .... 52 50N 140 14 E
Susanville 40 28N 120 40w
Susquehanna, R. .. 39 33N 76 5w
Susques 23 35s 66 25w
Sussex 45 45N 65 37w
Susuman .... 62 47N 148 10 E
Sutherland,
  S. Africa, ... 32 33s 20 40 E
Sutherland, Canada 52 15N 106 40w
Sutlej, R. .... 29 23N 71 2 E
Sutton-
  in-Ashfield 52 8N 1 16w

Suva .... 17 40s 178 8 E
Suwałki .... 54 8N 22 59 E
Suwannee, R. 29 18N 83 9w
Suwanose-Jima, I. . 29 26N 129 30 E
Suwarrow Is. 13 15s 163 5w
Suweilih .... 32 2N 35 50 E
Suweis, Kaŋg es.. 28 40N 33 0 E
Suwen .... 20 27N 110 2 E
Suwôn .... 37 17N 127 1 E
Suzdal .... 56 29N 40 26 E
Suzu .... 37 25N 137 17 E
Suzuka .... 34 55N 136 36 E
Svalbard, Is. .... 78 0N 17 0 E
Svappavaara ..... 67 40N 21 3 E
Svartisen, Mt. .... 66 40N 14 16 E
Svealand, Reg. ... 60 0N 15 0 E
Sveg .... 62 2N 14 21 E
Svendborg ...... 55 4N 10 35 E
Sverdlovsk ...... 56 50N 60 30 E
Sverdrup Is. 79 0N 97 0w
Svishtov .... 43 36N 25 23 E
Svobodnyy ...... 51 20N 128 0 E
Svolvaer .... 68 15N 14 34 E
Swabian Mts.=
  Scwäbische
  Alb., Mts. ..... 48 30N 9 30 E
Swakop, R. ..... 22 38s 14 36 E
Swakopmund .... 22 37s 14 30 E
Swale, R. 54 6N 1 20w
Swan Hill ...... 35 15s 143 31 E
Swan Hills 54 42N 115 49w
Swan Is. 17 22N 83 57w
Swan River 52 10N 101 25w
Swanage 50 36N 1 59w
Swansea, Australia 33 3s 151 35 E
Swansea, U.K. ... 51 37N 3 57w
Swartberge ..... 30 15s 29 23 E
Swartruggens .... 25 39s 26 42 E
Swatow = Shantow 23 25N 116 40 E
Swaziland ■ .... 26 30s 31 30 E
Sweden ■ ..... 67 0N 15 0 E
Swedru 5 32N 0 41w
Sweetwater 32 30N 100 28w
Swellendam ..... 34 1s 20 26 E
Swidnica .... 50 50N 16 30 E
Swiebodzin ..... 52 15N 15 37 E
Swift Current 50 20N 107 45w
Swindon 51 33N 1 47w
Swinoujście .... 53 54N 14 16 E
Switzerland ■ .... 46 30N 8 0 E

Swords 53 27N 6 15w
Sydney, Australia . 33 53s 151 10 E
Sydney, Canada .. 46 7N 60 7w
Sydney Mines ... 46 18N 60 15w
Syktyvkar ...... 61 45N 50 40 E
Sylacauga 33 10N 86 15w
Sylhet .... 24 43N 91 55 E
Sylvan Lake 52 20N 114 10w
Sym .... 60 20N 87 50 E
Syr Darya, R. ... 46 3N 61 0 E
Syracuse 38 0N 101 40w
Syria ■ .... 35 0N 38 0 E
Syul'dzhyukyor .. 63 25N 113 40 E
Syzran .... 53 12N 48 30 E
Szczecin .... 53 27N 14 27 E
Szechwan □ .... 30 15N 103 15 E
Szeged .... 46 16N 20 10 E
Székesfehérvár .. 47 15N 18 25 E
Szekszárd ...... 46 22N 18 42 E
Szemao .... 22 50N 101 0 E
Szengen .... 24 50N 108 0 E
Szentes .... 46 39N 20 21 E
Szeping .... 43 10N 124 18 E
Szolnok .... 47 10N 20 15 E
Szombathely .... 47 14N 16 38 E

T

Ta Hingan Ling,
  Mts. .... 48 0N 120 0 E
Ta Liang Shan, Mts. 28 0N 103 0 E
Tabacal 23 15s 64 15w
Tabagné........ 7 53N 3 7w
Tabasco □ 17 45N 93 30w
Taber 49 48N 111 5w
Tablas, I. .... 12 20N 122 10 E
Table Mt. ...... 34 0s 18 22 E
Tableland ...... 17 16s 126 51 E
Tabletop, Mt. ... 23 30s 147 0 E
Tábor .... 49 25N 14 39 E
Tabora .... 5 2s 32 57 E
Tabou 4 30N 7 20w
Tabriz .... 38 7N 56 20 E
Tabuk .... 28 30N 36 25 E
Tachira 8 7N 72 21w
Tacloban .... 11 1N 125 0 E
Tacna 18 0s 70 20w

Tacoma 47 15N 122 30w
Tacuarembó 31 45s 56 0w
Tademait, Plateau
  du .... 28 30N 2 30 E
Tadjoura .... 11 50N 44 55 E
Tadmor, N.Z. .... 41 27s 172 45 E
Tadmor, Syria ... 34 30N 37 55 E
Tadoussac 48 11N 69 42w
Tadzhik S.S.R. □ . 35 30N 70 0 E
Taegu .... 35 50N 128 25 E
Taejon .... 35 30N 127 22 E
Tafalla 42 30N 1 41w
Tafelbaai .... 33 35s 18 25 E
Taff, R. 51 27N 3 9w
Taftan, Küh-e, Mt. 28 36N 61 6 E
Taganrog .... 47 12N 38 50 E
Tagbilaran ...... 9 42N 124 3 E
Tagliamento, R. .. 45 38N 13 6 E
Taguatinga 12 26s 45 40w
Tahakopa .... 46 30s 169 23 E
Tahan, Gunong .. 4 38N 102 14 E
Tahcheng .... 46 50N 83 1 E
Tahiti, I. 17 45s 149 30w
Tahoe, L. 39 6N 120 0w
Tahoua .... 14 57N 5 16 E
Tahsien .... 31 12N 108 13 E
Tahta .... 26 44N 31 32 E
Tai Hu .... 31 10N 120 0 E
Taichow .... 32 30N 119 50 E
Taichung .... 24 10N 120 35 E
Taihan Shan, Mts. . 36 0N 114 0 E
Taihape .... 39 41s 175 48 E
Taiho .... 26 50N 114 54 E
Taiku .... 37 46N 112 28 E
Tailai .... 46 28N 123 18 E
Tailem Bend .... 35 12s 139 29 E
Taima .... 27 35N 38 45 E
Tain 57 49N 4 4w
Tainan .... 23 0N 120 15 E
Taínaron, Åkra .. 36 22N 22 27 E
Taipei .... 25 2N 121 30 E
Taiping .... 4 50N 100 43 E
Taitao, Pen. de .. 46 30s 75 0w
Taitung .... 22 43N 121 4 E
Taiwan ■ ...... 23 30N 121 0 E
Taiyiba, Israel ... 32 36N 35 27 E
Taiyiba, Jordan .. 31 55N 35 17 E
Taiyuan .... 38 0N 112 30 E
Ta'izz .... 13 38N 44 4 E
Tajo, R. 38 40N 9 24w

Tãjūra .... 32 51N 13 27 E
Tak .... 17 0N 99 10 E
Takachiho ..... 32 42N 131 18 E
Takada .... 37 7N 138 15 E
Takaka .... 40 51s 172 50 E
Takamatsu ...... 34 20N 134 5 E
Takaoka .... 36 40N 137 0 E
Takapuna .... 36 47s 174 47 E
Takasaki .... 36 20N 139 0 E
Takatsuki ...... 34 40N 135 37 E
Takaungu .... 3 38s 39 52 E
Takayama .... 36 10N 137 5 E
Takefu .... 35 50N 136 10 E
Takhar □ .... 36 30N 69 30 E
Takla Makan, Reg. 39 40N 85 0 E
Takum .... 7 18N 10 0 E
Talara 4 30s 81 10w
Talata Mafara .... 12 35N 6 2 E
Talaud, Kep. .... 4 30N 127 10 E
Talavera de la Reina 39 55N 4 46w
Talca 35 20s 71 46w
Talcahuano 36 40s 73 10w
Taldy Kurgan ..... 45 10N 78 45 E
Talfit .... 32 5N 35 17 E
Talguppa .... 14 11N 74 51 E
Tali, Shensi ..... 34 48N 109 48 E
Tali, Yunnan ... 25 50N 100 0 E
Taliabu, I. .... 1 45s 125 0 E
Talien .... 38 53N 121 35 E
Taliwang .... 8 50s 116 55 E
Talkeetna 62 20N 149 50w
Talladega ...... 33 28N 86 2 w
Tallahassee 30 25N 84 15w
Tallangatta .... 36 10s 147 14 E
Tallinn .... 59 29N 24 58 E
Tallulah 32 25N 91 12w
Talluza .... 32 17N 35 18 E
Taltal 25 23s 70 40w
Talwood .... 28 27s 149 20 E
Tamale 9 22N 0 50w
Tamano .... 34 35N 133 59 E
Tamanrasset .... 22 56N 5 30 E
Tamar, R. 50 22N 4 10w
Tamashima ...... 34 32N 133 18 E
Tamaské .... 14 55N 5 40 E
Tamatave .... 18 10s 49 25 E
Tamatave □ ..... 18 0s 49 0 E
Tamaulipas □ ... 24 0N 99 0w
Tambacounda 13 55N 13 45w

Tambellup .... 34 4s 117 37 E
Tambo .... 24 54s 146 14 E
Tambora, I. ..... 8 14s 117 55 E
Tambov .... 52 45N 41 20 E
Tamchaket 17 25N 10 40w
Tamiahua, Laguna
de 21 30N 97 30w
Tamil Nadu □ .... 11 0N 77 0 E
Taming .... 36 20N 115 10 E
Tammun .... 32 18N 35 23 E
Tampa 27 57N 82 30w
Tampere .... 61 30N 23 50 E
Tampico 22 20N 97 50w
Tamra .... 32 51N 35 12 E
Tamsagbulag ..... 47 15N 117 5 E
Tamworth,
Australia .. 31 0s 150 58 E
Tamworth, U.K. .. 52 38N 1 2w
Tana .... 70 23N 28 13 E
Tana, L. .... 12 0N 37 20 E
Tana, R. .... 2 32s 40 31 E
Tanabe .... 33 44N 135 22 E
Tanacross 63 40N 143 30w
Tanahgrogot .... 1 55s 116 15 E
Tanahmeroh ..... 6 0s 140 7 E
Tanami, Des. ... 23 15s 132 20 E
Tanana 65 10N 152 15w
Tanana, R. 64 25N 145 30w
Tananarive =
Antananarivo .. 18 55s 47 31 E
Tananarive □ ... 19 0s 47 0 E
Tánaro, R. ..... 44 9N 7 50 E
Tanda 7 48N 3 10w
Tandil 37 15s 59 6w
Tando Adam ..... 25 45N 68 40 E
Taneatua .... 38 4s 177 1 E
Tane-ga-Shima, I. . 30 30N 131 0 E
Tanen Tong
Dan, Mts. ...... 19 40N 99 0 E
Tanezrouft ..... 23 9N 0 11 E
Tanga .... 5 5s 39 2 E
Tanganyika■ =
Tanzania ■ .. 6 40s 34 0 E
Tanganyika, L. .. 6 40s 30 0 E
Tanger 35 50N 5 49w
Tangerang ...... 6 12s 106 39 E
Tanghla Shan, Mts. 33 10N 90 0 E
Tangiers=Tanger . 35 50N 5 49w
Tangshan, Anhwei. 34 23N 116 34 E
Tangshan, Hopei . 39 40N 118 10 E

Tangtu .... 31 37N 118 39 E
Tanguiéta ...... 10 37N 1 16 E
Tangyang .... 30 50N 111 45 E
Tanimbar, Kep. ... 7 30s 131 30 E
Tanjung .... 2 10s 115 25 E
Tanjungbalai ..... 2 55N 99 44 E
Tanjungkarang... 5 25s 105 16 E
Tanjungpandan .. 2 45s 107 39 E
Tanjungredeb ... 2 12N 117 35 E
Tanjungselor ..... 2 55N 117 25 E
Tannin .... 49 40N 91 0 E
Tanout .... 14 58N 8 53 E
Tanta .... 30 45N 30 57 E
Tanunda .... 34 30s 139 0 E
Tanzania ■ ..... 6 40s 34 0 E
Taonan .... 45 30N 122 20 E
Taoyuan .... 25 0N 121 4 E
Tapa Shan, Mts. .. 31 45N 109 30 E
Tapachula 14 54N 92 17w
Tapah .... 4 10N 101 17 E
Tapaktuan ...... 3 30N 97 10 E
Tapanui .... 45 56s 169 18 E
Tapti, R. ...... 21 5N 72 40 E
Tapuaenuka, Mt. .. 41 55s 173 50 E
Tara .... 6 55s 74 30 E
Tara, R. .... 56 42N 74 36 E
Tarabagatay,
Khrebet, Mts. .. 47 30N 84 0 E
Tarābulus, Lebanon 34 31N 35 52 E
Tarābulus, Libya . 32 49N 13 7 E
Tarago .... 35 6s 149 39 E
Tarakan .... 3 20N 117 35 E
Taranaki □ ..... 39 5s 174 51 E
Taranga Hill .... 24 0N 72 40 E
Táranto .... 40 30N 17 11 E
Táranto, G. di .. 40 0N 17 15 E
Tarapaca 2 56s 69 46w
Tarapoto 6 30s 76 20w
Tarawera .... 39 2s 176 36 E
Tarawera, L. .... 38 13s 176 27 E
Tarbat Ness 57 52N 3 48w
Tarbela Dam .... 34 0N 72 52 E
Tarbert 57 54N 6 49w
Tarbes .... 43 15N 0 3 E
Taree .... 31 50s 152 30 E
Tarifa 36 1N 5 36w
Tarija 21 30s 64 40w
Tarim, R. ...... 41 5N 86 40 E
Tarkastad ...... 32 0s 26 16 E
Tarkhankut, Mys. . 45 25N 32 30 E

Tarko Sale ...... 64 55N 77 50 E
Tarkwa 5 20N 2 0w
Tarlac .... 15 30N 120 25 E
Tarlton Downs ... 22 40s 136 45 E
Tarn, R. .... 44 5N 1 6 E
Tarn □ .... 43 50N 2 8 E
Tarn-et-Garonne □ 44 8N 1 20 E
Tarnobrzeg ..... 50 35N 21 41 E
Tarnów .... 50 3N 21 0 E
Tarnowskie Góry . 50 27N 18 54 E
Tarom .... 28 11N 55 42 E
Tarragona ...... 41 5N 1 17 E
Tarrasa .... 41 26N 2 1 E
Tarso Emissi .... 21 27N 18 36 E
Tarsus .... 36 58N 34 55 E
Tartagal 22 30s 63 50w
Tartu .... 58 25N 26 58 E
Tartūs .... 34 55N 35 55 E
Tarutung .... 2 0N 99 0 E
Tasāwah .... 26 0N 13 37 E
Taschereau 48 40N 78 40w
Tashauz .... 42 0N 59 20 E
Tashigong ...... 33 0N 79 30 E
Tashkent .... 41 20N 69 10 E
Tashkurgan ..... 37 51N 74 57 E
Tashkurghan .... 36 45N 67 40 E
Tashtagol ...... 52 47N 87 53 E
Tasikmalaya .... 7 18s 108 12 E
Taskan .... 63 5N 150 5 E
Tasman, B. ..... 40 59s 173 25 E
Tasman Glacier .. 43 45s 170 20 E
Tasman Sea ..... 42 0s 170 0 E
Tasmania, I. □ .. 49 0s 146 30 E
Tatabánya ...... 47 32N 18 25 E
Tatar A.S.S.R. □ . 55 30N 51 30 E
Tatarsk .... 55 50N 75 20 E
Tateyama .... 35 0N 139 50 E
Tatien .... 25 45N 118 0 E
Tatra Mts.=
Tatry, Mts. .. 49 20N 20 0 E
Tatry, Mts. ..... 49 20N 20 0 E
Tatsaitan ...... 37 35N 95 0 E
Tatui 23 25s 48 0w
Tatung .... 40 10N 113 10 E
Tatungkow ...... 39 55N 124 10 E
Taubaté 23 5s 45 30w
Taumarunui ..... 38 53s 175 15 E
Taumaturgo 9 0s 73 50w
Taung .... 27 33s 24 47 E
Taungdwingyi ... 20 1N 95 40 E

Taunggyi .... 20 50N 97 0 E
Taungup Taunggya 18 20N 93 40 E
Taunton, U.K. ... 51 1N 3 7w
Taunton, U.S.A. .. 41 54N 71 6w
Taunus, Mts. .... 50 15N 8 20 E
Taupo .... 38 41s 176 7 E
Taupo, L. ...... 38 46s 175 55 E
Tauranga .... 37 35s 176 11 E
Taurus Mts. =
Toros Daglari .. 37 0N 35 0 E
Tava Wan, G. .... 22 40N 114 40 E
Tavani 62 10N 93 30w
Tavda 58 7N 65 8w
Tavda, R. ...... 57 47N 67 16 E
Taveta .... 3 31N 37 37 E
Taveuni, I. 16 51s 179 58w
Tavira 37 8N 7 40w
Tavistock 50 33N 4 9w
Tavoy .... 14 7N 98 18 E
Taw, R. 51 4N 4 11w
Tawitawi, I. .... 5 2N 120 0 E
Tay, Firth of ... 56 25s 3 8w
Tay, L. 56 30N 4 10w
Tay, R. 56 37N 3 58w
Tayabamba ...... 8 15s 77 10 E
Taylor 30 30N 97 30w
Taylor, Mt. 35 16N 107 50w
Taylorville 39 32N 29 20w
Taymyr Pol. .... 75 0N 100 0 E
Tayport 56 27N 2 52w
Tayshet .... 55 58N 97 25 E
Tayside □ 56 30N 3 35w
Taytay .... 10 45N 119 30 E
Tayu .... 25 38N 114 9 E
Tayulehsze ..... 29 15N 98 1 E
Taza 34 10N 4 0w
Tazovskiy ...... 67 28N 78 42 E
Tbilisi .... 41 50N 44 50 E
Tchad ■ .... 12 30N 17 15 E
Tchad, L. ...... 13 30N 14 30 E
Tchibanga ...... 2 45s 11 12 E
Te Anau, L. .... 45 15s 167 45 E
Te Aroha .... 37 32s 175 44 E
Te Awamutu ..... 38 1s 175 20 E
Te Horo .... 40 48s 175 6 E
Te Kuiti .... 38 20s 175 11 E
Te Puke .... 37 46s 176 22 E
Tébessa .... 35 28N 8 9 E
Tebingtinggi ... 3 38s 102 1 E
Tecuala 22 24N 105 30w

Tecuci .... 45 51N 27 27 E
Tedzhen .... 37 23N 60 31 E
Tees, R. 54 34N 1 16w
Teesside 54 37N 1 13w
Tefé 3 25s 64 50w
Tegal .... 6 52s 109 8 E
Tegelen .... 51 20N 6 9 E
Tegina .... 10 5N 6 14 E
Tegucigalpa 14 10N 87 0w
Tehchow .... 37 28N 116 18 E
Tehrãn .... 35 44N 51 30 E
Tehrãn □ .... 35 30N 51 0 E
Tehtsin .... 28 45N 98 58 E
Tehuacán 18 20N 97 30w
Tehuantepec 16 10N 95 19w
Tehuntepec, Istmo
 de 17 0N 94 30w
Teifi, R. 52 7N 4 42w
Teign, R. 50 33N 3 29w
Teignmouth 50 33N 3 30w
Teixeira da Silva . 12 12s 15 52 E
Teixeira de Sousa . 10 42s 22 12 E
Tejo, R. 38 40N 9 24w
Tekapo, L. ..... 43 48s 170 32 E
Tekax 20 20N 89 30w
Tekeli .... 44 50N 79 0 E
Tekirdag .... 40 58N 27 30 E
Tekkali .... 18 43N 84 24 E
Tel Aviv-Yafo .. 32 4N 34 48 E
Tel Mond ...... 32 15N 34 56 E
Tela 15 40N 87 28w
Telanaipura =
 Jambi .... 1 38s 103 30 E
Telavi .... 42 0N 45 30 E
Telegraph Creek . 58 0N 131 10w
Telemark □ ..... 59 30N 8 30 E
Telford 52 42N 2 29w
Telisze .... 39 50N 112 0 E
Telkwa 54 41N 126 56w
Tell City 38 0N 86 44w
Tellicherry ..... 11 45N 75 30 E
Telok Anson .... 4 0N 101 10 E
Telsen 42 30s 66 50w
Telukbetung .... 5 29s 105 17 E
Telukbutun ..... 4 5N 108 7 E
Telukdalem ..... 0 45N 97 50 E
Tema .... 5 41N 0 0 E
Temanggung .... 7 18s 110 10 E
Tembuland ..... 31 30s 28 20 E
Teme, R. 52 9N 2 18w

Temerloh .... 3 27N 102 25 E
Temir .... 49 8N 57 6 E
Temirtou .... 53 10N 87 20 E
Temiskaming 46 44N 79 5w
Temora .... 34 30s 147 30 E
Tempe 33 26N 111 59w
Tempino .... 1 55s 103 23 E
Temple 31 5N 97 28w
Templemore 52 48N 7 50w
Temuco 38 50s 72 50w
Temuka .... 44 14s 171 17 E
Tenado .... 12 6N 2 38 E
Tenali .... 16 15N 80 35 E
Tenancingo 18 98N 99 33w
Tenango 19 0N 99 40w
Tenasserim ..... 12 6N 99 3 E
Tenby 51 40N 4 42w
Tenda, Col di ... 44 9N 7 34 E
Tende .... 44 5N 7 34 E
Tenerife, I. 28 20N 16 40w
Tengah□, Java .... 7 0s 110 0 E
Tengah□,
 Kalimantan .... 2 20s 113 0 E
Tengchung ...... 24 58N 98 30 E
Tenghsien ...... •35 10N 117 10 E
Tengiz, Oz. ..... 50 30N 69 0 E
Tenkasi .... 8 55N 77 20 E
Tenkodogo 11 55N 0 20w
Tennant Creek .. 19 30s 134 0 E
Tennessee, R. ... 37 0N 88 20w
Tennessee □ 36 0N 86 30w
Tenryū-Gawa, R... 34 39N 137 47 E
Tenterfield ..... 29 0s 152 0 E
Teófilo Otoni ... 17 15s 41 30w
Teotihuacan 19 44N 98 50w
Tepic 21 30N 104 54w
Teplice .... 50 39N 13 48 E
Ter, R. .... 42 1N 3 12 E
Téra .... 14 1N 0 50 E
Terang .... 38 3s 142 59 E
Terek, R. ...... 43 44N 46 33 E
Teresina 5 2s 42 45w
Termez .... 37 0N 67 15 E
Términi Imerese . 37 59N 13 51 E
Términos, L. de .. 18 35N 91 30w
Térmoli .... 42 0N 15 0 E
Ternate .... 0 45N 127 25 E
Terneuzen ...... 51 20N 3 50 E
Terni .... 42 34N 12 38 E
Terowie .... 38 10s 138 50 E

Terrace 54 30N 128 35w
Terracina .... 41 17N 13 12 E
Terralba .... 39 43N 8 37 E
Terre Adélie .... 67 0s 140 0 E
Terre Haute 46 30N 75 13w
Terrell 32 44N 96 19w
Terschelling, I. .. 53 25s 5 20 E
Teruel 40 22N 1 8w
Tervola .... 66 6N 24 59 E
Tessalit .... 20 12N 1 0 E
Tessaoua .... 13 45N 8 0 E
Test, R. 51 7N 1 30w
Tetas, Pta. 22 28s 70 38w
Tete .... 16 13s 33 33 E
Tete □ .... 16 20s 32 30 E
Tetouan = ... 35 30N 5 25w
Tetyukhe =
 Dalnergorsk .... 44 40N 135 50 E
Teuco, R. 25 35s 60 11w
Teulon 50 30N 97 20w
Teutoburger Wald . 52 5N 8 15 E
Tevere, R. ...... 41 44N 12 14 E
Teviot, R. 55 36N 2 26w
Tewantin .... 26 27s 153 3 E
Tewkesbury 51 59N 2 9w
Texarkana, Ark. . 33 25N 94 0w
Texarkana, Tex. . 33 25N 94 0w
Texas .... 28 49s 151 15 E
Texas □ 31 30N 98 30w
Texas City 27 20N 95 20w
Texel, I. .... 53 5N 4 50 E
Teziutlán 19 50N 97 30w
Tezpur .... 26 40N 92 45 E
Thabana Ntlenyana 29 30s 29 9 E
Thabazimbi ..... 24 40s 26 4 E
Thailand ■ ..... 16 0N 101 0 E
Thakhek .... 17 25N 104 45 E
Thal .... 33 28N 70 33 E
Thal Desert ..... 31 0N 71 30 E
Thallon .... 28 30s 148 57 E
Thame, R. 51 52N 0 47w
Thames .... 37 7s 175 34 E
Thames, R., Canada 42 19N 82 28w
Thames, R., U.K. . 51 28N 0 43 E
Than Hoa ...... 19 48N 105 46 E
Thana .... 19 12N 72 59 E
Thanet, I. ...... 51 21N 1 20 E
Thangoo P.O. ... 18 10s 122 22 E
Thangool .... 24 29s 150 35 E
Thanjavur ...... 10 48N 79 12 E

Thar Des.=
 Gt. Indian Des. . 28 25N 72 0 E
Thargomindah .... 27 58s 143 46 E
Tharrawaddy .... 17 30N 96 0 E
Thásos, I. ...... 40 40N 24 40 E
Thatcher 32 54N 109 46w
Thaton .... 17 0N 97 39 E
Thaungdut ...... 24 30N 94 30 E
Thayetmyo ..... 19 19N 95 11 E
Thazi .... 21 0N 96 5 E
The Bight 24 19N 75 24w
The Dalles 45 40N 121 11w
The Flatts 32 19N 64 45w
The Great Wall
 of China ...... 37 30N 109 0 E
The Grenadines ... 12 40N 61 15w
The Hague =
 s'Gravenhage ... 52 7N 7 14 E
The Johnston
 Lakes .... 32 25s 120 30 E
The Pas 53 45N 101 15w
Theebine .... 26 0s 152 30 E
Theodore .... 24 55s 150 3 E
Thermaikós Kól. . 40 15N 22 45 E
Thermopolis .... 43 14N 108 10 E
Thermopílai Giona,
 Mt. .... 38 48N 22 45 E
Thessalía □ ..... 39 30N 22 0 E
Thessalon 46 20N 83 30w
Thessaloníki .... 40 38N 23 0 E
Thetford .... 52 25N 0 44 E
Thessaly□=
 Thessalía □ .... 39 30N 22 0 E
Thetford Mines .. 46 8N 71 18w
Thevenard ...... 32 9s 133 38 E
Thibodaux 29 48N 90 49w
Thicket Portage .. 55 25N 97 45w
Thief River Falls . 48 15N 96 10w
Thiès 14 50N 16 51w
Thika .... 1 1s 37 5 E
Thionville ...... 49 20N 6 10 E
Thíra, I. .... 36 23N 25 27 E
Thirsk 54 15N 1 20w
Thisted .... 56 57N 8 42 E
Thíval .... 38 19N 23 19 E
Thomasville, Ala. . 31 55N 87 42w
Thomasville, Fla. . 30 50N 84 0w
Thomasville, N.C. . 35 5N 80 4w
Thompson 55 50N 97 34w
Thonon .... 46 22N 6 29 E

Thori .... 27 20N 84 40 E
Thornaby on Tees . 54 36N 1 19w
Thráki □ .... 41 9N 25 30 E
Three Forks 45 5N 111 40w
Three Hills 51 43N 113 15w
Three Points C. . 4 42N 2 6w
Thule 76 0N 68 0w
Thun .... 46 45N 7 38 E
Thunder Bay .... 48 25N 89 10 E
Thunder River ... 52 13N 119 20w
Thung Song .... 8 10N 99 40 E
Thüringer Wald . 50 35N 11 0 E
Thuringian Forest=
 Thüringer Wald . 50 35N 11 0 E
Thurles 52 40N 7 53w
Thursday I. ..... 10 59s 142 12 E
Thurso, Canada .. 45 36N 75 15w
Thurso, U.K. 58 34N 3 31w
Thurston I. 72 0s 100 0w
Tianjin=Tientsin . 39 10N 117 0 E
Tiaret .... 35 28N 1 21 E
Tiassalé 5 58N 4 57w
Tibati .... 6 22N 12 30 E
Tiber, R.=
 Tevere, R. ...... 41 44N 12 14 E
Tiberias .... 32 47N 35 32 E
Tibesti .... 21 0N 17 30 E
Tibet □ .... 32 30N 86 0 E
Tibet, Plateau of . 35 0N 90 0 E
Tibooburra ..... 29 26s 142 1 E
Tiburón, I. 29 0N 112 30w
Ticino, R. ...... 45 9N 9 14 E
Ticul 20 20N 89 50w
Tidjikdja 18 4N 11 35w
Tiehling .... 42 25N 123 51 E
Tiel .... 51 54N 5 5 E
Tielt .... 51 0N 3 20 E
Tien Shan, Mts. .. 42 0N 80 0 E
T'ienching=
 Tientsin .... 39 10N 117 0 E
Tienen .... 50 48N 4 57 E
Tienshui .... 34 30N 105 34 E
Tientsin .... 39 10N 117 0 E
Tientung .... 23 47N 107 2 E
Tierra de Campos . 42 5N 4 45w
Tierra del Fuego, I. 54 0s 69 0w
Tiétar, R. 39 55N 5 50w
Tiffin 41 8N 83 10w
Tifrah .... 31 19N 34 42 E
Tifton 31 28N 83 32w

Tifu .... 3 39s 126 18 e
Tignish 46 58n 63 57w
Tigris, R. =
  Dijlah, Nahr .. 31 0n 47 25 e
Tigu .... 29 48n 91 38 e
Tigyaing .... 23 45n 96 10 e
Tijuana 32 30n 117 10w
Tikal 17 2n 89 35w
Tikhoretsk ..... 45 56n 40 5 e
Tiko .... 4 4n 9 20 e
Tiksi .... 71 50n 129 0 e
Tilburg .... 51 31n 5 6 e
Tilbury, Canada . 42 17n 84 23 e
Tilbury, U.K. .. 51 27n 0 24 e
Tilichiki .... 61 0n 166 5 e
Tillabéri .... 14 10n 1 30 e
Tillsonburg 42 53n 80 55w
Tílos, I. .... 36 27n 27 27 e
Tilpa .... 30 58s 144 30 e
Timanskiy Kryazh . 65 58n 50 5 e
Timaru .... 44 23s 171 14 e
Timbuktu =
  Tombouctou ... 16 50n 3 0w
Timişoara ...... 4543 1 21 15 e
Timmins 48 28n 81 25w
Timok, R. ..... 44 13n 22 40 e
Timon 5 8s 42 52w
Timor, I. ...... 9 0s 125 0 e
Timor, Sea ..... 10 0s 127 0 e
Timris, C. 19 15n 16 30w
Timur□, Java ... 7 20s 112 0 e
Timur□,
  Kalimantan .... 1 15n 117 0 e
Tindouf 27 50n 8 4w
Tinkurrin ...... 33 0s 117 38 e
Tinnoset .... 59 45n 9 3 e
Tinogasta 28 0s 67 40w
Tínos, I. ...... 37 33n 25 8 e
Tinpak .... 21 40n 111 15 e
Tintinara ...... 35 48s 140 2 e
Tioman, Pulau .. 2 50n 104 10 e
Tipongpani ..... 27 20n 95 55 e
Tipperary 52 28n 8 10w
Tipperary □ 52 37n 7 55w
Tipton 52 32n 2 4w
Tíra .... 32 14n 34 56 e
Tîrân .... 32 45n 51 0 e
Tirana .... 41 18n 19 49 e
Tiraspol .... 46 55n 29 35 e
Tirat Karmel .... 32 46n 34 58 e

Tirat Tsevi ..... 32 26n 35 51 e
Tirat Yehuda .... 32 1n 34 56 e
Tire .... 38 5n 27 50 e
Tirebolu .... 40 58n 38 45 e
Tiree, I. 56 31n 6 49w
Tírgovişte ..... 44 55n 25 27 e
Tírgu-Jiu ...... 45 5n 23 19 e
Tirgu-Mureş ..... 46 31n 24 38 e
Tirich Mir, Mt. .. 36 15n 71 35 e
Tirol, Reg. ..... 46 50n 11 40 e
Tirol □ .... 47 3n 10 43 e
Tiruchchirappalli . 10 45n 78 45 e
Tirunelveli....... 8 45n 77 45 e
Tirupati .... 13 45n 79 30 e
Tisa, R. .... 45 15n 20 17 e
Tisdale 52 50n 104 0w
Tit-Ary .... 71 58n 127 1 e
Titicaca, L. 15 30s 69 30w
Titiwa .... 12 14n 12 53 e
Titlagarh .... 20 15n 83 5 e
Titograd .... 42 30n 19 19 e
Titov Veles ..... 41 46n 21 47 e
Titovo Uzice .... 43 55n 19 50 e
Titule .... 3 15n 25 31 e
Titusville 41 35n 79 39w
Tiverton 50 54n 3 30w
Tívoli .... 41 58n 12 45 e
Tiwi .... 22 45n 59 12 e
Tizi-Ouzou ..... 36 48n 4 2 e
Tizimín 21 0n 88 1w
Tlaxcala □ 19 30n 98 20w
Tlaxiaco 17 10n 97 40w
Tlemcen 34 52n 1 15w
Toay 36 50s 64 30w
Toba Kakar Ra... 31 30n 69 0 e
Tobago, I. 11 10n 60 30w
Tobelo .... 1 25n 127 56 e
Tobermorey,
  Australia ..... 22 12s 138 0 e
Tobermory, Canada 45 12n 81 40w
Tobermory, U.K. .. 56 37n 6 4w
Tobolsk .... 58 0n 68 10 e
Tobruk = Tubruq . 32 7n 23 55 e
Tocantinopolis ... 6 20s 47 25w
Tocantins, R. 1 45s 49 10w
Toccoa 34 35n 83 19w
Tochigi .... 36 25n 139 45 e
Tochigi □ ...... 36 45n 139 45 e
Tocopilla 22 5s 70 10w
Tocumwal ...... 35 45s 145 31 e

Todos os Santos,
  B. de 12 45s 38 40w
Togliatti .... 53 37n 49 18 e
Togo ■ .... 6 15n 1 35 e
Tohoku □ ...... 38 40n 142 0 e
Tokaj .... 48 8n 21 27 e
Tōkamachi ..... 37 8n 138 43 e
Tokar .... 18 27n 37 43 e
Tokara Kaikyō, Str. 30 0n 130 0 e
Tokara-Shima, I. . 29 0n 129 0 e
Tokarahi .... 44 56s 170 39 e
Tokat .... 40 22n 36 35 e
Tokelau Is. 9 0s 172 0w
Tokmak .... 47 16n 35 42 e
Tokombere ...... 11 18n 3 30 e
Toku-no-Shima, I. . 27 56n 129 2 e
Tokushima ..... 34 0n 134 45 e
Tokushima □ .... 35 50n 134 50 e
Tokuyama ...... 34 0n 131 50 e
Tōyama .... 35 45n 139 45 e
Tōkyō □ .... 35 40n 139 30 e
Tolaga .... 38 21s 178 20 e
Tolbukhin ...... 43 37n 27 49 e
Toledo, Spain ... 39 50n 4 2w
Toledo, U.S.A. .. 41 37n 83 33w
Toledo, Mts. de .. 39 30n 4 30w
Tolima, Mt. 4 40n 75 19w
Tolitoli .... 1 5n 120 50 e
Tolleson 33 29n 112 10w
Tolo, Teluk, G. .. 2 20s 122 10 e
Tolosa 43 8n 2 5w
Toluca 19 20n 99 50w
Tolun .... 42 22n 116 30 e
Tom Price ...... 22 50s 117 40 e
Tomar 39 36n 8 25w
Tombigbee, R. ... 32 0n 88 6 e
Tombouctou 16 50n 3 0w
Tombstone 31 40n 110 4w
Tomini, Teluk, G. . 0 10s 122 0 e
Tomintoul 57 15n 3 22w
Tommot .... 58 50n 126 30 e
Tomsk .... 56 30n 85 12 e
Tonalá 16 8n 93 41w
Tonantins ...... 2 45s 67 45 e
Tonawanda 43 0n 78 54w
Tonbridge ...... 51 12n 0 18 e
Tonga ■ 20 0s 173 0w
Tongaat .... 29 33s 31 9 e
Tongatapu, I. ... 20 0s 174 0w
Tongeren ...... 50 47n 5 28 e

Tonghing .... 21 30n 108 0 e
Tongking, G. of .. 20 0n 108 0 e
Tongoy 30 25s 71 40w
Tongue 58 29n 4 25w
Tonj .... 7 20n 28 44 e
Tonk .... 26 6n 75 54 e
Tonlé Sap, L. ... 13 0n 104 0 e
Tonopah 38 4n 117 12w
Tønsberg ...... 59 19n 11 3 e
Tooele 40 30n 112 20w
Toompine ...... 27 15s 144 19 e
Toowoomba ..... 27 32s 151 56 e
Top, Oz. ...... 65 35n 32 0 e
Topeka .... 39 3n 95 40 e
Topki .... 55 25n 85 20 e
Topley 54 32n 126 5w
Toppenish 46 27n 120 16w
Torata 17 3s 70 1w
Torbat-e
  Heydariyeh 35 15n 59 12w
Torbay, Canada .. 47 40n 52 42w
Torbay, U.K. ... 50 26n 3 31w
Tordesillas 41 30n 5 0w
Torgau .... 51 32n 13 0 e
Torhout .... 51 5n 3 7 e
Torino .... 45 4n 7 40 e
Torne, R. ...... 65 48n 24 8 e
Torneträsk, L. ... 68 20n 19 10 e
Tornio .... 65 57n 24 12 e
Tornquist 38 0s 62 15w
Toro, Cerro del ... 29 0s 69 50w
Toronáios Kól. .. 40 5n 23 30 e
Toronto, Canada . 43 39n 79 20w
Toronto, U.S.A. .. 40 28n 80 36w
Tororo .... 0 45n 34 12 e
Toros Dağlari, Mts. 37 0n 35 0 e
Torquay 50 27n 3 31w
Torre Annunziata . 40 45n 14 26 e
Tôrre de Moncorvo 41 12n 7 8w
Torrelavega 43 20n 4 5w
Torremolinos 36 38n 4 30w
Torrens, L. ..... 31 0s 137 45 e
Torreon 25 33n 103 25w
Torres Str. ..... 10 0s 142 0 e
Torres Vedras ... 39 5n 9 15w
Torrevieja 37 59n 0 42w
Torridge, R. 51 3n 4 11w
Torridon, L. 57 35n 5 50w
Torrington 41 50n 73 9w
Tortola, I. 18 19n 65 0w

Tortosa .... 40 49n 0 31 e
Tortosa, C. ..... 40 41n 0 52 e
Toruń .... 53 3n 18 39 e
Tosa-Wan, G. ... 33 15n 133 30 e
Toscana □ ...... 43 30n 11 5 e
Tostado 29 15s 61 50w
Toteng .... 20 22s 22 58 e
Totma .... 60 0n 42 40 e
Totnes 50 26n 3 41w
Totness 5 53n 56 19w
Totonicapán 14 50n 91 20w
Tottori .... 35 30n 134 15 e
Tottori □ ...... 35 30n 134 12 e
Toubkal,
  Djebel, Mt. ... 31 0n 8 0w
Touggourt ...... 33 10n 6 0 e
Tougué 11 25n 11 50w
Toul .... 48 40n 5 53 e
Toulon .... 43 10n 5 55 e
Toulouse ...... 43 37n 1 28 e
Toummo .... 22 45n 14 8 e
Toungoa .... 19 0n 96 30 e
Touraine, Reg. .. 47 20n 0 30 e
Tourane = Da Nang 16 10n 108 7 e
Tourcoing ...... 50 42n 3 10 e
Tournai .... 50 35n 3 25 e
Tournon .... 45 5n 4 50 e
Tours .... 47 22n 0 40 e
Touwsrivier ..... 33 20s 20 0 e
Towang .... 27 33n 91 56 e
Townsend, Mt. ... 36 25s 148 16 e
Townsville ..... 19 15s 146 45 e
Towson 39 26n 76 34w
Towyn 52 37n 4 8w
Toyama .... 36 40n 137 15 e
Toyama □ ...... 36 45n 137 30 e
Toyama-Wan, G... 37 0n 137 30 e
Toyohashi ...... 34 45n 137 25 e
Toyokawa ...... 34 48n 137 27 e
Toyonaka ...... 34 50n 135 35 e
Toyooka .... 35 35n 135 55 e
Toyota .... 35 5n 137 9 e
Tozeur .... 33 54n 8 4 e
Trabzon .... 41 0n 39 45 e
Tracy 44 12n 95 3w
Tradom .... 30 0n 83 59 e
Trafalgar ...... 38 14s 146 12 e
Trafalgar, C. 36 10n 6 2w
Traiguón 38 12s 72 40w
Trail 49 5n 117 40w

Tralee 52 16N 9 42w
Tramore 52 10N 7 10w
Tranås .... 58 3N 14 59 E
Trancas 26 11s 65 20w
Trang .... 7 33N 99 38 E
Trangan, I. ..... 6 40s 134 20 E
Trani .... 41 17N 16 24 E
Tranoroa .... 24 42s 45 4 E
Transcona 49 50N 97 0w
Transilvania, Reg.=
  Transylvania,
  Reg. .... 46 20N 25 0 E
Transkei □ ..... 32 15s 28 15 E
Transvaal □ .... 25 0s 29 0 E
Transylvania, Reg. 46 20N 25 0 E
Transylvanian
  Alps, Mts...... 45 30N 25 0 E
Trápani .... 38 1N 12 30 E
Traralgon ...... 38 6s 146 31 E
Tras os Montes Alto
  Douro, Reg.... 41 30N 7 5w
Trasimeno, L. ... 43 30N 12 5 E
Traverse City ... 44 45N 85 39w
Travnik .... 44 17N 17 39 E
Trayning .... 31 8s 117 42 E
Třebíč .... 49 13N 15 53 E
Trebinje .... 42 44N 18 22 E
Třeboň .... 48 59N 14 48 E
Tredegar 51 47N 3 16w
Tregaron 52 14N 3 56w
Treinta y Tres .. 33 10s 54 50w
Trekveld .... 30 35s 19 45 E
Trelew 43 10s 65 20w
Trelleborg ..... 55 20N 13 5 E
Tremonton 41 45N 112 10w
Trenggalek ..... 8 5s 111 44 E
Trenque Lauquen . 36 0s 62 45w
Trent, R. 53 40N 0 40w
Trentino-Alto
  Adige □ ...... 46 5N 11 0 E
Trento .... 46 5N 11 8 E
Trenton, Canada . 44 10N 77 40w
Trenton, U.S.A. . 40 15N 74 41w
Trepassey 46 43N 53 25w
Tres Arroyos 38 20s 60 20w
Três Corações ... 21 30s 45 30w
Três Lagoas 20 50s 51 50w
Tres Montes, C. . 47 0s 75 35w
Tres Puentes ... 27 50s 70 15w
Tres Puntas, C. . 47 0s 66 0w

Três Rios........ 22 20s 43 30w
Treungen .... 58 55N 8 27 E
Treviso .... 45 40N 12 15 E
Triabunna ...... 42 28s 148 0 E
Trichinopoly=
  Tiruchchirappalli 10 45N 78 45 E
Trichur .... 10 20N 76 18 E
Trier .... 49 45N 6 37 E
Trieste .... 45 39N 13 45 E
Triglav, Mt...... 46 30N 13 45 E
Trikkala .... 39 34N 21 47 E
Trikora,
  Puncak, Mt. ... 4 11s 138 0 E
Trim 53 34N 6 48w
Trincomalee ..... 8 38N 81 15 E
Trindade, I. 20 20s 29 50w
Trinidad, Bolivia . 14 54s 64 50w
Trinidad, Cuba .. 21 40N 80 0w
Trinidad, U.S.A. . 37 15N 104 30w
Trinidad, Uruguay 33 30s 56 50w
Trinidad I., Arg. . 39 10s 62 0w
Trinidad I.,
  Trinidad &
  Tobago 10 30N 61 20w
Trinidad &
  Tobago ■ 10 30N 61 20w
Trinity, R. 29 47N 94 42w
Trinity Is. 56 33N 154 25w
Tripoli, Lebanon=
  Tarābulus .... 34 34N 35 52 E
Tripoli, Libya=
  Tarābulus .... 32 49N 13 7 E
Trípolis .... 37 31N 22 25 E
Tripura □ ...... 24 0N 92 0 E
Tristan de Cunha, I. 37 6s 12 20w
Trivandrum ..... 8 31N 77 0 E
Trnava .... 48 23N 17 35 E
Trois Pistoles ... 48 5N 69 10w
Trois Rivières .. 46 25s 72 40w
Troitsk .... 54 10N 61 35 E
Troitsko Pechorsk . 62 40N 56 10 E
Trollhättan .... 58 17N 12 20 E
Trompsburg .... 30 2s 25 5 E
Troms .... 69 19N 19 0 E
Tromsø .... 69 40N 19 0 E
Tronador, Mt. ... 41 53s 71 0w
Trondheim ...... 63 25N 10 25 E
Trondheims, Fd. . 63 40N 10 45 E
Tróodos, Mt. ... 34 58N 32 55 E
Troon 55 33N 4 40w

Trossachs, Reg. .. 56 14N 4 24w
Trotternish, Reg. . 57 32N 6 15w
Trouville ...... 49 21N 0 54 E
Trowbridge 51 18N 2 12w
Troy, Ala. 31 50N 85 58w
Troy, N.Y. 42 45N 73 39w
Troy, Ohio 40 0N 84 10w
Troyes .... 48 19N 4 3 E
Truckee 39 29N 120 12w
Trujillo, Honduras . 16 0N 86 0w
Trujillo, Peru 8 0s 79 0w
Trujillo, Sp. ... 39 28N 5 55w
Trujillo, Ven. ... 9 22N 70 26w
Truk, I. .... 7 25N 151 46 E
Trung-Phan, Reg. . 16 0N 108 0 E
Truro, Canada ... 45 21N 63 14w
Truro, U.K. 50 17N 5 2w
Truslove .... 33 20s 121 45 E
Truth or
  Consequences ... 33 9N 107 16w
Tsaidam, Reg. ... 37 0N 95 0 E
Tsanghsien .... 38 24N 116 57 E
Tsangpo, R. ..... 29 40N 89 0 E
Tsaochwang .... 35 11N 115 28 E
Tsaratanana .... 16 47s 47 39 E
Tsaratanana, Mt. de 14 0s 49 0 E
Tsaring Nor, L. .. 35 0N 97 0 E
Tsau .... 20 12s 22 22 E
Tsavo .... 3 0s 38 27 E
Tselinograd .... 51 10N 71 30 E
Tsetserleg ..... 47 46N 101 32 E
Tsévié .... 6 25N 1 13 E
Tshabong .... 26 2s 22 29 E
Tshane .... 24 5s 21 54 E
Tshwane 22 24s 22 11N
Tsiaotso .... 35 11N 113 37 E
Tsihombé ...... 25 18s 45 29 E
Tsimlyanskoye,
  Vdkhr. .... 47 45N 42 0 E
Tsin Ling
  Shan, Mts. .... 34 0N 107 30 E
Tsinan .... 34 50N 105 40 E
Tsincheng ..... 35 30N 113 0 E
Tsinghai .... 36 56N 116 52 E
Tsinghai □ ..... 35 10N 96 0 E
Tsingkiang, Kiangsi 27 50N 114 38 E
Tsingkiang, Kiangsu 33 30N 119 2 E
Tsingning ..... 35 25N 105 50 E
Tsingshih ...... 29 43N 112 13 E
Tsingtao .... 36 0N 120 25 E

Tsining,
  Inner Mongolia . 40 59N 112 59 E
Tsining, Shantung . 35 30N 116 35 E
Tsinyang ...... 35 2N 112 59 E
Tsiroanomandidy . 18 46s 46 2 E
Tsitsihar....... 47 20N 124 0 E
Tsivory .... 24 4s 46 5 E
Tskhinvali ..... 42 14N 44 1 E
Tsna, R. .... 54 32N 42 5 E
Tsu .... 34 45N 136 25 E
Tsuchiura ...... 36 12N 140 15 E
Tsugaru-Kaikyo,
  Str. .... 41 30N 140 30 E
Tsuiluan ...... 47 58N 28 27 E
Tsumeb .... 19 9s 17 44 E
Tsungfa .... 23 35N 113 35 E
Tsungtso ...... 22 20N 107 25 E
Tsunyi .... 27 40N 107 0 E
Tsuruga .... 35 35N 136 0 E
Tsushima-Kaikyō,
  Str. .... 34 20N 130 0 E
Tsuyama .... 35 0N 134 0 E
Tswana □ ...... 24 0s 27 50 E
Tual .... 5 30s 132 50 E
Tuam 53 30N 8 50w
Tuamotu Arch. .. 17 0s 144 0w
Tuapse .... 44 5N 39 10 E
Tuatapere ..... 48 7s 167 43 E
Tubac 31 45N 111 2w
Tuban .... 6 57s 112 4 E
Tubarão 28 30s 49 0w
Tubas .... 32 20N 35 22 E
Tubayq, Jabal at . 29 40N 37 30 E
Tübingen ...... 48 31N 9 4 E
Tubo, R. .... 10 25N 7 10 E
Tubruq .... 32 7N 23 55 E
Tubuai Is. 23 20s 151 0w
Tucacas 10 48N 68 19w
Tuckanarra .... 27 8s 118 1 E
Tucker's Town .. 32 19N 64 43w
Tucson 32 14N 110 59w
Tucumcari 35 12N 103 45w
Tucupita 9 4N 62 0w
Tucurui 3 45s 49 48w
Tudela 42 4N 1 39w
Tugela, R. ..... 29 14s 31 30 E
Tuguegarao .... 17 35N 121 42 E
Tugur .... 53 50N 136 45 E
Tuhshan .... 25 40N 107 30 E
Tuktoyaktuk ... 69 15N 133 0w

Tukuyu .... 9 17s 33 35 E
Tula, Nigeria ... 9 51N 11 27 E
Tula, U.S.S.R. .. 54 13N 37 32 E
Tulan .... 37 24N 98 1 E
Tulare 36 15N 119 26w
Tulbagh .... 33 16s 19 6 E
Tulcán 0 48N 77 43w
Tulcea .... 45 13N 28 46 E
Tuléar .... 23 21s 43 40 E
Tuléar □ ...... 21 0s 45 0 E
Tuli .... 1 24s 122 26 E
Tülkarm .... 32 19N 35 10 E
Tullahoma 35 23N 86 12w
Tullamore 53 17N 7 30w
Tulle .... 45 16N 1 47 E
Tullow 52 48N 6 45w
Tully .... 17 30s 141 0 E
Tulymaythah .... 32 40N 20 55 E
Tulsa 36 10N 96 0w
Tulua 4 6N 76 11w
Tulun .... 54 40N 100 10 E
Tulungagung ... 8 5s 111 54 E
Tuma, R. 13 6N 84 35w
Tumaco 1 50N 78 45w
Tumatumari 5 20N 58 55w
Tumba, L. ..... 0 50s 18 0 E
Tumbes 3 30s 80 20w
Tumby Bay .... 34 21s 136 8 E
Tumen .... 42 46N 129 59 E
Tumeremo 7 18N 61 30w
Tumkur 13 18N 77 12w
Tummel, L. 56 43N 3 55w
Tump .... 26 7N 62 16 E
Tumpat .... 6 11N 102 10 E
Tumucumaque
  South 2 0N 55 0w
Tumut .... 35 16s 148 13 E
Tunduma ...... 9 20s 32 48 E
Tunbridge Wells . 51 7N 0 16 E
Tunduru ...... 11 0s 37 25 E
Tundzha, R. .... 41 40N 26 34 E
Tungabhadra, R. . 15 57N 78 15 E
Tungcheng ..... 31 0N 117 3 E
Tungchow ..... 39 58N 116 50 E
Tungchuan ..... 35 4N 109 2 E
Tungfanghsien .. 18 50N 108 33 E
Tunghwa ...... 41 46N 126 0 E
Tungkiang ..... 47 40N 132 30 E
Tungkwanshan .. 31 0N 117 45 E

Tungliao .... 43 42N 122 11 E
Tunglu .... 29 50N 119 35 E
Tungping .... 35 50N 116 20 E
Tungshan ...... 29 36N 144 28 E
Tungshan, I. ..... 23 40N 117 31 E
Tungsten 61 52N 128 1W
Tungtai .... 32 55N 120 15 E
Tungting Hu, L. .. 28 30N 112 30 E
Tungtze .... 27 59N 106 56 E
Tunhwa .... 43 27N 128 16 E
Tunhwang ...... 40 5N 94 46 E
Tunis .... 36 50N 10 11 E
Tunisia ■ ...... 33 30N   9 0 E
Tunja .... 5 40N 73 25 E
Tuoy-khaya 62 30N 111   0W
Tupelo 34 15N 88 42W
Tupik .... 54 26N 119 57 E
Tupiza 21 30s 65 40W
Tupper Lake 44 18N 74 30W
Tupungato, Mt. .. 33 15s 69 50W
Túquerres 1 5N 77 37W
Tur .... 31 47N 35 14 E
Tura, India ..... 25 30N 90 16 E
Tura, Tanz. ..... 5 15s 33 48 E
Turayf .... 31 45N 38 30 E
Turbaco 10 20N 75 25W
Turbo .... 8 6N 76 43 E
Turda .... 46 35N 23 48 E
Turek .... 52 3N 18 30 E
Turfan .... 43 6N 89 24 E
Turfan Depression . 43 0N 88 0 E
Tŭrgovishte ..... 43 17N 26 38 E
Turgutlu .... 38 30N 27 48 E
Turhal .... 40 24N 36 19 E
Turia, R. 39 27N   0 19W
Turiaçu 1 40s 45 28W
Turin=Torino .... 45 3N   7 40 E
Turkana, L. ..... 4 10N 36 10 E
Turkestan ...... 43 10N 68 10 E
Turkey ■ .... 39 0N 36 0 E
Turkey Creek P.O. 17 2s 128 12 E
Turkmen S.S.R. .. 39 0N 59 0 E
Turks Is. 21 20N 71 20W
Turku .... 60 27N 22 14 E
Turlock 37 30N 122 55W
Turneffe Is. 17 20N 87 50W
Turnhout 51 19N   4 57W
Tûrnovo .... 43 5N 25 41 E
Turnu Măgurele .. 43 46N 24 56 E
Turnu-Severin ... 44 39N 22 41 E

Turriff 57 32N   2 58W
Turtle 48 52N 92 40W
Turtleford 53 30N 108 50W
Turūbah .... 28 20N 43 15 E
Turun ja Pori □ .. 61 0N 22 30 E
Tuscaloosa 33 13N 87 31W
Tuskegee 32 26N 85 42W
Tutoja 2 45s 42 20W
Tuttlingen ...... 47 59N   8 50 E
Tutuala .... 8 25s 127 15 E
Tutuila, I. 14 19s 170 50W
Turukhansk ..... 65 55N 88 5 E
Tava, A.S.S.R. ... 52 0N 95 0 E
Tuvalu ■ .... 8 0s 176 0 E
Tuwaiq, Jabal .. 23 0N 46 0 E
Tuxpan 20 50N 97 30W
Tuxtla Gutiérrez . 16 50N 93 10W
Tuy 42 3N   8 39W
Tuyun .... 26 5N 107 20 E
Tuz Gölü .... 38 45N 33 30 E
Tuz Khurmātu ... 34 50N 44 45 E
Tweed, R. 55 46N   2 0W
Tweedsmuir Prov.
  Park 52 55N 126 5W
Tweeling .... 27 38s 28 30 E
Twin Falls 42 30N 114 30W
Two Rivers 44 10N 87 31W
Tyler 32 20N 95 15W
Tyndinskiy ..... 55 10N 124 43 E
Tyne, R. 55 1N   1 26W
Tyne & Wear □ .. 54 55N   1 35W
Tynemouth 55 1N   1 27W
Tyre =Sur ...... 33 19N 35 16 E
Tyrendarra ..... 38 12s 141 50 E
Tyrifjorden ..... 60 2N 10 3 E
Tyrol, Reg.=
  Tirol, Reg. ..... 46 50N 11 40 E
Tyrrhenian Sea .. 40 0N 12 30 E
Tyumen .... 57 0N 65 18 E
Tywi, R. 51 46N   4 22W
Tzaneen .... 23 47s 30 9 E
Tzeki .... 27 40N 117 5 E
Tzekung .... 29 25N 104 30 E
Tzekwei .... 31 0N 110 46 E
Tzepo .... 36 28N 117 58 E
Tzeyang .... 32 47N 108 58 E

U

Uarsciek .... 2 28N 45 55 E
Uaupés 0 8s 67 5W
Ubá 21 0s 43 0W
Ubaitaba 14 18s 39 20W
Ube .... 34 6N 131 20 E
Ubeda 38 3N   3 23W
Uberaba 19 50s 48 0W
Uberlândia 19 0s 48 20W
Ubiaja .... 6 40N   6 20 E
Ubon Ratchathani 15 15N 104 50 E
Ubundu .... 0 22s 25 30 E
Ucayali, R. 4 30s 73 30W
Uchi Lake 51 10N 92 40W
Uchiura-Wan, G.. 42 25N 140 40 E
Ucluelet 48 57N 125 32W
Udaipur .... 24 36N 73 44 E
Uddevalla ...... 58 21N 11 55 E
Uddjaur, L. ..... 65 55N 17 50 E
Udi .... 6 23N   7 21 E
Údine .... 46 5N 13 10 E
Udipi .... 13 25N 74 42 E
Udmurt A.S.S.R. □ 57 30N 52 30 E
Udon Thani ..... 17 29N 102 46 E
Udzungwa Ra. ... 8 30s 35 30 E
Ueda .... 36 30N 138 10 E
Uelen 66 10N 170 0W
Uelzen .... 53 0N 10 33 E
Uere, R. .... 3 42N 25 24 E
Ufa .... 54 45N 55 55 E
Uganda ■ .... 2 0N 32 0 E
Ugashik Lakes ... 57 0N 157 0W
Ugep .... 5 50N   8 1 E
Uglegorsk ...... 49 10N 142 5 E
Uitenhage ...... 33 40s 25 28 E
Ujiji=Kigoma-Ujiji 4 57s 29 40 E
Ujjain .... 23 9N 75 43 E
Ujpest .... 47 33N 19 6 E
Ujung Pandang .. 5 10s 119 0 E
Uka .... 57 50N 162 0 E
Ukerewe I. ...... 2 0s 33 0 E
Ukhrul .... 25 10N 94 25 E
Ukhta .... 63 55N 54 0 E
Ukiah 39 10N 123 9W
Ukrainian S.S.R. □ 48 0N 35 0 E
Ulaanbaatar =
Ulan Bator

= Ulaanbaatar .. 48 0N 107 0 E
Ulan Ude .... 52 0N 107 30 E
Ulanhot .... 46 5N 122 1 E
Ulhasnagar ..... 19 15N 73 10 E
Ulladulla .... 35 21s 150 29 E
Ullapool 57 54N   5 10W
Ullswater, L. 54 35N   2 52W
Ulm .... 48 23N 10 0 E
Ulricehamn ..... 57 46N 13 26 E
Ulrichsville 40 27N 81 30W
Ulster □ 54 45N   6 30W
Uluguru Mts. .... 7 15s 37 30 E
Ulverston 54 13N   3 7W
Ulverstone ..... 41 11s 146 11 E
Ulyanovsk ...... 54 25N 48 25 E
Uman .... 48 40N 30 12 E
Umaria .... 23 31N 80 40 E
Umba .... 42 53N 12 30 E
Umeå .... 63 45N 20 20 E
Umfuli, R. ...... 17 50s 29 40 E
Umkomaas ..... 30 13s 30 48 E
Umm al Qaiwain . 25 30N 55 35 E
Umm el Fahm ... 32 31N 35 9 E
Umm Keddada ... 13 36N 26 42 E
Umm Lajj ...... 25 0N 37 23 E
Umnak I. 53 0N 168 0W
Umniati, R. ..... 17 30s 29 23 E
Umtali .... 18 58s 32 38 E
Umtata .... 31 36s 28 49 E
Umuahia .... 5 33N   7 29 E
Umvuma .... 19 16s 30 30 E
Umzimvubu .... 31 38s 29 33 E
Umzinto .... 30 15s 30 45 E
Unac, R. .... 44 30N 16 9 E
Unalakleet 63 53N 160 50W
Unalaska I. 54 0N 164 30W
Uncompahgre Pk. 38 5N 107 32W
Underbool ...... 35 10s 141 51 E
Ungarie .... 33 38s 146 56 E
Ungava B. 59 30N 67 0W
Ungava Pen. 60 0N 75 0W
União 4 50s 37 50W
União da Vitória . 26 5s 51 0W
Unimak I. 54 30N 164 30W
Union 34 49N 81 39W
Union City, Pa. .. 41 53N 79 50W
Union City,
  Tenn. 36 35N 89 0W
Union Gap 46 38N 120 29W
Union of Soviet

Socialist
  Republics ■ ... 60 0N 60 0 E
Uniondale ...... 33 39s 23 7 E
Uniontown 39 54N 79 45W
United Arab
  Emirates ■ ... 24 0N 54 30 E
United Kingdom ■ 55 0N   3 0W
United States
  of America ■ ... 37 0N 96 0W
Unity 52 30N 109 5W
Unst, I. 60 50N   0 55W
Ünye .... 41 5N 37 15 E
Uozu .... 36 48N 137 24 E
Upata 8 1N 62 24W
Upington .... 28 25s 21 15 E
Upolu, I. 13 58s 172 0W
Upper □ .... 10 40N   2 0 E
Upper Hutt ..... 41 8s 175 5 E
Upper
  Musquodoboit . 45 10N 62 58W
Upper Volta ■ .. 12 0N   0 30W
Uppsala .... 59 53N 17 42 E
Uppsala □ ...... 60 0N 17 30 E
Ur .... 30 55N 46 25 E
Uracará 2 20s 57 50W
Ural, Mt. .... 33 21s 146 12 E
Ural Mts. =
  Uralskie Gory .. 60 0N 59 0 E
Ural, R. .... 47 0N 51 48 E
Uralla .... 30 37s 151 29 E
Uralsk .... 51 20N 51 20 E
Uralskie Gory ... 60 0N 59 0 E
Urandangi ...... 21 32s 138 14 E
Uranium City ... 59 28N 108 40W
Urawa .... 35 50N 139 40 E
Uray .... 60 5N 65 15 E
Urbana, Ill. 40 7N 88 12W
Urbana, Ohio ... 40 9N 83 44W
Urbino .... 43 43N 12 38 E
Ure, R. 54 1N   1 12W
Urengoy .... 66 0N 78 0 E
Urfa .... 37 12N 38 50 E
Urfahr .... 48 19N 14 17 E
Urgench .... 41 40N 60 30 E
Uribia 11 43N 72 16W
Urim .... 31 18N 34 32 E
Urmia, L. =
  Daryâcheh-ye
  Reza'iyeh .... 37 30N 45 30 E
Uruaca 14 35s 49 16W

Uruapán 19 30N 102 0w
Uruçui 7 20s 44 28w
Uruguay ■ 32 30s 55 30w
Uruguay, R. 34 0s 58 30w
Uruguaiana 29 50s 57 0w
Urumchi=
  Wulumuchi .... 43 40N 87 50 E
Urungu, R. .... 46 30N 88 50 E
Uruzgan □ .... 33 30N 66 0 E
Usa, R. .... 65 57N 56 55 E
Uşak .... 38 43N 29 28 E
Usakos .... 22 0s 15 31 E
Usambara Mts..... 4 50s 38 20 E
Usedom, I. .... 53 50N 13 55 E
Usfan .... 21 58N 39 27 E
Ush-Tobe .... 45 16N 78 0 E
Ushant, I.=
  Ouessant, I. d' . 48 28N 5 6w
Ushuaia 54 50s 68 23w
Ushuman .... 52 47N 126 32 E
Usk, R. 51 36N 2 58w
Üsküdar .... 41 0N 29 5 E
Usman .... 52 5N 39 48 E
Usoke .... 5 8s 32 24 E
Usolye Sibirskoye . 52 40N 103 40 E
Usoro .... 5 34N 6 13 E
Uspallata, P...... 32 30s 69 28w
Uspenskiy .... 48 50N 72 55 E
Ussuriysk .... 43 40N 131 50 E
Ust-Ilga .... 55 5N 104 55 E
Ust-Ilimsk ...... 58 3N 102 39 E
Ust Ishim .... 57 45N 71 10 E
Ust-Kamchatsk ... 56 10N 162 0 E
Ust Kamenogorsk . 50 0N 82 20 E
Ust-Kut .... 56 50N 105 10 E
Ust Kuyga .... 70 1N 135 36 E
Ust Maya .... 60 30N 134 20 E
Ust Olenek ...... 73 0N 120 10 E
Ust Port .... 70 0N 84 10 E
Ust Tsilma ...... 65 25N 52 0 E
Ust-Tungir ...... 55 25N 120 15 E
Ust Usa .... 66 0N 56 30 E
Ustchaun .... 68 47N 170 30 E
Ustí nad Labem ... 50 41N 14 3 E
Ustica, I. .... 38 42N 13 10 E
Ustye .... 55 30N 97 30 E
Usulután 13 25N 88 28w
Utah □ 39 30N 111 30w
Utara □ , Sulawesi 1 0N 120 3 E
Utara □ , Sumatera 2 0N 99 0 E

Utete .... 7 59s 38 47 E
Uthmaniya ...... 25 5N 49 6 E
Utica 43 5N 75 18w
Utrecht, Neth. .... 52 3N 5 8 E
Utrecht, Neth. □ .. 52 6N 5 7 E
Utrecht, S. Africa . 27 38s 30 20 E
Utrera 37 12N 5 48w
Utsunomiya ..... 36 30N 139 50 E
Uttar Pradesh □ .. 27 0N 80 0 E
Uttaradit .... 17 36N 100 5 E
Uttoxeter 52 53N 1 50w
Uudenmaa □ ..... 60 25N 23 0 E
Uuldza .... 49 8N 112 10 E
Uusikaupunki ... 60 47N 21 28 E
Uvalde 29 15N 99 48w
Uvat .... 59 5N 68 50 E
Uvinza .... 5 5s 30 24 E
Uvira .... 3 22s 29 3 E
Uvs Nuur, L. ..... 50 20N 92 30 E
Uwajima .... 33 10N 132 35 E
Uxmal 20 22N 89 46w
Uyo .... 5 1N 7 53 E
Uyuni 20 35s 66 55w
Uzbek S.S.R. ..... 40 5N 65 0 E

V

Vaal, R. .... 29 4s 23 38 E
Vaasa .... 63 10N 21 35 E
Vaasa □ .... 63 6N 23 0 E
Vác .... 47 49N 19 10 E
Vadodara .... 22 20N 73 10 E
Vadsø .... 70 3N 29 50 E
Váh, R. .... 47 55N 18 0 E
Vaigach .... 70 10N 59 0 E
Val d'Or 48 7N 77 47w
Val Marie 49 15N 107 45w
Valahia, Reg. .... 44 35N 25 0 E
Valchete 40 40s 66 20w
Val-d'Oise □ ..... 49 5N 2 0 E
Val-de-Marne □ .. 48 45N 2 28 E
Valdayskaya
  Vozvyshennost . 57 0N 33 40 E
Valdepeñas, Ciudad
  Real 38 43N 3 25w
Valdés, Pen. 42 30s 63 45w
Valdez 61 14N 146 10w

Valdivia 39 50s 73 14w
Valdosta 30 50N 83 48w
Valença, Brazil ... 13 20s 39 5w
Valença da Piaui . 6 20s 41 45w
Valence .... 44 57N 4 54 E
Valencia, Sp. 39 27N 0 23w
Valencia, Ven. ... 10 11N 68 0w
Valencia, G. de .. 39 30N 0 20 E
Valencia, Reg. ... 39 25N 0 45w
Valencia
  de Alcántara ... 39 25N 7 14w
Valenciennes .... 50 20N 3 34 E
Valentia, I. 51 54N 10 22w
Valentine 42 50N 100 35w
Valera 9 19N 70 37w
Valkenswaard ... 51 21N 5 29 E
Valladolid, Mexico 20 30N 88 20w
Valladolid, Sp. ... 41 38N 4 43w
Valle d'Aosta □ .. 45 45N 7 22 E
Valle de la Pascua . 9 13N 66 0w
Valle de Santiago . 20 25N 101 15w
Vallecas 40 23N 3 41w
Vallejo 38 12N 122 15w
Vallenar 28 30s 70 50w
Valletta .... 35 54N 14 30 E
Valley City 46 57N 98 0w
Valleyfield 45 15N 74 8w
Valleyview 55 5N 117 25w
Valls .... 41 18N 1 15 E
Valognes 49 30N 1 28w
Valparaíso 33 2s 71 40w
Valsbaai .... 34 15s 18 40 E
Valverde del
  Camino 37 35N 6 47w
Van Buren, Ark. .. 35 28N 94 18w
Van Buren, Me. ... 47 10N 68 1w
Van Diemen, C. .. 16 30s 139 46 E
Van Diemen, G. .. 12 0s 132 0 E
Van Gölü .... 38 30N 43 0 E
Van Wert 40 52N 84 31w
Vancouver, Canada 49 20N 123 10w
Vancouver, U.S.A. 45 44N 122 41w
Vancouver I. 49 50N 126 30w
Vandalia 38 57N 89 4w
Vanderbijlpark ... 26 42s 27 54 E
Vanderhoof 54 0N 124 0w
Vandyke .... 24 8s 142 45 E
Vänern, L. ...... 58 47N 13 50 E
Vänersborg ..... 58 26N 12 27 E
Vanga .... 4 35s 39 12 E

Vangaindrano .... 23 21s 47 36 E
Vankarem 67 51N 175 50w
Vankleek Hill 45 32N 74 40w
Vännäs .... 63 58N 19 48 E
Vannes 47 40N 2 47w
Vanrhynsdorp ... 31 36s 18 44 E
Vansbro .... 60 32N 14 15 E
Vanua Levu, I. ... 15 45s 179 10 E
Var □ .... 43 27N 6 18 E
Varanasi .... 25 22N 83 8 E
Varaždin .... 46 20N 16 20 E
Varberg .... 57 17N 12 20 E
Vardar, R. ...... 40 35N 22 50 E
Varese .... 45 49N 8 50 E
Värmlands □ .... 59 45N 13 0 E
Varna .... 43 13N 27 56 E
Värnamo .... 57 10N 14 3 E
Vascongadas, Reg. 42 50N 2 45w
Vaslui .... 46 38N 27 42 E
Västerås .... 59 37N 16 38 E
Västerbotten □ .. 64 58N 18 0 E
Västerdalälven, R. . 60 33N 15 8 E
Västernorrlands □ . 63 30N 17 40 E
Västervik .... 57 43N 16 43 E
Västmanlands □ .. 89 5N 16 20 E
Vasto .... 42 8N 14 40 E
Vatnajökull 64 30N 16 30w
Vatomandry ..... 19 20s 48 59 E
Vatra-Dornei .... 47 22N 25 22 E
Vättern, L. ...... 58 25N 14 30 E
Vaucluse □ ...... 44 3N 5 10 E
Vaughan 34 37N 105 12w
Vauxhall 50 5N 112 9w
Växjö .... 56 52N 14 50 E
Vaygach, Os. .... 70 0N 60 0 E
Vechte, R. ...... 52 35N 6 5 E
Vedea, R. .... 43 53N 25 59 E
Veendam .... 53 5N 6 25 E
Veenendaal ..... 52 2N 5 34 E
Vefsna, R. ...... 65 50N 13 12 E
Vega .... 65 37N 12 0 E
Vegafjord .... 65 37N 12 0 E
Vegreville 53 30N 112 5w
Vejer de la Frontera 36 15N 5 59w
Vejle .... 55 43N 9 30 E
Velay, Mts. du ... 45 0N 3 40 E
Velddrif .... 32 42s 18 11 E
Velebit Planina,
  Mts. .... 44 50N 15 20 E
Vélez 6 2N 73 43w
Vélez Málaga 36 48N 4 5w

Vélez Rubio 37 41N 2 5w
Velikiy Ustyug ... 60 47N 46 20 E
Velikiye Luki .... 56 25N 30 32 E
Velikonda Ra. .... 14 45N 79 10 E
Velletri .... 41 43N 12 43 E
Vellore .... 12 57N 79 10 E
Velsen .... 52 27N 4 40 E
Velsk .... 61 10N 42 5 E
Venado Tuerto ... 33 50s 62 0w
Vendée □ 46 40N 1 20w
Veneto □ .... 45 30N 12 0 E
Venézia .... 45 27N 12 20 E
Venézia, G. di ... 45 20N 13 0 E
Venezuela ■ 8 0N 65 0w
Venezuela, G. de .. 11 30N 71 0w
Vengurla .... 15 53s 73 45 E
Venice=Venézia . 45 27N 12 20 E
Venlo .... 51 22N 6 11 E
Venraij .... 51 31N 6 0 E
Ventnor 50 35N 1 12w
Ventspils .... 57 25N 21 32 E
Ventura 34 16N 119 25w
Vera, Arg. 29 30s 60 20w
Vera, Sp. 37 15N 1 15w
Veracruz 19 10N 96 10w
Veracruz □ 19 0N 96 15w
Veraval .... 20 53N 70 27 E
Vercelli .... 45 19N 8 25 E
Verde, R. 41 56s 65 5w
Verden .... 52 56N 9 15 E
Verdun .... 49 12N 5 24 E
Vereeniging ..... 26 38s 27 57 E
Verkhniy
  Baskunchak ... 48 5N 46 50 E
Verkhoyansk .... 67 50N 133 50 E
Verkhoyanskiy
  Khrebet .... 66 0N 129 0 E
Vermilion 53 20N 110 50w
Vermilion, R. 53 44N 110 18w
Vermilion Bay ... 49 50N 93 20w
Vermillion 42 50N 96 56w
Vermont □ 43 40N 72 50w
Vernal 40 28N 109 35w
Verner 46 25N 80 8w
Vernon, Canada .. 50 20N 119 15w
Vernon, U.S.A. .. 34 0N 99 15w
Verona .... 45 27N 11 0 E
Versailles ...... 48 48N 2 8 E
Verte, C. 14 45N 17 30w
Verulam .... 29 38s 31 2 E

Verviers .... 50 37N 5 52 E
Veselovskoye,
  Vdkhr. .... 47 0N 41 0 E
Vesoul .... 60 40N 6 11 E
Vest-Agde □ .... 58 30N 7 0 E
Vestfold □ ...... 59 15N 10 0 E
Vestmannaejar, Is. 63 27N 20 15w
Vesuvio, Mt. .... 40 50N 14 22 E
Vesuvius, Mt.=
  Vesuvio, Mt. .... 40 50N 14 22 E
Veszprém .... 47 8N 17 57 E
Vetlanda .... 57 24N 15 3 E
Vexin, Reg. ..... 49 20N 1 30 E
Viacha 16 30s 68 5w
Viana 3 0s 44 40w
Viana do Castelo . 41 42N 8 50w
Vianopolis 16 40s 48 35w
Viborg .... 56 27N 9 23 E
Vicenza .... 45 32N 11 31 E
Vich .... 41 58N 2 19 E
Vichy .... 46 9N 3 26 E
Vicksburg 32 22N 90 56w
Vicosa 9 28s 36 25w
Victor Harbour ... 35 30s 138 37 E
Victoria, Australia . 21 16s 149 3 E
Victoria, Cameroon 4 1N 9 10 E
Victoria, Canada . 48 30N 123 25w
Victoria, Chile .. 38 22s 72 29w
Victoria,
  Hong Kong .... 22 25N 114 15 E
Victoria, Malaysia . 5 20N 115 20 E
Victoria, Malta .... 36 2N 14 14 E
Victoria, U.S.A. ... 28 50N 97 0w
Victoria, L. ...... 1 0s 33 0 E
Victoria, R. ...... 15 12s 129 43 E
Victoria □ .... 20 55s 31 50 E
Victoria Beach 50 45N 96 32w
Victoria
  de las Tunas 20 58N 76 59w
Victoria Falls .... 17 58s 25 45 E
Victoria I. 71 0N 11 0w
Victoria Ld. ...... 75 0s 160 0 E
Victoria Nile, R. .. 2 14N 31 26 E
Victoria
  Taungdeik, Mt. . 21 15N 93 55 E
Victoria West .... 31 25s 23 4 E
Victorica 36 15s 65 30w
Victoriaville 46 4N 71 56w
Victorville 34 32N 117 18w
Vicuña 30 2s 70 44w

Vidalia 32 13N 82 25w
Vidin .... 43 59N 22 52 E
Viedma 40 50s 63 0w
Viedma, L. 49 30s 72 30w
Vienna = Wien .. 48 12N 16 22 E
Vienne .... 45 31N 4 53 E
Vienne, R. ...... 47 13N 0 5 E
Vienne □ .... 45 53N 0 42 E
Vientiane .... 18 7N 102 35 E
Vierzon .... 47 13N 2 5 E
Vietnam ■ ...... 16 0N 108 0 E
Vigan .... 17 35N 120 28 E
Vigia 0 50s 48 5w
Vigo 42 12N 8 41w
Vijayawada ...... 16 31N 80 39 E
Vikulovo .... 56 50N 70 40 E
Vila Cabral
  = Lichinga .... 13 13s 35 11 E
Vila da Maganja .. 17 18s 37 30 E
Vila de Manica ... 18 58s 32 58 E
Vila Franca de Xira 38 57N 8 59w
Vila Machado .... 19 15s 34 14 E
Vila Real 41 17N 7 48w
Vila Real
  de Sto. António . 37 10N 7 28w
Vilaine, R. 47 30N 2 27w
Viliga .... 60 2N 156 56 E
Villa Ángela 27 34s 60 45w
Villa Cisneros
  = Dakhla 23 50N 15 53w
Villa Colón 31 38s 68 20w
Villa Hayes 25 0s 57 20w
Villa Julia Molina . 19 5N 69 45w
Villa María 32 20s 63 10w
Villa Mazán 28 40s 66 10w
Villa Ocampo 28 30s 59 20w
Villach .... 46 37N 13 51 E
Villa de María ... 29 55s 63 45w
Villagarcía de
  Arosa 42 34N 8 46w
Villaguay 32 0s 58 45w
Villahermosa,
  Mexico 17 45N 92 50w
Villalba 40 36N 3 59w
Villanueva 35 16N 105 31w
Villanueva de
  la Serena 38 59N 5 50w
Villarreal 39 55N 0 3w
Villarrica 39 15s 72 30w
Villavicencio 4 9N 73 37w

Villaviciosa 43 32N 5 27w
Villazón 22 0s 65 35w
Ville Marie 47 20N 79 30w
Ville Platte 30 45N 92 17w
Villena 38 39N 0 52w
Villiers .... 27 2s 28 36 E
Vilna 54 7N 111 55w
Vilnius .... 54 38N 25 25 E
Vilvoorde .... 50 56N 4 26 E
Vilyuysk .... 63 40N 121 20 E
Viña del Mar 33 0s 71 30w
Vinaroz .... 40 30N 0 27 E
Vincennes 38 42N 87 29w
Vindhya Ra. ..... 22 50N 77 0 E
Vinh .... 18 45N 105 38 E
Vinh Loi .... 17 4N 107 2 E
Vinita 36 40N 95 12w
Vinkovci .... 45 19N 18 48 E
Vinnitsa .... 49 15N 28 30 E
Violet Town ..... 36 19s 145 37 E
Viqueque .... 8 42s 126 30 E
Viramgam .... 23 5N 72 0 E
Virden 49 50N 101 0w
Virgenes, C. 52 19s 68 21w
Virgin Gorda, I. .. 18 45N 64 26w
Virgin Is., Br. 18 40N 64 30w
Virgin Is., U.S. ... 18 20N 64 50w
Virginia, S. Afr. .. 28 8s 26 55 E
Virginia, U.S.A. .. 47 30N 92 32w
Virginia □ 37 45N 78 0w
Virginia Beach ... 36 54N 75 58w
Virginia City 45 25N 111 58w
Virton .... 49 35N 5 32 E
Virudunagar ..... 9 30N 78 0 E
Vis, I. .... 43 0N 16 10 E
Visalia 36 25N 119 18w
Visayan Sea ..... 11 30N 123 30 E
Visby .... 57 37N 18 18 E
Viscount
  Melville Sd. 78 0N 108 0w
Visé .... 50 44N 5 41 E
Viseu, Brazil 1 10s 46 20w
Viseu, Port. 40 40N 7 55w
Vishakhapatnam .. 17 45N 83 20 E
Visrivier .... 31 45s 25 20 E
Vistula, R.=
  Wisła, R. ...... 54 22N 18 55 E
Viso, Mte. ...... 44 40N 7 7 E
Vitebsk .... 55 10N 30 15 E
Viterbo .... 42 25N 12 8 E

Viti Levu, I. ...... 17 30s 177 30 E
Vitim .... 59 45N 112 25 E
Vitim, R. .... 59 26N 112 34 E
Vitoria, Brazil ... 20 20s 40 22w
Vitória, Sp. 42 50N 2 41w
Vitória da
  Conquista 14 51s 40 51w
Vitoria de Santo
  Antão 8 10s 37 20w
Vittória .... 36 58N 14 30 E
Vittório Véneto .. 45 59N 12 18 E
Vivero 43 39N 7 38w
Vizianagaram ... 18 6N 83 10 E
Vlaardingen ..... 51 55N 4 21 E
Vladimir .... 56 0N 40 30 E
Vladivostok .... 43 10N 131 53 E
Vlissingen ...... 51 26N 3 34 E
Vlóra .... 40 32N 19 28 E
Vogelkop, Mt.=
  Doberai,
  Djazirah ...... 1 25s 133 0 E
Vohémar .... 13 25s 50 0 E
Vohipeno .... 22 22s 47 51 E
Voi .... 3 25s 38 32 E
Volga, R. .... 45 55N 47 52 E
Volga Heights, Mts. 51 0N 46 0 E
Volgograd ...... 48 40N 44 25 E
Volgogradskoye,
  Vdkhr. .... 50 0N 45 20 E
Volksrust .... 27 24s 29 53 E
Vollenhove ...... 52 40N 5 58 E
Volochanka ..... 71 0N 94 28 E
Vologda .... 59 25N 40 0 E
Vólos .... 39 24N 22 59 E
Volsk .... 52 5N 47 28 E
Volta, L. .... 7 30N 0 15 E
Volta, R. .... 5 46N 0 41 E
Volta Noire, R. .. 8 41N 1 33w
Volta Redonda .. 22 31s 44 5w
Volterra .... 43 24N 10 50 E
Volzhskiy ...... 48 56N 44 46 E
Vondrozo ...... 22 49s 47 20 E
Voorburg .... 52 5N 4 24 E
Vor-Arlberg □ .. 47 15N 9 55 E
Vorkuta .... 67 48N 64 20 E
Voronezh ...... 51 40N 39 10 E
Voroshilovgrad .. 48 38N 39 15 E
Vosges, Mts. .... 48 20N 7 10 E
Vosges □ .... 48 12N 6 20 E
Voss .... 60 38N 6 26 E

Vostochnyy Sayan . 54 0N 96 0 E
Vostok, I. 10 5s 152 23w
Votkinsk .... 57 0N 53 55 E
Votkinskoye,
  Vdkhr. .... 57 30N 55 0 E
Vozhe, Oz. ...... 60 45N 39 0 E
Voznesenka ..... 46 51N 35 26 E
Voznesensk ..... 47 35N 31 15 E
Voznesenye ..... 61 0N 35 45 E
Vrangelya, Os. .. 71 0N 180 0 E
Vranje .... 42 34N 21 54 E
Vratsa .... 43 13N 23 30 E
Vrede .... 27 30s 29 6 E
Vredefort ...... 27 5s 27 16 E
Vredenburg ..... 32 51s 18 0 E
Vredendal ...... 31 41s 18 35 E
Vršac .... 45 8N 21 18 E
Vryburg .... 26 55s 24 45 E
Vryheid .... 27 54s 30 47 E
Vught .... 51 38N 5 20 E
Vulcan 50 25N 113 15w
Vulcano, I. ...... 38 27N 14 58 E
Vyatskiye ...... 56 5N 51 0 E
Vyazma .... 55 10N 34 15 E
Vyborg .... 60 42N 28 45 E
Východné Beskydy 49 30N 22 0 E
Vyg, Oz. .... 63 30N 34 0 E
Vyrnwy, L. 52 48N 3 30w
Vyshniy Volochek . 57 30N 34 30 E
Vytegra .... 61 15N 36 40 E

W

Wa 10 7N 2 25w
Waal, R. .... 51 55N 4 30 E
Wabana 47 40N 53 0w
Wabash 40 48N 85 46w
Wabash, R. 37 46N 88 2w
Wabowden 54 55N 98 35w
Wabrzeźno ...... 53 16N 18 57 E
Wabush City 52 40N 67 0w
Waco 31 33N 97 5w
Wad Banda ..... 13 10N 27 50 E
Wad Hamid ..... 16 20N 32 45 E
Wâd Medani .... 14 28N 33 30 E
Wadayama ...... 35 19N 134 52 E
Waddenladen, Is. . 53 30N 5 30 E

Waddenzee .... 53 15N   5 15 E
Wadderin Hill 32   0s 118 25 E
Waddington, Mt. .. 51 10N 125 20w
Wadena, Canada .. 52   0N 103 50w
Wadena, U.S.A. .. 46 25N 95   2w
Wadi Halfa .... 21 53N 31 19 E
Wageningen ...... 51 58N   5 40 E
Wager Bay 66   0N 91   0w
Wagga Wagga ... 35   7s 147 24 E
Wagin, Austral ... 33 17s 117 25 E
Wagin, Nigeria .... 12 45N   7   8 E
Wahai .... 2 48s 129 35 E
Wahpeton 46 20N 96 35w
Waiau .... 42 39s 173   5 E
Waiau, R. .... 42 46s 173 23 E
Waigeo, I. .... 0 20s 130 40 E
Waihi .... 37 23s 175 52 E
Waihou, R. ...... 37 10s 175 32 E
Waikaremoana, L. . 38 49s 177   9 E
Waikari .... 42 58s 72 41 E
Waikato, R. ...... 37 23s 174 43 E
Waikerie 34   9s 140   0 E
Waikokopu 39   3s 177 52 E
Waikouaiti ...... 45 36s 170 41 E
Waimakariri, R. ... 43 24s 172 42 E
Waimarino ...... 40 40s 175 20 E
Waimate .... 44 53s 171   3 E
Wainganga, R. ... 18 50N 79 55 E
Waingapu .... 9 35s 120 11 E
Wainwright 52 50N 110 50w
Waiouru .... 39 29s 175 40 E
Waipara 43   3N 172 46 E
Waipawa .... 39 56s 176 38 E
Waipiro 38   2s 176 22 E
Waipu .... 35 59s 174 29 E
Waipukurau 40   1s 176 33 E
Wairakei .... 38 37s 176   6 E
Wairau, .R. ...... 41 32s 174   7 E
Wairoa 39   3s 177 25 E
Waitaki, R. ...... 44 56s 171   7 E
Waitara .... 38 59s 174 15 E
Waiuku .... 37 15s 174 45 E
Waiyeung .... 23 12N 11432 E
Wajima .... 37 30N 137   0 E
Wajir .... 1 42N 40 20 E
Wakasa .... 35 20N 134 24 E
Wakasa-Wan .... 34 45N 135 30 E
Wakatipu, L. 45   6s 168 30 E
Wakaw 52 39N 105 44w
Wakayama ...... 34 15N 135 15 E

Wakayama □ ..... 34 50N 135 30 E
Wake, I. .... 19 18N 166 36 E
Wakefield, U.K. .. 53 41N   1 31w
Wakefield, N.Z. .. 41 24s 173   5 E
Wakeham Bay =
  Maricourt 61 36N 71 57w
Wakkanai ...... 45 28N 141 35 E
Wakkerstroom ... 27 24s 30 10 E
Wakre .... 0 30s 131   5 E
Walachia, Reg. =
  Valahia, Reg. .. 44 35N 25   0 E
Walbrzych ...... 50 45N 16 18 E
Walbury Hill 51 22N   1 28w
Walcha .... 30 55s 151 31 E
Walcheren, I. .... 51 30N   3 35 E
Walden 40 47N 106 20w
Waldron 50 53N 102 35w
Walebing .... 30 40s 116 15 E
Wales ■ 52 30N   3 30w
Walgett 30   0s 148   5 E
Walkaway 28 59s 114 48w
Walkerton 44 10N 81 10w
Walla Walla 46   3N 118 25w
Wallace 47 30N 116   0w
Wallaceburg 42 40N 82 30w
Wallal .... 26 32s 146   7 E
Wallal Downs ... 19 47s 120 40 E
Wallaroo .... 33 56s 137 39 E
Wallasey 3 26s   3   2w
Wallerawang .... 33 25s 150   4 E
Wallahallow .... 17 50s 135 50 E
Wallowa 45 40N 117 35w
Wallsend 54 59N   1 30w
Wallumbilla .... 26 33s 149   9 E
Walmer .... 33 57s 25 35 E
Walney, I 54   5N   3 15w
Walpeup .... 35 10s 142   2 E
Walsall 52 36N   1 59w
Walsenburg 37 42N 104 45w
Waltham 45 57N 76 57w
Walvisbaai 23   0s 14 28 E
Walvis Bay =
  Walvisbaai 23   0s 14 28 E
Wamba .... 2 10N 27 57 E
Wanaka, L. ..... 44 33s 169   7 E
Wanapiri .... 4 30s 135 50 E
Wanbi .... 34 46s 140 17 E
Wanderer ...... 19 37s 29 59 E
Wandoan 26   5s 149 55 E
Wanganui ...... 39 35s 175   3 E

Wangaratta ...... 36 21s 146 19 E
Wangary .... 34 33s 135 29 E
Wangtu .... 38 42N 115   4 E
Wanhsien .... 30 45N 108 20 E
Wankie .... 18 18s 26 30 E
Wanless 54 11N 101 21w
Wanning .... 18 45N 110 28 E
Wantsai 28   1N 114   5 E
Wanyang
  Shan, Mts. ..... 26 30N 113 30 E
Wanyuan 32   3N 108 16 E
Wapato 46 30N 120 25w
Warandab .... 7 20N 44   2 E
Warangal .... 17 58N 79 45 E
Ward .... 41 49s 174 11 E
Wardak □ .... 34 15N 68   0 E
Warden .... 27 56s 29   0 E
Wardha .... 20 45N 78 39 E
Warialda .... 29 29s 150 33 E
Warkopi .... 1 12s 134   9 E
Warkworth ...... 36 24s 174 41 E
Warley 52 30N   2   0w
Warman 52 25s 106 30w
Warmbad .... 24 51s 28 19 E
Warmbad, S.W.
  Africa .... 28 25s 18 42 E
Warmbad, S.W.
  Africa .... 19 14s 13 51 E
Warncoort ...... 38 30s 143 45 E
Warnemünde 54   9N 12   5 E
Warner Ra. 41 30s 120 20w
Warner Robins .. 32 41N 83 36w
Waroona .... 32 50s 115 55 E
Warragul .... 38 10s 145 58 E
Warrego, R. ..... 30 24s 145 21 E
Warren, Australia . 31 42s 147 51 E
Warren, Ohio 41 18N 80 52w
Warren, Pa. 41 52N 79 10w
Warren 33 35N 92   3w
Warrenpoint 54   7N   6 15w
Warrensburg 38 45N 93 45w
Warrenton, S.
  Africa 28   9s 24 47 E
Warrenton, U.S.A. 46 11N 123 59w
Warri .... 5 30N   5 41 E
Warrington, U.K. . 53 25N   2 38w
Warrington, U.S.A. 30 22N 87 16w
Warrnambool ... 38 25s 142 30 E
Warsak Dam .... 34 10N 71 25 E

Warsaw 41 14N 85 50w
Warsaw = Warszawa 52 13N 21   0 E
Warszawa ...... 52 13N 21   0 E
Warta, R. .... 52 35N 14 39 E
Warwick □ 52 20N   1 30w
Warwick, Australia 28 10s 152   1 E
Warwick, U.K. ... 52 17N   1 36w
Warwick, U.S.A. . 41 43N 71 25w
Wasa 49 45N 115 50w
Wasatch Mts. 40 30N 111 15w
Wasbank .... 28 15s 30   9 E
Wasco, Calif. 35 37N 119 16w
Wasco, Oreg. 45 45N 120 46w
Waseca 44   3N 93 31w
Wash, The ...... 52 58N   0   2 E
Washington □ ... 47 45N 120 30w
Washington, D.C. . 38 52N 77   0w
Washington, Ind.. 38 40N 87   8w
Washington, Iowa . 41 20N 91 45w
Washington, Mo.. 38 33N 91   1w
Washington, N.C. . 35 35N 77   1w
Washington, Ohio. 39 34N 83 26w
Washington, Pa... 40 10N 80 20w
Washington, Mt. .. 44 15N 71 18w
Wassenaar 52   8N   4 24 E
Waswanipi 49 30N 77   0w
Watangpone ..... 4 29s 120 25 E
Waterberg ...... 24 14s 28   0 E
Waterbury 41 32N 73   0w
Waterford 52 16N   7   8w
Waterford □ 51 10N   7 40w
Waterloo, Belgium 50 43N   4 25 E
Waterloo, Canada . 43 30N 80 32w
Waterloo, Iowa .. 42 27N 92 20w
Watertown, N.Y. .. 43 58N 75 57w
Watertown, S.D. .. 44 57N 97   5w
Watertown, Wis.. 43 15N 88 45w
Waterval-Boven .. 25 40s 30 18 E
Waterville 44 35N 69 40w
Watervliet 42 46N 73 43w
Wates .... 7 53s 110   6 E
Watford 51 38N   0 23w
Watheroo 30 15s 116   0w
Watkins Glen ... 42 25s 76 55 E
Watling, I. 24   0N 74 30w
Watrous 51 40N 105 25w
Watsa 3   4N 29 30 E
Watson .... 30 19s 131 41 E
Watson Lake ... 60 12N 129   0w
Watsonville 37 58N 121 49w

Waubra .... 37 21s 143 39 E
Wauchope ...... 31 28s 152 45 E
Waugh 49 40N 95 20w
Waukegan 42 22N 87 54w
Waukesha 43   0N 88 15w
Waupun 43 38N 88 44w
Wausau 44 57N 89 40w
Wauwatosa 43   6N 87 59w
Wave Hill ...... 17 32N 131   0 E
Waveney, R. .... 52 28N   1 45 E
Waverley ...... 39 46s 174 37 E
Waverly 42 40N 92 30w
Wavre .... 50 43N   4 38 E
Wāw .... 7 45N 28   1 E
Waxahachie 32 22N 96 53w
Wayatinah ..... 42 19s 146 27 E
Waycross 31 12N 82 25w
Waynesboro, Pa. . 39 46N 77 32w
Waynesboro, Va.. 38   4N 78 57w
Waynesville 35 31N 83   0w
Wazirabad,
  Afghanistan .... 36 44N 66 47 E
Wazirabad,
  Pak. .... 32 30N 74   8 E
Weald, The 51   7N   0   9 E
Wear, R. 54 55N   1 22w
Weatherford 32 45N 97 48w
Webster City ... 42 30N 93 50w
Webster Green .. 38 38N 90 20w
Weda .... 0 30N 127 50 E
Weddell I. 51 50s 61   0w
Weddell Sea ... 72 30s 40   0w
Wedderburn ... 36 20s 143 33 E
Wedgeport 43 44N 65 59w
Wee Waa ..... 30 11s 149 26 E
Weenen .... 28 57s 30   3 E
Weert .... 51 15N   5 43 E
Wei Ho, R. .... 35 45N 114 30 E
Weifang .... 36 47N 119 10 E
Weihai .... 37 30N 122 10 E
Weimar 51   0N 11 20 E
Weinan .... 34 30N 109 35 E
Weipa .... 12 24s 141 50 E
Weir River 57   0N 94 10w
Weiser 44 10N 117   0w
Wejherow ..... 54 35N 18 12 E
Wekusko 54 45N 99 45w
Welch 37 29N 81 36w
Welkom 28   0s 26 50 E

Welland 43 0N 79 10w
Welland, R. ..... 52 53N   0 2 E
Wellesley, Is. .... 17 20s 139 30 E
Wellingborough ... 52 18N 0 41w
Wellington,
   Australia ...... 32 30s 148 0 E
Wellington, Canada 43 57N 77 20w
Wellington, N.Z. . 41 19s 174 46 E
Wellington, U.K. .. 52 42N   2 31w
Wellington, U.S.A. 37 15N 97 25w
Wellington □ .... 40 8s 175 36 E
Wellington, I. ... 49 30s 75 0w
Wells, Norfolk .. 52 57N   0 51 E
Wells, Somerset .. 51 12N   2 39w
Wells, U.S.A. ... 41 8N 115 0w
Wells, L. 26 44s 123 15w
Wellsboro 41 45N 77 16w
Wellsville, N.Y. .. 42 9N 77 57w
Wellsville, Ohio .. 40 36N 80 40w
Wels .... 48 9N 14 1 E
Welshpool,
   Australia ...... 38 42s 146 26 E
Welshpool,
   U.K. 52 40N   3 9w
Wem 52 52N   2 45w
Wenatchee 47 30N 120 17w
Wenchang .... 19 38N 110 42 E
Wenchi 7 46N   2 8w
Wenchou=
   Wenchow ...... 28 0N 120 35 E
Wenchow .... 28 0N 120 35 E
Wendell 42 50N 114 51w
Wensiang .... 34 35N 110 40 E
Wensleydale 54 20N   2 0w
Wensu .... 41 15N 80 14 E
Wenteng .... 25 15s 23 16 E
Wentworth ..... 34 2s 141 54 E
Wepener .... 29 42s 27 3 E
Werda .... 25 15s 23 16 E
Werra, R. ...... 51 26N 9 39 E
Werribee .... 37 54s 144 40 E
Werris Creek ... 31 8s 150 38 E
Weser, R. ...... 53 32N   8 34 E
Wesleyville 49 8N 53 36w
Wessel, Is. ..... 11 10s 136 45 E
West Bend 43 25N 88 10w
West Bengal □ ... 25 0N 90 0 E
West Bromwich .. 52 32N   2 1w
West Des Moines . 41 30N 93 45w
West Falkland, I. . 51 30s 60 0w

West Frankfort 37 56N 89 0w
West Germany ■ .. 51 0N   9 0 E
West Glamorgan □ 51 40N   3 55w
West Helena 34 30N 90 40w
West Indies 20 0N 65 0w
West Memphis ... 35 5N 90 3w
West Midlands □ .. 52 30N   2 0w
West Monroe 32 32N 92 7w
West Palm Beach . 26 44N 80 3w
West Pt. 18 14N 78 30w
West Point, Miss. .. 33 36N 88 38w
West Point, Va. ... 37 35N 76 47w
West Sussex □ 50 55N   0 30w
West Virginia □ ... 39 0N 18 0w
West Wyalong ... 33 56s 147 10 E
West Yorkshire □ . 53 45N   1 40w
Westbrook 43 41N 70 21w
Westbury .... 41 30s 146 51 E
Western □ 6 0N   2 20w
Western
   Australia ...... 25 0s 118 0 E
Western Ghats,
   Mts. .... 15 30N 74 30 E
Western Isles □ ... 57 30N   7 10w
Western Samoa ■ . 14 0s 172 0w
Westerschelde, R. . 51 25N   4 0 E
Westerwald, Mts. .. 50 39N   8 0 E
Westland □ ...... 43 33s 169 59 E
Westlock 54 20N 113 55w
Westmeath □ 53 30N   7 30w
Westminster 39 34s 77 1w
Westmorland ... 33 2N 115 42w
Weston, Malaysia . 5 10N 115 35 E
Weston, U.S.A. .. 39 3N 80 29w
Weston-super-Mare 51 20N   2 59w
Westphalia□=
   Nordrhein-
   Westfalen □ .... 51 45N   7 30 E
Westport, Eire ... 53 44N   9 31w
Westport, N.Z. ... 41 46s 171 37 E
Westray, I. 59 18N   3 0w
Westview 49 50N 124 31w
Westwood 40 26N 121 0w
Wetar, I. .... 7 30s 126 30 E
Wetaskiwin 52 55N 113 24w
Wetteren .... 51 0N   3 53 E
Wetzlar .... 50 33N   8 30 E
Wewaka 35 10N 96 35w
Wexford 52 20N   6 28w
Wexford □ 52 20N   6 40w

Weyburn 49 40N 103 50w
Weymouth, U.K. .. 50 36N   2 28w
Whakatane ...... 37 57s 177 1 E
Whale, R. 57 40N 67 0w
Whale Cove 62 10N 93 0w
Whalsay, I. 60 22N   1 0w
Whangamomona . 39 8s 174 44 E
Whangarei ..... 35 43s 174 21 E
Whangaroa,
   Harbour........ 35 4s 173 46 E
Wharfe, R. 53 51N   1 7w
Wheatland 42 4N 105 58w
Wheeler Pk. 38 57N 114 15w
Wheeling 40 2N 80 41w
Whernside, Mt. .. 54 14N   2 24w
Whitby 54 29N   0 37w
White, R., Ind. .. 38 25N 87 44w
White, R., Ark. .. 33 53N 91 3w
White Cliffs .... 30 50s 143 10 E
White Horse,
   Vale of 51 37N   1 30w
White Nile, R. =
   Nîl el Abyad .... 9 30N 31 40 E
White River,
   Canada 48 35N 85 20w
White River, S. Afr. 25 20s 31 0 E
White Sea=
   Beloye More .... 66 30N 38 0 E
White Sulphur
   Springs 46 35N 111 0w
White Volta, R. .. 9 10N   1 5N
Whitecliffs ..... 43 26s 171 55 E
Whitefish 48 25N 114 22w
Whitehall, Wis. .. 44 20N 91 19w
Whitehaven 54 33N   3 35w
Whitehorse 60 45N 135 10w
Whiteshell
   Prov. Park 50 0N 95 25w
Whitewood ..... 21 28s 143 30 E
Whitewood 50 20N 102 20w
Whithorn 54 55N   4 25w
Whitianga ..... 36 47s 175 41 E
Whitney, Mt. ... 36 35N 118 14w
Whitstable ..... 51 21N   1 2 E
Whitsunday, I. .. 20 15s 149 4 E
Whittier 60 46N 148 48w
Whittle, C. 50 11N 60 8w
Whyalla .... 33 2s 137 30 E
Wiarton 44 50N 81 10w
Wiawso 6 12N   2 29w

Wichita .... 37 40N 97·29w
Wichita Falls 33 57N 98 30w
Wick 58 26N   3 5w
Wickenburg 33 58N 112 45w
Wickepin ...... 32 50s 117 30 E
Wicklow 53 0N   6 2w
Wicklow □ 52 59N   6 25w
Wicklow Mts. ... 53 0N   6 30w
Widgiemooltha .. 31 30s 121 34 E
Widnes 53 22N   2 44w
Wieliczka ...... 50 0N 20 5 E
Wieluń .... 51 15N 18 40 E
Wien .... 48 12N 16 22 E
Wiener Neustadt . 47 49N 16 16 E
Wierden .... 52 22N   6 35 E
Wiesbaden ..... 50 7N   8 17 E
Wigan 53 33N   2 38w
Wigtown 54 52N   4 27w
Wigtown B. 54 46N   4 15w
Wilcannia ...... 31 30s 143 26 E
Wildwood 39 5N 74 46w
Wilhelmshaven .. 53 30N   8 9 E
Wilkes-Barre ... 41 15N 75 52w
Wilkes Ld. ..... 69 0s 120 0 E
Wilkie 52 27N 108 42w
Willcox 32 13N 109 53w
Willemstad 12 5N 69 0w
Willeroo ...... 15 14s 131 37 E
William Creek .. 28 58s 136 22 E
Williams, Australia 33 0s 117 0 E
Williams, U.S.A. .. 35 16N 112 11w
Williams Lake .. 52 20N 122 10w
Williamsburg ... 37 17N 76 44w
Williamson 37 46N 82 17w
Williamsport 41 18N 77 1w
Williamstown,
   Australia ...... 37 46s 144 58 E
Williston, S. Afr. .. 31 20s 20 53 E
Williston, U.S.A. .. 48 10N 103 35w
Willits 39 28N 123 17w
Willmar 45 5N 95 0w
Willow Tree ... 31 40s 150 45 E
Willowmore .... 33 15s 23 30 E
Willows, Australia . 23 45s 147 25 E
Willows, U.S.A. .. 39 30N 122 10w
Wilmette 42 6N 87 44w
Wilmington, Del. .. 39 45N 75 32w
Wilmington, N.C. . 34 14N .77 54w
Wilmington, Ohio . 39 29N 83 46w
Wilson 35 44N 77 54w

Wilson, Mt. 37 55N 105 3w
Wilson's
   Promontory ..... 39 5s 146 28 E
Wilton 51 5N   1 52w
Wiltshire □ 51 20N   2 0w
Wiluna .... 26 40s 120 25 E
Winburg .... 28 30s 27 2 E
Winchester, U.K. .. 51 4N   1 19w
Winchester, Ind. . 40 10N 84 56w
Winchester, Ky. .. 38 0N 84 8w
Winchester, Va. .. 39 14N 78 8w
Windber 40 14N 78 50w
Windermere, L. .. 54 20N   2 57w
Windhoek ...... 22 35s 17 4 E
Windorah ...... 25 24s 142 36 E
Windrush, R. ... 51 42N   1 25w
Windsor, Australia 33 34s 150 44 E
Windsor,
   Nova Scotia .. 44 59N 64 5w
Windsor, Ont. .. 42 25N 83 0w
Windsor, U.K. .. 51 28N   0 36w
Windsor, U.S.A. .. 43 30N 72 25w
Windward Is. .. 13 0N 63 0w
Winfield, Canada . 52 58N 114 26w
Winfield, U.S.A. .. 37 15N 97 0w
Wingen .... 31 50s 150 58 E
Wingham 43 55N 81 25w
Winisk, R. 55 17N 85 5w
Winkler 49 15N 98 0w
Winneba 5 25N   0 36w
Winnemucca ... 41 0N 117 45w
Winnepegosis, L. .. 52 40N 100 0w
Winnetka 42 8N 87 46w
Winnfield 31 57N 92 38w
Winning .... 23 9s 114 32 E
Winnipeg 49 50N 97 15w
Winnipeg, L. 52 30N 98 0w
Winnipegosis ... 52 40N 100 0w
Winona 44 2N 91 45w
Winooski 44 31N 73 11w
Winschoten .... 53 9N   7 3 E
Winslow 35 2N 110 41w
Winston-Salem .. 36 7N 80 15w
Winter Haven .. 28 0N 81 42w
Winter Park ... 28 34N 81 19w
Winterhoek, Mt. .. 33 5s 19 35 E
Winterthur .... 47 30N   8 44 E
Winton .... 22 21s 143 0 E
Winton .... 46 8s 168 20 E
Wirrulla .... 32 24s 134 31 E

Wisbech . . . . 52 39N　0 10 E
Wisconsin □ . . . . . . 44 30N　90　0w
Wisconsin Rapids . 44 25N　89 50w
Wishaw . . . . 55 46N　3 55w
Wisła, R. . . . . 54 22N　18 55 E
Wismar . . . . 53 53N　11 23 E
Witbank . . . . 25 51s　29 14 E
Witham, R. . . . . . . 52 56N　0　4 E
Withernsea . . . . . . 53 43N　0　2w
Witney . . . . 51 47N　1 29w
Witsand . . . . 34 24s　20 50 E
Wittenberg . . . . . . 51 51N　12 39 E
Wittenberge . . . . . 53　0N　11 44 E
Wittenoom . . . . . . 22 15s 118 20 E
Witu . . . . 2 23s　40 26 E
Wlingi . . . . 8　5s 112 25 E
Włocławek . . . . . . 52　39　19　2 E
Włodawa . . . . 51 34N　23 32 E
Wodonga . . . . . . 36　5s 146 50 E
Wokam, I. . . . . . . 5 45s 134 28 E
Wolfe I. . . . . 44　7N　76 27 E
Wolin, I. . . . . 53 55N　14 31 E
Wollaston, Is. . . . 55 40s　67 30w
Wollaston L. 58 20N 103 30w
Wollaston Pen. . . . 69 30N 113　0w
Wollongong . . . . 34 25s 150 54 E
Wolmaransstad . . 27 12s　26 13 E
Wolseley, Canada . 44 25N 103 15w
Wolseley, S. Afr. . 33 26s　19 12 E
Wolstenholme, C. . 62 50N　78　0w
Wolverhampton . . 52 35N　2　6w
Wonarah P.O. . . . 19 55s 136 20 E
Wondai . . . . 26 20s 151 49 E
Wongan Hills . . . 30 53s 116 42 E
Wŏnju . . . . 37 30N 127 59 E
Wŏnsan . . . . 39 20N 127 25 E
Wonthaggi . . . . . 38 29s 145 31 E
Wood Buffalo Nat.
　Park . . . . 59 30N 113　0w
Woodanilling . . . 33 31s 117 24 E
Woodend . . . . . . 37 20N 144 33 E
Woodland 38 40N 121 50w
Woodridge . . . . . 49 20N　96 20w
Woodroffe, Mt. . . 26 20s 131 45 E
Woods, L. of the . 49 30N　94 30w
Woodstock,
　Australia . . . . 19 22s 142 45 E
Woodstock, Ont. . 43 10N　80 45w
Woodstock, N.B. . 46 11N　67 37w
Woodstock, U.K. . 51 51N　1 20w

Woodstock, Ill. . . 42 17N　88 30w
Woodville . . . . . 40 20s 175 53 E
Woodward . . . . . 36 24N　99 28w
Woolgangie . . . . 31 12s 120 35 E
Woolgoolga . . . . 30　7s 153 12 E
Woombye . . . . . 26 40s 152 55 E
Woomelang . . . . 35 37s 142 40 E
Woomera . . . . . 31　9s 136 56 E
Woonona . . . . . 34 32s 150 49 E
Woonsocket . . . . 42　0N　71 30w
Woonsockett . . . 44　5N　98 15w
Wooramel . . . . . 25 45s 114 40 E
Wooramel, R. . . . 25 47s 114 10 E
Wooroloo . . . . . 31 45s 116 25 E
Wooster . . . . . . 40 38N　81 55w
Worcester, S. Africa 33 39s　19 27 E
Worcester, U.K. . . 52 12N　2 12w
Worcester, U.S.A. . 42 14N　71 49w
Workington . . . . 54 39N　3 34w
Worksop . . . . . . 53 19N　1　9w
Worland . . . . . . 44　0N 107 59w
Worms . . . . 49 37N　8 21 E
Worsley . . . . . . 33 15s 116　2 E
Worthing . . . . . 50 49N　0 21w
Worthington . . . 43 35N　95 30w
Wosi . . . . 0 15s 128　0 E
Wrangell 56 30N 132 25w
Wrangell Mts. . . . 61 40N 143 30w
Wrath, C. . . . . . 58 38N　5　0w
Wrekin, The, Mt. . 52 41N　2 35w
Wrexham . . . . . 53　5N　3　0w
Wright, Canada . . 51 45N 121 30w
Wright, Philippines 11 42N 125　2 E
Wrigley . . . . . . 63　0N 123 30w
Wrocław . . . . . 51　5N　17　5 E
Września . . . . . 52 21N　17 36 E
Wubin . . . . 30　8s 116 30 E
Wuchang,
　Heilungkiang . . 44 51N 127 10 E
Wuchang, Hupei . 30 34N 114 25 E
Wuchow . . . . . . 23 26N 111 19 E
Wuchung . . . . . 38　4N 106 12 E
Wuhan . . . . 30 32N 114 22 E
Wuhsi=Wusih . . . 31 30N 120 30 E
Wuhu . . . . 31 21N 118 30 E
Wukari . . . . 7 57N　9 42 E
Wulumuchi . . . . 43 40N　87 50 E
Wum . . . . 6 23N　10　4 E
Wun . . . . 19 59N　78 52 E
Wuntho . . . . . . 23 55N　95 45 E

Wuppertal . . . . . 51 15N　7　8 E
Wurarga . . . . . 28 15s 116 12 E
Würzburg . . . . . 49 46N　9 55 E
Wusih . . . . 31 30N 120 30 E
Wusu . . . . 44 10N　84 55 E
Wutai Shan . . . . 39　4N 113 35 E
Wutunghliao . . . 29 25N 104　0 E
Wuwei . . . . 38　0N 102 30 E
Wuyi Shan, Mts. . 26 40N 116 30 E
Wuying . . . . . . 48 10N 129 20 E
Wuyo . . . . 10 25N　11 50 E
Wuyuan . . . . . . 41 45N 108 30 E
Wyalkatchem . . . 31　8s 117 22 E
Wyandotte . . . . 42 14N　83 13w
Wyandra . . . . . 27 12s 145 56 E
Wycheproot . . . 36　0N 143 17 E
Wye, R. . . . . . . 51 37N　2 39w
Wymondham . . . 52 34N　1　7 E
Wynberg . . . . . 34　0s　18 30 E
Wyndham . . . . . 15 33s 128　3 E
Wynnum . . . . . 27 29s 152 58 E
Wynyard,
　Australia . . . . 40 59s 145 45 E
Wynyard, Canada . 51 45N 104 10w
Wyoming □ . . . . 42 48N 109　0w
Wyong . . . . . . 33 14s 151 24 E
Wytheville . . . . 37　0N　81　3w

X

Xánthi . . . . 41 10N　24 58 E
Xenia . . . . 39 42N　83 57w
Xi'an=Sian . . . . 34　2N 109　0 E
Xieng Khouang . . 19 17N 103 25 E
Xinavane . . . . . 25　2s　32 47 E
Xingu, R. . . . . . 1 30s　51 53w
Xique-Xique . . . 10 40s　42 40w

Y

Yaamba . . . . . 23　8s 150 22 E
Yaan . . . . 30　0N 102 59 E
Yabassi . . . . . . 4 32N　10　2 E
Yablonovy

Khrebet . . . . . 53　0N 114　0 E
Ya'Bud . . . . . . 32 27N　35 10 E
Yacuiba . . . . . . 22　0s　63 25w
Yadgir . . . . 16 45N　77　5 E
Yagur . . . . 32 45N　35　4 E
Yaicheng . . . . . 18 14N 109　7 E
Yajua . . . . 11 25N　12 50 E
Yakima 46 42N 120 30w
Yako . . . . 13　2N　2 15w
Yakoshih . . . . . 49 13N 120 35 E
Yaku-Shima, I. . . 30 20N 130 30 E
Yakuluku . . . . . 4 22N　28 45 E
Yakut A.S.S.R. □ . 66　0N 125　0 E
Yakutat 59 50N 139 44w
Yakutsk . . . . . . 62　5N 129 40 E
Yala . . . . 6 45N 101 15 E
Yalboroo . . . . . 20 50s 148 30 E
Yalgoo . . . . . . 28 16s 116 39 E
Yalkubul, Pta. . . 21 32N　88 37w
Yallourn . . . . . 38 10s 146 18 E
Yalta . . . . 44 30N　34 10 E
Yalu, R. . . . . . . 47 30N 123 30 E
Yalung Kiang, R. . 32　0N 100　0 E
Yalutorovsk . . . 56 30N　65 40 E
Yamagata . . . . . 37 55N 140 20 E
Yamagata □ . . . 38 30N 140　0 E
Yamaguchi . . . . 34 10N 131 32 E
Yamaguchi □ . . . 34 20N 131 40 E
Yamal Pol. . . . . 71　0N　70　0 E
Yamama . . . . . 24　5N　47 30 E
Yamanashi □ . . . 35 40N 138 40 E
Yamba . . . . . . 29 30s 153 22 E
Yamdena, I. . . . 7 45s 131 20 E
Yamethin . . . . . 20 26N　96　9 E
Yamil . . . . 12 55N　8　5 E
Yampi, Sd. . . . . 15 15s 123 30 E
Yamhsien . . . . . 21 45N 108 31 E
Yamrat . . . . . . 10 10N　9 55 E
Yamun . . . . . . 32 29N　35 14 E
Yamuna, R. . . . . 27　0N　78 30 E
Yanaul . . . . . . 56 25N　55　0 E
Yanda Bayo . . . 11 30N　10 55 E
Yandanooka . . . 29 18s 115 29 E
Yandoon . . . . . 17　2N　95 39 E
Yangambi . . . . . 0 47N　24 20 E
Yangchow . . . . 32 25N 119 25 E
Yangchuan . . . . 38　0N 113 29 E
Yangi-Yer . . . . 40 17N　68 48 E

Yangtze Kiang, R. . 31 40N 122　0 E
Yankton . . . . . 42 55N　97 25w
Yanna . . . . 26 58s 146　0 E
Yanping . . . . . 22 25N 112　0 E
Yao Shan, Mts. . . 24　0N 110　0 E
Yaoundé . . . . . 3 50N　1 35 E
Yap Is. . . . . . . 9 30N 138 10 E
Yapen, I. . . . . . 1　50s 136　0 E
Yapen, Teluk, G. . 1 30s 136　0 E
Yaraka . . . . . . 24 53s 144　3 E
Yaransk . . . . . 57 13N　47 56 E
Yare, R. . . . . . 52 40N　1 45 E
Yarensk . . . . . 61 10N　49　8 E
Yarkand= Soche . 38 24N　77 20 E
Yarkhun, R. . . . 36 30N　72 45 E
Yarmouth . . . . 43 53s　65 45w
Yaroslavl . . . . . 57 35N　39 55 E
Yarra Yarra Lakes 29 12s 115 45 E
Yarraloola . . . . 21 34s 115 52 E
Yarraman . . . . 26 46s 152　1 E
Yar-Sale . . . . . 66 50N　70 50 E
Yartsevo . . . . . 60 20N　90　0 E
Yarumal . . . . . 6 58N　75 24w
Yasawa Is. . . . . 17　0s 177 23 E
Yashi . . . . 12 25N　7 58 E
Yass . . . . 34 50s 149　0 E
Yas'ur . . . . . . 32 54N　35 10 E
Yathkyed, L. . . . 63　0N　98　0w
Yatsushiro . . . . 32 30N 130 40 E
Yattah . . . . . . 31 27N　35　6 E
Yavne . . . . . . 31 52N　34 45 E
Yawatehama . . . 33 27N 132 24 E
Yazd . . . . 31 55N　54 27 E
Yazdan . . . . . . 33 30N　60 50 E
Yazoo City . . . . 32 48N　90 28w
Ye . . . . 15 15N　97 51 E
Yealering . . . . . 32 35s 117 30 E
Yebyu . . . . . . 14 15N　98 13 E
Yegros . . . . . . 26 20s　56 25w
Yehsien . . . . . . 37 12N 119 58 E
Yelanskoye . . . 61 25N 128　0 E
Yelarbon . . . . . 28 33s 150 49 E
Yelets . . . . . . 52 40N　38 30 E
Yell, I. . . . . . . 1　46 42N　2 20w
Yellow, R.=
　Hwang Ho, R. . 37 32N 118 19 E
Yellow Sea . . . . 35　0N 124　0 E
Yellowdine . . . . 31 18s 119 39 E
Yellowhead P. . . 53　0N 118 30w
Yellowknife . . . 62 30N 114 10w

Yellowknife, R. . . . 63 30N 113 30W
Yellowstone
  Nat. Park 44 35N 110 0W
Yellowtail Res. 45 6N 108 8W
Yelvertoft . . . . 20 13s 138 53 E
Yelwa . . . . 10 50N   4 50 E
Yemen ■ . . . . 15 0N 44 0 E
Yenangyaung . . . . . 20 30N 95 0 E
Yencheng . . . . . . 36 44N 110 2 E
Yendi . . . . 9 17N   0 22 E
Yeniseysk . . . . 58 39N 92 4 E
Yenisey, R. . . . . . . 68 0N 86 30 E
Yeniseyskiy Zaliv . 72 20N 81 0 E
Yenki . . . . 43 12N 129 30 E
Yentai . . . . 37 30N 121 22 E
Yenyuka . . . . 58 20N 121 30 E
Yeo, R. 51 1N   2 46W
Yeola . . . . 20 0N 74 30 E
Yeotmal . . . . 20 20N 78 15 E
Yeovil 50 57N   2 38W
Yeppoon . . . . 23 5s 150 47 E
Yerevan . . . . 40 10N 44 20 E
Yermakovo . . . . . . 52 35N 126 20 E
Yerofey Pavlovich . 54 0N 122 0 E
Yeroham . . . . 30 59N 34 55 E
Yershov . . . . 51 15N 48 27 E
Yerushalayim=
  Jerusalem . . . . . 31 47N 35 10 E
Yes Tor . . . . 50 41N   3 59 E
Yeu, Î.d' 46 42N   2 20W
Yeungchun . . . . . . 22 15N 111 40 E
Yeungkong . . . . . . 21 55N 112 0 E
Yeysk Stavo . . . . . 46 40N 38 12 E
Yiannitsa . . . . 40 46N 22 24 E
Yibal . . . . 22 10N 56 8 E
Yilan . . . . 24 47N 121 44 E
Yin Shan, Mts. . . . 41 0N 111 30 E
Yinchuan . . . . 38 30N 106 20 E
Yingcheng . . . . . . 31 0N 113 44 E
Yingkow . . . . 40 38N 122 30 E
Yingtan . . . . 28 12N 117 0 E
Yirga Alem . . . . . . 6 34N 38 29 E
Yíthion . . . . 36 46N 22 34 E
Yitu . . . . 36 40N 118 24 E
Yiyang . . . . 28 45N 112 16 E
Yizre'el . . . . 32 34N 35 19 E
Ylivieska . . . . 64 4N 24 28 E
Yoakum 29 20N 97 10W
Yobe, R. . . . . 13 0N 13 45 E
Yogyakarta . . . . . . 7 49s 110 22 E

Yokkaichi . . . . 35 0N 136 30 E
Yokohama . . . . . . 35 30N 139 32 E
Yokosuka . . . . . . 35 20N 139 40 E
Yola . . . . 9 10N 12 25 E
Yom, R. . . . . 16 40N 100 14 E
Yonago . . . . 35 25N 133 19 E
Yongchon . . . . . . 35 55N 138 55 E
Yonkers 40 57N 73 51W
Yonne □ . . . . 47 50N   3 40 E
Yonne, R. . . . . . . 48 23N   2 58 E
Yoqne'am . . . . . . 32 39N 35 7 E
York, Australia . . . 31 52s 116 47 E
York, U.K. 53 58N   1 7W
York, Nebr. 40 55N 97 35W
York, Pa. 39 57N 76 43W
York, C. 75 55N 66 25W
York, Sd. . . . . . . 14 30s 125 0 E
York Factory 57 0N 92 30W
York Wolds 54 0N   0 30W
Yorke, Pen. . . . . . 34 40s 137 35 E
Yorkton 51 11N 102 28W
Yornup . . . . 34 2s 116 10 E
Yosemite Nat. Park 31 50N 119 30W
Yoshkar Ola . . . . 56 49N 47 10 E
Yosu . . . . 34 47N 127 45 E
Yotvata . . . . 29 53N 35 2 E
Youghal 51 58N   7 51W
Young . . . . 34 19s 148 18 E
Younghusband,
  Pen. . . . . 34 45s 139 15 E
Youngstown 43 16N 79 2W
Yoweragabbie . . . 28 10s 117 30 E
Yoyang . . . . 29 27N 113 10 E
Ypsilanti 42 18N 83 40W
Yreka 41 44N 122 40W
Ystad . . . . 55 26N 13 50 E
Ythan, R. 57 26N   1 12W
Ytyk-kel . . . . 62 20N 133 28 E
Yu Shan, Mt. . . . 23 30N 121 0 E
Yuan Kiang, R. . . 28 40N 110 30 E
Yuanling . . . . . . 28 30N 110 5 E
Yuanyang . . . . . 23 10N 102 58 E
Yuba City 39 12N 121 45W
Yucatán □ 21 30N 86 30W
Yucatán, Canal de 21 30N 86 30W
Yucca 34 56N 114 6W
Yudino . . . . 55 10N 67 55 E
Yuendumu . . . . . 22 16s 131 49 E
Yugoslavia ■ . . . . 44 0N 20 0 E
Yukikow . . . . . . 31 29N 118 17 E

Yukon Territory □ 63 0N 135 0W
Yukon, R. 65 30N 150 0W
Yukti . . . . 63 20N 105 0 E
Yülin, Hainan . . . 18 10N 109 31 E
Yülin
  Kwangsi-Chuang 22 30N 110 50 E
Yuma, Ariz. 32 45N 114 45W
Yuma, Colo. 40 10N 102 43W
Yumen . . . . 41 13N 96 55 E
Yuna . . . . 28 20s 115 0 E
Yunndaga . . . . . 29 45s 121 0 E
Yungan . . . . 25 50N 117 25 E
Yungchun . . . . . 25 20N 118 15 E
Yungfu . . . . 24 59N 109 59 E
Yungshun . . . . . 29 3N 109 50 E
Yungtsi . . . . 34 50N 110 25 E
Yunlin . . . . 23 45N 120 30 E
Yunnan □ . . . . . 25 0N 102 30 E
Yunsiao . . . . . . 24 0N 117 20 E
Yunta . . . . 32 35s 139 33 E
Yurga . . . . 55 42N 84 51 E
Yuribei . . . . 71 20N 76 30 E
Yurimaguas 5 55s 76 0W
Yütu . . . . 5 0N 115 24 E
Yutze . . . . 37 45N 112 45 E
Yuyang . . . . 28 44N 108 46 E
Yuyao . . . . 30 0N 121 20 E
Yuzhno-Sakhalinsk 47 5N 142 5 E
Yvelines □ . . . . . 48 40N   1 45 E
Yvetot . . . . 49 37N   0 44 E

Z

Zaandam . . . . . . 52 26N   4 49 E
Zabaykalskiy . . . 49 40N 117 10 E
Zabid . . . . 14 10N 43 17 E
Zabol . . . . 31 0N 61 25 E
Zāboli . . . . 27 10N 61 35 E
Zabrzé . . . . 50 24N 18 50 E
Zabul □ . . . . 32 0N 67 15 E
Zacapa 14 59N 89 31W
Zacatecas 22 49N 102 34W
Zacatecas □ 23 30N 103 0W
Zacatecoluca . . . 13 29N 88 51W
Zadar . . . . 44 8N 15 8 E
Zadawa . . . . 11 30N 10 22 E
Zadetkyi Kyun, I. . 10 0N 98 25 E

Zafra 38 26N   6 30W
Zagań . . . . 51 39N 15 22 E
Zagazig . . . . 30 40N 31 12 E
Zagnanado . . . . . 7 15N   2 15 E
Zagreb . . . . 45 50N 16 0 E
Zagros, Kudhā-ye . 33 45N 47 0 E
Zahala . . . . 32 8N 34 49 E
Zāhedān . . . . . . 29 30N 60 50 E
Zahlah . . . . 33 52N 35 50 E
Zaïre ■ . . . . 3 0s 23 0 E
Zaïre, R. . . . . . . 6 4s 12 24 E
Zakamensk . . . . 50 23N 103 17 E
Zakavkazye . . . . 42 0N 44 0 E
Zākhū . . . . 37 10N 42 50 E
Zákinthos . . . . . 37 47N 20 54 E
Zákinthos, I. . . . 37 45N 27 45 E
Zalingei . . . . . . 13 5N 23 10 E
Zambeze, R. . . . . 18 46s 36 16 E
Zambézia □ . . . . 16 15s 37 30 E
Zambia ■ . . . . . 15 0s 28 0 E
Zamboanga . . . . 6 59N 122 3 E
Zamora, Mexico . 20 0N 102 21W
Zamora, Sp. 41 30N   5 45W
Zamość . . . . . . 50 50N 23 22 E
Zandvoort . . . . . 52 22N   4 32 E
Zanesville 39 56N 82 2W
Zanjan . . . . 36 40N 48 35 E
Zante, I.=
  Zákinthos, I. . . 37 47N 20 54 E
Zanthus . . . . . . 30 55s 123 29 E
Zanzibar . . . . . . 6 12s 39 12 E
Zanzibar, I. . . . . 6 12s 39 12 E
Zaouiet Reggane . 26 32N   0 3 E
Západné
  Beskydy, Mts. . . 49 30N 19 0 E
Zapadnyy Sayan . 53 0N 94 0 E
Zapala 39 0s 70 5W
Zapolyarnyy . . . 69 26N 30 48 E
Zaporozhye . . . . 47 50N 35 10 E
Zaragoza 41 39N   0 53W
Zarand . . . . 30 46N 56 34 E
Zaraza 9 21N 65 19W
Zari . . . . 13 5N 12 44 E
Zaria 11 0N   7 40W
Zaruma 3 40s 79 30W
Žary . . . . 51 37N 15 10 E
Zarzis . . . . 33 31N 11 2 E
Zashiversk . . . . 67 25N 142 40 E
Zastron . . . . . . 30 18s 27 7 E

Zavareh . . . . . . 33 35N 52 28 E
Zavitinsk . . . . . 50 10N 129 20 E
Zawiercie . . . . . 50 30N 19 13 E
Zayarsk . . . . . . 56 20N 102 55 E
Zaysan, Oz. . . . . 48 0N 83 0 E
Zduńska Wola . . 51 37N 18 59 E
Zealand=
  Sjaelland . . . . 55 30N 11 30 E
Zeballos 49 49N 126 50W
Zeebrugge . . . . 51 19N   3 12 E
Zeehan . . . . . . 41 52s 145 25 E
Zeeland □ . . . . . 51 30N   3 50 E
Zeerust . . . . . . 25 33s 26 6 E
Zefat . . . . 32 58N 35 29 E
Zeila . . . . 11 15N 43 30 E
Zeist . . . . 52 5N   5 15 E
Zeita . . . . 32 23N 35 2 E
Zemun . . . . 44 51N 20 23 E
Zerbst . . . . 51 59N 12 8 E
Zeya . . . . 54 2N 127 20 E
Zêzere, R. 40 0N   7 55W
Zhanatas . . . . . 43 11N 81 18 E
Zhdanov . . . . . . 47 5N 37 31 E
Zheleznogorsk-
  Ilimskiy . . . . . 56 34N 104 8 E
Zhigansk . . . . . 66 35N 124 10 E
Zhitomir . . . . . . 50 20N 28 40 E
Zhlobin . . . . . . 52 55N 30 0 E
Zhupanovo . . . . 51 59N 15 9 E
Zielona Góra . . . 51 57N 15 31 E
Ziguinchor 12 25N 16 20W
Zikhron Ya'aqov . 32 34N 34 56 E
Zile . . . . 40 15N 36 0 E
Žilina . . . . 49 12N 18 42 E
Zillah . . . . 28 40N 17 41 E
Zilling Tso, L. . . 31 40N 89 0 E
Zima . . . . 54 0N 102 5 E
Zimbabwe ■=
  Rhodesia ■ . . . 20 0s 28 30 E
Zimnicea . . . . . 43 39N 25 21 E
Zinder . . . . 13 48N   9 0 E
Ziniaré 12 35N   1 18W
Zinjibar . . . . . . 13 5N 46 0 E
Zion Nat. Park . . 37 25N 112 50W
Zipaquira 5 0N 74 0W
Zippori . . . . . . 32 64N 35 16 E
Zirko, I. . . . . . . 25 0N 53 30 E
Zitácuaro 19 20N 100 30W
Zlatoust . . . . . 55 10N 59 30 E
Zlitan . . . . 32 25N 14 35 E

Znojmo .... 48 50N 16 2 E
Zoar .... 33 30S 21 58 E
Zohar .... 31 36N 34 42 E
Zomba .... 15 30S 35 19 E
Zonguldak ...... 41 28N 31 50 E
Zorgo 12 15N   0 36W

Zorritos 3 50S 80 40W
Zouérabe 22 35N 12 30W
Zrenjanin .... 45 22N 20 23 E
Zuba .... 9 5N   7 10 E
Zuetina .... 30 58N 20 7 E
Zufar, Reg. ...... 17 40N 54 0 E

Zug .... 47 10N   8 31 E
Zuid Holland □ ... 52 0N   4 35 E
Zuider Zee=
  Ijsselmeer, L. ... 52 45N   5 20 E
Zula .... 15 17N 39 40 E
Zululand .... 28 15S 31 45 E

Zumbo .... 15 35S 30 26 E
Zürich .... 47 22N   8 32 E
Zuru .... 11 25N   5 12 E
Zutphen .... 52 9N   6 12 E
Zuwarah .... 32 58N 12 1 E
Zverinogolovskoye 55 0N 62 30 E

Zwettl .... 48 35N 15 9 E
Zwickau .... 50 43N 12 30 E
Zwolle .... 52 31N   6 6 E
Zyryanka .... 65 45N 150 51 E
Zyryanovsk ...... 49 43N 84 20 E
Żyrardów .... 52 3N 20 35 E

Roald Amundsen was born in Norway in 1877. In 1894 he broke off his medical studies to be trained as a polar explorer. His first journey was to the Antarctic and it was also here he made his greatest achievements. From 1897–99 he went as the first officer on the "Belgica" on an expedition to the Antarctic. The ship was ice-bound for 13 months so Amundsen took part, involuntarily, in the first wintering in the Antarctic. In 1903–06 he and the Dane Godfred Hansen were the first to sail through the North West Passage from Greenland to Alaska. En route they did some extensive magnetic measuring. In 1918–22 he sailed through the North East Passage from Norway past the northern coast of USSR. The ships were ice-bound on both voyages for long periods of time. Amundsen tried in vain to reach the North Pole by drifting with the ice, but he succeeded in crossing the North Pole in 1926 in the airship "Norge". Perhaps Amundsen's greatest achievement was during the 1910 –13 expedition, when he was the first to reach the South Pole on December 14th. 1911. The expedition travelled 1400 km. in 99 days in order to reach this objective. The Englishman Scott and his men died in an attempt to do the same thing, having crossed the South Pole one month after Amundsen.

Christopher Columbus was born in Genoa in Northern Italy in 1451, the son of a wool spinner. After an unsettled boyhood, during which on his many travels he learned to read and write, he married the daughter of a Portuguese courtier in 1479, thereby gaining access to the leading circles of society. However, his plan to find a passage to India by sailing west did not meet with favour in Portugal, and Columbus did not succeed in persuading the Spanish king and queen to equip an expedition until 1492. On August 3rd. 1492 3 ships (the Santa Maria, the Pinta and the Nina) with a crew of 100 men, under the command of Columbus, sailed across the Atlantic. The following year he returned home with 2 of the ships and had been to the Canary Islands, the Bahamas, Cuba and Haiti.

Columbus received a wonderful welcome and left again the same year (2nd. voyage, 1493–96), this time with 17 ships and 1500 men. On this voyage he visited the Lesser Antilles, Puerto Rico and Jamaica, but when he returned home without any wealth the enthusiasm was restrained. However, Columbus went on 2 more voyages (1498–1500 and 1502 –04), on which he discovered the mouth of the River Orinoco and visited Central America (Honduras). His last voyages were eclipsed by the achievements of other seafarers, and Columbus – who believed throughout his life that he had discovered India – died in 1506, a disappointed man.

James Cook, born in Yorkshire in England, the son of a farmer, worked his way up through the ranks in

his young days, first as the captain on colliers in English coastal waters and then in the Canadian Navy, for whom he did some very exact surveys of the coasts of New Foundland. Thus he was a very experienced navigator when he was given the task by the English government in 1768 of exploring the Pacific Ocean, which was still thought to be covered by large areas of land between the Equator and 50° southern latitude. Cook made his first voyage from August 1768 to June 1771. From England he sailed south of South America and via the Society Islands to areas where it was thought there was land, but where Cook found only water! And from there to New Zealand, where he discovered the passage between the 2 main islands (Cook Strait). During the following exploration of the east coast of Australia the ship ran aground on a coral reef, but came free and sailed to Batavia, where the damage was repaired. The crew, who had received exemplary treatment from Cook by the standards of those days, were afflicted by illness here, so many died before their return to England.

On the next voyage (1772–74) Cook had 2 ships – again of a rather broad, flat-bottomed type, which could sail close to the shore. This time Cook succeeded in making the first circumnavigation of the world from west to east, and by going far south in the Pacific Ocean finally killed the myth of the «southern continent". He also explored a large number of the islands in the ocean.

On his 3rd. voyage (1776–79) Cook tried in vain to find a passage from the Pacific Ocean to Hudson Bay (the North West Passage). On the way home he reached Hawaii, where he was killed by the natives in connection with a minor battle.

Leif Ericsson – was born in Iceland in about 970, the son of the chieftain Eric the Red. His father was banished, for committing murder, for 3 years from about 985. He travelled west and explored the coasts of Western Greenland during the following years. His son Leif, who went along on these expeditions as a grown boy, went off on long voyages himself in the years around 1000. In 999 he was in Norway, where he was baptised, and in the following years he went on his famous voyages to the east coast of North America. It is difficult to locate the places Leif Ericsson and his people visited from the sagas, but a settlement from about 1000, found on the northern point of New Foundland, is considered to be from his expedition, and it is likely that he was in Labrador and maybe even as far south as Cape Cod (near what is now Boston).

During their stay in Vinland (= grassland) the Norseman met the natives, with whom they had minor clashes. During the next decades the Norsemen from Greenland often sailed across to North America for timber, but they do not appear to have settled anywhere.

Vasco da Gama was born in 1469, the son of a high-ranking Portuguese court official.

In the latter half of the 14th. century the Portuguese were very intent on finding the passage south of Africa to India. Already in 1448 Bartolomeu Diaz rounded the southern point of Africa, but only in July 1497 when King Manoel sent Vasco da Gama off with 4 small ships and about 150 men, was there any great progress in the exploration of the Indian Ocean: the ships sailed via the Cape Verde Islands south of Africa and explored parts of the east coast of Africa, where they met Arab traders, from whom they tried to get information about a passage further across the Indian Ocean. On May 20th. 1498 the expedition landed at Calicut on the Malabar Coast. After what was often a dramatic journey along the coast (to Goa among other places), the expedition returned home in October, and reached Lisbon in July 1499, with vast supplies of spices. Vasco da Gama received a peerage, was appointed admiral and sent back to India in 1502–03, this time with a larger fleet. First they sailed to Brazil, down the coast of South America and from there via the Cape of Good Hope to India, where the Portuguese put down Indian and Arab resistance, often with great cruelty. Within a short time their fleet had military control of the Indian Ocean and its coasts, and their trade ships were able to return home with very handsome profits.

During the following years Vasco da Gama worked at home in Portugal planning voyages. When trouble broke out in India in 1524, he was sent out with the title of Viceroy, but died shortly after.

Alexander von Humboldt was born in Berlin in 1769 into a German noble family. After a successful career in the city administration, from 1797 he turned to research and became one of the greatest geographers and naturalists of his day. In the years 1799–1804 he travelled to Venezuela, where he made detailed studies and collected scientific material, especially from the Orinoco area. He also travelled to Columbia, Ecuador, Peru, Mexico and Cuba. These expeditions have been called the "second discovery of South America".

In 1829 he explored further West – and South Siberia. His aim was to write a book in which all aspects of nature – everything known both on Earth and in the Universe – were dealt with. The result: the work "Cosmos" in 5 volumes was of a fantastic quality for the times, and von Humboldt is considered a pioneer particularly within the fields of plant geography and climatology.

Ferdinand Magellan was born in about 1480 in Portugal. In his youth he went on voyages all the way to Malacca, but after several disappointing refusals from the Portuguese king, he entered the services of the king of Spain. Thus his dream of

looking for a passage to the Moluccas, south of America, came within his reach. On September 20th. 1519 5 ships with a crew of 270 men sailed from San Lucar in Spain, under the command of Magellan. On December 13th. they reached the Bay at Rio de Janeiro, but only on December 1st. the following year did the 3 remaining ships manage to sail through what later became known as the Magellan Strait. After much suffering in the form of hunger, thirst and illness Magellan reached the Mariana Islands on March 6th. 1521, and thus Europeans had crossed the Pacific Ocean for the first time. The voyage continued to the Philippines, where they made friends with the King of Cebu, who granted Spain a trade monopoly with the island. When Magellan wanted to help the king quell a local uprising, he was killed. The 2 remaining ships with 115 men sailed on to the Moluccas among other places, but only one – the Victoria – arrived back in Spain on September 6th. 1522 with 18 of the original 270 men. The first circumnavigation of the world was at an end. The Moluccas remained Portuguese, but Spain secured control of the Philippines.

The Nautilus expedition. During the years 1952–54 USA built the first nuclear-powered submarine in the world, and it was named after the submarine in Jules Verne's "Twenty Thousand Leagues Under the Sea" from 1870. Nautilus could sail fast (up to 20 knots) and, unlike other submarines, could stay under water for *long* periods of time. This attribute was made use of in 1958 when the submarine was the first to cross the Arctic Ocean *under* the ice. The voyage had both a military purpose and was also part of the intensive exploration of the sea bed which took place during the International Geophysical Year 1957/58. Nautilus sailed, under the command of Commander W. R. Anderson, from Pearl Harbour on July 23rd. 1958, dived under the ice at Point Barrow, Alaska, on August 1st. and reached the North Pole after 1830 miles on August 3rd. at 11.15pm (EDT). The voyage under the ice continued for a further 1200 miles until Nautilus reached open water between Svalbard and Greenland. The journey beneath the ice had taken 96 hours and in that time the crew had, by means of an echo sounder, gained further knowledge of the ranges of mountains and chasms which lie beneath the ice, the first of which was found by USSR in 1948 (the Lomonosov range). During later surveys both from stations on ice islands and from nuclear-powered submarines, this knowledge has been increased so that the Arctic Ocean has by and large been charted.

Robert E. Peary, born in 1856 in USA, started his career as a marine engineer and ended up as a rear-admiral. Inspired by the Swede Nordenskiöld's book about Greenland, he

travelled up there in 1886 and was so fascinated by the country that he spent almost all his life exploring the polar region. His main objective was to reach the North Pole itself – which he succeeded in doing on April 6th. 1909 – and was the first to do so.

There was a lot of lengthy preparation but this in itself led to several discoveries: during the 1891–95 expedition Peary proved that Greenland is an island, by exploring the northern coast right up to Independence Bay. From 1898–1902 he surveyed the northern coast even more thoroughly and the northernmost part of Greenland has since been called Peary Land.

Around the turn of the century there was a veritable race to get to the North Pole. During the 1890s it was established that the area round the North Pole is sea and not land. Therefore, meticulous preparation was necessary in order to be able to cross the ice to the North Pole. Peary had depots set up and sent reconnaissance teams in advance, so that it was easier for the actual expedition, and as the ice situation in 1909 was favourable, he and Matthew Henson succeeded in reaching their goal. They tried to sound the depth of the sea at the North Pole itself, but were only able to ascertain that their 2300 metre long sounding line was too short (the depth was later measured to be 4290 metres). Peary and Henson were only at the North Pole for a short time and travelled the 776 km. back in only 16 days.

Abel Janzoon Tasman, born in about 1603 in Groningen, is considered the greatest Dutch seafarer and discoverer. From the beginning of the 1630s he sailed for the Dutch East India Company to Thailand, Kampuchea and Japan among other countries.

In 1642 he was assigned the task of exploring the Antarctic Ocean and looking for the "southern continent", which was thought to exist as a southern extension of Australia. For this voyage he was given 2 extremely well-equipped ships. After sailing for 10 months only 10 men out of the crew of 110 had died of illness, a very small number in those days.

On October 8th. 1642 they sailed from Mauritius south east to latitude 44° and then east until on November 23rd. they reached the island which was named after the leader of the expedition, Tasmania. On December 13th. the ships reached New Zealand and from there sailed to New Guinea, via the Tonga Islands and the Fiji Islands. In June 1643 Tasman reached Batavia and had thus – without knowing it – sailed round Australia. The "southern continent", after this discovery, could not go further south than Tasmania, but it was not known how far east it extended. In 1644 Tasman was sent to explore the area between New Guinea and Australia. He did not find the Torres Strait, and when he observed barren coasts along the Gulf of Carpentaria and along the east coast of Australia, the

company was not interested in further voyages of discovery.

Tasman worked for the Company until 1653 and died in 1659.

Charles Wilkes, born in New York in 1798, started his career in the US Navy at the age of 20. In 1838 he was given the task of leading the first expedition sent by the American congress to the Antarctic continent. The expedition included people from many fields of science. They sailed from USA to Sydney and from there to the Antarctic, where they explored the ice barrier from 150 to 97 east. Since then the area has been called Wilkes Land. On the outward journey the expedition visited the Samoa Islands and New South Wales, and on the way north the Fiji Islands and Hawaii (1840) among other places. During 1841 he explored the west coast of USA and from there he sailed across the Pacific Ocean to the islands south of Asia and onwards south of Africa to New York, where Wilkes arrived in June 1842.

From 1844 to 1861 Wilkes worked on publishing 19 large volumes – 7 of which he wrote himself – on the results of the expedition.

Voyages of discovery:

Roald Amundsen	1897–1899
	1903–1906
Christopher Columbus	1492–1494
	1493–1496
	1498–1500
	1502–1504
James Cook	1768–1771
	1772–1774
	1776–1779
Leif Ericsson	about 1000
Vasco da Gama	1497–1499
	1502–1503
Alexander von Humboldt	1799–1804
	1829
Ferdinand Magellan	1519–1522
Nautilus Expedition	1952–1954
Robert E. Peary	1891–1895
	1898–1902
	1909
Abel Janzoon Tasman	1642–1643
	1644
Charles Wilkes	1838–1840
	1841–1842

Space Travel

Wostok 1	USSR	Gagarin	12.4.61.	The first man in space
Freedom 2	USA	Shepard	5.5.61.	The first american in space
Apollo 11	USA	Armstrong Collins Aldrin	16.7.69 to 24.7.69.	The first man on the Moon

Summary of the First Six Manned Apollo Experiments

name	Apollo 7	Apollo 8	Apollo 9	Apollo 10	Apollo 11	Apollo 12
sent up	11.10. 1968	21.12. 1968	3.3. 1969	18.5. 1969	16.7. 1969	14.11. 1969
taken down	22.10. 1968	27.12. 1968	13.3. 1969	26.5. 1969	24.7. 1969	24.11. 1969
duration	$10^d20^h09^m$	$6^d03^h00^m$	$10^d01^h01^m$	$8^d00^h03^m$	$8^d03^h18^m$	$10^d04^h36^m$
length (km)	7,200,000	990,000	6,800,000	1,220,000	1,170,000	1,360,000
orbited earth	163 times	2 times	151 times	2 times	2 times	2 times
orbited moon	no	10 –	no	31 –	30 –	45 –
carried sections	CM + SM	CM + SM	CM + SM + LM	CM + SM + LM	CM + SM + LM	CM + SM + LM
landing site on the earth	27°N, 64°W in western Atlantic	8°N, 165°W in central Pacific	23°N, 66°W in western Atlantic	15°S, 164°W in central Pacific	13°N, 169°W in central Pacific	15°S, 165°W in central Pacific
landing site on the moon	none	none	none	none	0.8°N, 23.5°E Mare Tranquillitatis	3.0°S, 23.4°W Oceanus Procellarum
commanding pilot in LM	Walter M. Schirra	Frank Borman	James A. McDivitt	Thomas P. Stafford	Neil A. Armstrong	Charles Conrad
CM-pilot	Donn E. Eisele	James A. Lowell	David R. Scott	John W. Young	Michael Collins	Richard F. Gordon
LM-pilot	R. Walter Cunningham	William A. Anders	Russell L. Schweickart	Eugene A. Cernan	Edwin E. Aldrin	Alan L. Bean

NB: Above CM means command module, SM service module, LM lunar module.